Man in Evolutionary Perspective

Man in Evolutionary Perspective

C. Loring Brace

Department of Anthropology
University of Michigan
Ann Arbor, Michigan

James Metress

Department of Anthropology
University of Toledo
Toledo, Ohio

JOHN WILEY & SONS, INC.
New York • London • Sydney • Toronto

Library of Congress Cataloging in Publication Data:

Brace, C   Loring, comp.
  Man in evolutionary perspective.

  Includes bibliographies.
  1. Somatology—Addresses, essays, lectures.
I. Metress, James F., joint comp.   II. Title.
GN60.B73 1973   573'.08   72-14184

ISBN 0-471-09419-6
ISBN 0-471-09420-X(pbk)

Printed in the United States of America

10 9 8 7 6 5 4 3 2 1

PREFACE

The readings included in this book were selected to represent the range of subject matter included in the field of physical anthropology, or biological anthropology, as many of its current practitioners prefer to call it. Biological anthropology is the study of the biological nature of man; what it is, what shapes it, and how it got this way. Although this is but a division of the larger field of anthropology as a whole, its scope is vast indeed, and the time has long since passed when a single scholar could claim to do justice to all of its aspects. And at the edges of the field, the specialists who contribute to the advances in our knowledge may not even be anthropologists. For example, some of the scholars whose work is reprinted here are primarily identified with fields such as paleontology, physiology, and psychology. The relevance of their contributions, however, should be obvious.

There are a number of books of readings in physical anthropology currently available. One might ask, then, why are we offering yet another one? Basically, there are two reasons. The first one is due to what has been called the information explosion. The pace of current research and resultant discovery is such that the most carefully prepared work can be out of date within a year or two. Many of the articles reprinted here are the most recent available, and, indeed, some have yet to appear in print at the time of this writing.

If the effort to be as up-to-date as possible is one of the reasons why we offer this collection, the other is the perspective emphasized. As our title states, we stress an evolutionary perspective for the study of the biological nature of man. Of course, virtually all works on physical anthropology claim an evolutionary theme. However, close examination often reveals that evolutionary principles are honored in name only while being slighted in practice. In article 19 we give an example of how this is done but, for the most part, we have tried to include works where practice follows theory.

Answers to the age-old question "What is man?" are very different from those proposed when the query was first framed in written form. The "erect and featherless biped" of the philosopher, "a little lower than the angels" in the words of the psalmist, now has been put in the perspective of a survey of geological time undreamed of scarcely more than a dozen years ago. Theorists who struggled to comprehend how man could have evolved from his prehuman ancestor in the relatively short span of half a million years have now been presented with a stretch of three to five million years and possibly more. The rate of change needed to produce man from not-man, once thought to be extraordinarily rapid, is now seen to have been quite comparable to that visible in other lineages of the animal kingdom.

If our perspective has undergone a revolutionary alteration from that recorded at the beginning of written history, we are still a long way from possessing a reliable picture of what actually happened in human evolution. There are many more gaps than pieces. Some theories are based on the flimsiest of evidence and can be overthrown by a single new find. But the picture is being put together bit by bit, with pieces being contributed both directly and indirectly from a wide variety of sources. Studies of evolutionary theory shape our expectations as can be seen from the papers in Section One. The study of man's primate relatives provides some insight into the basic potential which, when shaped, led to the development of human nature. The papers in Section Two display both the limitations inherent in, and the insights to be gained from, this direction of approach.

When we turn to the direct evidence itself,

the papers in Section Three show the effects of dealing with the frequently indeterminate and scrappy vestiges of the human past. Even when we consider the wealth of information available from living human populations, as sampled in Section Four, the origin and meaning of the human differences observed may remain obscure.

Before proceeding we should take a moment to explain ourselves on a basic linguistic matter. In this age of resurgent feminism, our use of the term "man" and "mankind" to include all human beings, male and female, may open us to charges of blatant discrimination. When that ponderous Edwardian wag defined anthropology as "the study of man embracing woman," he fully intended the sexism inherent in the remark. To avoid being accused of such attitudes, we considered "People in evolutionary perspective," or "Human Beings in Evolutionary Perspective," but the result is a kind of self-conscious clumsiness which borders on the ludicrous when used wherever the situation arises. The tradition of using the singular male noun "man" to stand for the totality of Homo sapiens may have sexist roots, but it is so firmly established in common usage that any attempt to change it would be an exercise in futility rivaling the legendary attempt by King Canute to command the tide not to come in. So, with apologies for its inadequacies, we shall continue to use the language as tradition has shaped it.

Finally, we should say something about the level of readership to which this book is directed. In our effort to cover as much of the field as possible with the most recent works available, we have included a few articles that the beginning student may find a bit technical and heavy going. To aid in their comprehension and to give a thread of continuity to the sprawl of many contributions by separate authors, we have added a few introductory and explanatory paragraphs before each chapter. We hope that this will make things easier for the student with no previous experience and allow the book to be used as a text for the introductory course in physical anthropology. Because the further ramifications of many of the topics treated are also mentioned in many of the essays, the book should also prove useful at more advanced levels where it is assumed that the student has already been introduced to the material covered at a basic level. Last but not least, we suspect that our professional colleagues will mine it for the evidence of bias in our choices and the preparation of their own counter-efforts.

To all our readers, the subject is a fascinating one and we hope you enjoy the collection we have assembled.

C. Loring Brace
James Metress

December, 1972

CONTENTS

Section FOUR   HUMAN DIVERSITY

Man in Evolutionary Perspective

1
PRINCIPLES OF HUMAN EVOLUTION

1

HUMAN POPULATIONS
Frank B. Livingstone

Past discussions have allowed, somewhat remotely, that evolutionary principles operated to shape the appearance of mankind. But the examples chosen to illustrate such principles were generally other than human. A partial reason for this was that control for the specifics of the various aspects under scrutiny was much easier to ensure when nonhuman cases were involved, it being considered fair game to experiment with fruit flies and rats, but bad form to manipulate people; but this was also due to a reluctance to admit that the mechanics that operated to shape the nonhuman world were sufficient to account in detail for the shaping of human form.

Recently, however, there have been repeated attempts to apply evolutionary principles to understand the human condition and, further, to use variations in the human condition to exemplify the operation of the principles themselves. Sometimes this has led to fundamental revisions in commonly held assumptions concerning the nature of mankind. We begin this section with an article by Frank B. Livingstone not only because it is a good example of the use of human data to provide examples of how evolution works, but also, as we shall later show in Section Four, because Livingstone himself, by the rigorous application of these principles to make sense out of human variation, has demonstrated that one of our most cherished assumptions concerning the nature of mankind is simply wrong. We refer to the widely held misconception that variation in Homo sapiens is best treated by recognizing a series of named races that are assumed to have some sort of biological validity. We shall not labor this matter here, but we do want to point out that this follows quite logically from the principles that Livingstone discusses.

At the end of Dr. Livingstone's article, we have added a list of sources for further reference. Most have been written recently, although the work by Simpson is actually a reprint of the 1953 edition. It applies as well today as it did twenty years ago and demonstrates the continuity and stability in the main aspects of the modern evolutionary synthesis. There have been some changes in emphasis during the last two decades, but we shall mention these when introducing later articles.

Cavalli-Sforza, L.L., and W.F. Bodmer. 1971. *The Genetics of Human Populations.* Freeman, San Francisco. 966 pp.

Dobzhansky, T. 1970. *Genetics of the Evolutionary Process.* Columbia University Press, New York. 505 pp.

Markert, C.L., and H. Ursprung. 1971. *Developmental Genetics.* Prentice-Hall, Englewood Cliffs, N.J. 215 pp.

Mayr, Ernst. 1972. The nature of the Darwinian revolution. *Science 176*:981–989.

Savage, Jay M. 1969. *Evolution,* 2nd ed. Holt, Rinehart and Winston, New York. 152 pp.

Simpson, George Gaylord. 1968. *The Major Features of Evolution.* Simon and Schuster, New York. 434 pp.

Williams, George C. (ed.). 1971. *Group Selection.* Aldine-Atherton, Chicago. 210 pp.

The study, by anthropologists, of the biological characteristics of the human species has

Reprinted from Sol Tax, ed. *Horizons of Anthropology* (Chicago: Aldine Publishing Company, 1964); copyright© 1964 by Aldine Publishing Company. Reprinted by permission of Aldine-Atherton, Inc.

been marked by significant changes in the postwar years. The basic change is reflected in the title of my essay: "Human Populations." Now we are attempting to describe human variability, or at least that of interest to anthropologists, in terms of the population as the unit of study. Previously the individual had been the unit of study; and human genetic variability was described in terms of races. In racial analysis the individual was the unit which was classified as belonging to this or that race or mixture of races. Of course, one still has to study individuals; but the basic datum which is the anthropologist's major concern refers to populations. One can blood type individuals as belonging to either blood group O, A, B, or AB, but it is the variability in the frequencies of the O, A, and B genes in the populations of the world which is our major concern. I have used this example because it was the discovery of such genes as the ABO blood groups that are found in all human populations but in different frequencies which necessitated this change to the study of the population and its characteristics.

In the postwar years the application of relatively simple biochemical techniques to the analysis of human proteins has resulted in the discovery of a great deal of human genetic variability which was heretofore undreamed of. Since the basic techniques of paper electrophoresis and paper chromatography are relatively inexpensive and easy to run, they have been widely used and great numbers of human populations have been studied. One of the most studied of human proteins is hemoglobin, and in the short space of ten years some twenty different varieties of adult hemoglobin have been discovered in the human species. Most of these hemoglobins appear to be due to the presence of a single gene. But while some of these genes are quite wide-spread among human populations, others seem to be restricted to a few groups.

In addition to simply bringing about an increase in our knowledge of the genetic variability of the human species, the studies of human hemoglobin genes have great theoretical significance and have played a major role in changing our thinking about the nature of human genetic variability and its explanation. The first of these hemoglobin genes to be discovered was the sickle cell gene. When the distribution of this gene in the populations of the world was first beginning to be known, the sickle cell gene was thought to have great anthropological significance, which means in other words that it was considered to be a racial trait or

restricted to one so-called primary race, the Negroids. Even today one can read in the newspapers and national magazines that the sickle cell gene is only found in Negroes. But this is simply not true; appreciable frequencies of this gene have been found in Portugal, Italy, Greece, Turkey, Arabia, Kuwait, and India, in addition to Africa. Attempts were made to explain these occurrences of the sickle cell gene by Negro admixture, but some of these populations would then have to be 150 per cent Negro. Thus, racial analysis could not explain this particular bit of human genetic variability. Prior to the discovery of the sickle cell gene, there were other known human traits which varied considerably in the populations of the world but which were unrelated to race, so that the sickle cell gene was only the last of a great number of traits which were not "useful" in anthropology. However, the sickle cell gene raised some disturbing questions about the nature of human genetic variability and in addition suggested an explanation of this variability other than that of race.

Since persons who are homozygous for the sickle cell gene have a very serious disease, sickle cell anemia, there is a constant loss of genes in each generation. With random mating, one can calculate for a given gene frequency how many individuals will die each generation from sickle cell anemia and hence how much the frequency of the sickle cell gene will decrease in the population. The presence of high frequencies of the sickle cell gene in many countries of the Old World thus raised the question of how they could be maintained in the presence of this adverse selection. As Dr. James V. Neel, who first worked out the mode of inheritance of the phenomenon, pointed out (1950), there were two outstanding possibilities for explaining these high frequencies: either a high mutation rate to the sickle cell gene from its normal alleles, or selection in favor of heterozygotes for the sickle cell gene. Although a high mutation rate could possibly explain the high frequencies, it would raise the further question of why the mutation rate seemed to vary so considerably in the populations of the world. Hence this possibility was scarcely considered, particularly since there was also no evidence in its favor. Despite many other attempts to explain the high frequencies of the sickle cell gene by race mixture, random gene drift, or meiotic drive, the most plausible explanation was natural selection in favor of heterozygotes for the sickle cell gene. And if this was the explanation of the distribution of the sickle cell gene, was it the explanation of much of the rest of human genetic variability? The demonstration by Dr. Anthony C. Allison and others (1955) that heterozygotes for this gene had a greater resistance to falciparum malaria showed that, indeed, natural selection and not race explained the high frequencies of the sickle cell gene. Thus, these discoveries concerning the sickle cell gene began a trend toward examining each gene or trait of human variability individually in an attempt to investigate the role of natural selection.

Previously human genetic variability had been used for taxonomic purposes in anthropology. Individual traits or genes were considered to have anthropological value or be useful to anthropology only if their variability could be used to divide the human populations of the world into races or if a particular trait was considered to be a marker of the racial origins of some groups.

When the world distribution of the ABO blood groups began to become fairly well mapped out, these genes were used in the same way, as tools in racial analysis. The blood groups were the first set of genes not concerned with external morphological characteristics to have their world distribution well known. The races which were discovered by examining their distributions were somewhat different than those based on morphology; but although the genes and races discovered were different, the concepts and methods of analysis were the same. With the discovery in the postwar years of many more genes which varied in their frequencies in the populations of the world, it was thought that the solution to the problem of race was near at hand. This followed from the idea that when we knew enough human genetic variability we would finally be in a position to discover how many races of man there really are. Genetic variability was conceived of in terms of races which were not human conceptions of reality but which actually existed out there. So that the question of how many races was quite legitimate. But the increases in knowledge did not seem to solve the problem, but only

to confound it. For each new gene, a new set of races was discovered, and thus the amount of human genetic variability which could not be explained in terms of the usually accepted races increased enormously. The situation became discouraging; so much so that a recent reappraisal of the value of these newer blood group and hemoglobin genes for taxonomic purposes has labeled them worthless. This means that their distributions are not related to the morphological characteristics by which races are usually constructed. But this does not mean that the genes are worthless; the racial classifications are.

Although genetic characteristics were used to discover the races of man, these races were also thought to explain the distribution of genetic traits in an historical way. Thus, populations were similar or different in several genetic characters according to whether or not they were members of the same race. Coupled with this use of race to explain similarities and differences was the widespread use of migration as an explanatory concept. The analysis of any particular group consequently consisted in separating out the racial elements in it and then postulating how these elements migrated into the area inhabited by the group from the race's original homeland. The group would be labeled di- or tri-hybrids or a primary race according to how many races were thought to have contributed to their ancestry. Most of human variability was thus explained by associating each trait with some primary race and its subsequent migrations. I think it is easily seen that this is an historical explanation. It does not attempt to explain why some people are dark-skinned or light-skinned, but only how dark and light skinned peoples got distributed the way they are. However, race and migration were considered to be the causes of human variability. But migration is not a principle or cause of anything, but just a simple fact; either it happened or it did not.

This type of racial analysis was not practiced in a vacuum but had many conceptual similarities to the cultural anthropology of the day. Independent invention, centers of civilization, and diffusion were the concepts then in vogue in cultural anthropology, and these concepts were utilized in both limited historical studies like Spier's study of the sun dance among the Plains Indians and grander historical schemes such as Elliot-Smith's diffusion of everything from Egypt, or the culture circle theory of Graebner and Schmidt. Thus, in all fields of anthropology cultural or biological variability was being explained by such postulated historical time-tables.

At the same time there was an almost complete rejection of any determinism. Perhaps the reason for this rejection is the incompatibility between determinism and racial analysis. One of the assumptions of racial analysis was that the traits or genes used to trace racial heritage were nonadaptive, which means, in other words, that the trait was not related to any environmental factor. If such traits were related to some selective factor in the environment, then the geographical distribution of this environmental variable would to a great extent explain the distribution of the trait, which would thereby not be an indication of common ancestry. In most racial analysis this alternative explanation was not even considered, or if so, dismissed as not proven. When the sickle cell gene was proven to most scientists' satisfaction to have a selective advantage in a malarious environment, it raised the question of how many others were also related to some selective factor in the environment.

While impossible canons of proof were required to show the presence of natural selection, the postulated migrations or diffusions did not require proof in the same sense. The observed similarities themselves were evidence for connections and hence proof. Usually migrations were attributed to the inner urgings of individuals, or man's eternal desire to see the other side of the mountain; but people do not migrate; they get pushed—and usually by their own over-breeding. Migrations, invasions, and expansions by animals other than man also occur and are explainable in terms of the ecology of the animal. Whether an animal population is increasing or decreasing its numbers or territory are functions of the availability of its ecological niche. When the population size is far below that which the niche can support, it will increase at an enormous rate which will at least double the population every generation.

This process of filling an ecological niche is extremely rapid in terms of geological time. In the past few centuries the filling of the Australian continent by the rabbit, or of practically the entire world by the brown rat are examples of this phenomenon among other mammals, while in the human species the recent Japanese expansion or the Irish expansion of the eighteenth- and early nineteenth centuries are examples. However, such population explosions are not characteristic of most animal populations most of the time, but instead these populations tend to remain fairly stable or fluctuate around some mean or optimum value. Of course as a result of the great technological advances during the last few hundred years, the human populations of the world have been far from either ecological or populational stability.

On the other hand, during the long paleolithic period of human history the hominids were undoubtedly part of a much more stable ecological community. Hence they occupied completely the available ecological niche—which appears to have been the tropical and temperate regions of the Old World—for much of the paleolithic period, and their populations were relatively stable. Although the fossil finds are sparse for much of this time, this does not mean that there were wide-open spaces which were inhabitable and accessible but unoccupied. The Australian aborigines, the last remaining people with a paleolithic culture, seem to accord with this view of the ecology of early man. Joseph B. Birdsell has demonstrated (1957) that it might take two thousand years to fill up the continent of Australia. Since the aborigines have lived there for much longer, their populations must have been comparatively stable and in biological equilibrium for a considerable length of time. Birdsell has also shown that the population density is significantly correlated with rainfall and hence with the food supply. This indicates that the food supply was the major determinant of population density, but it does not mean that the process by which the population size was controlled was starvation. Although disease, predators, starvation, and fighting mediated by territorialism control the populations of other animals, the Australian aborigines illustrate that even at their rudimentary level of culture, man is totally different from other animals in this respect. There is a famous quote from Spencer and Gillin that the Australian pulls in his belt and starves philosophically, but the ethnographic evidence clearly indicates that the major factor controlling aboriginal population size was infanticide. Thus, in man, cultural control has now superseded biological control. It is interesting to speculate how long this has been the case. In paleolithic sites many infant bones have been found—some even purposeful burials. Usually these are considered evidence of a high infant mortality rate due to other causes such as disease, but I think the Australian evidence indicates that they may more likely be cases of infanticide.

Among recent more developed societies, Ireland is a good example of the cultural control of population size. Prior to the potato famines of the mid-nineteenth century the population of Ireland rose from about one million to eight million in two hundred fifty years; however, for the last fifty to one hundred years the population of Ireland has been stable at about four million. After the famines the old practices of retaining the farm intact for the eldest son, dowry, and late marriage by males, which had been abandoned, were reinstituted. These have been the major factors determining the lower reproduction rate and hence population stability, but the "cause" of this stability has often been given as the food supply.

In preceding examples I have dealt with the demographic or ecological characteristics of human populations and attempted to show that culture was a major factor determining these biological variables in human populations. Since culture determines the sizes, densities, and reproduction rates of human populations, whether or not these populations expand, contract, survive, or migrate, are in turn determined to a large extent by their culture as it adapts to its environment. The next task is to consider the genetic variability among human populations in terms of this approach. Since the genetic variability, which we now express in terms of gene frequencies, is determined to a large extent by the ecological characteristics of human population, it too can be explained by cultural differences. It is the result of

culture and not the other way around as is usually supposed.

Modern population genetics attempts to explain gene frequency differences in terms of the factors which can change gene frequencies. These factors are: mutation, natural selection, gene flow, and gene drift. It should be noted that this is a very general theory which is capable of explaining *all* gene frequencies although, of course, for any particular gene the exact magnitudes of these factors which control gene frequencies are not known. All genes mutate, drift, flow, and for a given environment have fitnesses associated with their various genotypes. Hence differences in the frequency of any gene can be explained by these general factors. Thus, the problem becomes that of ascertaining how culture can influence these general factors and in this way determine to a great extent human genetic variability.

The first factor, mutation, is the source of all genetic variation. But since mutation tends to be repetitive and there is no good evidence for qualitative differences in mutation among the world's populations, this factor by itself cannot explain human genetic variation. In the past few years human cultural activity ranging from x-ray to nuclear bomb production may well have greatly affected human mutation rates. This may be a significant determinant of future human variation, but culturally determined differences in mutation rates do not appear to have affected present or past human genetic variability to any great extent.

Gene flow, which is defined to include the dispersal of genes among human populations by either migration or admixture, has certainly been an important factor determining the present-day distribution of gene frequencies. On the other hand, the role of gene drift, which is the tendency of gene frequencies to fluctuate from generation to generation in small populations, is much more difficult to ascertain. Today there is considerable disagreement among anthropologists and geneticists as to the extent gene drift has been important, but this controversy is beyond the scope of this essay. In any case, I think it can be seen that gene flow is a function of the demographic variables—population size, expansion rate, and density; and the amount of gene drift which can occur is also dependent on population size. Thus, culture plays an important role in determining these factors —gene flow and gene drift—which control gene frequencies.

Finally I want to consider the cultural determinants of the major factor controlling gene frequencies, natural selection. Up until a few years ago natural selection was not considered to have played an important role in determining human genetic variability, and even Darwin had abandoned his brainchild when it came to the human species. But the demonstration of the overwhelming importance of natural selection in determining the distribution of the sickle cell gene has changed our thinking. Now we do not speculate about how many races there are or where they migrated, but instead about the possible means by which natural selection could have produced the observable human differences.

Natural selection operates in any population in two ways: through either differential mortality or differential fertility. Thus, the direction and amount of natural selection which is occurring in any population is determined by the amount and causes of mortality and fertility. Again I think it is obvious that the variability in the causes of death among the human societies of the world are determined to a very considerable extent by cultural differences. Some causes of death such as infanticide, accidents, or warfare are the direct result of cultural activity, but even others, like measles, influenza, or the common cold, require the huge host population which is the result of the agricultural and industrial revolutions. When man was a hunter with the sparse population which is characteristic of large carnivores, the kinds and number of endemic diseases were undoubtedly very different from the present when he is the most populous large animal.

Natural selection can also be considered from another aspect as two different kinds of competition: first, as the competition between individuals within a single population; and second, as the competition between populations. Within a single population the amount of natural selection which is occurring is expressed by the relative fitnesses of the genotypes, while the average fitnesses of the populations are measures of the compe-

tition between populations. The classical model of population genetics was concerned with the first or intrapopulational aspect. When the concepts of population genetics first began to influence anthropology, cultural influences on biological variability were examined in terms of this model; however, culture is the property of a population, so that it is the competition between populations in which culture is the major determinant. The outcome of this competition between populations is determined by the ecological potentials of the cultures of the respective populations and not by their respective genes. For example the replacement of Bushman genes by Bantu genes over most of East and South Africa was not due to the superiority of Bantu genes, but to their association with a culture which could support higher population densities. In the competition with Bushman hunting-and-gathering culture, the agricultural-pastoral Bantu culture simply swamped the hunters, and the population density of the area increased at least tenfold. The fact that it was the ecological potentials of the respective cultures which determined this replacement is obvious since the Bantu have not replaced the Bushman in the Kalahari Desert where agriculture is impossible with the Bantu technology. Of course, the agricultural populations have adapted to the new selective factors which are characteristic of their ecological niche while the Bushman has not.

Perhaps the greatest change in the direction of natural selection is the great increase in infectious disease which has followed the development of agriculture with its more sedentary way of life. An increased resistance to infectious disease is one of the more important adaptations among agriculturalists, but this increased resistance is not the reason for agriculturalists replacing hunters in Africa or anywhere else. However, differential susceptibility to infectious disease has frequently been cited as the reason for the replacement of one culture or people by another. But this is simply one or more example of biological determinism as an explanation of culture change. Unfortunately, this way of thinking is ubiquitous in Western thought. Even the evolution of culture itself has been considered to be the result of the peculiar biology of *Homo sapiens*. For example, the usual explanation of the development of blade cultures in the upper paleolithic period and for the glorious art of this same period has held that *Homo sapiens'* "restless creativity" is the cause. This point of view—that man is responsible for culture and hence that man precedes culture—has led to the rejection of just about every well-defined fossil hominid population as our ancestors since such brutes could not possibly have had the brains or intellect to create culture. More recently the exactly reverse position is gaining acceptance; now culture and tools are regarded as responsible for man. For the upper paleolithic period instead of *Homo sapiens* being responsible for blade cultures, blade cultures are now thought responsible for *Homo sapiens*. Such an approach is more in accord with our newer concepts of the process of human biological evolution and the role of natural selection in that process. Man's genetic constitution, whether it is his brains, brawn, or blood, is the product of natural selection, and this natural selection is in turn the result of his environment and his way of life, which for man can be called his cultural ecology. Hence his genes are the result of his culture. Like other animals, man is what man does, and the fact that he has been doing cultural and intellectual things for the past millennia has resulted in his present proficiency in these activities.

BIBLIOGRAPHICAL NOTE

P.B. Medawar's little book, *The Future of Man* (1961), is an excellent introduction to the methodology and philosophy of the modern approach to human biology. S.M. Garn (1961), or the relevant chapters of T. Dobzhansky (1962) are good summaries of our knowledge of human genetic variability. For more detailed studies of specific genes or traits see G.A. Harrison (1961) or S.M. Garn (1959). Marston Bates (1955) is a good introduction to the biology and control of human populations, while A. Montagu (1962) contains specific studies of the interrelationships of man's biology and culture.

EDITORS' REFERENCES

Allison, A. C. 1955. Aspects of Polymorphism in Man. In *CSPSQB* 1955, pp. 239–255.

Birdsell, J. B. 1957. Some Population Problems Involving Pleistocene Man. In *CSPSQB* 1957, pp. 47–70.

Neel, James. V. 1950. The Population Genetics of Two Inherited Blood Dyscrasias in Man. In *CSPSQB* 1950, pp. 141–158.

2

STRUCTURAL REDUCTION IN EVOLUTION *
C. Loring Brace

When this paper was written ten years ago, it went counter to the trend of orthodox evolutionary thinking which tried to account for all the changes observed during the course of organic evolution by invoking the action of natural selection alone. Each such change, so the feeling went, was advantageous to the creature in whom it occurred even if the observing scientist could not figure out why. Mutations alone were not considered sufficient to produce change without selection. Underlying this position was the assumption that the effects of mutation away from a given condition were balanced by mutations back to the original state, the backward and forward mutations eventually reaching an equilibrium that prevented permanent change.

Since this paper was written, however, others too have challenged the old orthodoxy. This challenge has come principally from those schooled in the relatively new field of molecular biology. As a result of discoveries made in the last twenty years, the nature of minimal genetic changes—single mutations—is known with considerable precision, and it is clear that the probability of a back-mutation that would restore the original state is so low that it is effectively nonexistent. In the absence of selection, then, mutations can accumulate unopposed to produce cumulative change.

The argument in this article is in line with a growing movement that has been called "non-Darwinian evolution" (King and Jukes 1969; Wilson and Sarich 1969; Wilkens 1971). Its proponents do not deny the mechanisms of orthodox Darwinian theory but, to these, they add others such as the Probable Mutation Effect discussed in the article. Non-Darwinian evolution has not been without its critics (Richmond 1970), and we can anticipate many new developments in the near future but, as a result of the current disagreements, much new work has been undertaken, and our understanding of the mechanics of evolution has been appreciably enhanced.

King, Jack Lester, and Thomas H. Jukes. 1969. Non-Darwinian evolution. *Science* 164: 788–798.

Ohno, Susumu. 1970. *Evolution by Gene Duplication*. Springer-Verlag, New York. 160 pp.

Richmond, Rollin C. 1970. Non-Darwinian evolution: a critique. *Nature 225*: 1025–1028.

Wilkens, Horst. 1971. Genetic interpretation of regressive evolutionary processes: studies on hybrid eyes of two *Astyanax* cave populations (Characidae, Pisces). *Evolution 25*: 530–544.

Wilson, A.C., and V. M. Sarich. 1969. A molecular time scale for human evolution. *Proceedings of the National Academy of Science 63*: 1088–1093.

From *The American Naturalist* 97:39–49; Copyright 1963 by the University of Chicago. All rights reserved. Reprinted with the permission of the author and publisher.

*This paper is a revised version of one read at the meetings of the Southwestern Anthropological Association in Berkeley, California, on April 20, 1962. I wish to thank Professor Garrett Hardin of the Division of Biological Sciences at the University of California-Santa Barbara for his valuable comments and suggestions. He does not, however, completely agree with some of the ideas expressed, and therefore the responsibility for their statement is solely my own.

INTRODUCTION

Since the concern of this paper is with reductions in structures for which the selective importance has changed, it should be stated at the out-set that this is not a return to the views of Lamarck (Osborn, 1924), or to those of any proponent of orthogenesis (Carter, 1951; Simpson, 1953). On the other hand, since the influential publication of Fisher in 1930 emphasizing the positive action of natural selection, there has been a tendency to ignore the fate of phenotypic characters which, for reasons of environmental or other changes, have ceased to confer survival benefits upon the possessing organisms.

Immediately following the epochal publication of *The Origin of Species* by Darwin (1859), the reading public became aware of the importance of the operation of natural forces in producing the organic diversity evident in the world of nature (Brace, 1863). After the first flush of excitement over the implications of evolution by means of natural selection, there was a general waning of enthusiasm when the complexities of the ramifications of such a view were brought into consideration (Eiseley, 1958). From the biological point of view, Darwin's ideas had some of the aspects of a facile explanation which did not have sufficient basis in detailed mechanics to be finally convincing. The same obstacles lay in the way of serious consideration of the work of Gregor Mendel, since his major contribution was in the statistical analysis of natural phenomena and did not really explain *how* heredity worked. Studies relating to process in organic systems continued to be pursued but with increasing isolation, so that during the second decade of the twentieth century it seemed to some people that Mendelian genetics was not compatible with the kind of organic change required by the thesis of evolution (Pearson, 1930).

The identification of mutations (Muller, 1927; Ingram, 1957) and the realization that they could provide the morphological variation needed for natural selection to operate (Haldane and Huxley, 1927; Fisher, 1930; Wright, 1931, 1951) brought back a frame of reference quite similar to that proposed in the first edition of Darwin's work (1859). This time it was underlain by a sufficient body of controlled observation and experiment relating to the mechanics of organic perpetuation so that a view of evolution by means of natural selection was no longer *merely* one possible hypothesis.

While natural selection was regarded as the most important factor in accounting for the direction which evolution has taken, there was evidently some feeling that there also existed a good deal of naturally occurring variation which did not have any obvious selective advantage and may not have been the product of natural selection. Random genetic drift has been proposed as a mechanism for the production of such variants, but, while examples have been cited (Glass, 1956; Dobzhansky and Spassky, 1962), there has been considerable disagreement over the role which it has played in influencing the direction of evolution, and most authorities do not consider it to have decisive significance (Wright, 1951; Fisher and Ford, 1950).

PROBABLE MUTATION EFFECT

More recent developments in the basic mechanisms of heredity (Beadle, 1945a; Watson and Crick, 1953; Crick, Barnett, Brenner and Watts-Tobin, 1961) provide the basis for the possibility that the process whereby variation is produced may also determine the direction of the variation when selective factors are inoperative. Without the benefit of subsequent advances in the field of biochemical genetics, Sewall Wright (1929) clearly perceived the nature of such a process which he termed "mutation pressure." Wright (1931, 1929) recognized that, "Random changes in a complex organism are more likely to injure than to improve it," and proposed "mutation pressure" to describe the fact that most observed mutations "tend to reduce development of parts" and tend to be "in the direction of inactivation." Consistent with the recognition that most mutations are recessive, he (Wright, 1929) noted that ". . . for physiological reasons inactivation should generally behave as recessive."

Whether because the biochemistry of mutations was not more than speculation or because the inclusion of the term "pressure" in the label provided different connotations, the process which Wright originally described has been ignored or distorted. Recent discussions have assumed that mutation pressure refers to the *rate* of mutations (Boyd, 1950; Dempster, 1955; Moody, 1962), and since it is generally felt that known mutation rates are adequate as a source for the variability needed for natural selection to work (Simpson, 1953), differences in such rates are regarded as of only minor importance in current concerns with problems in evolutionary mechanics. This confusion seems to be an extension of the tendency discussed by Hardin (1960) where ideas or principles remain in obscurity because they have not been given concise labels. In this case, however, the label has been concise, but it has also been misleading. Perhaps the title "probable mutation effect" would be preferable.

More serious as an obstacle to the utility of the principle has been the tendency to project from the realization that mutations involve random changes in the character of genes (Neel and Schull, 1954) to an expectation that the phenotypic characters which the genes control will likewise vary in random fashion. Part of the trouble may be due to the fact that the word mutation is often used to designate inherited differences in phenotypic characters as well as changes in gene structure. At the level of the gene, it seems likely that mutations are truly random changes in the identity or number of the constituent units (Neel and Schull, 1954; compare Crick, et al., 1961). On the other hand, the effects of random heritable change on the observable phenotype are universally recognized as being deleterious with a high degree of probability (Wright, 1929; Fisher, 1930; Dobzhansky, 1955a). Despite the recent contention of Wright (1951) that "mutations merely furnish random raw material for evolution and rarely, if ever, determine the course of the process," this paper will attempt to show that current developments in biochemistry (Perutz, 1958; Anfinsen, 1959; Crick, et al., 1961; and Sutton, 1961) tend to support the earlier insight of Wright (1929) that, in the absence of selective factors, random mutation will produce progressive reduction of the corresponding phenotypic features. Although mutation is random, the probable effect is directional, that is, non-random.

DEVELOPMENT OF THE CONCEPT

Structural development has always been a focus for consideration by students of evolu-

tion. The development of such features as powerful canine teeth, laminated molars, horns, antlers, claws, hooves, prehensile appendages, long limbs and great body size (to name just a few) are obviously the result of natural selection and have been of survival value to their possessors as can be inferred from the picture of their emergence in the fossil record (Gregory, 1951; Simpson, 1953).

On the other hand, there are features which differ between related species in ways which appear so unimportant that selection is not likely to have been the mechanism which produced the differentiation. Variations in inherited features such as the numbers of incisors, premolars, and segments of the tail, or length-width proportions of the brain cavity, or the many details of coloring may have no adaptive significance. Where separate but related populations exhibit differences in such features, the mechanism of production is frequently cited as being "genetic drift," although no serious scholars grant it a very important role in evolution (Fisher and Ford, 1950; Simpson, 1953). Genetic drift, as it was originally conceived (Wright, 1931), was primarily concerned with the probabilities of sampling (Glass, 1956), and it was assumed to be effective in accounting for differences in adaptively unimportant features in small populations only. The accidental separation of members of a breeding population or chance failure of a given factor to reproduce in a small group must still be regarded in the light of the original conception of genetic drift, but the chance rise of differing mutations in isolated groups which had formerly been genetically identical (that is, 'identical' for purposes of the model) must be reconsidered utilizing recent increases in knowledge about the nature of the basic genetic material and its proposed mode of action (Watson and Crick, 1953; Crick, 1958; Hoagland, 1959).

Whether what has been regarded as a single gene turns out to be a single molecule of DNA, or a segment of a DNA molecule, or is in fact a statistical abstraction which loses meaning when pursued to such a level, remains to be determined (Anfinsen, 1959). In any event, it appears that changes in single sub-molecular units (nucleotides) may produce what have been called mutations

(Hoagland, 1959; Crick, et al., 1961; Lengyel, et al., 1962; Matthaei, et al., 1962; Nirenberg, et al., 1962; Speyer, et al., 1962a and 1962b).

At present it appears that the primary function of the basic genetic material is to serve as a blue-print for protein production (Crick, 1958; Anfinsen, 1959). Furthermore, the simplest form of modification of the basic genetic material accounts for single unit (amino acid) modifications in the corresponding protein (Ingram, 1956, 1957, 1959; Lehmann and Ager, 1960). Genetic units, then, only correspond directly with simple observable phenotypes where these latter are specific proteins (Crick, 1958; compare Harris, 1959). For example, the phenotypic phenomenon of sickle cell anemia is the product of the substitution of a single amino acid residue in the protein hemoglobin (Ingram, 1957).

To say that most facets of phenotypic morphology are determined by a multiplicity of genes is true (Boyd, 1950), but it does not adequately point out the fact that observable morphology is the end product of a process of growth and development influenced by the activity of a great many enzymes over a considerable period of time (Garn, 1957; Macy and Kelly, 1957). At any point in such an enzyme chain, development depends on the presence and activity of preceding enzymes, and a single modification in any of these is likely to prevent the completion of the enzyme chain or to allow a reduced version of the chain to continue (Stanbury, Wyngaarden, and Frederickson, 1960; Sutton, 1961).

Enzymes are proteins and many are under direct genetic control (Beadle, 1945a, 1945b; Crick, 1958). The effect of mutations relating to specific enzymes is to delete or substitute an amino acid (Ingram, 1957; Perutz, 1958) with the probable result that the enzyme will become a less efficient (if indeed operable) member of the chain to which it should belong. The chain in turn is likely to be terminated or to continue in altered form with reduced effectiveness.

As a result of these probable changes, the morphological end product of growth and development will probably be altered in the direction of reduction and simplification, if not of failure to occur (Beadle, 1945b; Anfinsen, 1959). This, of course, is just a more complete expression of the long-standing observation that the great majority of mutations will be disadvantageous (Wright, 1929; Fisher, 1930). The effect of most mutations, then, will be in the reduction if not the elimination of the structures to which they pertain, which is precisely what Sewall Wright described when he proposed the perhaps inappropriate term "mutation pressure" (Wright, 1929).

Under most circumstances, however, the reduction or elimination of organic structures will be detrimental to the survival potential of the organism involved. If, however, the circumstances under which a structure had evolved should suddenly (or even gradually) cease to exist, then the structure in question would be free to vary without having any influence upon the survival chances of the possessor. Subsequent variation will be at the mercy of random mutation, and, because of the probable mutation effect, reduction of the structure in question will be the inevitable result.

To illustrate with a hypothetical example which is extreme for purposes of emphasis, imagine the following situation. On a large island, a population of pigs is plagued by the depradations of a pack of dogs. In the course of time, the pigs develop a fairly effective form of dental defense—tusks. This of course occurs through the normal slow processes of mutation and selection with the dogs doing the negative part of the selecting. The populations remain in balance for a period of time until disaster in the form of a viral infection completely wipes out the canine population. The pigs continue and eventually achieve a new population balance maintained by seasonal availability of food supply, water, breeding territories, and other factors. Their tusks, however, serve them no useful purpose and are free to vary without having any effect on their survival. Since random variations are mostly detrimental to the structures involved for the reasons already citied, the tusks can be expected to reduce during the course of 50 to 100 thousand years.

GENERAL APPLICABILITY

Applying these findings to the evolutionary

picture, one can see how directional changes can occur without the operation of natural selection and without being confined to small breeding populations. Furthermore, the changes will be in a less random manner than those postulated by genetic drift. This does not contradict the fact that the great majority of the changes which have occurred during evolution have been the direct result of the aggregate of forces called natural selection operating on naturally occurring variation. If for any reason the selective advantage conferred by the possession of a given morphological character would have as much likelihood of surviving as the original form of the feature in question, in the course of time, the mutations would occur, and, following the argument developed above, reduction of the structure which they determine would take place. Since change of environment has been a major problem with which organic continuity has had to contend, the reduction of selective advantage formerly conferred by particular characters must have been a continually recurring process in organic evolution.

The picture of vertebrate evolution abounds with examples of structural reduction. While it might be argued that in the early stages of digital reduction among the ungulates there was selective pressure favoring such a development, yet the reduction continued far beyond the point at which non-functional digits had become adaptively unimportant (Gregory, 1951; Simpson, 1951). Snakes and Cetaceans (Gregory, 1951) show reductions in limb structure which have proceeded beyond the point where natural selection would play an obvious role. Many other less dramatic examples occur (canine teeth in bovids, tails in anthropoid apes, jaws in termites (Emerson, 1961), etc.) where the progress of reduction has been too consistent to be explained by genetic drift and where natural selection has apparently been unimportant.

POSSIBLE ROLE IN HUMAN EVOLUTION

To turn to anthropological matters, it should be possible to discover changes in the selective pressures which coincide with changes which have taken place in observable morphology. The relation of brain size increase in the human fossil record to cultural developments noted in the archaeological record has been cited as a probable example of natural selection (Tappen, 1953), and points to biological change coinciding with changes in major selective factors. This is a recognizable case of the operation of natural selection, and is not an example of structural reduction. The best illustration of structural reduction in man is in the face. Human dental and consequently facial size can also be linked to cultural development, but in a negative way (Brace, 1962a). As technology increasingly took over tasks formerly performed by the dentition, the adaptive advantage formerly inherent in the possession of large teeth decreased, and mutations affecting the face could occur without disadvantage to the possessors. Since the majority of such mutations will result in structural reduction (compare Garn and Lewis, 1962), it is no surprise to find that the human face has become smaller as human culture has become a more complete means for adaptation.

The reduction of robustness in skeleton and musculature may be another instance of change following the suspension of formerly selective factors, and the reduction of skin color among certain populations may be yet another example. Pigmentation gives no benefits to organisms which live in total darkness, hence mutations are allowed to accumulate in the enzyme chain which results in melanin. Accumulated changes eventually result in the reduction of or the failure to produce malenin (for details of melanin synthesis, see Fitzpatrick, 1960; Lerner, 1961). It is possible that a similar trend of development has started to occur in certain human populations.

With the appearance of extensive evidence for the use of fire and evident stone tool elaboration visible in the archaeological record (Movius, 1953; Clark, 1959), it is reasonable to regard the populating of the more northerly latitudes at the beginning of the Würm glaciation as a result of cultural-technological advances. If the Neanderthal peoples inhabiting western Europe, the Middle East, and Southern Russia at the beginning of the Würm glaciation were culturally (Bordes, 1958) and physically (Brace, 1962a, 1962b) the ancestors to much of the present-day populations there, then we may be able to trace the relative depigmentation of many of these people in these areas back to changes in selective factors dating from that time.

Evidence of Neanderthal tooth wear indicates that they used their front teeth for far more activities than simple eating (Stewart, 1959; Brace, 1962a). Professor Coon (1961) has suggested that the extraordinary rounding wear is due to their use in leather working, and it is reasonable to suppose that the Neanderthals tanned hides for use as clothing, which they certainly must have had in order to survive in such periglacial areas.

Although the exact adaptive significance of skin color is still a matter for debate (Baker, 1958a, 1958b; Cowles, 1958, 1959; Garn, 1961), there is general agreement that dark pigmentation is valuable if the skin is subjected to excessive solar radiation in regions of high temperatures. A population which, by the act of clothing itself, had suspended the adaptive advantage conferred by dermal melanin could be expected to have descendants among whom the enzyme chain resulting in malanin had been so modified by the accumulation. of chance mutations that little melanin was produced. If one can accept the onset of the last glaciation as having occurred on the order of 70,000 B.P. (Gross, 1961) and if one used the rough figure of five generations per century, then the selective advantage conferred by the possession of melanin has been suspended in the north temperate parts of the Old World for some 3,500 generations and perhaps much longer. The relatively pigmentless peoples of European origin may owe their present appearance to such a background.

One thing all this points up is the necessity of assessing the adaptive significances of outstanding morphological characteristics when the evolution of a particular organism is being considered. These of course will change with changes in the major relevant selective factors. Obviously, then, consideration of the morphology of an organism taken out of context will at best lead to an inadequate appraisal and will frequently lead to misinterpretation. However valuable the theoretical and mathematical models of evolutionary stystems may be (Dobzhansky, 1955b), there is always the danger that the models will acquire more importance than the reality which they are supposed to portray. While increased sophistication in mathematical genetics may be a good thing, it is urged that such improvements be made with an eye towards the organic systems being described and not from the point of view of refinements in probability statistics alone.

SUMMARY

1. While there is no doubt that currently accepted factors (mutation, selection, genetic drift, and migration) (Neel and Schull, 1954; Dobzhansky, 1955a) play a major role in determining the direction of evolution, it is suggested that a process of considerable importance has been overlooked. The probable effect of mutations will be towards structural reduction. If the structure controlled by the locus in question has no adaptive significance, then it will be reduced in the course of time.
2. It is suggested that some of the major and formerly unexplained changes which have occurred in human evolution are the results of probable mutation effect. Reduction in the size of the teeth and face and of the skeletal and muscular systems may have been brought about by such a mechanism, as a result of changes in the principal human adaptive merchanism, culture. The rise and distribution of depigmentation is treated in like manner.
3. Finally it is urged that changes in all outstanding morphological characteristics be reviewed, and considered in the light of changes in the major selective factors relating to the survival of the organisms under consideration.

LITERATURE CITED

Anfinsen, Christian B., 1959, The molecular basis of evolution. John Wiley and Sons, Inc., New York. 228 pp.

Baker, Paul T., 1958a, The biological adaptation of man to hot deserts. Am. Naturalist 92: 337–357.

1958b, Racial difference in heat tolerance. Am. J. Phys. Anthropol. n.s. 16: 287–306.

Beadle, G.W., 1945a, Biochemical genetics. Chem. Revs. 37: 15–96.

1945b, Genetics and metabolism in Neurospora. Physiol. Revs. 25: 643–663.

Bordes, Francois, 1958, Le passage du Paléolithique moyen au Paléolithique supérieur. pp.

175–181. *In* G.H.R. von Koenigswald [ed.], Hundert Jahre Neanderthaler. Kemink en Zoon N. V., Utrecht, Netherlands.

Boyd, William C., 1950, Genetics and the races of man, an introduction to modern physical anthropology. Little, Brown and Company, Boston. 453 pp.

Brace, C. L., 1863, The races of the old world, a manual of ethnology. Charles Scribner, New York. 540 pp.

Brace, C. L., 1962a, Cultural factors in the evolution of the human dentition. pp. 343–354. *In* M. F. A. Montagu [ed.], Culture and the evolution of man. Oxford University Press, New York.

1962b, Refocussing on the Neanderthal problem. Am. Anthropologist. 64: 729–741.

Carter, G. S., 1951, Animal evolution. Sidgwick and Jackson, London. 368 pp.

Clark, J. Desmond, 1959, The prehistory of Southern Africa. Penguin Books, Ltd., Harmondsworth, Middlesex, England. 341 pp.

Coon, Carleton S., 1961, Personal communication.

Cowles, Raymond B., 1958, Possible origin of dermal temperature regulation. Evolution 12: 347–357.

1959, Zulu journal, field notes of a naturalist in South Africa. Univ. of California Press, Berkeley. 267 pp.

Crick, F. H. C., 1958, On protein synthesis. pp. 138–163. Univ. Press, Cambridge. *In* Symp. Soc. Exptl. Biol., Number XII, The biological replication of macromolecules.

Crick, F. H. C., L. Barnett, S. Brenner, and R. J. Watts-Tobin, 1961, General nature of the genetic code for proteins. Nature 192: 1227–1232.

Darwin, C., 1859, On the origin of species by means of natural selection, or the preservation of favoured races in the struggle for life. John Murray, Albemarle Street, London. (See reprint of the first edition, Philosophical Library, New York, 1951).

Dempster, Everett R., 1955, Maintenance of genetic heterogeneity. Cold Spring Harbor Symp. Quant. Biol. 20: 25–32.

Dobzhansky, Theodosius, 1955a, Evolution, genetics, and man. John Wiley and Sons, New York. 398 pp.

1955b, A review of some fundamental concepts and problems of population genetics. Cold Spring Harbor Symp. Quant. Biol. 20: 1–15.

Dobzhansky, Theodosius, and N. P. Spassky, 1962, Genetic drift and natural selection in experimental populations of *Drosophila pseudoobscura*. Proc. Natl. Acad. Sci. U. S. 48: 148–156.

Eiseley, Loren, 1958, Darwin's century: evolution and the men who discovered it. Doubleday and Company, Inc., Garden City, New York. 378 pp.

Emerson, Alfred E., 1961, Vestigial characters of termites and processes of regressive evolution. Evolution 15: 115–131.

Fisher, R. A., 1930, The genetical theory of natural selection. Clarendon Press, Oxford. 272 pp.

Fisher, R. A., and E. B. Ford, 1950, The 'Sewall Wright' effect. Heredity 4: 117–119.

Fitzpatrick, Thomas B., 1960, Albinism. pp. 428–448. *In* J. B. Stanbury, J. B. Wyngaarden, and D. S. Frederickson [eds.], The metabolic basis of inherited disease. McGraw-Hill Book Company, New York.

Garn, Stanley Marion, 1957, Research in human growth. Human Biol. 29: 1–11.

1961, Human races. Charles C. Thomas, Springfield, Ill. 137 pp.

Garn, Stanley Marion, and Arthur B. Lewis, 1962, The relationship between third molar agenesis and reduction in tooth number. Angle Orthodontist 32: 14–18.

Glass, Bentley, 1956, On the evidence of random genetic drift in human populations. Am. J. Phys. Anthropol. n.s. 14: 541–555.

Gregory, William K., 1951, Evolution emerging: a survey of changing patterns from primeval life to man. 2 vols., Macmillan Co., New York.

Gross, Hugo, 1961, Comment in more on upper palaeolithic archaeology. Current Anthropol. 2: 428–434.

Haldane, J. B. S., and Julian Huxley, 1927, Animal biology. Clarendon Press, Oxford. 344 pp.

Hardin, Garrett, 1960, The competitive exclusion principle. Science 131: 1292–1298.

Harris, H., 1959, Human biochemical genetics. Univ. Press, Cambridge. 310 pp.

Hoagland, Mahlon B., 1959, Nucleic acids and proteins. Sci. American 201: 55–61.

Ingram, V. M., 1956, A specific chemical difference between the globins of normal human and sickle-cell anaemia haemoglobin. Nature 178: 792–794.

1957, Genic mutations in human haemoglobin: the chemical difference between normal and sickle-cell haemoglobin. Nature 180: 326–328.

1959, Chemistry of the abnormal human haemoglobins. Brit. Med. Bull. 15: 27–32.

Lehmann, Hermann, and J. A. M. Ager, 1960, The hemoglobinopathies and thalassemia. pp. 1086–1144. *In* J. B. Stanbury, J. B. Wyngaarden, and D. S. Frederickson [eds.], The Matabolic Basis of Inherited Disease. McGraw-Hill Book Co., New York.

Lengyel, Peter, Joseph F. Speyer, Carlos Basilio, and Severo Ochoa, 1962, Synthetic polynucleotides and the amino acid code, III. Proc. Natl. Acad. Sci. U. S. 48: 282–284.

Lerner, Aaron B., 1961, Hormones and skin color. Sci. American 205: 98–108.

Macy, Icie G., and Harriet J. Kelly, 1957, Chemical anthropology: a new approach to growth in children. Univ. Chicago Press, Chicago. 149 pp.

Matthaei, J. Heinrich, Oliver W. Jones, Robert G. Martin, and Marshall W. Nirenberg, 1962, Characteristics and composition of RNA coding units. Proc. Natl. Acad. Sci. U. S. 48: 666–677.

Moody, Paul Amos, 1962, Introduction to evolution. 2nd ed. Harper & Bros., New York. 553 pp.

Movius, Hallam L., 1953, Old world prehistory: paleolithic. pp. 163–192. In A. L. Kroeber [ed.], Anthropology today. Univ. Chicago Press, Chicago.

Muller, H. J., 1927, Artificial transmutations of the gene. Science 66: 84–87.

Neel, J. V., and W. J. Schull, 1954, Human heredity. Univ. Chicago Press, Chicago. 361 pp.

Nirenberg, Marshall W., J. Heinrich Matthaei, and Oliver W. Jones, 1962, An intermediate in the biosynthesis of polyphenylalanine directed by synthetic template RNA. Proc. Natl. Acad. Sci. U. S. 48: 104–109.

Osborn, Henry Fairfield, 1924, From the Greeks to Darwin. Charles Scribner's Sons, New York. 259 pp.

Pearson, Karl, 1930, On a new theory of progressive evolution. Ann. Eugenics 4: 1–40.

Perutz, M. F., 1958, Some recent advances in molecular biology. Endeavour 17: 190–203.

Simpson, G. G., 1951, Horses: the story of the horse family in the modern world and through sixty million years of history. Oxford Univ. Press, New York. 247 pp.

1953, The major features of evolution. Columbia Univ. Press, New York. 434 pp.

Speyer, Joseph F., Peter Lengyel, Carlos Basilio, and Severo Ochoa, 1962a, Synthetic polynucleotides and the amino acid code, II. Proc. Natl. Acad. Sci. U. S. 48: 63–68.

1962b, Synthetic polynucleotides and the amino acid code, IV. Proc. Natl. Acad. Sci. U. S. 48: 441–448.

Stanbury, J. B., J. B. Wyngaarden, and D. S. Frederickson, 1960, Inherited variation and metabolic abnormality. pp. 3–19. In J. B. Stanbury, J. B. Wyngaarden, and D. S. Frederickson [eds.], The metabolic basis of inherited disease. McGraw-Hill Book Co., New York.

Stewart, T. D., 1959, The restored Shanidar I skull. pp. 473–480. Smithsonian Report for 1958. Smithsonian Institution, Washington.

Sutton, H. Eldon, 1961, Genes, enzymes, and inherited diseases. Holt, Rinehart and Winston, New York. 120 pp.

Tappen, N. C., 1953, A mechanistic theory of human evolution. Am. Anthropologist 55: 605–607.

Watson, J. D., and F. H. C. Crick, 1953, Molecular structure of nucleic acids: a structure for deoxyribose nucleic acid. Nature 171: 737–780.

Wright, Sewall, 1929, Fisher's theory of dominance. Am. Naturalist 63: 274–279.

1931, Evolution in Mendelian populations. Genetics 16: 97–159.

1951, Fisher and Ford on "the Sewall Wright effect." Am. Scientist 39: 452–458.

3

THE EFFECT OF MUTATIONS UNDER CONDITIONS OF REDUCED SELECTION
Milford H. Wolpoff

An important matter was left out of the previous article in which the Probable Mutation Effect (PME) was proposed. This was the effect of pleiotropy, the tendency of a given gene to affect more than one trait. If pleiotropy were universal, that is, if every gene controlled more than a single trait, then even if selection were relaxed where a given trait is concerned, the gene would not be free to vary since selective forces would still operate on the other trait(s) under its control. The proponents of universal pleiotropy argue that this would prevent the PME from occurring, but there is a corollary. If natural selection promoted the increase of a particular trait, the alteration in the gene necessary to produce this increase would also have an effect on the other trait(s) under the gene's control, and it is quite unlikely that such extra alterations would be of advantage. It follows that if universal pleiotropy were the case, then evolution by means of natural selection would be just as impossible as structural reduction following selection relaxation as suggested by the PME. Obviously pleiotropy is not universal although we would not go quite so far as those (e.g., Sutton 1961) who have denied that it exists at all.

The following article by Milford Wolpoff develops the pleiotropy issue as well as others that arose following the original proposal of the Probable Mutation Effect.

Sutton, H. Eldon. 1961. *Genes, Enzymes and Inherited Diseases.* Holt, Rinehart and Winston, New York. 120 pp.

C.L. Brace has recently formulated a model of the mechanisms underlying structural reduction under conditions of reduced or suspended selection. His model consists of two distinct parts: (1) a consideration of the most probable effect of genetic mutation upon the size and form of the related phenotypic structure; and (2) a consideration of the nature and direction of the non-adaptive evolutionary change resulting from these effects in a population.

I propose to review and modify this model, and to discuss some of the criticisms leveled against it (Brues, 1966; Bailit and Friedlaender, 1966; Holloway, 1966; Prout, 1964; Wright, 1964). In addition, I intend to support the model, as well as the implications of its application for interpreting hominid evolution. However, it is first necessary to review and clarify the various formulations of Brace's proposals (1963; 1964a; Brace and Montagu, 1965) so that the

basis of their modification and defense can be achieved.

ORIENTED EVOLUTION

Brace originally claimed that his model is concerned with "reduction of structures for which the selective importance has changed" (1963, p. 39). However, its range of applicability must be made more specific. We find it necessary to restrict this range to structures for which selection has been reduced (or relaxed). It has long been recognized that such structures exist (Mayr, 1963); vestigial structures represent the extreme case. I would suggest that the same model applies to any reduction in selection, and that vestigial structures are probably the least important instance.

With reduction of selection, variability of the structure concerned inevitably increases (Simpson, 1953, p. 75). Factors responsible for this increase include both the variability already present in the gene pool (Mayr, 1963, p. 176), and the accumulation of additional mutation in the gene pool when such mutation is no longer selected against (Simpson, 1953, p. 76; Brace and Montagu, 1965, p. 57). Brace's model proposes that the accumulation of random mutation will eventually lead to the reduction and simplification of the structure concerned. There is some empirical evidence which motivates this proposition. Vestigial structures, an extreme result of relaxed selection, are always smaller and less complex than are their adaptive counterparts (Huxley, 1932; Van Valen, 1960). This reduction and simplification is certainly a *possible* consequence of reduced selection. The important question is a *necessary*, or even *frequent*, orientation of the nonadaptive evolutionary change which occurs when selection is relaxed.

The major set of problems to be considered concern the orientation of evolutionary change when selection is reduced. What, if not natural selection, orients the direction of such change? Is such an orientation an *inevitable* consequence of reduced selection (in the same sense that adaptation is an inevitable consequence of selection [see Simpson, 1953])? What is the frequency and evolutionary importance of any observed orientation?

THE "PROBABLE MUTATION EFFECT"

Brace has proposed that when selection is reduced, the direction of evolutionary change is oriented by the structured nature of genic action. Reduced selection allows a greater number of mutations to accumulate in the gene pool, and Brace has developed a model of genic action in order to predict the most probable effect of mutations upon the phenotype. This genic model is motivated by the observation that most mutations produce a "deleterious" net phenotypic result (Brace, 1963; Dobzhansky, 1955, 1962; Fisher, 1930; Stern, 1960; Wright, 1929). However, the matter is more complex than this implies (Mayr, 1963, pp. 168–176). "Deleterious" does not characterize the effect of mutation upon the phenotype, but rather characterizes the effect of mutation upon the *relation* of the phenotype to the environment.

It may seem paradoxical that the effect of a random process—mutation—is non-random. However, this apparent paradox is easily resolved. Mutations are random changes in

the developmental foundation of a very highly organized and structured system. For changes in these foundations to be interpretable within such a system, they must have interpretable, and thus nonrandom, results. Were random mutations not interpretable within the organism system, they would not affect the growth and development of the system. We are thus motivated to look for structure and organization in the effects of mutation. We already have the observation that mutation affects the relationship between the phenotype and its environment in a nonrandom (deleterious) manner. We should expect the effect of mutation upon the phenotype itself to also be nonrandom. We may also look within this structured system for the basis of the orientation of nonadaptive evolutionary change.

How can we then characterize the actual morphological, physiological, or behavioral effect of a genetic mutation upon the phenotypic expression—the so-called "trait"? In his original formulation, Brace claimed that the probable result of mutations is the reduction, simplification, or elimination of the phenotypic traits developmentally related to the mutated genetic material. Mutations have the immediate effect of amino acid substitution or deletion (Ingram, 1957; Jacob and Monod, 1961; Perutz, 1958)—except in those cases when mutation in a nucleotide triplet leads to a redundantly equivalent expression of the same information (i.e., amino acid) (Crick, 1966). This exception accounts, in part, for the observation of seemingly different mutation rates at different "loci." Otherwise, amino acid substitution or deletion will prohibit the altered protein from performing as it was coded to do in its developmental chain. Should this be the case, the chain will either terminate or continue only in altered form.

Even at this level, the effect of random mutation is highly structured. Brace contends that the alteration or termination of a developmental chain will lead to the eventual failure of its phenotypic "result" to develop completely, if at all. Thus, he claims that the most probable result of mutation is the reduction, simplification in complexity, or elimination of the phenotypic expression in question. He has termed this phenomenon the "probable mutation effect."

When selection for a structure is reduced,

the genetic basis of the structure is left free to vary and random mutations can accumulate. However, the effect of these mutations is structured, and it is this structure which provides the orientation for the direction of the resultant nonadaptive evolutionary change.

CRITICISMS RAISED BY BAILIT AND FRIEDLAENDER

Several authors have criticized portions of this reasoning. Bailit and Friedlaender (1966, p. 667–668) make three points in their discussion of Brace's model. First, they point out that reduction, or even complete termination, could lead to increase, or overdevelopment in the phenotype if the mutated genetic material influences an *inhibitory* process. This stands in apparent contrast to Brace's prediction of reduction. Jacob and Monod (1961) have established the existence of genetic bases for such inhibitory processes. Second, citing Waddington (1962), they point out that any significant increase or decrease in a field system (presumably a result of genetic mutation) leads to changes in structural *detail* as well as changes in structural size. Lastly, they conclude that "The accumulation of random mutation . . . would affect the final phenotype by causing wide variations in form as well as size" (p. 668).

The first criticism raises the question of inevitability. Is structural reduction an inevitable consequence of reduced selection? Brace's statement is unequivocal: "If the structure controlled by the locus in question has no adaptive significance, then it will be reduced in the course of time" (1963, p. 45). Perhaps much of the expressed negative reaction to the model actually represents a reaction to the unequivocal nature of this particular statement and its implications. Bailit and Friedlaender have adequately demonstrated that reduction is indeed *not* the inevitable result of alteration or termination in all developmental chains. Even without their arguments, mutations leading to structural increase, or to the development of new structures, have long been recognized. Prout (1964) also questions this inevitability and its implication of a necessary orientation to nonadaptive evolutionary change. Clearly, then, there seems sufficient reason, both

theoretical and empirical, to rule out so invariant a prediction.

On the other hand, I doubt that mutations which lead to the *increase* in size or complexity of a structure under reduced selection will be, with great regularity, selectively neutral. Indeed, whether due to the accumulation of mutations, or the positive effects of selection against increased size or complexity, or for that matter the selective disadvantage of maintaining an unimportant structure, I suspect that reduction *is* the most likely result of reduced selection.

The second criticism raised by Bailit and Friedlaender really agrees with Brace's conclusion that "the structure in question should be free to vary" (1963, p. 43). The genic model *does* predict variation in both size and detail. There is no conflict between their conclusions and Brace's predictions in this respect.

THE CRUCIAL EVIDENCE

Even though structural reduction is not an inevitable result of mutation accumulation, no one has questioned its occurrence as a *possible* result. The important question is thus one of significance, rather than one of existence. It follows that any information concerning the frequency or evolutionary importance of structural reduction under conditions of reduced selection is crucial. This is precisely what Bailit and Friedlaender have concluded: "When it comes to the determinants of alteration in the size or shape of developing organ systems, or their component parts, biologists are still very much at the level of description of empirically observed phenomena" (p. 667). Therefore, our best data consist of experimental or observational evidence on the frequency and evolutionary importance of structural reduction and simplification under conditions of reduced selection. Fortunately, the literature abounds in such evidence (Breder, 1944; Emerson, 1961; Huxley, 1932, 1942; deBeer, 1958; Gregory, 1951; Neel and Post, 1963; Post, 1962a, b, 1963a, b, 1964a, b, 1965, 1966a, b; Simpson, 1951, 1953; Tuttle and Rogers, 1966; Van Valen, 1960).

USE AND USELESSNESS OF THE MODEL

The model described here deals with the mechanisms of genic action. Mutations in the nucleotides of the DNA strand have highly structured effects upon the resultant developmental processes. Thus, the ultimate effects of such mutation upon the phenotypic expression is structured, as is the effect upon the relation between the phenotype and its environment. When selection for a particular structure is reduced, changes in it are less likely to be selected against and mutations occurring in its genetic basis allowed to accumulate. The structuring of the effects of mutation provide an orientation to the direction of change of the structure. Reduction in size and complexity is one of the possible orientations.

From this standpoint, we may best use this model to describe a mechanism to explain reduction or simplification *when it occurs as a result of reduced selection*. I would like to hold this view in contradistinction to Brace's original claim that reduction is an inevitable consequence in structures for which the selective importance has been reduced (1963, p. 39).

Perhaps the view suggested here is less general than that proposed by Brace. I suggest two ways in which the model is *not* to be used: (1) Reduction is not an inevitable result of reduced selection; and (2) reduced selection is not the unique cause of structural reduction. Holloway (1966) and Prout (1964) point out the many causes of reduction, as well as the multiple effects of reduced selection, and I am in complete agreement with their observations.

On the other hand, far from rendering the concept useless, this view allows the use of the model as a testable explanation of oriented evolutionary change under conditions of reduced selection. It is from the testability of this more limited hypothesis that its usefulness is derived. A trend toward structural reduction in a series of fossils is observable, whereas reduced selection in such a series is not.

We would like to be able to test which instances of structural reduction in evolution are due to the accumulation of mutations, and thus are taking place under conditions of reduced selection.

TAUTOLOGICAL OR TESTABLE?

Holloway (1966, p. 10) contends that Brace's original application of the model to historical phenomena is tautological; structural reduction is used as the criterion for claiming that selection has been reduced, and then the presence of reduced selection is used as an explanation of the structural reduction. Holloway goes on to say: "We need guidelines to avoid entanglement with this possible tautological framework" (p. 10).

Such guidelines can be, and indeed have been, developed from this consideration of the model. It is quite possible to test the hypothesis that a particular instance of reduction is the result of reduced selection.

The model predicts that when reduction occurs as a result of reduced selection, there will be a concomitant *increase* in the variability of the structure in question. Increased variability has long been associated with vestigial structures (Simpson, 1953, p. 75). The model predicts an increase of variability associated with *any* degree of selection relaxation.

For instance, were reduction the result of selection for reduced size (see Prout, 1964, pp. 242–243), there would instead be no concomitant increase in variability. Indeed, of all the possible mechanisms which can orient the direction of evolutionary change (Holloway, 1966; Prout, 1964; Simpson, 1953), *only* the accumulation of random mutation is accompanied by an increase in variability.

Therefore, we have a means of testing the hypothesis that a particular instance of structural reduction is the result of reduced selection.

MUTATION BALANCE AND UNIVERSAL PLEIOTROPY

Some authors have questioned whether a relaxation in selection will even *allow* the accumulation of sufficient mutations in a population to result in reduction (Prout, 1964; Wright, 1929, 1931). Their arguments are based on two separate assumptions: (1) Recurrent forward-backward mutations will lead to a balance of the alleles concerned, rather than to an eventual loss of genetic material; and (2) universal pleiotropy never allows selection to actually be reduced at any particular locus, although it may be reduced at the level of the phenotype. Let's take each assumption in turn.

The so-called "mutation balance formula"

(Li, 1955, pp. 243–244; Prout, 1964, pp. 246–248; Wright, 1964, p. 131) assumes a genetic system of two or more alleles, with recurrent mutations from each allele to each other. In such a system, each allele is interpretable as a polymorph. However, the assumption that small mutations on the level of the DNA base will always lead to an interpretable change in genetic information is now open to serious question.

According to Crick (1966), there are now known to be two normal types of small mutations. On the one hand, there are base substitution mutations which involve the changing of one base on the DNA molecule into another. This type of mutation is reversible, as no genetic material is actually lost (that is, the position for the original base is still present, although a different base occupies it), and the opposite base change can, and presumably does, occur. Thus, the base substitution mutation is the DNA level analogue of the situation which Wright (1931) mathematically analyzed. Experimental evidence indicates that this type of mutation will only lead either to an equivalent coding of the same information, or to a change of no more than one amino acid (Fraenkel-Conrat, 1964). It is easy to see why so small a change can often be interpreted as a polymorph on the phenotypic level.

On the other hand, the second normal type of mutation, the phase-shift mutation, involves an addition to, or a deletion from, the genetic material. The reading of the genetic message is then thrown "out of phase." With this type of mutation, a forward-backward mutation balance is much less likely. The lost genetic material can only be regained by a phase-shift mutation of the opposite sort at the *same* place, either adding or deleting the *same* material. Most phase-shift mutations are "corrected" by the occurrence of another opposite phase-shift mutation at *another* place, throwing the reading of the genetic code back into phase except for the section between the two mutations (Crick, 1966). There is, thus, an excellent chance that any genetic information lost or gained by a phase-shift mutation will remain respectively lost or gained. However, the extremely low probability of correction at the same place makes the creation of a forward-backward mutation balance based on phase-shift mutations extremely unlikely.

Because of the existence of two different types of mutation, it is quite possible that the genetic material responsible for some aspect of the phenotype which is not being maintained by selection can actually be lost. Furthermore, a mutation balance between the loss and gain of such material is, in many cases, improbable. Out of phase reading due to phase-shift mutation is most likely to be corrected by another phase-shift mutation at some other point along the DNA molecule. Only the genetic material between the two mutations remains affected. By limiting the amount of genetic material affected, the pleiotropic effects of the change are reduced, if not eliminated. In this manner, the chances of selection against the mutations are decreased.

The mechanisms whereby genetic material can be irrevocably lost through mutations are now understood in some detail. When selection is reduced, an increasing number of DNA level mutations responsible for reducing or simplifying the trait in question will not reduce the fitness of the population. Eventually, such mutations could accumulate in the gene pool until the structure was either reduced to the point where any further reduction *would* be selected against, or until the structure was entirely lost.

Some mutations lead to an increase of size or complexity, and even to the development of new structures. However, such mutations have a proportionately low frequency (Jacob and Monod, 1961). Of even greater importance, increase in size or complexity would probably be disadvantageous, even in a structure for which selection is reduced. Thus, there is a good possibility that mutations leading to an increase in size or complexity would be selected against. For this reason, I suggest that in most instances of reduced selection, the prevailing orientation will be toward reduction of the structure in question.

In sum, the possibility of mutation balance does not argue against the applicability of this model, but rather must itself be viewed with suspicion.

Referring to the question of universal pleiotropy, several authors have suggested that selection can never be reduced at any particular locus because of the pleiotropic effects which every locus exhibits (Prout, 1964; Wright, 1929, 1931, 1964).

Their argument is based upon the assumption that every locus has at least some pleiotropic effects. Given this assumption, certain conclusions can be shown to follow. Any mutation would have more than one effect upon the phenotype. If selection were reduced for the maintenance of a structure, there would be no reduction of selection for the genetic basis of the structure, but rather a shift in the balance of selective pressures acting upon this genetic material. Selection could only be relaxed for the genetic material if selection were concomitantly reduced for the maintenance of *all* phenotypic effects of this material. The probability of reduced selection occurring for all of these otherwise unrelated structures is close to zero. Thus, it is concluded that selection can never be relaxed with respect to the genetic material, mutations can never accumulate, and there is no nonadaptive orientation to evolutionary change. However, there are reasons to question both the applicability of this argument and the assumption of universal pleiotropy upon which it is based.

Even if the existence of such widespread pleiotropy is assumed, a completely different argument can be developed from it. As Brace (1964a) has pointed out, a change in selection acting upon one trait in a pleiotropically connected system can result in genetic changes which are random with respect to the other traits in the system. Thus, when there is any change in the direction or intensity of selection for one trait, the resultant changes in the genetic material will affect the other traits in the system in exactly the same manner as would a mutation. Were the selection for one trait relaxed, any change in selection acting upon the other traits in the system could, through changes in the common genetic material, lead to the eventual reduction of the structure in question. On the observational level, such reduction could not be distinguished from reduction due to random mutation unless the pleiotropic relations within the system were known. Brace (1964a) has suggested that reduction due to changes in the genetic material of a pleiotropic system due to shifts in selection acting upon the other traits in the system *may well be more common* than reduction due to the accumulation of mutations.

However, an even more damaging point can be raised against the assumption of universal pleiotropy itself. As Wright (1929,

p. 227) characterizes universal pleiotropy: "In general, every given gene has at least some effect on nearly all parts of the organism." If this were actually the case, it would be difficult to see how *any* change, adaptive or nonadaptive, could occur at all.

If we interpret Wright's statement more loosely, and simply consider the claim that every unit of genetic material ultimately influences the expression of more than one trait, the same problem arises. How could an adaptive change occur for one structure if selection acts upon the genetic material through many structures? Prout (1964) has made this point in the context of nonadaptive change, but the same arguments apply to the question of adaptive change. If the existence of such widespread pleiotropy is assumed, the chances of a change in the genetic material being advantageous for one trait, and at the same time not being *disadvantageous* for all other traits in the pleiotropic system (which, if we take Wright's claim literally, is the entire organism) are nil!

The assumption of pleiotropy for each genetic unit, even if it is not truly universal, apparently results in the conclusion that selection could only rarely lead to an adaptive change for any particular trait. Such a conclusion bars the possibility of evolution ever occurring!

The purpose of this discussion is not to discredit the concept of pleiotropy, for pleiotropic relations have been often observed and experimentally verified (Dobzhansky, 1955, 1962). I would suggest, however, that the notion of pleiotropy cannot be applied to the smallest bits of meaningful genetic information (nucleotide bases), but rather must apply only to larger units. Even a large amount of pleiotropy at the level of proteins and enzymes does not necessarily imply a large degree of pleiotropy for the constituent amino acids. Indeed, we can judge how *little* pleiotropy exists at the DNA level by how *readily* evolution occurs.

This interpretation allows the possibility of variation in part of the genetic material occurring without affecting more than one part of one trait, and thus describes a system in which evolution can take place. However, this system also allows the possibility that selection can be reduced, or even suspended, with respect to some of the genetic material. Selection permitting, random mutations can indeed accumulate in the genetic material and orient the direction of nonadaptive change. In this respect, the model proposed here has a firm theoretical basis.

EVOLUTIONARY IMPORTANCE OF PLEIOTROPY

There is, I believe, a great evolutionary advantage to the development and maintenance of multiple genic effects. This can be seen from the results of an experiment recently conducted by Hirsch at the University of Illinois (1963).

Hirsch reported a geotaxic (gravity oriented locomotion) experiment with Drosophila. A strong artificial selection (0.92) for the ability to distinguish "up" was applied to the flies. A vertically oriented two-branch maze with 15 nodes was used. The optimum response resulted from 15 consecutive upward turns through the maze. After fifteen generations of selection, the mean number of upward turns for the selected group was significantly greater than for the wild population. Selection was then relaxed, and the mean number of upward turns for the experimental population returned to the original value in one-third the time of the experimental selection. Dobzhansky (1967) suggests genetic homeostasis as the explanation of this rapid return to the original behavioral phenotype when experimental selection is relaxed.

Other experiments show the same phenomenon for morphological traits (Mather and Harrison, 1949). In general, when a population is experimentally exposed to a severe artificial selective pressure for a particular phenotypic trait, and selection is then discontinued, the phenotypic trait will rapidly return to the original condition (Mayr, 1963). Lerner (1954, p. 174) first suggested genetic homeostasis as the explanation for this rapid return, defining it as "the property of the population to equilibrate its genetic composition and to resist sudden changes."

This "explanation" itself requires an explanation (Waddington, 1957; Lewontin, 1957). For instance, Mayr (1963) interprets the phenomenon in terms of fitness. Because selection has already led to maximum fitness in a naturally occurring phenotype, selection for a new phenotype will presumably change

the "integrated genotype" and result in lower fitness. According to Mayr (1963, p. 288), the lowering of fitness is the result of "either an accumulation of homozygous recessives or a disharmony between the newly favored genes and the remainder of the genotype." When selection for the new phenotype is discontinued, natural selection acts to restore the original optimum fitness.

This explanation raises a number of questions. What allows the homozygous recessives to accumulate? In what sense are the newly favored genes in "disharmony" with the remainder of the genotype? However, the most puzzling question arises from Hirsch's results: How can natural selection act three times as fast as artificial selection with an intensity of 0.92?

Rather than viewing genetic homeostasis as a separate phenomenon and attempting to discover its underlying mechanisms, I believe that it can best be explained in terms of already known mechanisms, as a logical extension of the pleiotropic nature of much genetic material and the polygenic background for most phenotypic traits.

When selection acting upon one trait changes, there are two possible results. When genetic changes take place in pleiotropic material, the changes are random with respect to the other pleiotropically connected traits, and the fitness of the organism will probably be reduced. On the other hand, if the changed genetic material is not pleiotropic, no other traits will be affected. Because not all of the nucleotide bases are pleiotropic, both possibilities can occur.

I suggest that in wild populations under natural conditions with low levels of selection acting upon the organism as a whole, selection would act against changes in pleiotropic genetic material because of their overall effect on the organism. Thus, most adaptive changes are the result of genetic changes in nonpleiotropic material.

On the other hand, if selection is extreme, as in the artificial selection of Hirsch's geotaxic experiment, changes in the selective value of the organism *as defined by the experiment* outweigh any concomitant lowering of fitness resulting from changes in pleiotropic genetic material. Thus, under conditions of intense artificial selection for only a few traits, advantageous changes can occur in all the genetic material. When such selection is relaxed, selection for the pleiotropically connected traits should act to increase the fitness to its original level, reestablishing the original gene frequencies and phenotypic form of the trait in question. The later selection should be rapid because it acts through many traits.

Selection, then, acts only to affect pleiotropic genetic material under artificial laboratory conditions where only a few traits, rather than the entire organism, defines the direction and intensity of the selective process. I suggest that genetic homeostasis is a laboratory artifact and would only be rarely observed in wild populations. It is, rather, the effects of pleiotropy which protect the population from the short-term effects of vacillating changes in selection. I believe that this function is the fundamental evolutionary importance of pleiotropy.

PLEIOTROPY AND REDUCED SELECTION

We have come to view pleiotropy as one possible limitation to the amount of reduction that can occur when selection is relaxed (Huxley 1932; Wright 1929), rather than as a factor barring its occurrence. A nonadaptive structure which is maintained as the result of selection acting upon pleiotropic expressions of the genetic material should be highly variable, as most vestigial structures are (Simpson, 1953, p. 148; Huxley, 1932; Van Valen 1960). However, if a reduced structure is maintained by direct selection acting against any further reduction, one would not expect unusual variation since the genetic basis for the larger or more complex polymorphs formerly selected for will eventually be lost. This latter phenomenon may characterize several trends observable in human evolution (Brace, 1962, 1964b; Dahlberg, 1964; Garn, 1964; Brace and Montagu, 1965).

THE EVIDENCE ON RECORD

It only remains for us to demonstrate the existence in nature of a nonadaptive orientation toward reduction and simplification when selection is reduced. Reduction in size or complexity is the most probable, although not unique, result of the accumulation of mutations when selection is reduced. Reduction under these conditions can be distinguished from reduction due to direct selection, correlated adaptive change, meiotic

drive, genetic drift (and other sampling errors), and functionally correlated change (see Holloway, 1966; Prout, 1964; and Simpson, 1953, for further discussion of reduction not due to the accumulation of mutations). The distinguishing criterion is variability. Only mutation accumulation, when selection is reduced, results in a concomitant increase in population variability with respect to the structure concerned.

Through the application of the criteria discussed above to the data collected from fossils or modern populations it is possible to determine whether or not any reduction which has occurred is the result of relaxation of selection, without invoking tautological arguments. With this determination, we can bring evidence to bear upon the crucial questions of the frequency and importance of this postulated evolutionary orientation.

A large body of zoological literature supports several contentions relevant to the discussion above. It has been predicted that in instances of reduction due to relaxed selection, the structures undergoing reduction should tend to be more variable than those either maintained by, or reduced as a result of, selection. This phenomenon of increased variability in structures undergoing reduction has been consistently observed in such varied organisms as termites (Emerson, 1961); cave fish (Breder, 1944); frog tadpoles (DeBeer, 1958); horses (Simpson, 1951); certain snakes (Gregory, 1951); hind limbs of the whale (Huxley, 1932); functionless teeth in *Hoplophoneus* and *Ptilodus* (Simpson, 1953). It has been shown in respect to colorblindness, visual acuity, auditory acuity, breast cancer and other diseases of lactation, and the nasal septum in living human beings (Neel and Post, 1963; Post, 1962a, b, 1963a, b, 1964a, b, 1966a, b). For almost every case mentioned, the investigator has suggested that reduction occurred when a formerly maintained selective pressure was relaxed. In addition, there are many reports in the literature, such as the study of orangutan hallucal reduction conducted by Tuttle and Rogers (1966), in which reduction associated with increased variability is observed and possible selective factors are mentioned. I suggest a closer examination of the postulated selective factors in the light of the observed variability.

Thus, there is widespread confirmation of

the predictions generated by the model of genic action discussed here *already present* in the literature. These instances present data which are incompatible with the interpretation that direct selection, or any other possible orientation other than that of relaxed selection allowing the accumulation of mutations, has caused the reduction (see Emerson, 1961; Van Valen, 1960).

In Post's work we can find an additional confirmation of reduced selection. The distribution of visual and auditory acuity shows the most reduction, and the greatest variability, in precisely those populations which have not required these abilities for their survival over the longest period of time. The distribution of lactation abnormalities and breast cancer indicates the same pattern of distribution. Thus, there is an even more direct confirmation of reduced selection.

SUMMARY

While there are many causes of structural reduction in evolution, the accumulation of mutations when selection is relaxed is a differentiable mechanism. Such reduction is terminated by (a) the eventual loss of the structure in question, along with the loss of some of the genetic material responsible for it, (b) the maintenance of the structure in a reduced form with a high degree of variability, due to selection acting upon the pleiotropic effects of part of the genetic material this is the so-called "vestigial structure" or (c) the maintenance of the structure in its reduced or simplified form as a result of positive selection against any further reduction. Some evidence indicates the third possibility as the most common one (Brace and Montagu, 1965).

A consideration of the studies of structural reduction in evolution already present in the literature shows reduction due to the accumulation of mutations to be widespread and common. Reduced selection is thus not a rare evolutionary phenomena.

APPLICATION TO HUMAN EVOLUTION

While we have answered the question of frequency, we must yet consider the importance of this nonadaptive evolutionary orientation. One would expect that this phenomenon would be particularly characteristic of human evolution. There has been an increas-

ing capacity of culture to act as man's major adaptive mechanism. The course of human evolution has been largely oriented by increasing selection for man's capacity to be an effective culture-bearing creature. With this orientation has come an associated relaxation of the selective pressures acting upon those morphological features whose function has been supplemented or replaced by behavioral or technological cultural innovations.

Post's studies of selection relaxation in recent populations adequately demonstrate this point. Cultural innovations have increasingly reduced selection for the maintenance of visual and auditory acuity. I suggest that the same results can be found in the analysis of any abnormality for which there is a cultural compensation.

Peering further into the past, this interpretation has been applied to the reconstructed evolutionary history of many morphological traits. Perhaps the most highly criticized application has been in the interpretation of the observed trend toward dental reduction (Brues, 1966; Bailit and Friedlaender, 1966). The hypothesis that this trend is the result of reduced selection for a larger dentition due to the increasingly efficient replacement of the teeth as tools or weapons by culture has been proposed by many authors in addition to Brace (1962, 1964b), even without considering *why* reduced selection might result in size reduction (Dahlberg, 1964; Garn, 1964; Hooton, 1931).

If relaxed selection is to be proposed as the cause of hominid dental reduction without invoking tautological reasoning, an associated increase in dental variability must be shown for at least the period of reduction. The period of reduction varies for different portions of the dentition and among different populations. However, Dahlberg (1964, p. 22) observes relaxed selection for molar and premolar crown grinding area in some extant populations.

Brace (1964; Brace and Montagu, 1965) finds the beginnings of the reduction of selection resulting in the current degree of dental reduction to be in the technological innovations following the development of Upper Paleolithic blade-burin industries. I think this hypothesis may be modified. The transitional and unusually variable nature of the skeletal material at Mount Carmel (Brothwell, 1961; McCown and Keith, 1939) and Broken Hill (Clark et al., 1950; Pycraft, 1928), and the cultural associations of these materials with Middle Paleolithic industries (Garrod, 1962; Garrod and Bate, 1937; Higgs, 1961; Clark, 1960; Clark et al., 1950) indicates a reduction of selection originating in the more advanced facies of the Middle Paleolithic. In any event, Dahlberg (1964) observes the most extreme dental reduction in those populations that have been associated with an Upper Paleolithic blade-burin industry for the longest period of time (p. 21). Both the earliest and subsequently the greatest dental reductions can be found among populations in the Near East and Europe (p. 20)—areas in which the earliest Upper Paleolithic industries have been found (Garrod, 1962; Howell, 1959; Pradel, 1966; Muller-Beck, 1966).

In spite of the suggestive nature of these observations, I feel compelled to point out, contrary to Brues (1966) and Bailit and Friedlaender (1966), that the information necessary either to corroborate or to refute this interpretation has not been gathered or correctly utilized. Bailit and Friedlaender base their conclusions on population averages and ranges for dental dimensions not even corrected for body size. They claim a lack of relation between tooth size and body size. However, there is not a study in the literature which, in attempting to find a relation between tooth size and body size, holds constant factors causing independent variation of these traits. Their claim of no relation is unfounded, and reasonable doubt may be cast upon their conclusions. Brues, on the other hand, suggests selective factors which could be responsible for dental reduction. I suggest that the question of whether or not reduced selection was responsible for any particular trend toward reduction can only be answered by examining the nature of the data, and not by postulating possible, but untestable, selective pressures. As Holloway concluded, this procedure can only lead to tautological reasoning (1966, p. 10).

SUGGESTIONS FOR FURTHER RESEARCH

Population averages and ranges are not sufficient for testing this model. Estimates of population variability are of crucial importance. Factors which can cause the independent variation of the traits studied

must be controlled or isolated. Most of these data are already available, but many must be regathered so that we may be able to adequately test the model.

We need not stop with the testing of population data. A computer simulation of the Watson-Crick DNA model could be of crucial importance. We could test the degree of mutation accumulation associated with various amounts of pleiotropy at the nucleotide base level, and various reductions of selection for the phenotypic traits.

A well-grounded and potentially useful evolutionary mechanism has been found in this development of Brace's "probable mutation effect." Specific criteria for the testing of the model have been generated. I hope that the appropriate data will be tested, and further light thus may be shed upon the factors which have oriented the direction of human evolution.

ACKNOWLEDGMENTS

I would like to acknowledge my sincere indebtedness to Dr. Arthur H. Rohn of the Department of Anthropology at the University of Illinois for the very great amount of help extended to me in the preparation of this work, and to Dr. C.L. Brace of the University of Michigan for our conversations which have inspired many of the ideas developed here. Responsibility for the contents of this paper is solely my own. This study was supported in part by United States Public Health Service Grant 5 FI GM–30, 854–03.

REFERENCES

Bailit, H.L., and J.S. Friedlaender. 1966. Tooth size reduction: A hominid trend. Amer. Anthropol. 68:665–672.

Brace, C.L. 1962. Cultural factors in the evolution of the human dentition, p. 343–354. M.F. Ashley Montagu (ed.), Oxford, New York.

———. 1963. Structural reduction in evolution. Amer. Natur. 97:39–49.

———. 1964a. The probable mutation effect. Amer. Natur. 98:453–455.

———. 1964b. The fate of the "classic" Neanderthals: A consideration of hominid catastrophism. Curr. Anthropol. 5:3–43, 7:204–214.

Brace, C.L., and M.F. Ashley Montagu. 1965. Man's evolution: An introduction to physical anthropology. Macmillan, New York.

Breder, C.M. 1944. Ocular anatomy and light

sensitivity studies on the blind fish from Cueva de los Sabinos, Mexico. Zoologica 94:131–143.

Brothwell, D.R. 1961. The people of Mount Carmel. Proc. Prehist. Soc. 27:155–159.

Brues, A.M. 1966. "The probable mutation effect" and the evolution of hominid teeth and jaws. Amer. J. Phys. Anthropol. 25:169–171.

Clark, J.D. 1960. Further excavations at Broken Hill, Northern Rhodesia. J. Roy. Anthropol. Inst. 89:201–231.

Clark, J.D., K.P. Oakely, L.H. Wells, and J.A.C. McClelland. 1950. New studies on Rhodesian man. J. Roy. Anthropol. Inst. 77:7–32.

Crick, F.H.C. 1966. The genetic code III. Sci. Amer. 215:55–62.

Dahlberg, A.A. 1964. Dental evolution and culture, p. 19–31. In S.M. Garn (ed.) Culture and the direction of human evolution. Wayne State, Detroit.

DeBeer, G.R. 1940. Embryology and taxonomy, p. 365–393. In J.S. Huxley (ed.), The new systematics. Clarendon, Oxford.

———. 1958. Embryos and ancestors. Clarendon, Oxford.

Dobzhansky, T. 1955. Evolution, genetics, and man. Wiley, New York.

———. 1962. Mankind evolving. Yale Univ. Press, New Haven.

———. 1967. Lecture given at the 36th meeting of the American Association of Physical Anthropologists.

Emerson, A.E. 1961. Vestigial characters of termites, and processes of regressive evolution. Evolution 15:115–131.

Fisher, R.A. 1930. The genetical theory of natural selection. Clarendon, Oxford.

Fraenkel-Conrat, H. 1964. The genetic code of a virus. Sci. Amer. 213:55–67.

Garn, S.M. 1964. Culture and the direction of human evolution, p. 3–18. In S.M. Garn (ed.), Culture and the direction of human evolution. Wayne State, Detroit.

Garrod, D.A.E. 1962. The middle paleolithic of the Near East and the problem of the Mount Carmel man. J. Roy. Anthropol. Inst. 52:232–259.

Garrod, D.A.E., and D.M.A. Bate. 1937. The stone age of Mount Carmel, Vol. I. Excavations of the Wady El-Mughara. Oxford, New York.

Gregory, W.K. 1951. Evolution emerging: A survey of changing patterns from primeval life to man. 2 vols. Macmillan, New York.

Higgs, E.S. 1961. Some pleistocene faunas from the Mediterranean coastal areas. Proc. Prehist. Soc. 27:144–154.

Hirsch, J. 1963. Behavior genetics and individuality understood. Science 142:1436–1442.

Holloway, R.L., Jr. 1966. "Structural reduction" through the probable mutation effect. Amer. J. Phys. Anthropol. 25:7–11.

Hooton, E.A. 1931. Up from the ape. Macmillan, New York.

Howell, F.C. 1959. Upper pleistocene stratigraphy and early man in the Levant. Proc. Amer. Phil. Soc. 103:1–65.

Huxley, J.S. 1932. Problems of relative growth. Methuen, London.

———. 1942. Evolution, the modern synthesis. Allen, London.

Ingram, V.M. 1957. Genetic mutations in human haemoglobin: The chemical difference between normal and sickle-cell haemoglobin. Nature 180:326–328.

Jacob, F., and J. Monod. 1961. On the regulation of gene activity. Cold Spring Harbor Symposium on Quantitative Biology 26:318–356.

Lerner, I.M. 1954. Genetic homeostasis. Oliver and Boyd, Edinburgh.

Lewontin, R.C. 1957. The adaptations of populations to varying environments. Cold Spring Harbor Symposium on Quantitative Biology 22:395–408.

Li, C.C. 1955. Population genetics. Univ. of Chicago Press, Chicago.

McCown, T., and A. Keith. 1939. The stone age of Mount Carmel, Vol. II. The fossil human remains from the Levalloiso-Mousterian. Oxford, New York.

Mather, K., and B.J. Harrison. 1949. The manifold effects of selection. Heredity 3:1–52, 131–162.

Mayr, E. 1963. Animal species and evolution. Belknap, Cambridge.

Müller-Beck, H. 1966. Paleohunters in America: Origins and diffusion. Science 152:1191–1210.

Neel, J.V., and R.H. Post. 1963. Transitory "positive" selection for colorblindness? Eugen. Quart. 10:33–35.

Perutz, M.F. 1958. Some recent advances in molecular biology. Endeavour 17:190–203.

Post, R.H. 1962a. Population differences in red and green color vision deficiency: A review and a query on selection relaxation. Eugen. Quart. 9:131–146.

———. 1962b. Population differences in vision acuity: A review with speculative notes on selection relaxation. Eugen. Quart. 9:189–212.

———. 1963a. "Colorblindness" and relaxed selection. Eugen. Quart. 10:84–85.

———. 1963b. "Colorblindness" in Britain, France, and Japan: A review with notes on selection relaxation. Eugen. Quart. 10:110–118.

———. 1964a. Hearing acuity among Negroes and whites. Eugen. Quart. 11:65–81.

———. 1964b. Appraisals of civilized man and savages. Eugen. Quart. 11:168–169.

———. 1965. Jews, genetics, and disease. Eugen. Quart. 12:162–164.

———. 1966a. Breast cancer, lactation, and genetics. Eugen. Quart. 13:1–29.

———. 1966*b*. Deformed nasal septa and relaxed selection. Eugen. Quart. 13:101–112.

Pradel, L. 1966. Transition from the Mousterian to the Perigordian. Curr. Anthropol. 7:33–50.

Prout, T. 1964. Observations on structural reduction in evolution. Amer. Natur. 98:239–249.

Pycraft, W.P. (ed.). 1928. Rhodesian man and associated remains. British Museum, London.

Simpson, G.G. 1951. Horses. Oxford Univ. Press, New York.

———. 1953. The major features of evolution. Columbia Univ. Press, New York.

Stern, C. 1960. Principles of human genetics. 2nd ed. W. Freeman, San Francisco.

Tuttle, R.H., and C.M. Rogers. 1966. Genetic and selective factors in reduction of the hallux in *Pongo pygmaeus*. Amer. J. Phys. Anthropol. 24:191–198.

Van Valen, L. 1960. Nonadaptive aspects of evolution. Amer. Natur. 94:305–308.

Waddington, C.H. 1957. The strategy of the genes. Allen and Unwin, London.

———. 1962. New patterns in genetics and development. Columbia Univ. Press, New York.

Wright, S. 1929. Fisher's theory of dominance. Amer. Natur. 68:274–279.

———. 1931. Evolution in Mendelian populations. Genetics 16:97–159.

———. 1964. Pleiotropy in the evolution of structural reduction and of dominance. Amer. Natur. 98:65–69.

4

GENETIC EFFECTS OF POPULATION SIZE REDUCTION
D. F. Roberts

*Before the recent focus on non-Darwinian factors in evolution, the only change-pro-
ducing mechanism other than natural selection that was given even a tentative hearing
was the phenomenon called genetic drift. As Roberts notes in his article, this concept
was proposed and developed by the American geneticist, Sewall Wright. Specifically it
was based on the recognition that chance alone could affect the genetic structure of a
small population. Failure to reproduce by one individual in a group of only a few people
of breeding age could materially alter the proportions of genes in the succeeding
generation without any regard as to whether the alteration would benefit the
population or not. Accidental death, chance alterations in the ratio of males to females,
and other such factors could cause such changes.*

*Sewall Wright's formulations met with vehement opposition from British geneticists,
led by the late R.A. Fisher, who denied that evolution could occur by any mechanism
other than the operation of natural selection. One of the problems that plagued the
supporters of Sewall Wright was the lack of any clear-cut examples that could
demonstrate that genetic drift had occurred. In the following essay, British
anthropologist D.F. Roberts produces one of the most convincing examples offered so
far.*

*Since genetic drift, by definition, is not a positive response, nor, because it is
random, is it cumulative in any direction, there is some real question as to how
important a role it has played in evolution. But throughout by far the greater part of
human evolution, people lived in small groups between which contact was intermittent
and upon which chance could have played a considerable part in determining gene
frequencies. Some of the differences between modern human populations do not
appear to have any clear-cut adaptive meaning, and many an anthropologist suspects
that these differences may be the results of genetic drift acting on the small, local,
semi-isolated ancestral groups. Certainly the possibility cannot be denied out of hand.*

Cavalli-Sforza, L.L. 1969. "Genetic drift" in an Italian population. *Scientific
American* 221(2):30–37.

Fisher, R.A., and E.B. Ford. 1950. The "Sewall Wright" effect. *Heredity* 4:117–119.

Simmons, R.J., N.B. Tindale, and J.B. Birdsell. 1962. A blood group genetical
survey in Australian aborigines of Bentinck, Mornington and Forsyth islanders,
Gulf of Carpinteria. *American Journal of Physical Anthropology* 20:303–320.

For evolutionary thought, the proof by
Wright that non-adaptive differentiation can
occur as the result of genetic accident
appears in retrospect to be among the most
important results of the application of mathematical analyses to the facts of genetics.
Random processes, to whose results the
term "genetic drift" has come to be applied,
play a part in determining the character of
populations. In theory, their role is particularly important in small and entirely isolated
groups, whereas with a larger population
distributed uninterruptedly over a wide
territory their effects tend to be overshad-
owed by those of selection. The argument
that random drift can occur is, however,
different from establishing the fact that it has
occurred in any given instance; the latter has
proved unexpectedly difficult, even in human populations which according to Maryr [1]
provide some of the best evidence for
random fluctuations of gene frequency.
Indeed, it has been argued (for example,

From *Nature* 220: 1084–1088; reprinted with permission
of the author and publisher.

refs. 1–3) that drift is of inconsequential influence in the evolution of populations.

Part of the difficulty lies in the way in which the term "random drift" is used to cover various interrelated genetic phenomena. More than two decades were required to appreciate their variety and elucidate their effects. The importance of random factors in the balance of those bringing about evolutionary advance was recognized by Wright[4] in 1932, though not fully. Random fluctuation in intensity or direction of selection had been touched on the year before,[6] but was not stressed until 1935 (ref. 7). In 1938 Wright[5] published a method for dealing with several different types of random processes mathematically. The practically complete indeterminacy of events that are unique was not recognized until 1949 (ref. 8). Today "random drift" is taken to represent the cumulative effects of all the random processes affecting gene frequencies. These may be summarized as follows. (a) The random variation that occurs in the sampling process of passing on gametes from one generation to the next. This is the component to which the term "drift" is frequently restricted in common parlance. (b) Random variation in the magnitude and direction of selective and other systematic forces; these include random fluctuations in mutation rate, in selection pressures, and in rates of population movement. (c) Random unique events. These comprise category I 3 of Wright's[9] classification; here are included novel favourable mutations, unique hybridizations, swamping of a population by mass immigration, unique selective incidents, and unique reductions in numbers. The last of these is often termed the "founder" effect or the "bottleneck" effect, which represent the one phenomenon but at different points in a population's history in a given territory.

STUDIES OF DRIFT

Discussion of drift as a mechanism for genetic differentiation in human groups has come from three different types of studies.

1. Variations in gene frequency between local populations, and between offshoot and parent populations, have been attributed to drift. For example, Birdsell's[10] survey in south-west central Australia of forty-two tribes showed sharp blood group gene frequency differences which he attributed to drift, recognizing, however, that it could "be no more than suggested in terms of broad probabilities". Glass et al.[11] showed in their Dunker study what seemed to be drift of MN gene frequencies. Giles et al.[12] demonstrated differences in several blood group systems between New Guinea villages of common history and environment, differences which they felt to be due to drift. In these studies, drift has merely been invoked, not proved or measured; there are at best only pointers to the type of random process involved. In the third study, it was felt that the founder principle, or population size reduction by epidemics, was the cause of the differences, though no numerical details were given. In the second study, the authors recognized the difficulty of distinguishing the founder effect from that of accumulated gamete sampling over several generations, and their subsequent attribution to the latter[13] of part of the MN frequency change was later questioned.[14]

2. The demographic and mating structures of particular societies have been examined to show the magnitude of drift that could occur (for example, refs. 15–19). Here the restriction was to random variation that occurs in gamete sampling from one generation to the next. The net outcome of these was to show that the mating structure of the societies examined would only allow drift of very small degree to occur, though there were extremely segmented societies where the effect might be stronger.

3. Mathematical models have been applied to populations for which genetic, numerical and mating data are available to enquire whether the observed variations in gene frequencies are explicable by drift alone. For example, Cavalli-Sforza et al.[20] found that in North Italy they are greater than might be expected by drift alone, and attributed this extra dispersion to overestimation of the effective size of the population concerned. But because what was measured was the accumulated effects of intergenerational gamete sampling, the finding could have reflected other components of drift. None of these

studies, however, has yet demonstrated conclusively that drift has occurred; only the last has attempted to compare observed variation with expected drift magnitude. None, moreover, gives sufficient attention to the category (c) of drift processes, the random unique events. These are almost completely indeterminate statistically, and are therefore not adequately covered in any models so far applied, being treated as negligible components of q, the random portion of gene frequency change per generation, by Wright.[9] The genetic effects of these processes are illustrated and quantified in this article. It concerns the effects of accidents of the genetic constitution of a population, and in particular how these effects have been brought about through the resulting diminution of numbers, the "bottleneck" phenomenon.

POPULATION AND PROCEDURE

To identify the effects of a bottleneck in terms of the frequency of, say, blood group genes, the investigator would have to be extremely fortunate. He would have to know the gene frequencies in the population immediately before, and immediately after, the bottleneck occurred. He would require foresight to know that the size of the population is about to change, and hindsight to know that it had finished changing. The same results, however, can be demonstrated if the genetic constitution of the population is specified in a way other than by the usual array of frequencies of particular alleles and genotypes. This can be done if the population pedigree is known.

A parent passes to his child half of his chromosomes and therefore virtually half of his genes. When the child himself reproduces he again passes on half his genes, so a grandchild derives on average a quarter of his genes from each grandparent. The probability that any autosomal allele present in a grandparent is present in any one of his grandchildren is one quarter, and the probable genetic contribution of any grandparent to the gene pool of his grandchildren is a quarter. The genetic constitution of any generation of descendants can therefore be specified in terms of the contributions to it from particular ancestors, and, by extension,

the same method can be applied to any group of individuals but covering more than one generation. Thus the genetic constitution of a population at any moment is regarded as comprising a pack of probable ancestral contributions which can be calculated. They reflect the relative fertilities of the ancestors concerned and their descendants. Allowance can be made for the effects of mortality and migration, though not for other mechanisms of gene frequency change, notably for the random variation that occurs in the sampling process of passing on gametes from one generation to the next, for mutation, or for selection through differential mortality. Thus calculation of these probable contributions at a series of points in time, tracing their secular variation, shows how the genetic constitution of the population so defined varies during the period. The calculations are simple, and multiple lines of descent must be allowed for where the population is in any way inbred.

This procedure has been applied to the population of Tristan da Cunha. From the detailed data that are available for this population, from the records kept by the earliest settlers, the observations of visitors and official reports, the lists that at periods were kept of births, deaths, baptisms and marriages, and the investigations of genealogies by Dr. Woolley, Dr. Loudon and Dr. Munch, it is possible to obtain the necessary data for the analysis. First, a complete, albeit highly complex pedigree of the whole population since its founding can be established. Second, the numerical evolution of the population from its founding can be traced. Figure 1 shows the size of the population on December 31 of each year from 1816 to 1961. There have been three phases of increase in the population, one lasting until 1855, one until 1884 and one until October 1961, these three periods being separated by sudden and drastic population reductions—true bottlenecks.

BOTTLENECKS AT TRISTAN DA CUNHA

In the first of these the numbers dropped from 103 at the end of 1855 to thirty-three in March 1857 (these figures include men temporarily absent from the island). This massive reduction seems to have been due to a combination of two principal factors, the

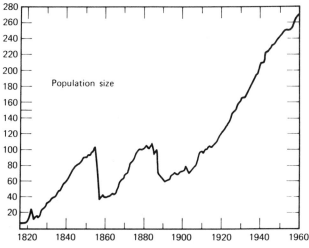

Figure 1. The size of the population of Tristan da Cunha on December 31 of each year from 1816 to 1960.

death of one man and the presence of another. In 1851 the first missionary arrived, and in 1853 the founder, W. G., died. After his death the cohesion of the community appears to have relaxed, and twenty-five of his descendants left for America in 1856. The pastor who remained on the island until 1857 became increasingly convinced that emigration was necessary for the population. Whether this was true, or whether it was a projection of his discontent with his own lot there, will never be known, but he noted that there were "more than a dozen adult females here, with no prospect of a comfortable provision for life" and "it will be a happy day when this little lonely spot is once more left to those who probably always were . . . its only fit inhabitants—the wild birds of the ocean." Under his influence, when he departed, another forty-five islanders left with him for the Cape, settling at Mossel Bay and Riversdale. The presence of a pastor of this opinion at a time when the population was reorganizing itself after the death of its dominant character can only be regarded as a chance combination of chance occurrences. The growth curve of population size to this date shows no sign of flattening, and no indication that numbers were approaching the limit that the island could support.

The second bottleneck was neither quite so extreme nor quite so abrupt. It was triggered by a disaster. The island has no natural harbour, and any vessels that called stood offshore while the islanders put out to them in their small boats. Sometimes they also put out to board passing vessels, for trade. On November 28, 1885, a boat manned by fifteen adult males set off to intercept a passing vessel but, in full view of the watching remaining islanders, vanished beneath the waves. Not one man was saved. This disaster made Tristan an "island of widows" and depleted the population of its adult providers. It left on the island four adult men, of whom one was insane and two were very aged, to support the remaining population. Despite the considerable distress that immediately followed, by August of the next year the population as a whole had accommodated to the situation—for example, adolescent boys had taken over crew duties in the boat—and a petition, organized by those who had emigrated to South Africa, formally to evacuate the island was rejected. During the next few years, however, many of the widows and their offspring left the island of their own accord, and the population declined to a second minimum in 1891. The reduction in numbers this time was not by two-thirds but by a little less than half, from 106 to 59. Again, this reduction is a direct result of accident. The population thereafter began its most recent phase of increase.

EFFECTS ON THE GENE POOL

The genetic constitution of the population in 1855 is shown in the second column of Table 1. Twenty ancestors had contributed genes, their respective probable contributions to the gene pool varying from 0.005 to 0.137; the two greatest contributions were from the two original settlers, W. G. and his wife, M. L., and the next three from two of the women from St Helena, S. W. and S. K., and from R.

R., the earliest of the men to arrive after the founding of the settlement. These five individuals contributed more than half the genes in the gene pool of the population at the end of 1855.

The effect of the first reduction in population is shown by comparison of the third with the second column of Table 1. The primary effect was deprivation of the population of eight of its founder ancestors and a recent arrival whose total contributions in 1855 had been more than one-third—genes from only eleven were to be found in the new gene pool. Second, there was a change in their relative contributions. Genes from two of the principal contributors were among those that completely disappeared. The greatest contribution now was from S. W. (0.191), and the next three largest were from her husband, T. S., her sister, M. W., and her husband, A. C. (0.139 each)—the contributions from these three individuals were more than doubled. These four individuals together now contributed 60 per cent of the genes in the new population compared with their previous total of less than 29 per cent. The contributions of the first two settlers were halved, and that of a former minor contributor (T. R.) multiplied nearly three-fold (from 0.005 to 0.014).

In the phase of increase that followed this first reduction, the contribution of one further ancestor was lost, but new contributions to the island's gene pool came from six more arrivals. The relative contributions from the original ancestors correspondingly declined with the exception of one (T. R.). By the end of 1884 the gene pool derived from sixteen individuals. It was relatively little affected by the boat disaster itself—the greatest changes were in the contributions of S. P. (0.061 to 0.071), W. G. and M. L. (0.055 to 0.047)—but the subsequent population size reduction had a much more pronounced effect, shown by comparison of columns 4 and 5. Again, there was loss of all the genes from several contributors, and again there was a rearrangement of the relative contributions of the remainder. The contributions (totalling some 8 per cent) lost were from four relatively recent arrivals, so that in 1891 the gene pool derived from only twelve individuals. The greatest contribution was still that from S. W., increasing from 0.139 to 0.186, the second largest from her husband

T. S., increasing from 0.094 to 0.144. But the third largest was from a much later immigrant woman, S. P., which nearly doubled, from 0.061 to 0.119, while the former principal contributors, M. W. and A. C., dropped to fifth and eighth places, respectively, from 0.138 to 0.081 and from 0.129 to 0.064.

THE GENE POOL IN 1961

The final column of Table 1 shows the probable contributions to the gene pool in October 1961, when the island was evacuated. In the intervening period all the genes from one earlier arrival had been lost, and eight new arrivals had contributed 22.4 per cent of the total to the gene pool, which thus derived from nineteen ancestors. The principal changes were the diminution in the contributions of A. H. and M. W. by about half, and of P. G. and A. C. by about one-third, and the great contributions (sixth and seventh in order of size) made by two of the new arrivals. But the three greatest contributions were made by the same individuals as in 1891. Indeed, there is a marked overall similarity between the figures for 1961 and those for 1891.

Tracing the contributions of particular ancestors (Fig. 2), it was the first exodus that halved the contributions of the first two settlers, and then, after a period of slight decline, the second size reduction increased them to nearly the 1961 figure. The predominance of the two principal contributors to the 1961 population is traceable to the first exodus that doubled their original contribution, and then, after a decline, to the second exodus that elevated them to the 1961 values. From the minor contributor, T.R. (No. 8), nearly 4 per cent of the 1961 gene pool derives, largely because the first exodus nearly trebled his contribution and the second exodus multiplied it by another 2.5 times. Two of the most prolific of the early settlers, M. W. and A. C. (Nos. 9 and 10), contribute only a little more than 4 per cent each to the 1961 gene pool; their contribution was doubled by the first exodus and then halved again by the second.

The overall effect is shown in Fig. 3. The gene pool of the population is taken as unity, and the proportion of it derived from each ancestor is shown to scale by the width of the band; time along the abscissa is not to scale.

Table 1

PROBABLE CONTRIBUTIONS TO THE GENE POOL
OF THE POPULATION
IN 1855, 1857, 1884, 1891 AND 1961

Ancestor		1855	1857	1884	1891	1961
W.G.	1	0.1275	0.0625	0.0548	0.0657	0.0691
M.L.	2	0.1373	0.0625	0.0548	0.0657	0.0691
T.S.	3	0.0662	0.1389	0.0943	0.1441	0.1339
S.W.	4	0.0907	0.1910	0.1392	0.1864	0.1602
F.M.W.	5	0.0245	0.0521	0.0448	0.0424	0.0263
R.R.	6	0.0637	—	—	—	—
S.K.	7	0.0858	—	—	—	—
T.R.	8	0.0049	0.0139	0.0177	0.0424	0.0382
M.W.	9	0.0637	0.1389	0.1380	0.0805	0.0424
A.C.	10	0.0637	0.1389	0.1285	0.0636	0.0424
P.G.	11	0.0490	0.1042	0.0896	0.0847	0.0526
C.T.	12	0.0490	—	—	—	—
P.M.	13	0.0441	—	—	—	—
W.D.	14	0.0588	—	—	—	—
M.F.	15	0.0049	—	—	—	—
G.	16	0.0049	—	—	—	—
A.H.	17	0.0245	0.0833	0.0684	0.0890	0.0365
F.R.C.	18	0.0049	0.0139	—	—	—
F.F.K.	19	0.0221	—	—	—	—
B.	20	0.0098	—	—	—	—
J.B.	21	—	—	0.0472	—	—
S.P.	22	—	—	0.0613	0.1186	0.1045
F.R.	23	—	—	0.0283	0.0170	—
R.A.B.	24	—	—	0.0142	—	—
M.J.	25	—	—	0.0142	—	—
F.S.G.	26	—	—	0.0047	—	—
A.R.	27	—	—	—	—	0.0626
E.S.	28	—	—	—	—	0.0445
G.L.	29	—	—	—	—	0.0435
G.C.	30	—	—	—	—	0.0126
A.S.	31	—	—	—	—	0.0543
R.L.	32	—	—	—	—	0.0037
F.P.S.	33	—	—	—	—	0.0019
J.B.	34	—	—	—	—	0.0019

Both the exoduses exerted a considerable effect on the genetic constitution. This effect was two-fold: (a) the elimination of all genes derived from an appreciable proportion of the ancestors and (b) alteration of the actual and relative sizes of the contributions from other ancestors. Immigration in the periods 1857–84 and 1891–1961, although diminishing the contribution of each pre-existing ancestor, did not, it seems, appreciably change the size of these contributions in relation to each other, although further work is required to establish this point. But at the present state of the analysis it seems to be chiefly the two reductions in population size which bring this about. Furthermore, the effects of these size reductions persist, as comparison of the 1961 figures with those for each other year shows. The general similarity of the 1961 figures to those for 1891 implies that, apart from the contributions of the recent immigrants, the gene pool of the 1961 population

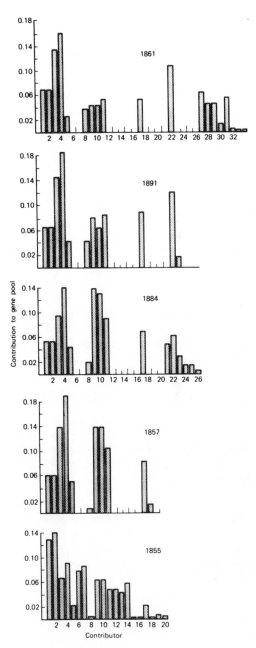

Figure 2. Contributions of particular ancestors to the gene pool.

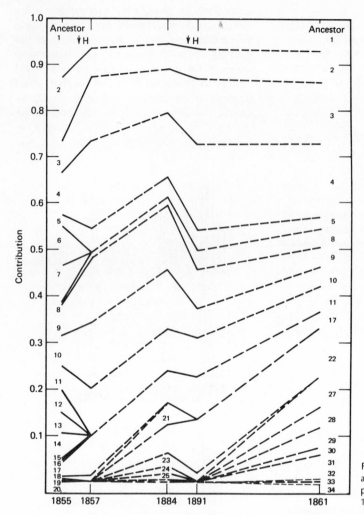

Figure 3. Overall contributions of ancestors to the gene pool of the population in 1855, 1857, 1884 and 1961. H shows serious bottleneck.

derives in its major features principally from the reduction in population that occurred between 1884 and 1891, and the modification that occurred then acted on the gene pool the features of which had been chiefly derived from the effects of the earlier exodus.

REDUCTION OF POPULATION AND GENETIC DRIFT

I have documented here, perhaps for the first time in a human population, the effects of drastic population reduction on the genetic constitution of the population. In both of the bottlenecks there are two primary effects: (a) deprivation of the population of the genetic contribution of some founder ancestors, that is, a reduction in the number of contributing ancestors, and (b)

change in the relative contributions of the remainder. The effects of these size reductions persist and, in accumulation, shape the profile of ancestral contributions to the gene pool of the present population; this in 1961 bears much more resemblance to the 1891 profile than to that of 1855. The present profile bears little relationship to the fertility of the ancestors, though further analysis is in progress to assess the relative importance of accumulated differential fertility effects. But there can no longer be any doubt that reduction in population size of the magnitude that occurs in nature must have a severe effect on the genetic constitution of a population.

There are, of course, drawbacks to this method of envisaging the gene pool as a pack of probable ancestral contributions. It obviously depends on the reliability of the pedigree. All possible steps were taken to ensure accuracy by comparison of the accounts of descent collected by different investigators, by checking these against the known movements of individuals to and away from the island, and by comparing all pedigrees with the information on the large number of genetic markers that is available for this population. In the few cases where paternity remained in doubt, it was possible to assign the most probable father on the basis of the known genotypes. No other population has been so intensively studied and the pedigree information now available can be regarded as the most reliable possible. The second drawback is that the work is couched in terms of probabilities. Although on average a child possesses a quarter of the genes of each grandparent, it is an extremely remote possibility that a given child actually carries no gene derived from a particular grandparent. While this would be quite unlikely taken over all loci, on the other hand, it is much more likely for a single locus. It is therefore interesting to compare observed numbers of genes with the probable numbers expected from the present work. The C_5 serum cholinesterase phenotype occurs in thirty-six individuals out of 213 tested;[21] there is little doubt that this gene was introduced by S.W., whose contribution to the 1961 population was 0.16; this gives an expected number of thirty-four heterozygous carriers in the population, instead of the observed thirty-six. The very slight gain of the C_5 gene is perhaps a result of intergenerational gamete sampling, or perhaps of selection. The pack method taken as a starting point for this analysis of the effects of population size reduction is obviously a powerful one for the elucidation of the effects of other processes on the gene pool.

This example illustrates the difficulty of assigning any given gene frequency change to any one category of evolutionary processes. Although the reduction in population was in both cases brought about by accident, there was a large non-accidental component to the reduction itself. In both cases family groups emigrated, so which genes and what proportions of them were lost from the population's gene pool were a partly random, partly non-random array. The families that departed obviously included individuals who felt they could no longer accept the

conditions on the island or its prospects for them, so the non-random component in part may be identified as selective. The fact that man is a social animal, that individuals tend to move and often act as family units, brought about, in this population, what may be termed a "booster" effect, whereby, although the genes lost from the population by accident were in actuality a random sample, the loss of some of them was exaggerated by consequent deliberate emigration of families.

This study therefore shows that there is no doubt as to the importance of drastic reductions of population in shaping the genetic constitution of an isolated population. The gene frequency changes they bring about, however, can only be attributed to drift when drift is defined so as to incorporate all random unique events, for there may be an appreciable selective component and in man there is also an exaggeration of the effects of both these processes by family ties and relationships. In populations such as that discussed here, drift so defined cannot be regarded as of inconsequential influence on their genetic evolution, at least in the short term.

I thank Dr. H. E. Lewis, the coordinator of the investigations of the Medical Research Council working party on Tristan da Cunha, for his help, and Dr. Robson for her original pedigree diagrams, Dr. Loudon and Dr. Mourant for making available results of unpublished investigations, and Mrs Majorie Smith for computational assistance.

REFERENCES

[1]Mayr, E., *Animal Species and Evolution* (Harvard University Press, Cambridge, Massachusetts, 1963).

[2]Sheppard, P. M., *Natural Selection and Heredity* (Hutchinson, London, 1958).

[3]Ford, E.B., *Ecological Genetics* (Methuen, London, 1964).

[4]Wright, S., *Proc. Sixth Intern. Cong. Genet.*, 1, 356 (1932).

[5]Wright, S., *Proc. US Nat. Acad. Sci.*, 24 253 (1938).

[6]Wright, S., *Genetics*, 16, 97 (1931).

[7]Wright, S., *J. Genet.*, 30, 257 (1935).

[8]Wright, S., *Proc. Amer. Phil. Soc.*, 93, 471 (1949).

[9]Wright, S., *Cold Spring Harbor Symp. Quant. Biol.*, 20, 16 (1955).

[10]Birdsell, J. B., *Cold Spring Harbor Symp. Quant. Biol.*, 15, 259 (1950).

[11]Glass, B., Sacks, M. S., Johns, E. F., and Hess, C., *Amer. Nat.*, 86, 145 (1952).

[12]Giles, E., Walsh, R. J., and Bradley, M. A., *Ann. NY Acad. Sci.*, 134, 655 (1966).

[13]Glass, B., *Amer. J. Phys. Anth.*, 14, 541 (1956).

[14]Roberts, D. F., *J. Roy. Anth. Inst.*, 95, 87 (1965).

[15]Lasker, G. W., *Amer. Anth.*, 54, 433 (1952).

[16]Roberts, D. F., *Hyman Biol.*, 28, 325 (1956).

[17]Roberts, D. F., *Acta Genetica Stat. Med.*, 6, 446 (1956).

[18]Alstrom, C. H., *Acta Genetica Stat. Med.*, 8, 295 (1958).

[19]Bonne, B., *Human Biol.*, 35, 61 (1963).

[20]Cavalli-Sforza, L. L., Barrai, I., and Edwards, A. W. F., *Cold Spring Harbor Symp. Quant. Biol.*, 29, 9 (1964).

[21]Harris, H., Hopkinson, D. A., Robson, E. B., and Whittaker, M., *Ann. Human Genet.*, 26, 359 (1913).

5

SOMATIC PATHS TO CULTURE
J. N. Spuhler [1]

Man is but one of the myriad creatures in the animal kingdom. While the forces that have shaped his development are no different in general from those that have shaped the other groups of living things, certain of the specifics are unique. Of course, this can be said of almost any group, but our concern here is with human evolution and, consequently, we have chosen Spuhler's essay for its focus on those particular capacities that have been especially crucial to the development of the condition we call human.

The reader should be aware that Spuhler wrote this article more than a dozen years ago. As some of the subsequent essays will show, his acceptance of Proconsul and Pithecanthropus as valid genera has not stood the test of time, the specimens included now being regarded respectively as belonging to Dryopithecus and Homo. This reduces the number of genera to be considered, and that, plus some recent Pliocene finds and a considerable lengthening of the period under consideration, indicates that the amount and rate of change in the line leading to modern man has differed less from those of other animals than was once thought.

Despite these changes in perspective, Spuhler's focus on the seven general capacities that were necessary for the development of what became peculiarly human is as valid today as when it was written. And, in fact, his cautious stance recognizing that the form of the human larynx may have influenced the sounds but probably not the capacity for human speech is far more defensible than the recent bizarre claims that the speech capabilities of certain fossil groups can be assessed from an examination of the shape of the skull and jaw. This latter view appears to be a bit of neo-phrenology of the sort that has been surfacing periodically for the last century, as it has done again recently (Hill 1972; Lieberman, Crelin, and Klatt 1972), and which seems impossible to squelch. Even though it is not the most recent writing on this subject, we prefer Spuhler's more balanced presentation.

Hill, Jane H. 1972. On the evolutionary foundation of language. *American Anthropologist* 74: 308–317.

Lieberman, Philip, E. S. Crelin, and D. H. Klatt. 1972. Phonetic ability and related anatomy of the newborn adult human, Neanderthal man, and the chimpanzee. *American Anthropologist* 73: 287–307.

For the present discussion, I am going to assume that culture is a biological adaptation, with non-genetic modes of transmission, which greatly supplements somatic evolution. Viewed in this way, there is a gap between cultural behavior and non-cultural behavior. The two sides of the gap are defined in terms of symbol and lack of symbol. Also, viewed in this way, we see that the gap is bridged. The gap was crossed in the past by the human species, and it is still being crosed by babies as they learn to become human.

Now certainly the behavior we observe in all human societies is fundamentally different in some respects from the behavior we observe in societies of monkeys, apes, and insects. We all recognize the rich symbolic character of human behavior. But I want to stress the bridge—the crossing of the gap from non-symbolic to symbolic behavior—

[1]Aside from minor changes, the present paper is the version presented in the American Anthropological Association symposium on the "Evolution of Man's Capacity for Culture," Chicago, 29 December 1957.

and not the gap itself. To me it appears absolutely necessary to consider both in the history of the species and of the individual that certain conditions are prerequisites for the full acquisition of culture whether by individuals or by the species. And we find these elements in babies before they begin to use symbols and we find certain of them in the behavior of monkeys and apes. Of course the above statements refer to culture in the specific sense of that variety of culture realized by members of the genus *Homo* and not to culture in the generic sense, not to all conceivable varieties of culture.[2]

Since all agree that modern man has culture, or is cultural, the easiest way in which I could discuss the morphological paths to culture would be to summarize the evidence which supports some particular phylogeny leading to man. The argument would then be: 1) Man has culture. 2) This or that phylogenetic diagram tells us how man changed from some non-cultural stem primate in the Paleocene to what he looks like today. In one sense this would be a proper discussion of the somatic paths to culture. It is important, and perhaps lucky, that we can make such pictures of man's biological history with a considerable amount of credibility. But this approach, while valuable, is not sufficient to help us understand the historical biology of human behavior, and I am not going to give it much attention here.

In thinking about human phylogeny, I believe in using all, or nearly all, the hominoid fossils we know about, so long as they are not fragments. To argue that none of the known man-like fossils are in *the* human phylogenetic line seems to me obscurantist. To argue that the fossils we know about are "somewhat near" but not exactly on the main line seems unnecessarily cautious and hedging and may give the unknown greater weight than the known. Perhaps Weidenreich (1946) and Heberer (1950) went too far in using all known hominid specimens they considered authentic. But I prefer their use of all of them to Wood Jones' (1948) use of almost none.

[2]In a more extended treatment it would be useful to make "society" a level of integration between biology and culture. There are a number of recognizable and important primate "social paths to culture."

There is not space here to give a review of new developments in human paleontology. In the last few years we have acquired a wealth of new specimens and new ideas and we have also been able to discard some old specimens and ideas with good cause. If additional fossils become available it may be necessary to make major revisions in what I am about to say. By taking an abstract level—the level of the taxonomic genus—I can avoid some undecided issues on the phylogenetic placement of individual specimens. For the moment I am going to assume a human evolutionary sequence of 4 or 5 genera (Clark, 1955):

1. Leaving out the periods before the Miocene, we start with *Proconsul*, the earliest ape whose skull is known (Clark and Leakey, 1951). I assume *Proconsul* had precursors who developed the general features of a man-like thorax and arms as we know them today, but that these terrestrial apes were not highly specialized as brachiators. There is no reason to suppose that any human ancestors since the Miocene have been arboreal to the extent characteristic of living gibbons, orangutans, or chimpanzees (Leakey, 1952; Washburn, 1951).
2. We don't know what happened in the Pliocene.
3. At least by Early Pleistocene there is *Australopithecus*, now known from dozens of good, or as Broom would say, "beautiful," specimens, and the earliest evidence of man-like animals with bipedal locomotion.
4. By Early Pleistocene times, and lasting into Middle Pleistocene in parts of Asia, we have the genus *Pithecanthropus*. From the neck down they were very like the genus *Homo* and like him they were tool makers, fire users, and hunters. Their brain volume was intermediate between *Australopithecus* and *Homo*.
5. At least by Middle Pleistocene we have the genus *Homo*, represented by such forms as Swanscombe, Fontéchevade, the Neanderthals, and Upper Paleolithic man. Everyone agrees that some, if not all, members of the genus *Homo* have culture.

Now, in the context of this sequence of 4

known genera, and with comparisons from living monkeys and apes, I want to discuss 7 biological topics which are preconditions for the beginning of culture. They are:

1. Accomodative vision,
2. Bipedal locomotion,
3. Manipulation,
4. Carnivorous-omnivorous diet,
5. Cortical control of sexual behavior,
6. Vocal communication,
7. Expansion of the association areas in the cerebral cortex.

Of course, these 7 conditions alone did not make a population of apes lacking culture into a population of men with culture. The evolution of man was not predetermined by a few conditions in a population of Miocene apes. Mutations are the fundamental genetic events in the historical process of the acquisition of the capacity for culture. Mutations are random events that do not point in an orthogenetic direction. But mutations are limited by the structure of the gene which mutates and this structure is determined by the evolutionary forces, especially selection, active in the history of the gene. In this way populations that survive accumulate genes which are favorable in the prevailing environment of the population.

To illustrate the complexity of human evolution since the Miocene as seen at the mutational level, let me do some speculative arithmetic—using figures that have fair justification and are conservative (Spuhler, 1948, 1956; Simpson, 1953). From the Miocene to now there must have been at least two million generations in the hominoid line. If the total breeding population in successful phyla was 10 thousand, we have 20 billion individuals as real or potential ancestors of modern man. If genes at the average locus mutate at a rate of 1 in 100,000, and if only 1 in 200,000 of these result in new and favorable steps (and that is a low estimate), we still could have about 20 thousand "visible," favorable mutational steps (in all loci) since the Miocene in the hominoid line.

Thus when we talk about 7 conditions we are perhaps oversimplifying the matter. But there is not time for further discussion, even if we knew what to say. And, I should add, the 7 conditions I list do not represent unit mutations, although mutation is the ultimate source of the genetic variation in each condition. Further, the order of listing is not strictly chronological. Evolutionary changes in the 7 conditions were interdependent and roughly synchronous.

1. *Accommodative vision.* Vision has been the primary sense in vertebrates as far back as we know them (Polyak, 1957). It makes possible their great mobility. The most complex vertebrates, birds and mammals, interact with their external environment predominantly *via* their eyes. Under the influence of the arboreal habitat, primate vision was perfected into a leading sense. Visual behavior is one key difference between the nocturnal, mostly solitary Prosimians, and the diurnal, more social Anthropoidea. The difference between these two is perhaps the largest gap in non-human Primate social behavior. With upright, or sitting-up posture, vision in the Anthropoidea gained strict control of manipulation—it became *supervision*, a guide and control of fine manipulation.

The relationship between the evolution of keen vision and fine manipulation is two-directional. As Polyak (1957) says: ". . . vision itself [became] more refined and the intellectual absorption and mental utilization more complete and lasting, as the skilled movements became more complex and more efficient." We will find that this kind of both-way causation with two or more systems evolving simultaneously, where progress in each stimulates change in the other, is important to the understanding of many topics in this symposium.

Before taking up bipedal locomotion, let me mention one good thing that came out of the Piltdown affair. It was the insight given, for example in Hooton's excellent paper of 1925, on the asymmetrical character of human evolution. Hooton was right, mostly for the wrong reason (Piltdown), but he was early to stress that different regions of the human body change at different rates. Many workers today would follow Washburn's (1951) separation of the human body into three regions distinct in phylogeny, with arms and thorax the oldest, the bipedal complex of pelvis and legs later, and the head and face latest of all to reach their modern form.

2. *Bipedal locomotion.* Although functional

differentiation of the front and hind limbs started with the first tetrapods where the front legs reach out and the hind legs push, *Australopithecus* is the first primate with upright bipedal locomotion (the tarsiers are bipedal hoppers). The australopithecine pelvis, sacrum, and femur resemble modern man in those features which make his upright posture possible. There are some features of full bipedalism not found in *Australopithecus*—these are fully developed in *Pithecanthropus* from Java and Peking. Australopithecine locomotion was certainly more similar to that of *Pithecanthropus* and *Homo* than to any of the quadrumanus primates. We must conclude that, by the early Pleistocene, hominoids were bipedal with free hands which could be used to handle tools. We will see that this was a master adaptation that demanded other adaptations leading to man's capacity for culture.

3. *Manipulation.* A good start toward precise manipulation is seen in monkeys. When monkeys sit up their hands are temporarily free and are used to bring objects close to the organs of touch, vision, taste, and smell. But something like a quantum jump is made when the hands are continually free for such activity as they are in an upright, fully bipedal hominoid. Then the arms and hands—under the guidance of binocular vision with good accommodation—are principal organs for interaction with the immediate physical environment. Getting food, eating, grooming, fighting, making, using, and carrying tools, these manipulations, accompanied by a rich flow of sense data including those from the more developed proprioceptive arm-and-hand muscle sense, enlarge the flow of information to the brain which in turn fosters development of association areas for storage of past experience with the hands and guides and initiates new hand movements. The neural delay required when some extra-organic tool is interposed between stimulus and response probably had much to do with the first ability to use symbols and the start of language.[3] The co-adaptation of the

[3]Probably no one today knows the exact significance of this. See C. Judson Herrick, The Evolution of Human Nature, University of Texas Press, Austin, 1956 for suggestions on the evolution of human mentation.

hands, senses, and association areas in precise manipulation seems a first basis for the subsequent development of human intelligence.

4. *Carnivorous-omnivorous diet.* Man and the tarsier are unusual among primates in being carnivores. Many monkeys are omnivores and take small animals as prey. Man is unique among living primates in taking large animals for food and these in large numbers.

Fortunately we have some fossil evidence on the problem of diet. It is still an open question whether the Australopithecines were hunters or the hunted. But by Middle Pleistocene times the *Pithecanthropus* of Peking were hunters of large mammals as well as gathers of hackberries and other plant food.

The change to a partially carnivorous diet had extremely broad implications for the social organization of early hominoids. Carnivores get a large supply of calories at each kill. This concentrated food is more easily transported to a central, continually used shelter than is low-calorie plant food, especially before containers were available.

Whoever killed the baboons and bucks associated with the Australopithecines must have been tool carriers as well as tool users. Tool carrying implies a degree of conceptualization not required in the occasional use of tools (White, 1942; Bartholomew and Birdsell, 1953). Before starting on the hunt there must be a minding which associates the tool with an event which is to occur in the future. This type of mentation has not been observed in captive chimpanzees or monkeys, and certainly not in wild non-human primates. The archaeological record shows it was a consistent part of *Pithecanthropus* behavior by Middle Pleistocene times.

Compact animal protein high in calories is a good basis for food sharing. Of non-human mammals it is only the carnivores that share gathered food. It is unlikely that the long dependency of human children—so important in the acquisition of culture by individuals—could develop in a society without food sharing. And the amount of information which needs to be transduced in a communication system for plant eaters like the gibbons is small compared to that needed in group-hunting of large animals. Gibbons share, by vocal communication, knowledge about the location of food collected and eaten individually on the site; hominoids share in the location, collection, and consumption of food.

5. *Cortical control of sexual behavior.* There seems little danger that modern anthropologists will overlook the importance of sex in the evolution of culture. Some of us fail to emphasize that, with regard to the physiology of sexual behavior, man is neither a) completely like most other beasts, nor b) completely different from non-human animals. Here, as in many other biological characters, the apes and man are alike and man and the apes are unlike other mammals. In the majority of mammals sexual behavior is seasonal and the sexual periods correspond to times when the female has high probability of ovulation and conception. In such mammals including the lower primates, copulation is evoked by an increase of gonadal hormones in the body fluids. In such animals we can bring about, or prevent, copulation by gonadectomy and hormonal injections. But in man and the chimpanzee, and probably also in other apes, copulation is strongly under cortical control and is not prevented by gonadectomy (Ford and Beach, 1951).

An important adaptation for culture is the change from built-in nervous pathways to neural connections over association areas (where learning and symboling can be involved) in the physiological control of activities like sleep, play, and sex. Cortical rather than gonadal control of female sexual receptivity may not be essential to the hominoid family (observations on other animals suggest not), but cortical dominance in sexual activity may have contributed to the easy transition of the family from a social unit where sex and reproduction were more important than food economy to a unit where subsistence is the dominant familial function.

6. *Vocal communication.* Human speech is an overlaid physiological function. It uses a set of body parts of quite diverse primary action. Consider the muscles used in speaking. Most of our coordinated muscular movement involves corrections and adjustments from proprioceptors. But the laryngeal muscles lack proprioceptors, and feedback control of speech comes by way of the ear and the 8th cranial nerve. When we talk, the voice box, tongue, and lips must work together smoothly and precisely. The 10th nerve controls the adjustment of the vocal cords and the 5th nerve the movement of the lips. Both of these involve branchial muscle while the 12th nerve moves the tongue with somatomotor muscle. The neurological basis of speech is not clear, but it is clear that the only place where the motor organs and steering apparatus of speech are wired together is in the cerebral cortex. Perhaps hand-tool manipulation in group activities like hunting coordinated by vocalization may have helped to make the connections.

Although the larynx is homologous in all primates its position in the throat differs in man. The larynx of quadrapedal primates from the lemur to the chimpanzee is in close to slight contact with the soft palate. This is why chimpanzees cannot make long, resonant sounds. As a consequence of upright posture and flexion of the craniofacial base, the larynx in man is moved down the throat away from contact with the soft palate, and an oral chamber is formed which makes possible resonant human phonation (Kelemen, 1948; von Bonin, 1955).[4]

This is not to deny a rich variety of vocal production to the chimpanzee and other primates. The position of the larynx, however, is one reason why attempts to teach chimpanzees English have failed. Unfortunately no one has tried seriously to teach a chimpanzee to learn to speak using chimpanzee "phonemes."

7. *Expansion of the cerebral cortex.* Current statements in the anthropological literature regarding the size of man's brain often involve misintepretations in one or the other of two directions. On one extreme, some investigators stress the fact that, compared with *mammals* in general, especially large mammals, man's brain is unusually large, both absolutely and relatively. For example, a 150 pound man has a three pound brain, while a 150 pound

[4]This was written before the publication of E. Lloyd DuBrul, Evolution of the Speech Apparatus, Charles C. Thomas Publisher, Springfield, 1958.

sheep has a one-quarter pound brain, and a 1500 pound cow has a one pound brain (Brody, 1945). On the other extreme, the stress is put on the conclusion that man's brain is indeed large, but not unexpectedly so. For example, when the log of brain weight in *primates* is plotted against the log of body weight, the slope of the regression line is steeper than it is among mammals in general (proportional to the 0.79th power of body weight in primates, the 0.66th power in mammals), and on visual inspection the plot shows—as log transformations often do—remarkably little scatter (see von Bonin, 1952, Fig 2), suggesting that brain weight in modern man is just about what would be predicted given the general regression of brain on body weight in primates and a knowledge of man's body weight alone (von Bonin, 1945, 1955). But if we take 1345 gm as a brain weight typical for modern man, say of 60 or 70 kg body weight (Bailey and von Bonin, 1951), we find man's brain is significantly larger than the value of 1095 gm of brain for 70 kg of body, predicted by von Bonin's (1955) regression formula: log brain weight=0.79 log body weight—1.00. A conclusion which avoids both extremes might stress at least two reasons for man's large brain weight: a) about 80% of man's brain weight may be explained because he is a primate of large body size, and b) about 20% of man's brain weight results from an evolutionary increase in the relative size of hominid brains—resulting in a total brain weight which is vast compared with mammals in general, and is significantly large compared with primates in general.[5] One reason we have overstressed the size of man's brain, even among primates, is that the chimpanzee and gorilla have relatively small brains, especially for primates. Similar arguments suggest that the frontal lobes in man, while well developed, are not of extraordinary and unexpected volume compared with other higher primates.

The distinctive feature of the human cerebral cortex is not so much in overall volume nor in relative size of the frontal lobes, but rather in the way that the projection areas are connected with association areas, especially in the temporal lobes, and in the way the whole thing works. I want only to point to these gross anatomical facts; Doctors Gerard and Washburn will take up their interpretation for cultural behavior.

RATES OF HUMAN EVOLUTION

In closing let me call attention to two sets of observations about rates of human evolution, one from paleontology and one from neontology. The first has to do with the rate of hominoid evolution as measured in genera per million years. Consider some sequence like this one (based on chronological data from Zeuner, 1954):

Period	Million Years Ago	Genus
Miocene	12 (25)	*Proconsul*
Lower Pleistocene	1	*Australopithecus*
Middle Pleistocene	0.5	*Pithecanthropus*
Upper Pleistocene	0.25	*Homo*

Using only known forms, without guesses about unknown ones, this sequence of 4 genera is close to a minimum one for hominoid evolution. Almost everyone would agree that these are good genera, although the taxonomic distance between *Pithecanthropus* and *Homo* is not so great as between the others. If one insists that additional genera must be put in (and probably there ought to be at least one more for the Pliocene) it will only strengthen the conclusion I want to draw. The point is that there has been an unusually rapid rate of hominoid evolution as measured in genera during the past 12 million years, and especially in the past million. This is apparent when we compare hominoid rates with those for horses, chalicotheres, and ammonites (Table 1). Something has speeded up hominoid evolution. I would guess that selection (perhaps within-species or inter-group selection) for a new type of environment—a cultural environment—has a lot to do with it.[6]

[6]C. H. Waddington has suggested a non-Lamarckian mechanism whereby variations in ontogenetic pattern initially brought about by environmental influence may, if subjected to strong selection, undergo genetic assimilation. See his The Strategy of the Genes, George Allen and Unwin Ltd., London, 1957.

[5]In the oral presentation of this topic, I put more emphasis than now seems justified on the thesis that man's brain is only as big as one would predict for a large and typical primate.

Table 1
RATES OF EVOLUTION IN TERMS OF GENERA PER MILLION YEARS
(Data, except hominoids, from Simpson, 1953)

Line	Number of Genera	Millions of Years	Genera Per Million Years[a]
Ammonites	8	160	0.05
Horses	8	60	0.13
Chalicotheres	5	38	0.13
Hominoids	4	12	0.25
Hominids	3	1	2.00

[a]For extant lines: Number of genera minus one per million years.

ONTOGENETIC RATES

Insofar as phylogenetic information can be deduced from observations on living animals, there exists among primates a general evolutionary trend to increase the duration of the main periods of the life cycle. The evidence is presented in Table 2. In the great apes the gestation period is lengthened to at least 34 weeks, full growth is attained by the end of the 11th year, and animals in their 3rd decade are senile. In man the duration of the prenatal period has changed little, if any, from that characteristic of the great apes, but the duration of the period of postnatal growth has almost doubled, and the total life span has more than doubled. Man is not unique with regard to the gestation period, but he is specialized in the marked elongation of postnatal growth and the long postponement of the onset of senility. These human specializations are extremes of trends found to lesser degrees in the evolutionary history of other primates (Schultz, 1956).

Man, then, is not much different from other primates, especially the apes, in the general sequence of events from conception to birth. After birth, the ontogenetic pattern in man differs markedly from that of all non-human primates but differs in a direction forecast by the general trend of primate evolution. I would guess that this elongation of the life periods after birth is a consequence of physiological adaptation to the acquisition of culture. Culture is a biological adaptation with a non-genetic mode of inheritance depending on symbolic contact rather than fusion of gametes. It has greatly supplemented somatic evolution. In all known human societies, individuals participate in social systems whose members represent more than a single biological family in which all are connected (as the social insects are) by gametes from one parental set. No human family is a self-sufficient system of social action. Symbols rather than gametes make this so. It may be assumed that the genes controlling the growth cycle in man have been changed through selection to man's *human, cultural* environment.

LITERATURE CITED

Bailey, P. and G. von Bonin 1951 The isocortex of man. Illinois Monogr. in Med. Sci., 6: Nos. 1–2.

Bartholomew, G. A. and J. B. Birdsell 1953 Ecology

Table 2
AVERAGE DURATION OF PRENATAL AND POSTNATAL GROWTH PERIODS AND OF LIFE SPAN IN DIFFERENT PRIMATES (SCHULTZ, 1956)

Primate Species	Gestation (weeks)	Menarche (years)	Eruption of First and Last Permanent Teeth (years)	Completion of General Growth (years)	Life Span (years)
Lemur	18	?	?	3	14
Macaque	24	2	1.8–6.4	7	24
Gibbon	30	8.5	?–8.5	9	30
Orang-utan	39	?	3.0–9.8	11	30
Chimpanzee	34	8.8	2.9–10.2	11	35
Gorilla	?	9	3.0–10.5	11	?
Man	38	13.7	6.2–20.5	20	75

and the protohominids. Amer. Anthrop., *55*: 481–498.

von Bonin, G. 1945 The cortex of Galago. Illinois Monogr. In Med. Sci., *3*.

——. 1952 Notes on cortical evolution. Amer. Med. Assn. Arch. Neurol. and Psychiat., *67*: 135–144.

——. 1955 Toward an anthropology of the brain. Annuals New York Acad. Sci., *63*: 505–509.

Brody, S. 1945 Bioenergetics and Growth. Reinhold Publishing Corp., New York.

Clark, W. E. LeGros 1955 The Fossil Evidence for Human Evolution: An Introduction to the Study of Paleoanthropology. University of Chicago Press.

—— and L. S. B. Leakey 1951 The Miocene Hominoidea of East Africa. London: British Museum (Natural History), Fossil Mammals of Africa, *1*.

Ford, C. S. and F. A. Beach 1951 Patterns of Sexual Behavior. Harper and Brothers, New York.

Heberer, G. 1950 Das Präsapiens-Problem. In: H. Grüneberg and W. Ulrich, eds. Moderne Biologie, Festschrift zum 60. Geburtstag von Hans Nachtsheim, Peters, Berlin, pp. 131–162.

Hooton, E. A. 1925 The asymmetrical character of human evolution. Amer. J. Phys. Anthrop., *8*: 125–141.

Kelemen, G. 1948 The anatomical basis of phonation in the chimpanzee, J. Morphol., *82*: 229–256.

Leakey, L. S. B. 1952 The Environment of the Kenya Lower Miocene Apes. IIe Congrès Panafrican de Préhistoire, Livret-Guide, Alger, p. 77.

Polyak, S. 1957 The Vertebrate Visual System. University of Chicago Press.

Schultz, A. H. 1956 Postembryonic age changes. Primatologia: Handbook of Primatology, *1*: 837–964.

Simpson, G. G. 1953 The Major Features of Evolution. Columbia University Press, New York.

Spuhler, J. N. 1948 On the number of genes in man. Science, *109*: 279–280.

——. 1956 Estimation of mutation rates in man. Clinical Orthopaedics, *8*: 34–43.

Washburn, S. L. 1951 The new physical anthropology. Trans. New York Acad. Sci., Ser. II, *13*: 298–304.

Weidenreich, F. 1946 Apes, Giants and Man. University of Chicago Press.

White, L. A. 1942 On the use of tools by primates. J. Comparative Psychol., *34*: 369–374.

Wood Jones, F. 1948 Hallmarks of Mankind. Bailliere, Tindall and Cox, London.

Zeuner, F. E. 1954 Chronological tables. In: C. Singer, et al., eds., A History of Technology, Oxford University Press, Vol. 1, pp. xlviii-lv.

6

CULTURE AND THE DIRECTION
OF HUMAN EVOLUTION
Stanley M. Garn

The previous essay emphasized the unique degree to which the hominid line has pushed the development of the basic capacities shared with the rest of the animal world; the present essay shows that for any given trait, and allowing the perspective of the hominid fossil record, there is no unbridgeable gap between the human and the nonhuman condition. Instead, it is the cumulative impact of the configuration produced by hominid trait development that is unique to mankind. The consequence of this trait configuration is culture. In the recent past, definitions of culture tended to stress its tool-making aspects, but it still seems most pertinent to quote the definition proposed a century ago by the pioneering English anthropologist, E.B. Tylor: "Culture . . . is that complex whole which includes knowledge, belief, art, morals, law, custom, and any other capabilities and habits acquired by man as a member of society" (1871, reprinted in 1958, p.1).

Our reason for preferring the broader, early definition is related to Garn's observations concerning the lack of specific gaps in the development of the human condition. Since the writing of Spuhler's and Garn's articles, studies of wild-living chimpanzees have revealed that they not only make and use rudimentary tools, but that they do so in the anticipation of their use and that this behavior is learned within the context of specific chimpanzee societies. Evidently there are pieces of knowledge that chimpanzees acquire as members of their groups (Goodall 1963, 1967; van Lawick-Goodall 1971). To be sure, the chimpanzee reliance on culture does not approach the human degree of total dependence, but it is consistent with Garn's cautions about claims made concerning the gap between man and non-man.

However, it is worth stressing the fact that human dependence on culture is unique and, as Garn notes, substantially alters the way in which the forces of selection impinge on human form. In recognition of this, one anthropologist (Brace 1967, Chapter 8) has suggested that man can be regarded as inhabiting a cultural ecological niche. Although this suggestion has brought some uncomplimentary comments, we still feel that it is of use in assessing the way in which selective forces have operated during human evolution.

Brace, C.L. 1967. *The Stages of Human Evolution: Human and Cultural Origins.* Prentice-Hall, Englewood Cliffs, N.J. 116 pp.

Goodall, Jane. 1963. Feeding behavior of wild chimpanzees, a preliminary report. *Symposia of the Zoological Society of London,* No. 10, pp. 39–47.

———. 1967. *My Friends the Wild Chimpanzees.* The National Geographic Society, Washington, D.C. 204 pp.

Tylor, Sir Edward Burnett. 1958 (originally published in 1871). *The Origins of Culture.* Reprinted with an introduction by Paul Radin. Harper Torchbooks, New York. 416 pp.

van Lawick-Goodall, Jane. 1971. *In the Shadow of Man.* Houghton-Mifflin, New York. 297 pp.

In the last million years, our own genus *Homo* has made considerable and apparently rapid evolutionary progress. From a rather small ground-scampering animal, man has emerged as a distance runner, attaining an adult fat-free weight of over 55 kilograms. Starting with a small brain of no more than

From *Human Biology* 31:1–13. Copyright 1963 by The Wayne State University Press. Reprinted with permission of author and publisher.

pongid proportions, there has been a three-fold increase in human brain-volume. And, from a molar row not far from 60 mm in length, there has been a full 50% linear reduction. Truly, evolution has reshaped us at both ends of the vertebral column, increasing our capacities to plan and to pursue, but decreasing our capacities to masticate.

Now it is tempting to speculate about the various directions that human evolution has taken, and to fit our trends into the broader picture of animal evolution. The human size increase during the Pleistocene may well be viewed as an example of Predator's Progress. The larger brain may represent organizational success on the part of smarter and less tolerant hominids. The smaller teeth we now possess may be due to relaxation of selection pressure following the development of food technology. But when we come to super-theories of human evolution, attempts to explain diverse trends in terms of a single set of adaptations, the probability of intellectual success becomes small. The literature now constitutes a graveyard of explanations for human evolution, explanations that no longer hold promise for explaining the multiple directions of evolutionary change. To quote Darwin on this matter, "Any fool can speculate." And sheer speculation we must conscientiously avoid.

And I think that it is important that many of the older speculations about the causes of evolutionary change in man were based upon the assumption of maximum differences between the fossils and us. Textbooks still emphasize these differences, and college students parse them at the tone of a Pavlovian bell. But, like the reports of Mark Twain's death, the morphological gap between Pleistocene man and contemporary man has been exaggerated and inflated. It is now necessary to adjust our thinking to the evidence that the major, postcranial reshaping of man was largely complete with *Homo erectus*, that despite changes in the way of life since the fossils from Java and China, man has remained very much the same below the cranial base.

But to speak of higher things, when we turn to the size of the brain there is no doubt of an increase from the African and Asiatic megadonts through the Javanese and Chinese fossils and on through to the forms we

accept as cospecific with us today. Some of this increase in brain size is necessarily allometric, the simple growth-associated relationship between bigger frames and bigger brains. Some of this brain increase, perhaps the largest portion, is a true increase in the volume of the brain; and here we must rack our brains to explain our brains. It is no longer enough to attribute even the first increase of hominid brain size to the mere rudiments of technology, and certainly not the second increase that followed Pithecanthropus. Surely man did not double and nearly redouble his cerebral volume merely to pick up sticks.

When we look upon the social adaptations man has made, adaptations to the improbable rules of his own making, when we observe (in even simplest societies) the highly complicated game of human relations, we wonder about the alterations in brain structure and brain physiology necessary to make such behaviors possible. The ability to adjust to complex relationships with an ever-changing set of age-specific rules, the needs for imagining, worrying, dreaming, and even speculating seem more closely related to our direction of brain evolution than simply using tools.

And now, in studies of ongoing human evolution, we have succeeded in climbing out of the bones and into the laboratory-based area of bio-chemical evolution. The clear fact is that man continually changes in response to new directions of selection. Over the last few thousand years, the rate of biochemical change in some populations has certainly been rapid, a rate attributable to intensive disease-selection. And, we now can demonstrate that the directions of disease-selection are due to changes in the way of life. Thus, the role of culture in directing the course of human evolution has first become clear for serological factors, for the hemoglobins, and for various enzymatic polymorphisms, rather than for the classical parameters of skulls and bones and teeth.

CULTURE AND THE PROBLEM OF FOSSIL DIFFERENCES

In describing the Pithecanthropus-Sinanthropus fossils from Java and China and the various "Neanderthals," much is commonly made of differences between them and us.

According to textbook descriptions (usually copied from previous textbook descriptions), these old-world fossils were unique in various ways. "Fossils" are supposedly characterized by unusually thick skulls, exceptionally large teeth, extra-massive mandibular symphyses, and patterns of tooth size and of tooth eruption not found in living man. Such characterizations heighten student acceptance of the notion that a taxonomic "chasm" separates the classical old-world fossils from contemporary man. And they suggest that selection pressure had to go far to convert palaeanthropic hominids into us.

But the fossils that achieve textbook immortality (like those that have gained newspaper notoriety) are a picked-over lot, remembered primarily because they were (or were once said to be) most unusual. Less extreme fossils have drifted into monographic obscurity and in some cases have not even been described at all. Fossil collections reviewed at a later date frequently reveal a cache of neglected breccia-mates, whose existence becomes known too late to change the taxonomic position now ascribed to the type specimen.

And fossil describers have rarely enjoyed the large comparative collection we have in our great museums today. Far too often, the past standard of comparison has been the dissecting-room pauper (plus an occasional "Hindoo" or "Kaffir" for skeletal variety). With inadequate facilities to compare the fossils, and inadequate bases to judge fossil variability against that of living hominids, it is not surprising that characterizations made fifty, thirty, and in some cases only ten years ago tend to exaggerate the picture of fossil uniqueness.

Now many of the fossils selected for description were thick-skulled, if published measurements can be trusted. But they were not so unique in skull thickness as we were wont to believe. And it is not necessary to search museums for isolated cranial extremes simply to demonstrate this important point, nor is it necessary to center upon thick-vaulted Florida and California coastal Indians. A contemporary series of living Americans extends well into the fossil range of skull thickness. With due precautions to exclude possible cases of Paget's disease, it is quite possible to show that contemporary Americans and palaeanthropic fossils do not

form separate distributions: the fossils are quite overlapped by living men and women.

Many fossils have been described as big-toothed, and surely the megadonts of Asia and Africa were as big-toothed as their name properly suggests. But from Pithecanthropus on, the exceptional nature of fossil tooth size (at least for the premolars and molars) is again open to question. With perhaps one classical exception (Pithecanthropus 4) modern and fossil tooth sizes quite overlap. The Neanderthals, as variously described, fit comfortably within contemporary ranges, and this observation is remarkably true for the Lower-Cave teeth from Choukoutien. The metrical position of these fossil teeth can best be portrayed and appreciated by a new comparison with living Americans who are by no means huge in tooth size (Figure 1). It is clear that the distribution of tooth sizes in contemporary American whites encompasses the "fossil" range to the extent that, as with skull thickness, there is no suggestion of a true taxonomic chasm.

Certain fossil teeth have been described as "taurodont" with pulp cavities huge by contemporary adult standards. Taurodont teeth are indeed remarkable, with enlarged pulp cavities extending deep into the root area. But the many allegedly "taurodont" fossil teeth are those of children, and it is with respect to children that comparisons should properly be made. Early in tooth formation, shortly after the bifurcate roots of the molars begin to calcify, enlarged pulp cavities may still be seen in occasional modern American boys and girls (Figure 2). With 45 degree-oblique views of developing dentitions, it should be possible to make a careful comparison of pulp-cavity growth in fossil children and contemporary Americans. Meanwhile, the term "taurodontism" should be restricted to those situations where pulp cavity enlargement extends well into the root area, after apical union is complete.

For some years, too, the notion has been current that fossil man and modern man were differentiated by the order of tooth eruption. Franz Weidenreich championed such a belief, arguing a real taxonomic "chasm" in this respect. Broom and Robinson (1951) and Dart (1962), in turn, have gone further by suggesting different sequences of

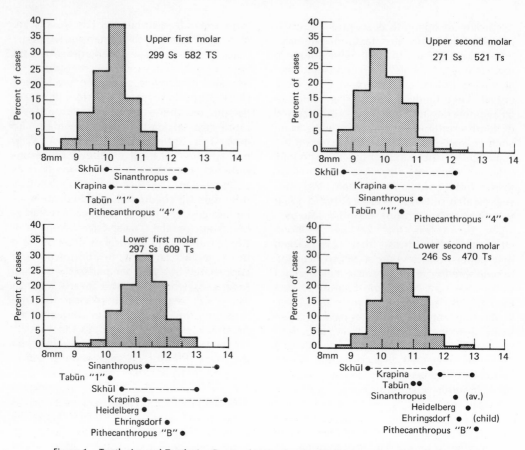

Figure 1. Tooth-size and Tooth-size Range of Major Fossils (data from Keith and McCown, 1939, Weidenreich, 1945, and Coon, 1962) Plotted against the Combined-Sex Frequency Distributions for Contemporary American Whites. While these fossils do tend to be large-toothed by our standards, it is clear that the majority of them fall within the contemporary range. (Mesio-distal crown measurements of more than 300 modern subjects made by Arthur B. Lewis.)

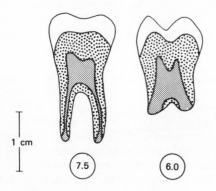

Figure 2. Example of Mild "Taurodontism" in a Set of Fels Siblings Aged 6.0 and 7.5 Years, respectively. Compare with Figure 7 in Dahlberg (1960), and Figure 4 in Lysell (1962). Mild taurodontism is by no means uncommon in contemporary populations, and is particularly obvious during the early stages of root information when the pulp chamber is at maximum size.

tooth eruption for individual Australopithecines, sequences which they claim to be "unknown in modern man." But the idea of one tooth-eruption sequence for fossils and another for modern man falls when subjected to careful review. It is a mistake to compare the order of eruption of the teeth through the jaws (that is, alveolar eruption) with the order of eruption of the teeth through the gums (i.e., gingival eruption). The two orders are not the same. Actually, and as we have shown, the M_2P_2 or "fossil" order is the usual order of alveolar eruption in modern children (Figure 3). And in ascertaining these facts we have further shown that the alleged uniqueness of fossil eruption-sequences is merely a lack of knowledge of the normal progress of the developing human dentition (Garn, Koski and Lewis, 1957; Koski and Garn, 1957; Garn and Lewis, 1963). Once again, and in a respect previously held to have great taxonomic importance, the fossils prove to be qualitatively not different from us.

Now this particular example, wherein an information gap simulates a basic biological difference, can easily be duplicated in yet another area of presumed taxonomic significance. Palaeanthropic fossils, according to the textbooks, are said to have massive mandibular symphyses, and high mandibular symphyses as well, as befits forms with supposedly massive dentition. Yet, by comparison to a rather small series of contemporary American adults ($N=258$) it would seem that we hold equal claim to the extremes of symphyseal size and massivity (Figure 4). All except one or two fossil specimens fall within the contemporary combined-sex bivariate distribution. All other euhominids, *erectus* or *sapiens* (taken from the listing of Weidenreich, 1945), fall well into the contemporary American white distribution. Many of the fossils (we might add) fall into the area that we now consider to be female by analysis of discriminant functions. Once again it would appear that the fossils are not qualitatively different from us.

Now I am not interested in displacing our ossified ancestors from their hard-won phylogenetic position. Nor am I interested in deflating their devoted describers, who worked without the manifold investigative advantages we enjoy today. Rather, it is my purpose to show particular respects in which the differences between the fossils and us are less than onetime claimed.

And if these famous fossils were not so uniquely thick of skull, so large of tooth, so massive of mandibular symphysis, or so different in the order of tooth eruption, how hard did culture have to work to convert them into us? I think that we all now realize that the *postcranial* skeleton of Pithecanthropus was contemporary in every respect. We no longer utter *caveats* about the limb bone of Sinanthropus, nor do we now picture Neanderthals as slouching, bent-knee half-men. And now, it would appear appropriate to observe that the facial skeletons of fossil and modern man are by no means so greatly different. Has culture modified man so very much below the cranial base?

The proposition is open that changes in the way of life have been concerned much more with modifying the brain of man than his jaws or teeth, at least since *Homo erectus*. And even here we must reconsider the evidence that still assigns the Java-China fossils to a separate species from us. Just as the provisional genus *Pithecanthropus* (DuBois) was ultimately reassigned to *Homo* (Linn) (Weidenreich, 1945), one may question the extent of differentiation between *H. erectus* (Weidenreich) and the successional species *H. sapiens* (Linn).

CULTURE AND THE DIRECTION OF BRAIN EVOLUTION

After reviewing tooth-size, symphysis-size, skull-thickness and tooth-eruption data on the Sinanthropus-Pithecanthropus fossils from Java and China, and on various "Neanderthals" and Neanderthal-like fossils, it is difficult to remain convinced of a major taxonomic gap between them and us. Depending upon the modern population selected for comparison, and exigencies of sampling within that population, it is easy to

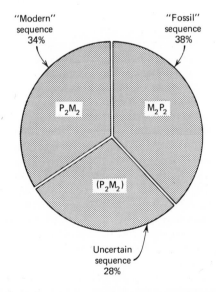

Figure 3. Frequency of the P_2M_2, (P_2M_2) and M_2P_2 Sequences of Alveolar Eruption in Contemporary Children. Although the M_2P_2 sequence has been claimed to be characteristic of fossil man, (Weidenreich, 1937; Schultz, 1944) this order of eruption *through the bone* is actually the most common sequence in contemporary Whites. Paradoxically, the M_2P_2 order is not diagnostic of the very fossils for which it was claimed (Garn, Koski and Lewis, 1957; Garn and Lewis, 1963).

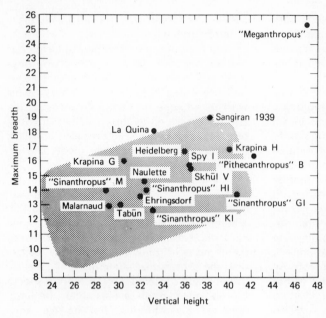

Figure 4. Bivariate Distribution of Symphyseal Sizes Showing Major Fossils (data from Weidenreich, 1945, Table VI) Plotted against Combined-Sex Data for 258 Fels Adults. While it is true that these fossils tend to cluster above the combined-sex contemporary means, it is also true that many fall below the discriminant line for American females. Note that Sinanthropus specimens G, H, K and M have narrow symphyseal widths compared to modern Americans, even though the technique of measurement used for the fossils tends to maximize this mandibular dimension. (Shaded area denotes contemporary adult data.)

surpass individual fossils with individual Americans or whole groups of Australians. I am inclined to agree with Weidenreich (1951, p. 226), therefore, that *all* the hominids now known belong morphologically to a single species, or successional species at most, and to suggest that below the braincase macro-evolution in the genus *Homo* came to an early end.

But the cranial contents provide a qualitatively different picture. The Javanese fossils within or slightly beyond the American range in tooth size had vastly smaller cranial capacities. The Lower-Cave finds from Choukoutien had smaller brains too. Now it is possible that some part of the smallness was allometric in nature, the natural consequence of small body size (*cf.* Jerison, 1955). Unfortunately, good stature estimates do not exist for the "Sinanthropus" fossils, the oft-quoted estimate of 165 cm being based on but one bone (*cf.* LeGros Clark, 1955). The estimate of 175–178 cm for Pithecanthropus is again a very limited estimate (*cf.* Garn and Lewis, 1958). Still, it would appear that no great correction need be made for body size in these fossils, and that subsequent human evolution raised cranial volume from below 1000 cc to perhaps 1400 cc, or roughly by one-half.

It does not seem sufficient to explain this cerebral increase by a simple improvement in manipulative skills. There is no reason to believe that the Java-China fossils were less handy with their hands than we. It is impossible to gauge linguistic skills by gazing at the backside of a mandible, so I will make no effort to introduce language. And, since neither Sinanthropus B-I nor the Ehringsdorf child was buried with a grave marker giving the true age at death, there is no confirmation for the belief that brain evolution has been paralleled by an increase in the period of juvenile dependency.

What, we may ask, is the adaptive advantage of more brains? Here we are truly stumped for a testable hypothesis. Do more brains make a better hunter? Does a more capacious skull make a more provident food gatherer? Do the personal qualities associated with more brains give greater access to females, and therefore more living children? What is the value of a 500 cc increase in brain volume, having 800 cc of brains to begin with? Does brain size have taxonomic meaning within the Pithecanthropus-sapiens range?

It may well be that early hominids with more brains were so intolerant of those with less as to eliminate them in wars of intellectual superiority, as Mayr (1950) has suggested. This presupposes an early origin of the battle between eggheads and pinheads, for which we have but one bit of evidence—the incidence of abrupt death and subsequent dismemberment in so many fossil remains.

We should have to grant the larger-brained hominids the advantages of deviousness, cunning and guile—preaching peace while practicing war. This is no flattering portrait of our forebears, arguing that they were no better then than we are now.

But these Pleistocene ancestors of ours were moving into an era of complex societies, an era in which equally complex rules were increasingly the way of life. As we know now, life in a horde is hemmed about by rules no less complicated than life in Outer Suburbia. Exactly how much brains does it take to learn that one's father's sister's daughter (if of appropriate totem) is fair sexual game, but one's mother's brother's daughter, not?

There is a need, even in the least complex cultures, to accept age-grading, otherwise the Leopard Society (or the accrediting board) will make short work of the upstart. There is a need to accept property rights, to observe tabus, and to cut the lawn at least once a week. There is a need for the young to recognize kinfolk (and therefore potential supporters), especially kinfolk with political power. But how much brains does political consciousness need?

There is a positive value in worry, if we mean by worry the vicarious living-through of potential events. There is a value in enjoying purely social and non-utilitarian games that mark one as a good guy (one might say a potential Dean). But does the game of power politics require more than 1000 cc of brains; and if it does, do the advantages accrue early enough to guarantee differential survivorship? Given the early average age at death in man till quite recently, plus the retention of fertility through the fifties at least, it is possible that in fossil years such intellectual abilities *did* convey an appreciable adaptive advantage.

When we view the increase in human-brain size from 900 cc to 1400 cc, it is natural for us to equate the additional volume with increased intelligence; but increased intelligence for what? Is intelligence as we customarily measure it by the Binet or Wechsler scales inherently adaptive? Or is intelligence, the function that we now test for, a chance by-product of brain changes that were truly adaptive during the middle Pleistocene?

Technically and technologically it is by no means certain that the hominids of Java and China (the small-brained men) were so far behind the larger-brained hominids that we all accept as co-specific with us. But social and even intercultural relations did increase, if we can judge from sites like the Shanidar Cave, bringing with them heightened interpersonal relations, with exponentially increasing possibilities for interpersonal conflict. With increasing chances for conflict, there obviously arose rules for minimizing conflict (as Etkin, 1954, and Chance and Mead, 1953, have suggested) and hence the need for a personality structure that could withstand both conflict and rules.

It is no secret that we are today surrounded by an extraordinary amount of informational noise, thousands of bits of information that are effectively irrelevant to survival or even to personal competence. But the signal-to-noise ratio is low, thus requiring (by analogy with vacuum-tube systems) rather complex circuitry to operate at a low signal-to-noise (S/N) ratio. Moreover, in a system where "information" is buried, there is need for a further type of circuitry, one that scans incoming signals for *pattern*. In the chaos of exhortations to buy this, do that, or vote for somebody, there are some few bits that are important (like the date for filing income tax), and some patterns that must be recognized (such as repeated failures to get grants). Circuits that discriminate at a low S/N ratio and circuits that are pattern-reading as well tend to be bulky. Is this the meaning of our 50% larger brain, as cyberneticists have been wont to suggest?

With increasing social (as against technological) complexity, it was inevitable that information input increased, and with it that kind of information that is effectively noise. This noisiness, we may presume, put a premium on the ability to discriminate between signal and noise. As total input increased, with larger groups and with more social complexities, the ability to discern pattern became of further use. Is this the key to human brain changes, *i.e.*, finer tuning, noise limiters, cathode followers and the like, all of them requiring more complicated and hence more bulky cerebral circuitry, neural component size being fixed?

The fact is that human-brain size did increase, either because brainier *individuals* were at an adaptive advantage, or because *groups* with larger brains survived and groups with smaller brains did not. It gratifies our ego to believe that selection favored intelligence, that our own ancestral lines came to genetic fulfillment because they were so very smart. But it may be that our vaunted intelligence is merely an indirect product of the kind of brain that can discern meaningful signals in a complex social context generating a heavy static of informational or, rather, misinformational noise.

CULTURE AND BIOCHEMICAL EVOLUTION IN RECENT MAN

In contrast to older and more familiar concerns with the skulls, teeth and jaws of fossil hominids, the newer interest in biochemical evolution may seem far removed. Substantively, the amino acids, hemoglobins and tissue enzymes represent an invisible world to paleontologists accustomed to osseous ontogeny. Methodologically, chromatography and electrophoresis are procedures a planet apart from skeletal comparisons and odontometrics. Even the time depth considered, thousands of years, at best, is minuscule to specialists who have pictured man over his million-year existence. But the biochemical and immunochemical evidence returns us to the initial quest for source and direction in human evolution. For the biochemical evidence clearly points to culture (i.e., the way of life) as the directing force in recent evolutionary change.

The abnormal hemoglobin S in Africa, the abnormal hemoglobin responsible for thalassemia in Europe and the Middle East, and red-cell phosphate dehydrogenase deficiency are all examples of adaptive polymorphisms. Elevated gene frequencies for hemoglobins S and E and G6PD deficiency similarly owe their existence to the fact that the heterozygotes are relatively protected against malaria (Motulsky, 1960). But, while malaria is the immediate agent of natural selection (with respect to these particular polymorphisms), it is man and his way of life that made malaria an important disease.

Malaria, and therefore hemoglobin S in Africa, may be traced to slash-and-burn agriculture which opened the forest floor to the stagnant pools in which the larvae of A. gambiae breed (Livingstone, 1958). Elsewhere man made malaria important by developing agricultural techniques that sup-

ported large human populations in potentially malarial areas (Garn, 1962). Such technological advances brought man to the insects and vice versa and they built populations of sufficient size to maintain a reservoir of infection. It is not the scattered nomadic tribesmen in Saudi Arabia who are the sicklers, but rather the inhabitants of settled oasis villages who have traded mosquito-free poverty for an enriched if more malarial existence.

Population size is crucial in disease selection. Small, isolated or nomadic human populations are effectively isolated both from each other and from infectious diseases as well. And hunting-and-gathering populations, limited by the amount of game a man can kill and carry, or the roots and fruits a woman can gather and pack, are likely to remain both small and isolated. But with the advent of agriculture, especially cereal-crop agriculture, larger populations eventuate and such larger populations constitute a disease reservoir. Permanent populations, moreover, attract traders who dispense both trinkets and microorganisms along their yearly trading rounds.

The impact of cultural level on disease and disease-selection is perhaps best shown for the African Bushmen. Continually on the move and few in numbers the South African Bushmen do not overtax the ability of dung-burying beetles to do an adequate sewage-disposal job (Heinz, 1961). But in contrast to the Bushmen, stable agricultural populations in Africa have a permanent sanitary problem to the point where intestinal parasites (coupled with protein malnutrition) become an important cause of death. Nomadic and peregrinating peoples outwalk and outrun both parasites and vermin, twin hazards of permanent civilization. Villages set in forest clearings, mud houses, and granaries all attract mice, rats, cockroaches and other domesticable insect vectors of disease. So it is that the great technological advances that made civilization possible brought with them diseases in turn, some carried by man, some by flies and mosquitoes, some by rodents and some by snails. Each of these communicable diseases, malaria, typhus, typhoid, paratyphoid and many others became actual or potential directors of human evolution.

Now the shift from hunting and gathering

to genuine food producing has had a profound directional impact on human evolution. The populations that acquired animal husbandry first, or those who learned to till the ground first, expanded first and thus achieved genetic predominance over the others. In history, as we know it, gene flow has generally been outward from the food producers. And more effective techniques of food producing brought new directions of selection in the form of disease, and (perhaps) a relaxation of certain other previously important directions of natural selection in man.

But agriculture, especially cereal and root agriculture, carries with it a potential danger, the ubiquitous danger of exclusive reliance upon a single crop. With the surrounding game exhausted, and with an increasing population to support, there is a too-common tendency to rely almost exculsively on the one crop that produces the greatest caloric yield. This tendency toward crop exclusiveness we see in the rice areas of Asia and corn areas of the Americas, particularly in the *Altaplana*. One-crop dependence carries disadvantages for each cereal has its own limiting amino acids. Moreover, the one crop of major importance tends to be deified, exalted out of all reasonable proportion, and ultimately viewed as an all-purpose food good for man, beast and in particular, child. And so in many parts of the world one-crop agriculture has resulted in protein-deficiency anemia (Scrimshaw and Behar, 1961), kwashiorkor, in part stemming out of the low-protein content of a particular grain or root, and in part stemming out of the culturally induced belief in this grain as the perfect food for the weaning and post-weaning period.

I need merely point out here the interaction between protein-deficiency disease, infection and the dysenteries. The evidence is now considerable that infection is more morbidogenic in areas of protein deficiency and that protein deficiency, in turn, constitutes a greater health hazard in areas where dysentery is common (Scrimshaw et al., 1959). Thus the very cultural advances that have resulted in large populations supported on a single climatologically adapted, highly productive crop constitute a directing force affecting both the tempo and the mode of recent human evolution.

We may view much of recent human evolution as a series of local adaptations (primarily in food-producing peoples) to disease situations arising out of food producing. In some cases man has made room for his diseases simply by favoring the insect or rodent vectors of the disease. In other cases man has moved to potential disease areas in actual pursuit of some particular food-producing economy. In general he has favored disease by increasing his numbers and by increasing the number of contacts with other populations. And he has favored disease-selection by developing dietaries that are themselves growth-limiting, and inimical to the maintenance of an optimum immuno-chemical (defense) system.

With respect to the cultural direction of hominid evolution in the early Pleistocene, we have at best speculations and conjectures. For the later Pleistocene we may postulate certain directions of cultural selection favoring increased brain size and (by relaxation of selection pressure) allowing reduction of tooth size. But all in all, and recognizing the extent to which the fossils are not as different from us as we once thought, the evidence for cultural direction of paleoanthropic evolution is far from good today. Yet, by the very same standards, it is apparent that the recent evolution of man has been profoundly influenced by a succession of psychological and cultural events. The very advances that made large populations possible brought about intensified disease-selection and rapid genetic change, as is now being demonstrated by students of geographical medicine today.

LITERATURE CITED

Broom, R., and J.T. Robinson 1951 Eruption of the permanent teeth in the South African ape-men. Nature, *167*:443.

Chance, M.R.A., and A.P. Mead 1953 Social behavior and primate evolution. *In* Symposia Soc. Exper. Biol., R. Brown and J.F. Danielli (ed.), VII, Evolution, 395–439.

Clark, W.E. LeGros 1955 The Fossil Evidence for Human Evolution. Univ. Chicago Press, Chicago.

Coon, C.S. 1962 The Origin of Races. Alfred A. Knopf, Inc., New York.

Dahlberg, A.A. 1960 The dentition of the first agriculturists (Jarmo, Iraq). Am. J. Phys. Anthropol., *18*:243–256.

Dart, R.A. 1962 A cleft adult mandible and nine other lower jaw fragments from Makapansgat. Am. J. Phys. Anthropol., n.s. 20:287–295.

Etkin, W. 1954 Social behavior and the evolution of man's mental faculties. Am. Nat., 80:129–142.

Garn, S.M. 1962 Human Races. 2nd revised printing. Charles C Thomas, Springfield, Ill.

Garn, S.M., and K. Koski 1957 Tooth eruption sequence in fossil and recent man. Nature, 180:442–443.

Garn, S.M., K. Koski and A.B. Lewis 1957 Problems in determining the tooth eruption sequence in fossil and modern man. Am. J. Phys. Anthropol., n.s. 15:313–331.

Garn, S.M., and A.B. Lewis 1958 Tooth-size, body-size and "giant" fossil man. Am. Anthropol., 60:874–880.

———. 1963 Phylogenetic and intraspecific variations in tooth sequence polymorphism. In Dental Anthropology, D.R. Brothwell (ed.). Pergamon Press, London.

Heinz, H.J. 1961 Factors governing the survival of Bushmen worm parasites in the Kalahari. S. Afr. J. Sci., No. 8:207–213.

Jerison, H.J. 1955 Brain to body ratios and the evolution of intelligence. Science, 121:447–449.

Keith, A., and T.D. McCown 1939 The Stone Age of Mt. Carmel. Vol. 2. Clarendon Press, Oxford.

Koski, K., and S.M. Garn 1957 Tooth eruption sequence in fossil and modern man. Am. J. Phys. Anthrop., 15:469–488.

Livingstone, F.B. 1958 Anthropological implications of sickle-cell gene distribution in West Africa. Am. Anthropol., 60:533–622.

Lysell, L. 1962 Taurodontism. Odontologisk Revy, 13:158–174.

Mayr, E. 1950 Taxonomic categories in fossil hominids. Cold Spring Harbor Symposium on Quant. Biol., 15:109–118.

Motulsky, A.G. 1960 Metabolic polymorphisms. Human Biol., 32:28–62.

Schultz, A.H. 1944 Age changes and variability in gibbons. Am. J. Phys. Anthropol., n.s. 2:1–129.

Scrimshaw, N.S., C.E. Taylor and J.E. Gordan 1959 Interactions of nutrition and infection. Am. J. Med. Sci., 237:367–403.

Scrimshaw, N.S., and M. Behar 1961 Protein malnutrition in young children. Science, 133:2039–2047.

Weidenreich, F. 1937 The dentition of Sinanthropus pekinensis: a comparative odontography of the hominids. Palaeontol. Sinica, n.s. 1:120–180.

———. 1945 Giant early man from Java and South China. Anthropol. Papers, Am. Mus. Nat. Hist., 40 (1).

———. 1951 Morphology of Solo man. Anthropol. Papers, Am. Mus. Nat. Hist., 43:205–290.

7

THE EVOLUTION OF HUNTING
Sherwood L. Washburn and C. S. Lancaster

No informed person now questions the fact that the modern human condition owes much to the shaping effects of a life-way that included hunting as a major component. Despite references in the press to "killer-apes" and visions of primeval violence embodied in King Kong and his ilk, these are largely unwarranted projections. The regularly manifest human capacity for lethal activity has no parallel among the nonhuman primates and almost certainly is an evolutionary legacy from the half-million years or more that the human line spent as the only primate who practiced hunting as a major part of its subsistence activities.

Many scholars have dealt with these matters, but none have done so as effectively as Sherwood L. Washburn. Over the past two decades and more, Washburn, often with the aid of his students, has shown a positive genius for zeroing in on crucial aspects of research on human evolution and articulating the key findings and consequent insights with unmatched clarity (e.g., Washburn 1951a, 1951b, 1953, 1959, 1960; Washburn and Avis 1958; Washburn and DeVore 1961; Washburn and Howell 1960). In many instances (including the present essay), the points, once stated, seem so self-evident that they quickly become incorporated into the very fabric of the thought of other scholars in the field.

The following essay, although not presented at the Man the Hunter symposium held in Chicago in 1966, was prepared for the volume, edited by Washburn's former students Richard B. Lee and Irven DeVore, that presented the results of that symposium.

Washburn, S.L. 1951a. The analysis of primate evolution with particular reference to the origin of man. *Cold Spring Harbor Symposia on Quantitative Biology* 15:67–77.

———. 1951b. The new physical anthropology. *Transactions of the New York Academy of Science* 13:298–304.

———. 1953. The strategy of physical anthropology. *in* A.L. Kroeber (ed.) *Anthropology Today*. University of Chicago Press, Chicago. pp. 714–727.

———. 1959. Speculations on the interrelations of the history of tools and biological evolution. *Human Biology* 31:21–31.

———. 1960. Tools and human evolution. *Scientific American* 203(3):63–75.

Washburn, S.L., and V. Avis. 1958. Evolution and human behavior. *in* A. Roe and G.G. Simpson (eds.) *Behavior and Evolution*. Yale University Press, New Haven. pp. 421–436.

Washburn, S.L., and I. DeVore. 1961. The social life of baboons. *Scientific American* 204(6):62–71.

Washburn, S.L., and F. Clark Howell. 1960. Human evolution and culture. *in* Sol Tax (ed.) Evolution After Darwin, Vol. II, *The Evolution of Man: Man, Culture and Society*. University of Chicago Press, Chicago. pp. 33–56.

It is significant that the title of this symposium is Man the Hunter for, in contrast to carnivores, human hunting, if done by males, is based on a division of labor and is a social and technical adaptation quite different from that of other mammals.[1] Human hunting is made possible by tools, but it is far more than a technique or even a variety of techniques. It is a way of life, and the success of this adaptation (in its total social, technical, and psychological dimensions) has dominated the course of human evolution for hundreds of thousands of years. In a very real sense our intellect, interests, emotions, and basic social life—all are evolutionary products of the success of the hunting adaptation. When anthropologists speak of the unity of mankind, they are stating that the selection pressures of the hunting and gathering way of life were so similar and the result so successful that populations of *Homo sapiens* are still fundamentally the same everywhere. In this essay we are concerned with the general characteristics of man that we believe can be attributed to the hunting way of life.

Perhaps the importance of the hunting way of life in producing man is best shown by the length of time hunting has dominated human history. The genus *Homo*[2] has existed for some 600,000 years, and agriculture has been important only during the last few thousand years. Even 6,000 years ago large parts of the world's population were nonagricultural, and the entire evolution of man from the earliest populations of *Homo erectus* to the existing races took place during the period in which man was a hunter. The common factors that dominated human evolution and produced *Homo sapiens* were preagricultural. Agricultural ways of life have dominated less than 1 per cent of human history, and there is no evidence of major biological changes during that period of time. The kind of minor biological changes that occurred and which are used to characterize modern races were not common to *Homo sapiens*.

[1]This paper is part of a program on primate behavior, supported by the United States Public Health Service (Grant No. 8623) and aided by a Research Professorship in the Miller Institute for Basic Research in Science at the University of California at Berkeley. We wish to thank Dr. Phyllis C. Jay for her helpful criticism and suggestions about this paper.

[2]The term *Homo* includes Java, Pekin, Mauer, etc., and later forms.

The origin of all common characteristics must be sought in preagricultural times. Probably all experts would agree that hunting was a part of the social adaptation of all populations of the genus *Homo*, and many would regard *Australopithecus*[3] as a still earlier hominid who was already a hunter, although possibly much less efficient than the later forms. If this is true and if the Pleistocene period had a duration of three million years, then pre-*Homo erectus* human tool using and hunting lasted for at least four times as long as the duration of the genus *Homo* (Lancaster, MS). No matter how the earlier times may ultimately be interpreted, the observation of more hunting among apes than was previously suspected (Goodall, 1965) and increasing evidence for hunting by *Australopithecus* strengthens the position that less than 1 per cent of human history has been dominated by agriculture. It is for this reason that the consideration of hunting is so important for the understanding of human evolution.

When hunting and the way of life of successive populations of the genus *Homo* are considered, it is important to remember that there must have been both technical and biological progress during this vast period of time. Although the locomotor system appears to have changed very little in the last 500,000 years, the brain did increase in size and the form of the face changed. But for present purposes it is particularly necessary to direct attention to the cultural changes that occurred in the last ten or fifteen thousand years before agriculture. There is no convenient term for this period of time, traditionally spoken of as the end of the Upper Paleolithic and the Mesolithic, but Binford and Binford (1966a) have rightly emphasized its importance.

During most of human history, water must have been a major physical and psychological barrier and the inability to cope with water is shown in the archeological record by the absence of remains of fish, shellfish, or

[3]Using the term to include both the small *A. africanus* and large *A. robustus* forms. Simpson (1966) briefly and clearly dicusses the taxonomy of these forms and of the fragments called *Homo habilis*.

any object that required going deeply into water or using boats. There is no evidence that the resources of river and sea were utilized until this late preagricultural period, and since the consumption of shellfish in particular leaves huge middens, the negative evidence is impressive. It is likely that the basic problem in utilization of resources from sea or river was that man cannot swim naturally but to do so must learn a difficult skill. In monkeys the normal quadrupedal running motions serve to keep them afloat and moving quite rapidly. A macaque, for example, does not have to learn any new motor habit in order to swim. But the locomotor patterns of gibbons and apes will not keep them above the water surface, and even a narrow, shallow stream is a barrier for the gorilla (Schaller, 1963). For early man, water was a barrier and a danger, not a resource. (Obviously water was important for drinking, for richer vegetation along rivers and lakeshores, and for concentrating animal life. Here we are referring to water as a barrier prior to swimming and boats, and we stress that, judging from the behavior of contemporary apes, even a small stream may be a major barrier.)

In addition to the conquest of water, there seems to have been great technical progress in this late preagricultural period. Along with a much wider variety of stone tools of earlier kinds, the archeological record shows bows and arrows, grinding stones, boats, houses of much more advanced types and even villages, sledges drawn by animals and used for transport, and the domestic dog. These facts have two special kinds of significance for this symposium. First, the technology of *all* the living hunters belongs to this late Mesolithic era at the earliest, and many have elements borrowed from agricultural and metal-using peoples. Second, the occasional high densities of hunters mentioned as problems and exceptions at the symposium are based on this very late and modified extension of the hunting and gathering way of life. For example, the way of life of the tribes of the Northwest Coast, with polished stone axes for woodworking, boats, and extensive reliance on products of the river and sea, should be seen as a very late adaptation. Goldschmidt's distinction (1959,

pp. 185–93) between nomadic and sedentary hunting and gathering societies makes this point in a slightly different way. He shows the social elaboration which comes with the settled groups with larger populations. The presence of the dog (Zeuner, 1963) is a good index of the late preagricultural period, and domestic dogs were used by hunters in Africa, Australia, and the Americas. Among the Eskimo, dogs were used in hunting, for transportation, as food in time of famine, and as watchdogs. With dogs, sleds, boats, metal, and complex technology, Eskimos may be a better example of the extremes to which human adaptation can go than an example of primitive hunting ways. Although hardly mentioned at the symposium, dogs were of great importance in hunting, for locating, tracking, bringing to bay, and even killing. Lee (1965, p. 131) reports that one Bushman with a trained pack of hunting dogs brought in 75 per cent of the meat of a camp. Six other resident hunters lacked hunting packs and accounted for only 25 per cent of the meat. Dogs may be important in hunting even very large animals; in the Amboseli Game Reserve in Kenya one of us saw two small dogs bring a rhinoceros to bay and dodge repeated charges.

With the acquisition of dogs, bows, and boats it is certain that hunting became much more complex in the last few thousand years before agriculture. The antiquity of traps, snares, and poisons is unknown, but it appears that for thousands of years man was able to kill large game close in with spear or axe. As Brues (1959) has shown, this limits the size of the hunters, and there are no very large or very small fossil men. Pygmoid hunters of large game are probably possible only if hunting is with bows, traps, and poison. It is remarkable that nearly all the estimated statures for fossil men fall between 5 feet 2 inches and 5 feet 10 inches. This suggests that strong selection pressures kept human stature within narrow limits for hundreds of thousands of years and that these pressures relaxed a few thousand years ago, allowing the evolution of a much wider range of statures.

Gathering and the preparation of food also seem to have become more complex during the last few thousand years before agriculture. Obviously gathering by nonhuman primates is limited to things that can be eaten immediately. In constrast, man gathers a wide range of items that he cannot digest without soaking, boiling, grinding, or other special preparation. Seeds may have been a particularly important addition to the human diet because they are abundant and can be stored easily. Since grinding stones appear before agriculture, grinding and boiling may have been the necessary preconditions to the discovery of agriculture. One can easily imagine that people who were grinding seeds would see repeated examples of seeds sprouting or being planted by accident. Grinding and boiling were certainly known to the preagricultural proples, and this knowledge could spread along an Arctic route, setting the stage for a nearly simultaneous discovery of agriculture in both the New and Old Worlds. It was not necessary for agriculture itself to spread through the Arctic but only the seed-using technology, which could then lead to the discovery of seed planting. If this analysis is at all correct, then the hunting-gathering adaptation of the Indians of California, for example, should be seen as representing the possibilities of this late preagricultural gathering, making possible much higher population densities than would have been the case in pregrinding and preboiling economy.

Whatever the fate of these speculations, we think that the main conclusion, based on the archeological record, ecological considerations, and the ethnology of the surviving hunter-gatherers, will be sustained. In the last few thousand years before agriculture, both hunting and gathering became much more complex. This final adaptation, including the use of products of river and sea and the grinding and cooking of otherwise inedible seeds and nuts, was worldwide, laid the basis for the discovery of agriculture, and was much more effective and diversified than the previously existing hunting and gathering adaptations.

Hunting by members of the genus Homo throughout the 600,000 years that the genus has persisted has included the killing of large numbers of big animals. This implies the efficient use of tools, as Birdsell stressed at the symposium. The adaptive value of hunting large animals has been shown by Bourlière (1963), who demonstrated that 75 per cent of the meat available to human hunters in the eastern Congo was in elephant, buffalo, and hippopotamus. It is some measure of the success of human hunting that when these large species are protected in game reserves (as in the Murchison Falls or Queen Elizabeth Parks in Uganda), they multiply rapidly and destroy the vegetation. Elephants alone can destroy trees more rapidly than they are replaced naturally, as they do in the Masai Amboseli Reserve in Kenya. Since the predators are also protected in reserves, it appears that human hunters have been killing enough large game to maintain the balance of nature for many thousands of years. It is tempting to think that man replaced the saber-toothed tiger as the major predator of large game, both controlling the numbers of the game and causing the extinction of Old World sabertooths. We think that hunting and butchering large animals put a maximum premium on cooperation among males, a behavior that is at an absolute minimum among the nonhuman primates. It is difficult to imagine the killing of creatures such as cave bears, mastodons, mammoths—or Dinotherium at a much earlier time—without highly coordinated, cooperative action among males. It may be that the origin of male-male associations lies in the necessities of cooperation in hunting, butchering, and war. Certainly butchering sites, such as described by F. Clark Howell in Spain, imply that the organization of the community for hunting large animals goes back for many, many thousands of years. From the biological point of view, the development of such organizations would have been paralleled by selection for an ability to plan and cooperate (or reduction of rage). Because females and juveniles may be involved in hunting small creatures, the social organization of big-game hunting would also lead to an intensification of a sexual division of labor.

It is important to stress, as noted before, that human hunting is a set of ways of life. It involves divisions of labor between male and female, sharing according to custom, cooperation among males, planning, knowledge of many species and large areas, and technical skill. Goldschmidt (1966, p. 87 ff.) has stressed the uniqueness and importance of human sharing, both in the family and in the wider society, and Lee (personal communication) emphasizes orderly sharing as fundamental to human hunting society. The importance of seeing human hunting as a whole social pattern is well illustrated by the old idea, recently revived, that the way of life of our ancestors was similar to that of wolves rather than that of apes or monkeys. But this completely misses the special nature of the human adaptation. Human females do not go out and hunt and then regurgitate to their young when they return. Human young do not stay in dens but are carried by mothers. Male wolves do not kill with tools, butcher, and share with females who have been gathering. In an evolutionary sense the whole human pattern is new, and it is the success of this particularly human way that dominated human evolution and determined the relation of biology and culture for thousands of years. Judging from the archeological record, it is probable that the major features of this human way, possibly even including the beginnings of language, had evolved by the time of *Homo erectus*.[4]

[4]In speculations of this kind, it is well to keep the purpose of the speculation and the limitation of the evidence in mind. Our aim is to understand human evolution. What shaped the course of human evolution was a succession of successful adaptations, both biological and cultural. These may be inferred in part from the direct evidence of the archeological record. But the record is very incomplete. For example, Lee (personal communication) has described, for the Bushmen, how large game may be butchered where it falls and only meat brought back to camp. This kind of behavior means that analysis of bones around living sites is likely to underestimate both the amount and variety of game killed. If there is any evidence that large animals were killed, it is probable that far more were killed than the record shows. Just as the number of human bones gives no indication of the number of human beings, the number of animal bones, although it provides clues to the existence of hunting, gives no direct evidence of how many animals were killed. The Pleistocene way of life can only be known by inference and speculation. Obviously, speculations are based on much surer ground when the last few thousand years are under consideration. Ethnographic information is then directly relevant and the culture bearers are of our own species. As we go farther back in time, there is less evidence and the biological and cultural difference becomes progressively greater. Yet it was in those remote times that the human way took shape, and it is only through speculation that we may gain some insights into what the life of our ancestors may have been.

THE WORLD VIEW OF THE HUNTER

Levi-Strauss urged that we study the world view of hunters, and, perhaps surprisingly, some of the major aspects of world view can be traced from the archeological record. We have already mentioned that boats and the entire complex of fishing, hunting sea mammals, and using shellfish was late. With this new orientation, wide rivers and seas changed from barriers to pathways and sources of food, and the human attitude toward water must have changed completely. But many hundreds of thousands of years earlier, perhaps with *Australopithecus*, the relation of the hunters to the land must also have changed from an earlier relationship which may be inferred from studies of contemporary monkeys and apes. Social groups of nonhuman primates occupy exceedingly small areas, and the vast majority of animals probably spend their entire lives within less than four or five square miles. Even though they have excellent vision and can see for many miles, especially from tops of trees, they make no effort to explore more than a tiny fraction of the area they see. Even for gorillas the range is only about fifteen square miles (Schaller, 1963), and it is of the same order of magnitude for savanna baboons (DeVore and Hall, 1965). When Hall tried to drive a troop of baboons beyond the end of their range, they refused to be driven and doubled back into familiar territory, although they were easy to drive within the range. The known area is a psychological reality, clear in the minds of the animals. Only a small part of even this limited range is used, and exploration is confined to the canopy, lower branches, and bushes, or ground, depending on the biology of the particular species. Napier (1962) has discussed this highly differential use of a single area by several species. In marked contrast, human hunters are familiar with very large areas. In the area studied by Lee (1965), eleven waterholes and 600 square miles supported 248 Bushmen, a figure less than the number of baboons supported by a single waterhole and a few square miles in the Amboseli Reserve in Kenya. The most minor hunting expedition covers an area larger than most nonhuman primates would cover in a lifetime. Interest in a large area is human. The small ranges of monkeys and apes restrict the opportunities for gathering, hunting, and meeting conspecifics, and limit the kind of predation and the number of diseases. In the wide area, hunters and gatherers can take advantage of seasonal foods, and only man among the primates can migrate long distances seasonally. In the small area, the population must be carried throughout the year on local resources, and natural selection favors biology and behavior that efficiently utilize these limited opportunities. But in the wide area, natural selection favors the knowledge that enables a group to utilize seasonal and occasional food sources. Gathering over a wide and diversified area implies a greater knowledge of flora and fauna, knowledge of the annual cycle, and a different attitude toward group movements. Clearly one of the great advantages of slow maturation is that learning covers a series of years, and the meaning of events in these years become a part of the individual's knowledge. With rapid maturation and no language, the chances that any member of the group will know the appropriate behavior for rare events is greatly reduced.

Moving over long distances creates problems of carrying food and water. Lee (1965, p. 124) has pointed out that the sharing of food even in one locality implies that food is carried, and there is no use in gathering quantities of fruit or nuts unless they can be moved. If women are to gather while men hunt, the results of the labors of both sexes must be carried back to some agreed upon location. Meat can be carried away easily, but the development of some sort of receptacles for carrying vegetable products may have been one of the most fundamental advances in human evolution. Without a means of carrying, the advantages of a large area are greatly reduced, and sharing implies that a person carries much more than one can use. However that may be, the whole human pattern of gathering and hunting to share—indeed, the whole complex of economic reciprocity that dominates so much of human life—is unique to man. In its small range, a monkey gathers only what it itself needs to eat at that moment. Wherever archeological evidence can suggest the beginnings of movement over large ranges, cooperation, and sharing, it is dating the origin of some of the most fundamental aspects of human behavior—the human

world view. We believe that hunting large animals may demand all these aspects of human behavior which separate man so sharply from the other primates. If this is so, then the human way appears to be as old as *Homo erectus.*

The price that man pays for his high mobility is well illustrated by the problems of living in the African savanna. Man is not adapted to this environment in the same sense that baboons or vervet monkeys are. Man needs much more water, and without preparation and cooking he can only eat a limited number of the foods on which the local primates thrive. Unless there have been major physiological changes, the diet of our ancestors must have been far more like that of chimpanzees than like that of a savanna-adapted species. Further, man cannot survive the diseases of the African savanna without lying down and being cared for. Even when sick, the locally adapted animals are usually able to keep moving with their troop; and the importance to their survival of a home base has been stressed elsewhere (DeVore and Washburn, 1963). Also man becomes liable to new diseases and parasites by eating meat, and it is of interest that the products of the sea, which we believe were the last class of foods added to human diet, are widely regarded as indigestible and carry diseases to which man is particularly susceptible. Although many humans die of disease and injury, those who do not, almost without exception, owe their lives to others who cared for them when they were unable to hunt or gather, and this uniquely human caring is one of the patterns that builds social bonds in the group and permits the species to occupy almost every environment in the world.

A large territory not only provides a much wider range of possible foods but also a greater variety of potentially useful materials. With tool use this variety takes on meaning, and even the earliest pebble tools show selection in size, form, and material. When wood ceases to be just something to climb on, hardness, texture, and form become important. Availability of materials is critical to the tool user, and early men must have had a very different interest in their environment from that of monkeys or apes. Thus, the presence of tools in the archeological record is not only an indication of technical progress but also an index of interest in inanimate objects and in a much larger part of the environment than is the case with non-human primates.

The tools of the hunters include the earliest beautiful manmade objects, the symmetrical bifaces, especially those of the Acheulian tradition. Just how they were used is still a matter of debate, but, as contemporary attempts to copy them show, their manufacture is technically difficult, taking much time and practice and a high degree of skill. The symmetry of these tools may indicate that they were swung with great speed and force, presumably attached to some sort of handle. A tool that is moved slowly does not have to be symmetrical, but balance becomes important when an object is swung rapidly or thrown with speed. Irregularities will lead to deviations in the course of the blow or the trajectory of flight. An axe or spear to be used with speed and power is subject to very different technical limitations from those of scrapers or digging sticks, and it may well be that it was the attempt to produce efficient high-speed weapons that first produced beautiful, symmetrical objects.

When the selective advantage of a finely worked point over an irregular one is considered, it must be remembered that a small difference might give a very large advantage. A population in which hunters hit the game 5 per cent more frequently, more accurately, or at greater distance would bring back much more meat. There must have been strong selection for greater skill in manufacture and use, and it is no accident that the bones of small-brained men (Australopithecus) are never found with beautiful, symmetrical tools. If the brains of contemporary apes and men are compared, the areas associated with manual skills (both in cerebellum and cortex) are at least three times as large in man. Clearly, the success of tools has exerted a great influence on the evolution of the brain, and has created the skills that make art possible. The evolution of the capacity to appreciate the product must evolve along with the skills of manufacture and use, and the biological capacities that the individual inherits must be developed in play and practiced in games. In this way, the beautiful, symmetrical tool becomes a symbol of a level of human intellectual achieve-

ment, representing far more than just the tool itself.

In a small group like the hunting band, which is devoted to one or two major cooperative activities, the necessity for long practice in developing skills to a very high level restricts the number of useful arts, and social organization is relatively simple. Where there is little division of labor, all men learn the same activities, such as skill in the hunt or in war. In sports (like the decathlon) we take it for granted that no one individual can achieve record levels of performance in more than a limited set of skills. This kind of limitation is partially biological but it is also a matter of culture. In warfare, for example, a wide variety of weapons is useful only if there are enough men to permit a division of labor so that different groups can practice different skills. Handedness, a feature that separates man from ape, is a part of this biology of skill. To be ambidextrous might seem to be ideal, but in fact the highest level of skill is attained by concentrating both biological ability and practice primarily on one hand. The evolution of handedness reflects the importance of skill rather than mere use.

Hunting changed man's relations to other animals and his view of what is natural. The human notion that it is normal for animals to flee, the whole concept of animals being wild, is the result of man's habit of hunting. In game reserves many different kinds of animals soon learn not to fear man, and they no longer flee. James Woodburn took a Hadza into the Nairobi Park, and the Hadza was amazed and excited, because although he had hunted all his life, he had never seen such a quantity and variety of animals close at hand. His previous view of animals was the result of his having been their enemy, and they had reacted to him as the most destructive carnivore. In the park the Hadza hunter saw for the first time the peace of the herbivorous wold. Prior to hunting, the relations of our ancestors to other animals must have been very much like those of the other noncarnivores. They could have moved close among the other species, fed beside them, and shared the same waterholes. But with the origin of human hunting, the peaceful relationship was destroyed, and for at least half a million years man has been the enemy of even the largest mammals. In this way the whole human view of what is normal and natural in the relation of man to animals is a product of hunting, and the world of flight and fear is the result of the efficiency of the hunters.

Behind this human view that the flight of animals from man is natural lie some aspects of human psychology. Men enjoy hunting and killing, and these activities are continued as sports even when they are no longer economically necessary. If a behavior is important to the survival of a species (as hunting was for man throughout most of human history), then it must be both easily learned and pleasurable (Hamburg, 1963). Part of the motivation for hunting is the immediate pleasure it gives the hunter, and the human killer can no more afford to be sorry for the game than a cat can for its intended victim. Evolution builds a relation between biology, psychology, and behavior, and, therefore, the evolutionary success of hunting exerted a profound effect on human psychology. Perhaps, this is most easily shown by the extent of the efforts devoted to maintain killing as a sport. In former times royalty and nobility maintained parks where they could enjoy the sport of killing, and today the United States government spends many millions of dollars to supply game for hunters. Many people dislike the notion that man is naturally aggressive and that he naturally enjoys the destruction of other creatures. Yet we all know people who use the lightest fishing tackle to prolong the fish's futile struggle, in order to maximize the personal sense of mastery and skill. And until recently war was viewed in much the same way as hunting. Other human beings were simply the most dangerous game. War has been far too important in human history for it to be other than pleasurable for the males involved. It is only recently, with the entire change in the nature and conditions of war, that this institution has been challenged, that the wisdom of war as a normal part of national policy or as an approved road to personal social glory has been questioned.

Human killing differs from killing by carnivorous mammals in that the victims are frequently of the same species as the killer. In carnivores there are submission gestures or sounds that normally stop a fatal attack (Lorenz, 1966). But in man there are no effective submission gestures. It was the Roman emperor who might raise his thumb; the victim could make no sound or gesture that might restrain the victor or move the crowd to pity. The lack of biological controls over killing conspecifics is a character of human killing that separates this behavior sharply from that of other carnivorous mammals. This difference may be interpreted in a variety of ways. It may be that human hunting is so recent from an evolutionary point of view that there was not enough time for controls to evolve. Or it may be that killing other humans was a part of the adaptation from the beginning, and our sharp separation of war from hunting is due to the recent development of these institutions. Or it may be simply that in most human behavior stimulus and response are not tightly bound. Whatever the origin of this behavior, it has had profound effects on human evolution, and almost every human society has regarded killing members of certain other human societies as desirable (D. Freeman, 1964). Certainly this has been a major factor in man's view of the world, and every folklore contains tales of culture heroes whose fame is based on the human enemies they destroyed.

The extent to which the biological bases for killing have been incorporated into human psychology may be measured by the ease with which boys can be interested in hunting, fishing, fighting, and games of war. It is not that these behaviors are inevitable, but they are easily learned, satisfying, and have been socially rewarded in most cultures. The skills for killing and the pleasures of killing are normally developed in play, and the patterns of play prepare the children for their adult roles. At the conference Woodburn's excellent motion pictures showed Hadza boys killing small mammals, and Laughlin described how Aleuts train boys from early childhood so that they would be able to throw harpoons with accuracy and power while seated in kayaks. The whole youth of the hunter is dominated by practice and appreciation of the skills of the adult males, and the pleasure of the games motivates the practice that is necessary to develop the skills of weaponry. Even in monkeys, rougher play and play fighting are largely the activities of the males, and the young females explore less and show a greater interest in infants at an early age.

These basic biological differences are reinforced in man by a division of labor which makes adult sex roles differ far more in humans than they do in nonhuman primates. Again, hunting must be seen as a whole pattern of activities, a wide variety of ways of life, the psychobiological roots of which are reinforced by play and by a clear identification with adult roles. Hunting is more than a part of the economic system, and the animal bones in Choukoutien are evidence of the patterns of play and pleasure of our ancestors.

THE SOCIAL ORGANIZATION OF HUMAN HUNTING

The success of the human hunting and gathering way of life lay in its adaptability. It permitted a single species to occupy most of the earth with a minimum of biological adaptation to local conditions. The occupation of Australia and the New World was probably late, but even so there is no evidence that any other primate species occupied more than a fraction of the area of *Homo erectus*. Obviously, this adaptability makes any detailed reconstruction impossible, and we are not looking for stages in the traditional evolutionary sense. However, using both the knowledge of the contemporary primates and the archeological record, certain important general conditions of our evolution may be reconstructed. For example, the extent of the distribution of the species noted above is remarkable and gives the strongest sort of indirect evidence for the adaptability of the way of life, even half a million years ago. Likewise all evidence suggests that the local group was small. Twenty to fifty individuals is suggested by Goldschmidt (1959, p. 187). Such a group size is common in nonhuman primates and so we can say with some assurance that the number did not increase greatly until after agriculture. This means that the number of adult males who might cooperate in hunting or war was very limited, and this sets limits to the kinds of social organizations that were possible. Probably one of the great adaptive advantages of language was that it permits the planning of cooperation between local groups, temporary division of groups, and the transmission of information over a much

wider area than that occupied by any one group.

Within the group of the nonhuman primates, the mother and her young may form a subgroup that continues even after the young are fully grown (Sade, 1965, 1966; Yamada, 1963). This grouping affects dominance, grooming, and resting patterns, and, along with dominance, is one of the factors giving order to the social relations in the group. The group is not a horde in the nineteenth-century sense, but it is ordered by positive affectionate habits and by the strength of personal dominance. Both these principles continue into human society, and dominance based on personal achievement must have been particularly powerful in small groups living physically dangerous lives. The mother-young group certainly continued and the bonds must have been intensified by the prolongation of infancy. But in human society, economic reciprocity is added, and this created a wholly new set of interpersonal bonds.

When males hunt and females gather, the results are shared and given to the young, and the habitual sharing between a male, a female, and their offspring becomes the basis for the human family. According to this view, the human family is the result of the reciprocity of hunting, the addition of a male to the mother-plus-young social group of the monkeys and apes.

A clue to the adaptive advantage and evolutionary origin of our psychological taboo on incest is provided by this view of the family. Incest prohibitions are reported universally among humans and these always operate to limit sexual activity involving subadults within the nuclear family. Taking the nuclear family as the unit of account, incest prohibitions tend to keep the birth rate in line with economic productivity. If in creating what we call the family the addition of a male is important in economic terms, then the male who is added must be able to fulfill the role of a socially responsible provider. In the case of the hunter, this necessitates a degree of skill in hunting and a social maturity that is attained some years after puberty. As a young man grows up, this necessary delay in his assumption of the role of provider for a female and her young is paralleled by a taboo which prevents him from prematurely adding unsupported members to the family. Brother-sister mating could result in an infant while the brother was still years away from effective social maturity. Father-daughter incest could also produce a baby without adding a productive male to the family. This would be quite different from the taking of a second wife which, if permitted, occurs only when the male has shown he is already able to provide for and maintain more than one female.

To see how radically hunting changed the economic situation, it is necessary to remember that in monkeys and apes an individual simply eats what it needs. After an infant is weaned, it is on its own economically and is not dependent on adults. This means that adult males never have economic responsibility for any other animal, and adult females do only when they are nursing. In such a system, there is no economic gain in delaying any kind of social relationship. But when hunting makes females and young dependent on the success of male skills, there is a great gain to the family members in establishing behaviors which prevent the addition of infants, unless these can be supported.

These considerations in no way alter the importance of the incest taboo as a deterrent to role conflict in the family and as the necessary precondition to all other rules of exogamy. A set of behaviors is more likely to persist and be widespread, if it serves many uses, and the rule of parsimony is completely wrong when applied to the explanation of social situations. However, these considerations do alter the emphasis and the conditions of the discussion of incest. In the first place, a mother-son sexual avoidance may be present in some species of monkeys (Sade, 1966) and this extremely strong taboo among humans requires a different explanation than the one we have offered for brother-sister and father-daughter incest prohibitions. In this case, the role conflict argument may be paramount. Second, the central consideration is that incest produces pregnancies, and the most fundamental adaptive value of the taboo is the provision of situations in which infants are more likely to survive. In the reviews of the incest taboo by Aberle and others (1963) and Mair (1965), the biological advantages of the taboo in controlling the production of infants are not adequately considered, and we find the treatment by Service (1962) closest to our own. In a society

in which the majority of males die young, but a few live on past forty, the probability of incest is increased. By stressing the average length of life rather than the age of the surviving few, Slater (1959) underestimated the probability of mating between close relatives. Vallois (1961, p. 222) has summarized the evidence on length of life in early man and shows that "few individuals passed forty years, and it is only quite exceptionally that any passed fifty."

That family organization may be attributed to the hunting way of life is supported by ethnography. Since the same economic and social problems as those under hunting continue under agriculture, the institution continued. The data on the behavior of contemporary monkeys and apes also show why this institution was not necessary in a society in which each individual gets its own food.[5] Obviously the origin of the custom cannot be dated, and we cannot prove *Homo erectus* had a family organized in the human way. But it can be shown that the conditions that make the family adaptive existed at the time of *Homo erectus*. The evidence of hunting is clear in the archeological record. A further suggestion that the human kind of family is old comes from physiology; the loss of estrus is essential to the human family organization, and it is unlikely that this physiology, which is universal in contemporary mankind, evolved recently.

If the local group is looked upon as a source of male-female pairs (an experienced hunter-provider and a female who gathers and who cares for the young), then it is apparent that a small group cannot produce

[5]The advantage of considering both the social group and the facilitating biology is shown by considering the "family" in the gibbon. The social group consists of an adult male, an adult female, and their young. But this group is maintained by extreme territorial behavior in which no adult male tolerates another, by aggressive females with large canine teeth, and by very low sex drive in the males. The male-female group is the whole society (Carpenter 1941; Ellefson, 1966). The gibbon group is based on a different biology from that of the human family and has none of its reciprocal economic functions. Although the kind of social life seen in chimpanzees lacks a family organization, to change it into that of a man would require far less evolution than would be required in the case of the gibbon.

pairs regularly, since chance determines whether a particular child is a male or female. If the number maturing in a given year or two is small, then there may be too many males or females (either males with no mates or females with no providers). The problem of excess females may not seem serious today or in agricultural societies, but among hunters it was recognized and was regarded as so severe that female infanticide was often practiced. How grave the problem of imbalance can become is shown by the following hypothetical example. In a society of approximately forty individuals there might be nine couples. With infants born at the rate of about one in three years, this would give three infants per year, but only approximately one of these three would survive to become fully adult. The net production in the example would be one child per year in a population of forty. And because the sex of the child is randomly determined, the odds that all the children would be male for a three-year period are 1 in 8. Likewise the odds for all surviving children being female for a three-year period are 1 in 8. In this example the chances of all surviving children being of one sex are 1 in 4, and smaller departures from a 50/50 sex ration would be very common.

In monkeys, because the economic unit is the individual (not a pair), a surplus of females causes no problem. Surplus males may increase fighting in the group or males may migrate to other groups.

For humans, the problem of imbalance in sex ratios may be met by exogamy, which permits mates to be obtained from a much wider social field. The orderly pairing of hunter males with females requires a much larger group than can be supported locally by hunting and gathering, and this problem is solved by reciprocal relations among several local groups. It takes something on the order of 100 pairs to produce enough children so that the sex ratio is near enough to 50/50 for social life to proceed smoothly, and this requires a population of approximately 500 people. With smaller numbers there will be constant random fluctuations in the sex ratio large enough to cause social problems. This argument shows the importance of a sizable linguistic community, one large enough to cover an area in which many people may find suitable mates and make alliances of many kinds. It does not mean either that the large community or that exogamy does not have many other functions, as outlined by Mair (1965). As indicated earlier, the more factors that favor a custom, the more likely it is to be geographically wide-spread and long lasting. What the argument does stress is that the finding of mates and the production of babies under the particular conditions of human hunting and gathering favor both incest taboo and exogamy for basic demographic reasons.

Assumptions behind this argument are that social customs are adaptive, as Tax (1937) has argued, and that nothing is more crucial for evolutionary success than the orderly production of the number of infants that can be supported. This argument also presumes that, at least under extreme conditions, these necessities and reasons are obvious to the people involved, as infanticide attests. The impossibility of finding suitable mates must have been a common experience for hunters trying to exist in very small groups, and the initial advantages of exogamy, kinship, and alliance with other such groups may at first have amounted to no more than, as Whiting said at the conference, a mother suggesting to her son that he might find a suitable mate in the group where her brother was located.

If customs are adaptive and if humans are necessarily opportunistic, it might be expected that social rules would be particularly labile under the conditions of small hunting and gathering societies. At the conference, Murdock pointed out the high frequency of bilateral kinship systems among hunters, and the experts on Australia all seemed to believe that the Australian systems had been described in much too static terms. Under hunting conditions, systems that allow for exceptions and local adaptation make sense and surely political dominance and status must have been largely achieved.

CONCLUSION

While stressing the success of the hunting and gathering way of life with its great diversity of local forms and while emphasizing the way it influenced human evolution, we must also take into account its limitations. There is no indication that this way of life could support large communities of more than a few million people in the whole world.

To call the hunters "affluent" is to give a very special definition to the word. During much of the year, many monkeys can obtain enough food in only three or four hours of gathering each day, and under normal conditions baboons have plenty of time to build the Taj Mahal. The restriction on population, however, is the lean season or the atypical year, and, as Sahlins recognized, building by the hunters and the accumulation of gains was limited by motivation and technical knowledge, not by time. Where monkeys are fed, population rises, and Koford (1966) estimates the rate of increase on an island at 16 per cent per year.

After agriculture, human populations increased dramatically in spite of disease, war, and slowly changing customs. Even with fully human (*Homo sapiens*) biology, language, technical sophistication, cooperation, art, the support of kinship, the control of custom and political power, and the solace of religion—in spite of this whole web of culture and biology—the local group in the Mesolithic was no larger than that of baboons. Regardless of statements made at the symposium on the ease with which hunters obtain food some of the time, it is still true that food was the primary factor in limiting early human populations, as is shown by the events subsequent to agriculture.

The agricultural revolution, continuing into the industrial and scientific revolutions, is now freeing man from the conditions and restraints of 99 per cent of his history, but the biology of our species was created in that long gathering and hunting period. To assert the biological unity of mankind is to affirm the importance of the hunting way of life. It is to claim that, however much conditions and customs may have varied locally, the main selection pressures that forged the species were the same. The biology, psychology, and customs that separate us from the apes—all these we owe to the hunters of time past. And, although the record is incomplete and speculation looms larger than fact, for those who would understand the origin and nature of human behavior there is no choice but to try to understand "Man the Hunter."

BIBLIOGRAPHY

Aberle, D. F. et al. 1963. The incest taboo and the mating patterns of animals. Amer. Anthrop. 65:253–65.

Binford, L. and S. Binford. 1966. The predatory revolution: a consideration of the evidence for a new subsistence level. Amer. Anthrop. n.s., 68(2), pt. I:508–512.

Bourlière, F. 1963. Observations on the ecology of some large African mammals. In F. C. Howell and F. Bourlière (Eds.), African Ecology and Human Evolution. Chicago: Aldine.

Brues, A. 1959. The spearman and the archer, an essay on selection in body build. Amer. Anthrop. (n.s.), 61:457–69.

Carpenter, C. 1941. A Field Study in Siam of the Behavior and Social Relations of the Gibbon (Hylobates lar). Baltimore: Johns Hopkins Press.

DeVore, I. and K. R. L. Hall. 1965. Baboon ecology. In I. DeVore (Ed.), Primate Behavior. New York: Holt, Rinehart and Winston.

DeVore, I. and S. L. Washburn. 1963. Baboon ecology and human evolution. In F. C. Howell and F. Bourliere (Eds.), African Ecology and Human Evolution. Chicago: Aldine.

Ellefson, J. O. 1966. A natural history of gibbons in the Malay Peninsula. Unpublished doctoral dissertation, University of California, Berkeley.

Freeman, D. 1964. Human aggression in anthropological perspective. In J. D. Carthy and F. J. Ebling (Eds.), The Natural History of Aggression. New York: Academic Press.

Goldschmidt. W. 1959. Man's Way: A Preface to the Understanding of Human Society. New York: Henry Holt.

———. 1966. Comparative Functionalism: An Essay in Anthropological Theory. Berkeley and Los Angeles: University of California Press.

Goodall, J. and H. van Lawick. 1965. My Life with Wild Chimpanzees.

Goodall, J. 1965. Chimpanzees on the Gombe Stream reserve. In I. DeVore (Ed.), Primate Behavior. New York: Holt, Rinehart and Winston.

Hamburg, D. 1963. Emotions in the perspective of human evolution. In P. H. Knapp (Ed.), Expression of the Emotions in Man. New York: International Universities Press.

Koford, C. 1966. Population Changes in Rhesus Monkeys: Cayo Santiago, 1960–1964. Tulane Studies in Zoology, 13:1–7.

Lancaster, J. MS. The evolution of tool-using behavior: primate field studies, fossil apes and the archaeological record.

Lee, R. 1965. Subsistence ecology of Kung Bushmen. Unpublished doctoral dissertation, University of California, Berkeley.

Lorenz, K. 1966. On Aggression. Trans. by Marjorie K. Wilson. New York: Harcourt, Brace and World.

Mair, L. 1965. An Introduction to Social Anthropology. Oxford, Clarendon Press.

Napier, J. 1962. Monkeys and their habitats. New Scientist, 15:88–92.

Sade, D. 1965. Some aspects of parent-offspring and sibling relations in a group of rhesus monkeys, with a discussion of grooming. AJPA (n.s.), 23(1): 1–17.

———. 1966. Ontogeny of social relations in a group of free ranging Rhesus monkeys (Macaca mulatta Zimmerman). Unpublished doctoral disseration, University of California, Berkeley.

Schaller, F. 1963. The Mountain Gorilla: Ecology and Behavior. Chicago: University of Chicago Press.

Service, E. 1962. Primitive Social Organization: An Evolutionary Perspective. New York: Random House.

Simpson, G. G. 1966. The biological nature of man. Science, 152 (3721): 472–78.

Slater, M. 1959. Ecological factors in the origin of incest. Amer. Anthrop. (n.s.), 61:1042–59.

Tax, S. 1937. Some problems of social organization. In F. Eggan (Ed.), Social Anthropology of North American Tribes. Chicago: University of Chicago Press.

Vallois, H. 1961. The social life of early man: the evidence of skeleton. In S. L. Washburn (Ed.), Social Life of Early Man. Chicago: Aldine.

Yamada, M. 1963. A study of blood-relationships in the natural society of the Japanese macaque. Primates (Journal of Primatology), 4:43–66.

Zeuner, F. 1963. A History of Domesticated Animals. New York: Harper and Row.

2
MAN'S PRIMATE RELATIVES

8

COMMUNICATION SYSTEMS OF OLD WORLD MONKEYS AND APES[1]
Jane B. Lancaster

Ever since Darwin, it has been realized that the anatomical and behavioral similarities of the various primates to one another and to man were more than accidental. Similarity of traits not only indicates a common heritage, but is also the result of adaptation to similar circumstances. The structure of the human arm, shoulder, and trunk; and the organization of the human sensory system, stressing diurnal, color discriminating and stereoscopic vision, not only bespeaks man's primate heritage but reflects a prolonged period in man's past when he was shaped extensively by the pressures of life in an arboreal environment.

The implications of anatomical similarities were realized immediately after the publication in 1859 of Darwin's Origin of Species. *Monkeys and apes were compared with men, muscle by muscle and bone by bone, and the implications for heritage and adaptation were correctly drawn. Darwin's defender, Thomas Henry Huxley, wrote* Evidence as to Man's Place in Nature *in 1863, which still stands as a model for this approach.*

Anatomical comparisons are relatively easy to make. Preserved specimens can easily be measured, drawn, and photographed. But behavioral comparisons are much more difficult to demonstrate. Observations of monkeys in zoo cages tell us no more about the spectrum of normal monkey behavior than observations of humans in prison cells would tell us about the spectrum of normal human behavior. Starting in the 1930s, the American psychologist C. R. Carpenter initiated what has become a series of studies of primate behavior done under unmodified conditions. The movement was slow to catch on, but, with the prodding of Washburn, it eventually gained momentum. As a result, we now know a good deal about the natural behavior of most major categories of primates thanks to field studies done mostly within the last twelve years.

Although these studies have greatly increased our insight into the aspects of primate behavior that help explain the origins of certain human behavioral propensities, we have yet, as Lancaster notes, to find out much about the background for that most human of all capacities, language. There appears to be no counterpart in wild primates, and all attempts to instruct tame individuals in the rudiments of speech have ended in frustration. Recently there has been some success in getting chimpanzees to use symbolic behavior via sign language (Kellogg 1968; Gardner and Gardner 1969) and the use of plastic tokens (Premack 1971), but the significance of such efforts has been seriously questioned (Bronowski and Bellugi 1970). As Lancaster reports, despite the extensive use of vocalizations for communicative purposes among the nonhuman primates, there is no counterpart to human linguistic behavior.

Bronowski, J., and U. Bellugi. 1970. Language, name, and concept. *Science* 168:669–673.

Gardner, R.A., and B.T. Gardner, 1969. Teaching sign language to a chimpanzee. *Science* 165:664–672.

Huxley, T.H. 1863. *Evidence as to Man's Place in Nature*. Williams and Norgate, London. 159 pp.

Kellogg, Winthrop N. 1968. Communication and language in the home-raised chimpanzee. *Science* 162:423–427.

Premack, David. 1971. Language in chimpanzee? *Science* 172:802–822.

Reprinted from *International Social Science Journal*, Volume XIX, No. 1, 1967. Reproduced by permission of Unesco and the author.

[1]This paper is part of a programme on primate behaviour supported by Grant Number MH 8623, United States Public Health Service.

STUDIES OF PRIMATE COMMUNICATION

The study of the communication systems of Old World monkeys and apes is a new and rapidly expanding field. Until recently most studies of communicative gestures and sounds were done either on caged animals in an impoverished social environment or in a group of free-ranging animals as a preliminary part of a larger study of social behavior. Valuable information has come from both these kinds of studies. Workers such as Andrew (1962, 1963a, b, c, d), Bolwig (1964), and van Hooff (1962) have been able to record a variety of sounds, gestures and facial expressions of caged monkeys and apes. They have been successful in sampling a wide variety of genera and species and in gaining useful insights into the possible evolutionary history of particular gestures or vocalizations. Many recent field workers have also attempted to describe the communication system of a single species and to show how it relates to the social system of the group under study (Hall and DeVore, 1965; Goodall, 1965; Kummer and Kurt, 1965; Jay, 1965; Schaller, 1963). These field workers have had to present the communication system as a given, and their focus was necessarily on patterns that tended to be of high frequency and often on those that were least variable. Their interest lay in regularities in social interactions and in social systems—to them understanding the communication system provided a means of entrance into the workings of the social system but it was not an object of study in itself.

Only a few workers have focused on the communication system itself—recording a large sample of sounds, gestures and expressions and struggling seriously with the infinite variety of problems of description and analysis. A number of studies have now been made on colonies living in outdoor compounds (Goustard, 1963; Hinde and Rowell, 1962; Rowell, 1962; Rowell and Hinde, 1962; Zhinkin, 1963), on free-ranging groups that are artificially fed (Altmann, 1962, 1965; Itani, 1963) and on free-ranging groups living in their natural habitats (Struhsaker, 1966). With the single exception of Struhsaker's work on vervets, all these studies have been on either baboons or macaques—two closely-related genera of terrestrial Old World monkeys. A second sampling bias has also developed because of the comparative ease of recording and describing the morphology of communicative sounds through the use of electronic recording equipment and the sound spectrograph. Although photographic equipment is easily used, there is no photographic equivalent of the sound spectrograph when it comes to describing and analysing complex patterns of movement. The result of these two biases in sampling is that we know a fair amount about the nature of the vocalizations of two genera of Old World monkeys and much less about the communication systems of most of the Old World monkeys and apes.

THE SOCIAL CONTEXT

Most acts of communication in a social group of primates occur in a context of long-term social relations (DeVore, 1965; Washburn, Jay and Lancaster, 1965). Monkey and ape societies are usually composed of animals of both sexes and all ages. Most members of the group have spent their entire lives within the same social context. Even in species where there may be no encompassing stable group, there are still stable sub-groups with continuing, long-term social relationships. Communication rarely occurs between strangers but for the most part is between animals that have known each other as individuals over long periods of time. The context, then, of any communicative act includes a network of social relations that have a considerable history behind them, all of which is relevant to the message and how it is received and responded to.

THE FORM AND NATURE OF THE SIGNALS

Marler (1965) presented a summary and interpretation of the nature of primate communication systems based on field accounts and laboratory studies published before 1963. One of the most significant generalizations, which he found demonstrated over and over again, is that the communication systems of higher primates are extraordinarily complex compared to that of a gull or rat, for example, and that they rely heavily on multimodal signals. A vocalization, a gesture or a facial expression in itself usually does not represent a complete signal but is only a part of a complex constellation of sound, posture, movement and facial expression. Parts of such a complex pattern may vary independently and may help to express changes in intensity or level of motivation. Sometimes olfactory elements are also present in the signal pattern but in monkeys and apes and in man the senses of vision, audition and touch are important in receiving communicative signals. Marler (1965) has emphasized that the complex multimodal signal is eminently suited to the kind of social system typical of monkeys and apes, where groups or at least sub-groups are in relatively continuous, long-term contact. Most group members are within sight of the rest of the group most of the time. This close-range continuous contact with other group members means that complex multimodal signals can be easily received and comprehended. When signals have to pass over greater distances or between animals that may be strangers, multimodal constellations of signal elements become difficult to receive and interpret correctly. In such situations unambiguous signals sent in a single optimal modality are likely to evolve. Furthermore, vocalizations that are often very important in long-distance signals are much less significant in close-range systems. Many field and laboratory workers (Hall and DeVore, 1965; Rowell, 1962) have emphasized that vocalizations do not carry the major burden of meaning in most social interactions but function instead either to call visual attention to the signaller or to emphasize or enhance the effect of visual and tactile signals. In other words, a blind monkey would be greatly handicapped in his social interactions whereas a deaf one would probably be able to function almost normally.

Another important generalization that has emerged from the field studies of higher primates is the major role that context plays in the total meaning of the signal pattern (Altmann, 1965; Marler, 1965). The receiver of a signal is presented with an extremely complex pattern of stimuli. Not only are the posture, gestures, vocalization and facial expression of the signalling animal important, but also the total context of that pattern is an essential part of the message. The immediately preceding events, the social context and the environmental context, all play major roles in the way a signal is received, interpreted and responded to. A threat display given by a juvenile may be ignored in one context, whereas if the same display is given again when he is near his mother, and if she shows some interest in what he is doing, it may produce an entirely different response in the animal receiving the threat. The major function of context in the total meaning of the signal makes the study of primate communication systems very difficult. Responses to a signal pattern may seem highly variable and erratic until a large number have been sampled and the relevant aspects of the varying contexts of the signal have been taken into account.

Besides being multimodal, primate signals are often graded in form (Marler, 1965), that is, variations that reflect differences in meaning occur in a single behaviour pattern, such as a threat gesture. In a graded or continuous system of behaviour patterns each grade or degree has at least the potential for expressing slight differences in intensity of motivation. The advantage of discrete non-graded signals, of the sort typical of many passerine birds, is that their lack of ambiguity makes them easy to receive and to comprehend. Graded signals place greater demands on the receiver of the signal but they have great value in their ability to express slight shifts in motivation. In a complex, enduring social system in which individuals are obliged to make a continuous series of adjustments and accommodations to each other, it is important to be able to express not just that one is aroused or frightened but also the degree and direction of changes in motivation. A good documentation of graded signals is found in Rowell and Hinde's description of communication in a colony of rhesus macaques (Hinde and Rowell, 1962; Rowell, 1962; Rowell and Hinde, 1962). In this system many signals were not only graded in form but also intergraded with each other. Rowell and Hinde demonstrated this by making spectrographs of all sounds that occurred in agonistic situations. They found what they thought were nine harsh sounds ranging from a growl to a squeal. After a large number of these had been recorded and analysed with a sound spectrograph, they discovered that the sounds in fact formed a single intergrading system that seemed to be expressive of the full range of emotions usually associated with agonistic interactions. These agonistic sounds were linked by a continuous series of intermediates and apparently each grade along the continuum potentially expressed a slightly different level of emotion. There was also one example of a multidimensional variation in which the pant-threat graded independently into three other calls. With such a system, a rhesus monkey is able to express quite complex patterns of motivation but most of the variations in signal form rest on contrasts in intensity of one or more of the components of the motivational state. In concert, this use of intergrading signals and of composites from several sensory modes produces a rich potential for the expression of very slight but significant changes in the intensity and nature of the mood of the signalling animal. Slight shifts or vacillations in arousal can be expressed by slight shifts in the vocalizations and gestures.

Not all primate signals belong to graded systems, and there are undoubtedly species differences in how much use is made of discrete and graded signals. Struhsaker (1966) has described the vocalizations of vervets, which he recorded in their natural free-ranging situation. He found thirty-six different sounds that were comparatively distinct both to the human ear and when analysed by a sound spectrograph. The majority of vervet sounds seem to be of the discrete type although there were two groups of sounds that may form graded systems. With more and more study on primates it will probably be shown that their communication systems tend to be of mixed type in which both graded and discrete signal patterns are used depending on the relative efficiency of one or the other form in serving a specific function. In such systems of communication as those of the monkeys and apes, complexity and subtlety of expression are always bought at a sacrifice to clarity and specificity. With complexity comes ambiguity, and greater burdens of reception and interpretation are placed on the nervous system of the receiver of the signal, which in turn places limits on the potential of the communication system.

THE NATURE OF THE MESSAGES

It is clear that the communication systems of monkeys and apes are rich in their ability to express the motivational state of the animals.

Most of these messages facilitate social interactions. In baboons and macaques, motivational information, particularly in relation to dominance and subordinance relationships, constitutes the largest category of messages (Itani, 1963: Marler, 1965: Rowell, 1962). Even greetings and other messages exchanged when one animal approaches another often serve to reassert recognized differences in dominance between two animals. Sometimes the dominant animal will gesture or indicate in some other way the pacific nature of his intentions at the same time that he displays his dominance. Compared to birds or primitive mammals, monkeys and apes have developed very highly evolved signal patterns expressing submission, aggression, anxiety, fear, and other motivational states associated with agonistic situations; in addition they also use a limited number of signal patterns in mating and mother-infant interactions. There are also signals that keep the group together and co-ordinate group movement. In most primate species these signals are generally only a small part of the total repertoire compared to the part devoted to agonistic communication (Marler, 1965).

Non-human primates can send complex messages about their motivational states but they communicate almost nothing about the state of their physical environments. Marler (1965, p. 584) in his review of research on primate communication systems concluded: "Environmental information, present or past, figures very little in the communication systems of these animals, and a major revolution in information content is still required before the development of a variety of signals signifying certain objects in the environment and a system of grammar to discourse about them can be visualized."

It may not even be accurate to speak about such a simple reference to the environment as a food call. Human beings possess a communication system that is highly evolved in its ability to make environmental references but this is a distinctively human specialization that should not be taken for granted in monkeys and apes. Marler was unable to find any clear examples of food calls and it is probable that what have been labelled food calls by many field workers are really expressions of a general level of excitement, which is often associated with food but which may be given in other circumstances as well. For example, Andrew (1962) reports that in many species of primate the same sounds that are given at the sight of food are also given in greeting a fellow animal. In both instances the animal vocalized upon perceiving a desired object; it was not giving a food call in the sense of making reference to specific items in its environment.

Even in a call warning of a threat of predation on the group, not much specific information about the danger itself is necessarily given. In baboons when an alarm cry is made the other animals try to see what the calling animal is looking at (Hall and DeVore, 1965). The cry itself gives no specific information about the form or position of the danger, but only indicates the level of excitement or alarm of the animal that first gave the call. Only by looking does the rest of the group learn what is the cause of the state of alarm in one of its members. Alarm cries of birds and other mammals are just as informative to a baboon as are the alarm cries given by a member of his own social group.

There are a few calls given by non-human primates that convey some information about the physical environment. They are rare and they represent important specializations of the few species that use them. In situations where monkeys are preyed upon by different kinds of predators an elaboration of alarm cries may occur. Struhsaker (1966) describes three high-intensity alarm cries of vervet monkeys that are very different in form and that evoke very different responses: a snake chutter, another call given when an airborne predator is seen, and a chirp that signals a terrestrial predator. There is an appropriate and different response to each of these calls. The snake call evokes a mobbing response similar to owl mobbing by birds. On hearing the call signalling an airborne predator, vervets seek cover either by running into tall grass or by dropping out of the tree branches into the dense thickets below, depending on where they were when they first heard the alarm. The response to the chirp warning of a terrestrial predator is exactly the opposite of that elicited by the call for an airborne predator—the vervets run to the trees and go out on to the ends of branches, which would be a dangerous place if the predator were

airborne (a monkey-eating eagle, for example), but which is safe if the predator, such as a lion, is on the ground. This kind of specialization in vervets in which some limited but vital information about the environment is communicated has occurred in many different species of animals ranging from chickens to rodents and can be expected when a species is hard pressed by such different kinds of predators as snakes, birds, and large mammals (Collias, 1960). This differentiation of high-intensity alarm calls to communicate some information about the environment is a specialization that should not be thought of as pointing toward the kind of major revolution in information content suggested by Marler as a requisite of human language.

Aside from predator alarms, Old World monkeys and apes probably have little ability to communicate about their environment. The ecology of non-human primates is such that communication about the environment can be, and is, very restricted, whereas exactly the opposite is true of man and human language. For monkeys and apes events inside the social group are of geat importance and their communication systems, therefore, are highly evolved in their capacity to express motivation of individuals and to facilitate social relations. Without this ability to express emotion, monkeys and apes would not be able to engage in the subtle and complex social interactions that are a major feature of their adaptations.

The more that is known about the communication systems of non-human primates the more obvious it is that these systems have little relationship with human language but much with the ways human beings express emotion through gesture, facial expression, and tone of voice. There is no evidence that human displays expressing emotion, such as laughter, smiling or weeping, are any less highly evolved than are displays of monkeys and apes or that they differ in form or function to any significant degree (Bastian, 1965). The communication systems of monkeys and apes are not steps toward language and they have much more in common with the communicative displays of other animals and of man than with human language. It is human language, a highly specialized aspect of the human system of communication, that has no obvious counterpart in the communication systems of man's closest relatives, the Old World monkeys and apes.

BIBLIOGRAPHY

Altmann, S.A. 1962. A field study of the sociobiology of rhesus monkeys, *Macaca mulatta. Ann. N.Y. Acad. Sci.*, 102:338–435.

———. 1965. Sociobiology of rhesus monkeys. II. Stochastics of social communication. *J. Theor. Biol.*, 8:490–522.

Andrew, R.J. 1962. The situations that evoke vocalization in primates. *Ann. N.Y. Acad. Sci.*, 102:296–315.

———. 1963a. The displays of primates. In: J. Buettner-Janusch (ed.), *Evolutionary and genetic biology of the primates.* New York, Academic Press, Vol. II.

———. 1963b. Evolution of facial expression. *Science*, 142:1034–41.

———. 1963c. The origin and evolution of the calls and facial expressions of the primates. *Behaviour*, 20:1–111.

———. 1963d. Trends apparent in the evolution of vocalization in the Old World monkeys and apes. *Symp. Zool. Soc. Lond.*, 10:89–101.

Bastian, J.R. 1965. Primate signaling systems and human language. In: I. DeVore (ed.), *Primate behavior: field studies of monkeys and apes.* New York, Holt, Rinehart.

Bolwig, N. 1964. Facial expression in primates with remarks on a parallel development in certain carnivores. *Behaviour*, 22:167–93.

Collias, N.E. 1960. An ecological and functional classification of animal sounds. In: W.E. Lanyon, W.N. Tavolga (eds.), *Animal sounds and communication.* Washington, D.C., American Institute of Biological Sciences.

DeVore, I. (ed.). 1965. *Primate behavior: field studies of monkeys and apes.* New York, Holt, Rinehart.

Goodall, J.M. 1965. Chimpanzees of the Gombe Stream Reserve. In: I. DeVore (ed.), *Primate behavior: field studies of monkeys and apes.* New York, Holt, Rinehart.

Goustard, M. 1963. Introduction à l'étude de la communication vocale chez *Macaca irus. Ann.* *Sci. Nat., Zool. et Biol. Animale*, 12ᵉ série, tome 5, fascicule 4.

Hall, K.R.L.; DeVore, I. 1965. Baboon social behavior. In: I. DeVore (ed.), *Primate behavior: field studies of monkeys and apes.* New York, Holt, Rinehart.

Hinde, R.A.; Rowell, T.E. 1962. Communication by postures and facial expressions in the rhesus monkey (*Macaca mulatta*). *Proc. Zool. Soc. Lond.*, 138:1–21.

Itani, J. 1963. Vocal communication of the wild Japanese monkey. *Primates*, 4:11–67.

Jay, P. 1965. The common langur of North India. In: I. DeVore (ed.), *Primate behavior: field studies of monkeys and apes.* New York, Holt, Rinehart.

Kummer, H.; Kurt, F. 1965. A comparison of social behavior in captive and wild Hamadryas baboons. In: H. Vagtborg (ed.), *The Baboon in Medical Research.* Austin, University of Texas Press.

Marler, P. 1965. Communication in monkeys and apes. In: I. DeVore (ed.), *Primate behavior: field studies of monkeys and apes.* New York, Holt, Rinehart.

Rowell, T.E. 1962. Agonistic noises of the rhesus monkey (*Macaca mulatta*). *Symp. Zool. Soc. Lond.*, 8:91–6.

———. Hinde, R.A. 1962. Vocal communication by the rhesus monkey (*Macaca mulatta*). *Proc. Zool. Soc. Lond.*, 138:279–94.

Schaller, G. 1963. *The mountain gorilla: ecology and behavior.* Chicago, University of Chicago Press.

Struhsaker, T.T. 1966. Auditory communication among vervet monkeys (*Cercopithecus aethiops*). In: S.A. Altmann (ed.), *Social communication among primates.* Chicago, University of Chicago Press.

Van Hooff, J.A.R. 1962. Facial expressions in higher primates. *Symp. Zool. Soc. Lond.*, 8:97–125.

Washburn, S.L.; Jay, P.C.; Lancaster, J.B. 1965. Field studies of Old World monkeys and apes. *Science*, 150:1541–7.

Zhinkin, N.I. 1963. An application of the theory of algorithms to the study of animal speech: methods of vocal intercommunication between monkeys. In: R.G. Busnel (ed.), *Acoustic behaviour of animals.* Amsterdam, Elsevier.

9

ON THE EVOLUTION OF TOOL-USING BEHAVIOR[1]
Jane B. Lancaster

If people would not be fully human without language, humanity itself would not be a viable phenomenon without tools. At one time, anthropologists suspected that tool-making and linguistic behavior developed at about the same time in the course of human evolution. Now, however, the educated guesswork on the origin of language tends to place it in the Middle Pleistocene along with the development of systematic hunting—or possibly even more recently and associated with the final achievement of modern brain size and the beginnings of the dramatic increases in population size that started with the Upper Pleistocene.

Words when spoken leave no trace, and we shall never know when language began. Stone tools, however, are practically indestructible and provide a permanent record of the activities of their makers. During the last decade, radiometric dating techniques, especially the potassium-argon method, have been applied to the strata in which the suspected earliest stone tools have been found. As a result, we know that tools were being made as early as 2 million years ago at Olduvai Gorge in Tanzania, the Omo River area of southern Ethiopea, and 2.6 million years ago just east of Lake Rudolf in nothern Kenya (Isaac, Leakey, and Behrensmeyer 1971). Evidently, tool-making behavior is much older than was previously suspected.

As with linguistic capacity, so with tool-making ability, repeated attempts have been made to assess possible performance from anatomy alone. When a fossil hominid is examined, any difference from the modern condition in jaw form or thumb joint form is taken to indicate less than modern speaking or manipulating ability, respectively (for the latter, see Musgrave 1971). In both matters, however, the principal factors that influence performance are more mental than anatomical. Lancaster makes this point well in discussing the manipulating behavior of baboons and chimpanzees. If anything, the chimpanzee hand is an even less promising manipulatory organ than the baboon hand. This further underscores Lancaster's observation that the difference in manipulating behavior is entirely due to the greater mental capacity of chimpanzees.

Isaac, Glynn L., R.E.F. Leakey, and A.K. Behrensmeyer. 1971. Archeological traces of early hominid activities east of Lake Rudolf, Kenya. *Science 173*:1129–1134.

Musgrave, Jonathan H. 1971. How dextrous was Neanderthal man? *Nature 233*:538–541.

This paper directs attention to the theoretical importance of recent discoveries and observations—especially those in primate field studies—to the interpretation of the fossil record. It is intended not as a review but simply as a discussion of the implications of recent developments.

TIME AND THE NEW METHODS OF DATING

The estimate of the amount of time occupied

Reproduced by permission of the American Anthropological Association from *American Anthropologist*, Vol. 70, No. 1, 1968. Reprinted with permission of the author and publisher.

by the Pleistocene has steadily increased. In 1932 Keith thought that the Pleistocene might have lasted 200,000 years and the Pliocene an additional 250,000. Then for a long time the Pleistocene was estimated at one million years and the Pliocene ten times that long (Zeuner 1959). According to that view, the Pleistocene was divided into two approximately equal parts: the first 500,000 years contained at least some very simple tool traditions, but these were of uncertain date and duration; the second 500,000 years spanned three glacials and contained all the tools of the Acheulian and later tool-making traditions. With the advent of potassium-argon dating, now partly supported by the fission-track method, radiometric dates rather than relative estimates could be given for these two parts of the Pleistocene (Butzer 1964, Evernden and Curtis 1965, Fleischer et al. 1965). The dates and duration of the last part of the Pleistocene have not been greatly altered but the early part has been radically extended in time. The new radiometric dating suggests well over two million years ago as a probable date for the Pliocene-Pleistocene boundary, but keeps 700,000–500,000 B.P. as likely for the onset on the First Interglacial period (Table 1). Two million years ago, according to Evernden and Curtis (1965), is a minimal estimate for the start of the Pleistocene and it may well have begun more than three million years ago. Estimates of the extent of the Lower Pleistocene, especially of the earliest part, the Villafranchian, have been the most radically affected by radiometric dating. The Villafranchian, which was once considered a relatively brief period preliminary to the major events and time spans of the Pleistocene, is now seen as lasting perhaps 2.5 million years and comprising three quarters of the total length of the Pleistocene.

While the radiometric chronology of the late Tertiary and Pleistocene stratigraphic unit is not finally settled, it is very clear that the time spans involved in the early stages of the Pleistocene have been seriously underestimated in the past. Geophysical age determinations indicate the need for a radical revision in our conception of the rate of development of tool-using abilities and techniques and in our understanding of the interrelation of tool types to the biology of

their makers. At Olduvai Gorge, chopping tools, trimmed and utilized flakes, polyhedral "flaked" stones, and other utilized stones are found near the base of Bed I in layers dated between 1.9 and 1.75 million years (Evernden and Curtis 1965, M.D. Leakey 1966). From these same stratigraphic levels fossils of two distinct hominid forms have been recovered. Regardless of the ultimate classification of the hominid forms found in Bed I, there are none with large brains. Tobias' most generous estimate for the cranial capacity of the juvenile parietal fragments is still only 725 cc. His more conservative estimate is 670 cc. (Tobias 1964).

The Oldowan industries from Bed I are at present the oldest radiometrically dated stone artifacts, but they need not necessarily represent the very beginning of stone flaking traditions, which we can expect to extend to perhaps a quarter to a half million years earlier. At Olduvai these industries persisted into the time of deposition of the lower part of Bed II, while in upper Bed II early hand-axe industries occur.[2] The age of the transition from Oldowan to Acheulian has not been directly determined at Olduvai[3] but archeological and faunal correlations can be made with other strata for which geophysical data indicate an age of between 700,000 and 500,000 B.P. (Isaac 1965). The elementary stone techniques and poorly standardized tool-making tradition of the Oldowan appears in East Africa to have lasted at least one million years and quite probably for more than double that time with little change or advance in their manufacture or in the biology of their makers. We can assign a time span for Oldowan tools from probably earlier

Table 1
CHRONOLOGY OF THE PLEISTOCENE
(After Butzer 1964, Evernden and Curtis 1965)

Upper	Third Interglacial (Ecmian)	100,000 B.P.	
Middle	Second Interglacial (Holstein)	255,000 B.P. or more	
	First Interglacial (Cromerian)	700,000–500,000 B.P.	Acheulian and later traditions
		1,000,000 B.P.	
Lower	Villafranchian	2,000,000 B.P.	Oldowan tools
	(Early Villafranchian?)	3,000,000–2,500,000 B.P. ???	

than 2,000,000 B.P. up to 500,000 B.P., the time when the first hand-axe cultures and the remains of larger-brained men classified as *Homo erectus* began to appear. The only possible makers of the Oldowan tools are small-brained forms (*Australopithecus*, in the broad sense).

There is reason to think that Oldowan tools were used for much longer than the 1.5 million years that passed between the lowest levels of Bed I and the beginning of the European First Interglacial period. Tools similar to the Oldowan may also date from the same or an earlier period at other African sites, such as Laetolil, Omo, Kanam, Ain Hanech, and elsewhere (Cooke 1963). Furthermore, the small incisors and canines of *Australopithecus* suggest that members of this genus had been using tools for a very long period of time and that the use of tools had almost entirely relieved their dentition of the functions of food getting and self protection. An estimate of two million years of tool use prior to hand-axe cultures and *Homo erectus* is undoubtedly conservative. This would mean that the stage of human evolution in which small-brained men used pebble tools and walked bipedally lasted at least four times as long as have all the subsequent stages. The early part of the evolution of stone tools and of man must have proceeded at a rate very different from the later stages and advances must have come very much more slowly.

To summarize to this point, the archeological discoveries from Bed I in Olduvai Gorge and the advent of new dating techniques have radically altered our conceptions of the duration of the early, primitive stages of tool using and tool making. The natural assumption has always been that tool use was so highly adaptive that once it had been firmly established as part of the normal behavior of the species the pace of evolution quickened immediately. Advances were assumed to have come in rapid succession as the brain, tool-making techniques, and cultural traditions interacted in a mutually stimulating feedback relationship. Events of the past, however, apparently did *not* move this rapidly, at least not in the beginning.

TOOL USE BY THE AFRICAN APES

In the same years that discoveries at Olduvai

Gorge and advances in the techniques of radiometric dating were being made, field workers were making new efforts to study the behavior of contemporary monkeys and apes in their natural habitats. Most of these modern field studies report very little object-manipulation in nonhuman primates except that directly involved in feeding activity (Hall 1963b, Menzel 1966). In feeding, nonhuman primates will turn over rocks, probe fingers into holes, and pull off bark or shells in search of food, but even here they are only manipulating objects and not using tools. In contrast to the findings of field workers on other primate species, Goodall (1964) has found that tool use in the chimpanzee is an important behavior pattern. Goodall (1962, 1963, 1965) over a period of six years has observed the behavior of a single population of approximately 60 free-ranging chimpanzees in the Gombe Stream Reserve in Tanzania. There can be little doubt now that tool-using performances by chimpanzees excel those reported for all other animals except man in both variety and complexity. They are also very close to man in many other measures: anatomy of the body, serum proteins, chromosome number and form, and dentition. Therefore it is not surprising that chimpanzees are closest to man in some aspects of behavior as well.

It may well be that further observations on the behavior of gorillas in the wild will produce evidence of tool-using behavior paralleling the performances of the chimpanzees. Schaller (1963) with 500 hours of observations of the behavior of the mountain gorilla reported that he never saw gorillas use or show interest in objects except vegetation for nest building and for throwing in aggressive display. The aggressive display of the gorilla is a highly stereotyped sequence of behavior patterns that usually includes the throwing and tossing of vegetation just before a running charge (Emlen 1962, Schaller 1963). Many of the same elements, including the throwing of vegetation followed by a charge, constitute the most essential parts of the chimpanzee aggressive display. At least in this one context both species show a strong tendency to manipulate and throw objects. It should be noted that what appear to be species differences in behavior between chimpanzees and gorillas may in part merely reflect

Goodall's unique long-term observations; in the first year of her study she only saw one kind of tool use, termiting. Moreover, there may have been important ecological differences between the two study areas. Schaller worked in a region of lush evergreen vegetation of herbs and vines, where rocks, sticks, and other hard objects were rare. Food plants were abundant and everywhere at hand. The feeding pattern of the gorillas was simply a leisurely grazing through the lush vegetation. In contrast, the Gombe Stream Reserve includes valleys of dense gallery forests and higher points of open woodland and grassy slopes where wood and stone are readily available materials. Food items are often seasonal, concentrated, and hard to get. The chimpanzees make an effort to locate and to gather their food; this is exactly the sort of situation where tool use in food getting might be likely to appear. Finally, the behavior of young gorillas in captivity is very similar to that of young chimpanzees in their interest in and manipulation of objects (Schenkel 1964, Glickman and Sroges 1966). In captivity both chimpanzees and gorillas spontaneously learn to throw dirt and food with considerable accuracy at visitors.

Goodall's most remarkable observations of chimpanzee tool use are of the use of twigs and grass blades for "fishing" ants or termites out of their nests. She has collected more than 1000 of these tools and on over a hundred occasions has observed actual termiting. Chimpanzees are very efficient in getting the termites. The animal takes a piece of twig and puts it in the termite hole where the insects seize the end of the stick with their mandibles. The chimpanzee then takes it from the hole and leisurely eats the termites that are clinging to the tip. Not only do the chimpanzees use these twigs very effectively as tools but they also will frequently improve the bit of twig or grass before using it. The animal will break off a piece of vine or a twig and prepare it by stripping away any side branch or leaf that might get in the way and by breaking it to the appropriate length, which differs by a foot or more for anting as opposed to termiting. There is much individual variation in the skill and care with which a tool is made. Some animals will take nearly anything at hand; others will search carefully for just the right

piece and then spend some time in preparing it. A few prepare a little pile of stems before starting to termite and some make the twig even before a nest is found. Goodall saw one male carry a termiting twig in his mouth for more than half a mile while he went from nest to nest looking for one that was ready to work.

The actual grip used to hold the twig for termiting is standardized among adults who hold it between the thumb and the side of the bent index finger (Goodall, personal communication). Infants who have not fully mastered the adult technique may grip the tool using only four fingers and not using the thumb at all. Chimpanzees are ambidextrous in their termiting; all animals can use either hand although there may be some individual preference for one hand over the other (Goodall, personal communication). This absence of handedness may be indicative of the limitations that the chimpanzee's brain places on its ability to develop highly skilled tool use. By human standards these termiting movements and other kinds of tool-using behavior in chimpanzees always appear clumsy, like the use of tools by a human child. Tool use is learned by the chimpanzee, improves with practice, but never develops the deftness either of human skill or of highly stereotyped innate motor patterns.

Goodall was fortunate enough to observe a one-and-a-half-year-old female in the process of learning how to use the termiting twig. The infant's technique was imperfect. She made tools that were too short to more than just enter the hole; the longest was only two inches whereas the adults always use 6- to 12-inch twigs. The infant's motor patterns were imperfectly coordinated and sometimes she would jerk the twig out of the hole so quickly that the termites were knocked off. Her attention span was very short as well; she would termite for a few minutes and then break off to play. In contrast, adults often work with great concentration for more than an hour without stopping. Goodall also observed that young animals try to termite out of season in what may have been a form of play activity. She is convinced that much of the ability to termite is learned by young animals by observing the adult technique and then practicing it. She often saw infants intently watching an adult termiting and then, when the adult had moved off leaving the twig or grass blade by the nest, the infant would pick up the abandoned tool and try termiting too.

Chimpanzees are not the only primates that like termites, and Goodall has seen baboons near chimpanzees while they are at work. Baboons are eager to eat termites, but they have never been observed trying to fish for termites themselves. The baboons do occasionally watch the chimpanzees termiting but not as intently as do young chimpanzees who will peer at working adults for minutes at a time (Goodall, personal communication).

Termiting is a seasonal activity, coming just before the termites begin their nuptial flights, which occur about eight times for each termite heap over a period of four months or more during the rainy season. During most of the year the termites are protected by a concrete-like shell that covers their nests, but for the flights the workers tunnel out to the surface. After each flight, the holes are sealed over until the next. Chimpanzees are able to scratch off the thin covering at the end of the tunnel and thus, by using the fishing technique, are able to eat termites throughout the entire season. Birds, monkeys, and other animals can feast on the termites only during the actual flights. The simple technique of fishing for termites assures the chimpanzees of a protein-rich diet for several months out of every year without competition from other species, and the inability of the baboons to imitate the chimpanzee behavior robs them of the extra protein.

Termiting is only one example of tool use by chimpanzees. Goodall saw them make sponges for dipping water out of crevices and boles of trees that were too small to let them put their faces down to the water. They would take a handful of leaves, chew them slightly, dip the wad into the water and then suck it. Goodall tried the same thing and found it seven to eight times more efficient than the technique used by many nonhuman primates of dipping the hand or fingers into water and letting the water drip into the mouth. Besides using leaves as sponges for drinking water, chimpanzees use them to wipe water or dirt from the body or sticky substances from the fingers. This use of objects to groom the body is more unusual than it seems. Although some species of bird are known to rub ants in their feathers as a part of grooming and elephants sometimes use objects to scratch themselves, man is the only animal reported to habitually use objects in grooming (Hall 1963b).

One other way in which chimpanzees use objects as tools is in aggressive display (Kortlandt and Kooij 1963, Goodall 1964). This behavior is particularly interesting because it suggests that tools for defense may have been developed just as early in man's history as tools for food-getting. Random throwing of objects—anything that comes to hand such as stones, sticks or other vegetation—is a common element in the excited displays of many primates, and chimpanzees are no exception (Hall 1963b). They tend to throw things when meeting other groups after a separation or when being annoyed by baboons (and probably by predators, Kortlandt and Kooij 1963). Sometimes an animal will even take some care in aiming the object; instead of just tossing it into the air, he will throw it toward the animal at which the display is aimed. Goodall saw chimpanzees aim and throw stones, both overhand and underhand, at baboons and at humans as part of such a sequence of aggressive display. This behavior pattern is significant because, as Washburn (1963b) has pointed out, it suggests the possible first steps in the evolution of weapons. If an animal is displaying to intimidate an aggressor, object throwing as a part of that display is effective whether he hits the other animal or not. If the total display is not intimidating enough, the chimpanzee is still able to flee or to fight with his canines. It is easy to imagine how the ability to develop skill in aimed throwing of sticks and rocks could gradually evolve until it became so effective that the creature need no longer rely on his canines. Only then would the selective pressure on large canines be relaxed and a behavior pattern, defense with weapons, could ultimately replace the behavioral and morphological pattern of defense by fighting with canines.

These examples of tool use in chimpanzees, when taken together, provide a good starting place for answering questions about how and why tools were used by man's earliest ancestors. It is true that some birds and other mammals use tools, but in any one tool-using species there is likely to be only one kind of tool. There is no nonprimate that uses such disparate objects as termiting twigs, leaf sponges, and stone projectiles. And, conversely, in the chimpanzee there is no single, highly evolved, stereotyped sequence of movements of the sort common in other vertebrate tool users such as the deft twist of a cactus spine used by finches to dig grubs from bark or even the much more complex but still relatively stereotyped patterns of nest building found in many mammals. In the chimpanzee there is a far more generalized tendency to manipulate objects and to use them in many different situations. And, if Goodall is correct, these different ways to use tools constitute a tradition based on biology but transmitted from adults to young by observational learning and practice.

Chimpanzees use tools in an impressive number of different situations, when they are compared with the rest of the animal kingdom in this respect (Hall, 1963b). By far the most common types of tool use in vertebrates are in feeding behavior or in preparation of nests or dens. The use of objects in self-grooming is almost unknown in animals and in aggressive display it has been observed only in monkeys, apes, and man. Goodall's single population of chimpanzees performed more complex kinds of tool use, and in a wider variety of situations, than has been observed for any other animal; that is true even though tool use is a very small part of their behavior repertoire and is a comparatively rare event. This small group of apes over a period of a few years was seen to use tools in agonistic display, in aimed throwing, in a variety of food-getting situations, in drinking, and in self-grooming. Perhaps the making of nests or sleeping platforms should be included in this list too, since it is very similar to these other forms of tool use in that objects are manipulated and modified to perform some important activity better—in this case the nest is a tool for sleeping.

CHIMPANZEE LEARNING OF TOOL-USING TRADITIONS

It would be interesting to know why chimpanzees seem to be able to learn the use of objects more readily than do many other primates. There are important biological limitations on learning abilities that vary from

species to species and do not reflect differences in intelligence so much as differences in specialization. Hall (1963b) has argued that in themselves tool-using performances give no indication of relative intelligence. A finch that uses a cactus spine to extract grubs is no more intelligent than other finches; the species has simply evolved a behavioral pattern rather than a morphological pattern to aid in its feeding. Nevertheless, chimpanzees do have large brains and the great apes have a much longer maturation period than do other nonhuman primates; certainly both these characteristics are related to greater learning abilities.

Undoubtedly there are many factors that contribute to the ontogeny of such an important adaptive pattern as the use of objects as tools. Schiller (1957) and more recently Chance (1960) have emphasized the importance of certain motor patterns occurring in the tool-using performances of captive chimpanzees that appear to be largely determined by heredity and that require only the opportunity for play for their perfection. For example, the tendency to manipulate sticks, to lick the ends, and to poke them into any available hole are responses that occur over and over again in captive chimpanzees. These responses are not necessarily organized into the efficient use of sticks to probe for objects but they probably form the basis of complex motor patterns such as termiting.

Certain kinds of human-like tool use such as overhand and underhand throwing are easier for an ape than for a monkey. The anatomy of the shoulder girdle of man and the apes enables them to throw or toss objects using powerful movements, something which is much more awkward and difficult for a quadrupedal monkey (Washburn and Jay 1967). In contrast, differences between chimpanzees and monkeys in manipulative abilities of the hands are based not so much on anatomical differences in the forelimbs as on the brain and the ability to learn different kinds of object manipulations. The hands of monkeys and apes are equally suited to picking up a stick and making poking or scratching movements with it but differences in the brain make these much more likely behavior patterns for the chimpanzee.

Another factor, one that may be just as

important in tool use as genetic tendencies toward motor patterns, is the degree to which chimpanzees can learn by observing the activities of other animals. Hall (1963a) has emphasized that observational learning is rarer in nonhuman primates than one might expect and that the ability to learn in this way varies tremendously according to the task to be learned and the context in which this learning takes place. Monkeys and apes seem to have greater abilities in this direction than do most other mammals, and Hall has suggested that these abilities are most often demonstrated when the animals are in the relaxed, protected atmosphere of a social group formed of animals linked by close affectional bonds. This is a situation that is common in the natural environment of monkeys and apes, but it is rarely duplicated in the laboratory. Monkeys and apes learn emotional attitudes, such as fear of particular objects or situations, with great ease from other group members as might be expected in animals for which group life is an important adaptive mechanism (Hamburg 1963).

Other, more complex kinds of observational learning in monkeys and apes are much more rare. Frequently the activities of one animal will stimulate another animal to do the same thing, but this sort of social facilitation is often merely a matter of a focusing of the attention of the second animal on a stimulus that then elicits a parallel response. For example, Hall (1963a) reported an experiment in which a young baboon, raised in captivity, was released near a wild troop. The young animal had been fed the diet of a pet and was unfamiliar with the wild foods of the area in which it was released. It learned how to dig for bulbs and roots by watching the other animals closely and then going over and digging beside them, but, as Hall emphasized, it did not learn how to dig, but rather where and for what to dig. The ability to mimic a novel motor pattern demonstrated by another animal has not conclusively been shown for any nonhuman primate except the chimpanzee. Studies of captive chimpanzees (Köhler 1925, Yerkes and Yerkes 1929, Hayes and Hayes 1952) point toward their considerable abilities in all the forms of observational learning mentioned above, ranging from the simpler kinds of attention focusing to some-

thing that must be genuine imitation of novel motor patterns. It is likely, then, that both these factors—the existence of simple hereditary motor acts that form the basis of more complex motor patterns of tool use and the ease with which one chimpanzee can learn by observing the activities of another chimpanzee—play important roles in the development of tool-using traditions within local populations of chimpanzees.

Tool-using behavior by chimpanzees is remarkable in the multiplicity of forms it takes, but it is very different from human use of tools in degree if not in kind. Chimpanzees, like men, both use and make tools, but man's brain is highly evolved and highly specialized to learn many different skilled uses of objects. For a species to depend on tool use as a way of life—for obtaining food and for defense—such tool use must be skillful. A spear has to be thrown just as skillfully as a baboon wields its canines in fighting, or the behavior pattern could never replace the morphological pattern in agonistic situations. Skill is a matter of evolutionary changes in the brain that do not fossilize. There are really only two indirect lines of evidence of skill from the past: (1) relative brain size of the tool makers and (2) the tools themselves, in the techniques by which they were made and in the complexity and specializations of the tool assemblages. The specializations of modern man's brain that allow him to learn many different skilled uses of tools may have come relatively late in the history of tool use, perhaps not until *Homo erectus*, when the rate of change in tool traditions became so rapid and when a major increase in cranial capacity occurred. The slow pace of evolution in tools and in their makers before that time may well reflect a lack of ability to use them skillfully.

The tool-using behavior of chimpanzees suggests the kind of ape ancestor that might be postulated for the origin of the hominid line—an ape that used tools for many different reasons and in many different ways, no matter how insignificant the tool, like leaf sponges, or how undramatic, like termiting twigs, or inefficient, like a clumsily swung stick. The more kinds of tools this ape used the more likely his ancestral role, because it would have been the accumulated influence of many reasons for using tools and many ways of using them that would have taken selective pressure off the specific situation, the specific tool, and the specific movement. Selective pressure was put on a hand that could use many tools skillfully and on a brain capable of learning these skills. Natural selection would then have acted upon a broader category of behavior, one involving the brain, the hand, many objects, and a wide variety of social and ecological situations and problems. The evolution of skilled tool using marks a major change from the kind of tool use that is incidental to the life of a chimpanzee to the kind that is absolutely essential for survival of the human individual.

PROBLEMS OF INTERPRETATION IN THE EVOLUTION OF TOOL USE

Chimpanzee tool-using behavior raises the question of how many millions of years of this sort of casual tool use and object manipulation by apes has existed. It also raises the problem of whether the ancestors of chimpanzees and man used tools before their separation or whether tool use evolved independently in the two species. Any reconstruction of evolutionary events can be guarded against the possibility of parallelism and convergence only by an evaluation of the degree of similarity between two species in as many different and unrelated systems as possible. The greater the number of similarities that can be found, in as many unrelated biological systems as possible, the higher the chances that one is dealing with true genetic affinities between species and not superficial similarities due to parallel evolution. A large number of such similarities between two species also suggests a shallow time depth of separation in which minor and random differences have not had a chance to accumulate.

Anatomical affinities between man and the apes have long been recognized both in dentition (Le Gros Clark 1962) and in the anatomy of the shoulder girdle (Grand 1964, Washburn 1963a). Washburn (1963a) noted that similarities between man and apes in the shoulder girdle involve fine details in a series of highly specialized modifications of the shoulder, elbow, and wrist joints. The full complement of these modifications was not present in the apes of the Miocene and may not have been established until the Miocene-

Pliocene border, perhaps 13 million years ago. Washburn argued that man is likely to have separated from the African apes sometime in the early Pliocene, perhaps several million years after the establishment of a modern shoulder girdle in the family Pongidae.

The number of similarities between man and the great apes is extremely impressive. Besides the affinities in dentition and the anatomy of the shoulder girdle mentioned above, man is closer to the great apes than to any other animal in susceptibility to special kinds of viral disease (Hsiung, Black, and Henderson 1964), in blood groups (Franks 1963), and in the glands of the axilla, the form of the hair follicles, the chemicals found at the ends of nerves, and many other details of the skin (Montagna and Ellis 1963).

The African apes are often specifically cited as being the most similar to man and the orangutan has never been mentioned as being closer to man than are the African apes. In respect to chromosome number and form, the chimpanzee is almost identical to man with only one extra set of arocentric chromosomes (Klinger et al. 1963, Chiarelli 1962). Dunn (1966) compared the internal parasites of man and apes and found that man and the African apes shared in common a much greater number of species of parasites, especially the host-specific ones, than do the Asiatic apes and man. Man living in the tropical forests of Southeast Asia shares many more species of helminths with African apes than with the Asiatic apes who are living in the same forest. Thus even when sharing his habitat with the Asiatic apes, man carries the internal parasites of the African apes. Goodman (1963) came to the conclusion that man and the African apes are so similar in their serum proteins that Pan and Gorilla should be classified in the Hominidae, whereas Pongo should be left in the Pongidae. Other workers on primate hemoglobins (Zuckerkandl 1963, Buettner-Janusch and Buettner-Janusch 1964, Hafleigh and Williams 1966) agree on the close affinities between man and the African apes as opposed to the Asiatic apes but do not take such an extreme taxonomic position. Sarich (1966) in a quantitative assessment of differences among the apes and man in serum albumins and gamma globulin found that man was very similar to the African apes and much less closely related to the Asiatic apes. The order of magnitude of these differences suggested a separation between man and the African apes going back perhaps 8 million years and a common ancestor for all modern apes and man coming from the Miocene-Pliocene border. There is no reason to think that all the different biological systems mentioned above are either genetically or functionally linked. Thus, an evolutionary change in one of these systems should not necessarily involve corresponding changes in the others. So many similarities between these systems can only be interpreted as reflecting close genetic relationships between man and the African apes, a relationship in which the time of separation is small enough that minor or random differences have not had a chance to accumulate.

The lack of divergence in many different systems strongly supports the idea of an end of the Miocene or early Pliocene (but no earlier) division between man and the African apes, somewhere on the order of 10 million years ago. If this is so, then it may be worth considering the possibility that casual, unskilled tool use might have been typical of many species of apes during the Pliocene. It should be remembered that the late Miocene and early Pliocene represent a time when apes were abundant, diverse, and widely spread over much of the Old World (Simons 1963a, 1963b). Fossil apes have been found in Europe, Africa, India, and China—a much larger geographical distribution than that of the modern apes, which live only in restricted areas of Africa and Southeast Asia (Simons and Pilbeam 1965). The number of different forms of apes was also much greater than today. From a single site, Rusinga Island in

Lake Victoria, there are at least two species from the genus *Dryopithecus* as well as one or more species of gibbonlike apes. The modern apes are only remnants, survivors of a time when the family was highly successful and diverse. Table 2 suggests that a kind of unskilled ape tool use continued without major changes for millions of years and has continued down to the present in one or more of the surviving, descendant species of ape.

The onset of the Pleistocene witnessed the emergence of perhaps one or more forms of bipedal hominid that, although possessing relatively small brains, had come to rely on tool use for much of their food getting and defense. Clearly, specializations in the hand and especially the thumb (Napier 1962), the reduction in the canines and incisors (Robinson 1963), and bipedalism (Napier 1964), all point toward the importance of tools to their way of life. Both the small brains and the tools themselves suggest a lack of skill in the way these tools were made and used. These hominids of the Early Pleistocene should not be thought of as merely forms transitional to man. They were highly successful, judging by their wide geographic distribution, and they lasted without major changes in either anatomy or tool traditions for a long time, perhaps 2.5 million years. Then, about half a million years ago, a rapid rate of evolutionary development in brain size and complexity of tool assemblages seems to have begun. This later period is associated with the emergence of a single species of tool user, *Homo erectus*, dominating much of the Old World. Remnant species of ape also survived but with quite restricted geographic distribution. Perhaps a new efficiency in the skilled use of

Table 2
CHRONOLOGY OF THE EVOLUTION OF TOOL-USING BEHAVIOR

Geological Time Divisions	Radiometric Age Estimates	Tool-Using Species of Primates	Types of Tool-Using Traditions
Pleistocene	700,000–500,000 B.P.	*Homo erectus* (1 species only)	Hand-axe and later traditions
	2,000,000 B.P.	*Australopithecus* (more than 1 species)	Oldowan industries
Pliocene	13,000,000 B.P.	Pongid and Hominid (many species)	Unskilled, ape tool use (hypothetical)

tools effectively closed the niche to competition. It probably left no room within the broad niche created by tools for separate species to develop specialized applications. Any possibility for different kinds of tool users—perhaps an open savanna, a woodland, and a forest form (a possibility that may have been realized in *Australopithecus* during the Early Pleistocene)—disappeared and a single species of Hominid, using various tool traditions, spread across the Old World. The increase of efficiency and skill with which tools were used, a trend that probably began in the early Pliocene, may well have been associated with a gradual decrease in the number of primate species able to command a portion of the niche open to tool users. At an early, inefficient stage many species may have tried using tools with variable degrees of success but, as skill and efficiency increased, the competition between tool-using species also increased and the possibility of many forms sharing the niche disappeared.

SUMMARY

Our conceptions of the conditions under which tools first evolved have been radically altered by recent archeological discoveries, new methods of dating, and primate field studies. All point toward a single conclusion—that in itself tool use does not cause a major change in the history of a species. Man is not the only primate to use tools and probably many species of ape have in time past used tools to some degree. The new radiometric dating by potassium-argon and fission-track methods indicates that the Early Pleistocene lasted for at least 2.5 million years and that during that time small-brained men used simple tools with little change or advance. The rapid acceleration of cultural advances, once traditionally thought to be a natural consequence of tools of any sort, came late in the history of tool use and was probably associated with specializations in the human brain that allowed the skilled use of many different kinds of tools. This evolutionary advance occurred in only one genus and species, *Homo erectus*, that preempted the entire niche once open to a number of different kinds of tool users. As Oakley (1954) argued some years ago, it is the skill with which man uses his tools that best

reflect man's specializations for a human way of life.

NOTES

[1] I am most grateful for the helpful comments and criticisms on the manuscript from A. Brower, P. Jay, L. Klein, and V. Sarich. I especially wish to thank S.L. Washburn for his continuing encouragement and criticism throughout the writing of this paper. Finally, I am particularly indebted to Glynn Isaac and to Jane Goodall van Lawick for many helpful comments and suggestions. This paper is part of a program on primate behavior supported by the United States Public Health Service.

[2] The early handaxe industries are designated Lower or Early Acheulian, the term Chellean having been abandoned by workers in many parts of Africa (Biberson 1961, Mason 1962, Leakey and Leakey 1965).

[3] There is only a single sample from Olduvai for which dates ranging from 500,000—300,000 B.P. have been published (Hay 1963, Evernden and Curtis 1965).

REFERENCES CITED

Biberson, P. 1961. Le Paléolithique inférieur du Maroc Atlantique. Pub. Serv. Antiquités Maroc, Mem. 17.

Buettner-Janusch, J., and V. Buettner-Janusch 1964. Hemoglobins of primates. In Evolutionary and genetic biology of primates, Vol. II. J. Buettner-Janusch, ed. New York, Academic Press.

Butzer, K.W. 1964. Environment and archeology: an introduction to Pleistocene geography. Chicago, Aldine.

Chance, M.R.A. 1960. Köhler's chimpanzees—how did they perform? Man 60:130–135.

Chiarelli, B. 1962. Comparative morphometric analysis of primate chromosomes. I. The chromosomes of anthropoid apes and of man. Caryologia 15:99–121.

Clark, W.E. LeGros. 1962. The antecedents of man. 2nd ed. Edinburgh University Press.

Cooke, H.B.S. 1963. Pleistocene mammal faunas of Africa, with particular reference to Southern Africa. In African ecology and human evolution. F.C. Howell and F. Bourlière, eds. Viking Fund Publications in Anthroplogy No. 36.

Dunn, F.L. 1966. Patterns of parasitism in primates: phylogenetic and ecological interpretations, with particular reference to the Hominoidea. Folia Primatologia 4:329–345.

Emlen, J.T. 1962. The display of the gorilla. Proceedings, American Philosophical Society 106:516–519.

Evernden, J.F., and G.H. Curtis 1965. Potassium-argon dating of Late Cenozoic rocks in East Africa and Italy. Current Anthropology 6:343–385.

Fleischer, R.L., L.S.B. Leakey, P.B. Price, and R.M. Walker 1965. Fission track dating of Bed I, Olduvai Gorge. Science 148:72–74.

Franks, D. 1963. The blood groups of the primates. In The primates. J. Napier and N.A. Barnicot, eds. Symposium, Zoological Society of London 10:221–250.

Glickman, S.E., and R.W. Sroges 1966. Curiosity in zoo animals. Behaviour 26:151–188.

Goodall, J.M. 1962. Nest building behavior in the free ranging chimpanzee. Annals, New York Academy of Science 102:455–467.

———. 1963. Feeding behaviour of wild chimpanzees. Symposium, Zoological Society of London 10:39–48.

———. 1964. Tool-using and aimed throwing in a community of free-living chimpanzees. Nature 201:1264–1266.

———. 1965. Chimpanzees of the Gombe Stream Reserve. In Primate behavior: field studies of monkeys and apes. I. DeVore, ed. New York, Holt, Rinehart. Pp. 425–473.

Goodman, M. 1963. Serological analysis of the phyletic relationships of recent Hominoids. Human Biology 35:377–436.

Grand, T.I. 1964. The functional anatomy of the shoulder of the chimpanzee. Doctoral dissertation, University of California, Berkeley.

Hafleigh, A.S., and C.A. Williams, Jr. 1966. Antigenic correspondence of serum albumins among the primates. Science 151:1530–1535.

Hall, K.R.L. 1963a. Observational learning in monkeys and apes. British Journal of Psychology 54. 3:201–226. 1963b. Tool-using performances as indicators of behavioral adaptability. Current Anthropology 4:479–494.

Hamburg, D.A. 1963. Emotions in the perspective of human evolution. In Expression of the emotions in man. P.H. Knapp, ed. New York, International Universities Press.

Hay, R.L. 1963. Stratigraphy of Beds I through IV, Olduvai Gorge, Tanganyika. Science 139:829–833.

Hayes, K.J., and C. Hayes 1952. Imitation in a home-raised chimpanzee. Journal of Comparative and Physiological Psychology 45:450–459.

Hsiung, G.D., F.L. Black, and J.R. Henderson 1964. Susceptibility of primates to viruses in relation to taxonomic classification. In Evolutionary and genetic biology of primates. Vol. II. J. Buettner-Janusch, ed. New York, Academic Press.

Isaac, G. 1965. The stratigraphy of the Peninj Beds and the provenance of the Natron Australopithecine mandible. Quaternaria 7:101–130.

Keith, A. 1932. The antiquity of man. Vol. 1. Philadephia, Lippincott.

Klinger, H.P., J.L. Namerton, D. Mutton, and E.M. Lang 1963. The chromosomes of the Hominoidea. In Classification and human evolution. S.L. Washburn, ed. Viking Fund Publications in Anthropology No. 37.

Köhler, W. 1925. The mentality of apes. New York, Harcourt Brace.

Kortlandt, A., and M. Kooij 1963. Protohominid behaviour in primates. In The primates. J. Napier and N.A. Barnicot, eds. Symposium, Zoological Society of London 10:61–88.

Leakey, M.D. 1966. A review of the Oldowan culture from Olduvai Gorge, Tanzania. Nature 210:462–466.

Leakey, L.S.B. 1965. Olduvai Gorge 1951–1961: A preliminary report on the geology and fauna. Vol. 1. Cambridge University Press.

Leakey, L.S.B., and M.D. Leakey 1965. Personal communication. Quoted in G. Isaac, The stratigraphy of the Peninj Beds and the provenance of the Natron Australopithecine mandible. Quaternaria 7:118.

Mason, R. 1962. Prehistory of the Transvaal. Witwatersrand, Witwatersrand University Press.

Menzel, E.W., Jr. 1966. Responsiveness to objects of free-ranging Japanese monkeys. Behaviour 26:130–150.

Montagna, W., R.A. Ellis 1963. New approaches to the study of the skin of primates. In Evolutionary and genetic biology of primates. Vol. 1. J. Buettner-Janusch, ed. New York, Academic Press.

Napier, J.R. 1962. Fossil hand bones from Oduvai Gorge. Nature 196:409–411. 1964. The evolution of bipedal walking in the hominids. Archives de Biologie 75: Supplement:673–708.

Oakley, K.P. 1954. Skill as a human possession. In A history of technology. Vol. 1. C. Singer, E.J. Holmyard, and A.R. Hall, eds. Oxford, Clarendon Press.

Robinson, J.T. 1963. Adaptive radiation in the Australopithecines and the origin of man. In African ecology and human evolution. F.C. Howell and F. Bourlière, eds. Viking Publications in Anthropology No. 36.

Sarich, V. 1966. Quantitative immunochemistry and the evolution of the Anthropoidea. Paper presented at the 35th Annual Meeting of the American Association of Physical Anthropologists, April 4–6, 1966, Berkeley, California. Abstracted in American Journal of Physical Anthropology 25:208.

Schaller, G. 1963. The mountain gorilla: ecology and behavior. Chicago, University of Chicago Press.

Schenkel, R. 1964. Zur Ontogenese des Verhaltens bei Gorilla und Mensch. Zeitschrift für Morphologie und Anthropologie 54:233–259.

Schiller, P.H. 1957. Innate motor action as a basis of learning. In Instinctive behavior. C.H. Schiller, ed. New York, International Universities Press.

Simons, E.L. 1963. A critical reappraisal of tertiary primates. *In* Evolutionary and genetic biology of primates. Vol. I. J. Buettner-Janusch, ed. New York, Academic Press.

———. 1963b. Some fallacies in the study of hominid phylogeny. Science 141:879–889.

Simons, E.L., and D.R. Pilbeam 1965. Preliminary revision of the Dryopithecinae (Pongidae, Anthropoidea). Folia Primatologia 3:81–152.

Tobias, P.V. 1963. Cranial capacity of *Zinjanthropus* and other Australopithecines. Nature 197:743–746.

———. 1964. The Olduvai Bed I Hominine with special reference to its cranial capacity. Nature 202:3–4.

Washburn, S.L. 1963. Behavior and human evolution. *In* Classification and human evolution. S.L. Washburn, ed. Viking Fund Publications in Anthropology No. 37. 1963b. Comment. Current Anthropology 4:492.

Washburn, S.L., and P. Jay 1967. More on tool use among primates. Current Anthropology 8:253–254.

Yerkes, R.M., and A.W. Yerkes 1929. The great apes. New Haven, Yale University Press.

Zeuner, F.E. 1959. The Pleistocene period: its climate, chronology, and faunal successions. London, Hutchinson and Co.

Zuckerkandl, E. 1963. Perspectives in molecular anthropology. *In* Classification and human evolution. S.L. Washburn, ed. Viking Fund Publications in Anthropology No. 37.

10

DIMENSIONS OF A COMPARATIVE BIOLOGY OF PRIMATE GROUPS
Hans Kummer

Not too long ago, years went by between field studies on primates in the wild, and there simply were not enough studies to allow a comparative discussion of the various kinds of social groupings. Now, however, there are whole journals devoted to primate studies and enough work is being done so that symposia can be devoted to primate research. The Symposium on Primate Studies in Anthropology was held at the annual meetings of the American Association of Physical Anthropologists at Chapel Hill, North Carolina, in 1967. Kummer's paper, part of this symposium, was subsequently published in the American Journal of Physical Anthropology.

For the interested reader, a recent review by Eisenberg, Muckenhirn, and Rudran (1972) offers the most complete and up-to-date list of published accounts of the various kinds of social structure recorded for primate groups. The source listed is equally applicable as a supplement to Crook's article, which follows the one by Kummer.

Eisenberg, J.F., N.A. Muckenhirn, and R. Rudran. 1972. The relation between ecology and social structure in primates. *Science 176*:863–874.

ABSTRACT. *The possible contributions of a comparative study of primate social organization to anthropology are many. Such a study may elucidate the repertory of motivational and organizational raw materials present among primates; it may show us the forms of society that have evolved from this raw material; it may show us the kinds of inhibitions and functional readjustments of phylogenetically old motivations that lead to the types of societies found among primates. These general aims are based upon analysis of specific primate groups. The analysis of a primate group as a functioning system leads to consideration of the anatomy and physiology of groups, the reasons for differences in types of groups, the ontogeny of a group, environmental modifications of types of groups, and the evolution of the adaptive function of groups.*

Eight years have now passed since field studies on primate behavior became the active concern of a group of anthropologists in this country, and the broader anthropological audience may rightly ask what this group has done and where they are heading.

In asking a zoologist but not an anthropologist to answer such questions, the organizers of this symposium have obviously not wished for a *pro domo* speech but for a broad discussion in terms of our common biological background. This paper, therefore, is not a review of facts but an attempt to familiarize the morphologist and physiologist with the special nature of our task in the field.

Let us first ask why we seek our subjects in their native habitats. Every biologist knows that a living system should be grown and studied in as many different environments as possible. No single environment reveals all the phenotypic modifications of which a genotype is capable. Captive animals may develop adaptive behavior patterns that are never observed in their wild conspecifics, and vice versa. It follows that there is nothing basically superior or sacred about studying animals in their natural habitat. Any controversy about a general superiority of either laboratory or field studies is pointless if we agree that our ultimate aim is not a description of one single modification, but an idea of the full genetic potential of our species.[1] A particular environment is a good or a bad

From *American Journal of Physical Anthropology* 27:357–366. Copyright by THE WISTAR PRESS 1967. Reprinted with permission of the author and the publisher.

[1]For a discussion of the relationship of field and laboratory work, see Menzel (1967).

choice only in relation to the questions we ask.

The biologist interested in primate behavior has two reasons for going to the field. The first is his interest in behavior as a means of survival. Behavior can become adaptive in a particular environment either because its genetic substrate was selected by this or a similar environment or because the environment evokes adaptive modifications from the genetic substrate of the present generation. The highest degree of adaptiveness will generally be found in an environment that shaped both the genotypes and the modifications of the genetic substrate of the animals studied. For a given population, this environment is most likely the one in which it presently occurs.

The second reason for field studies is the need to observe *group* behavior. We may without difficulty buy individuals for our laboratory studies, but as yet no dealer sells us an entire group as he found it in the wild. We may have the courage to assemble the system which we are going to study, but before we do so we should learn as much as possible about these fragile structures in their native habitat. For this second reason, the study of social groups may be considered the typical task of field work on primates. The study of social groups will also be the frame of this discussion.

As a first approximation, a social group can be approached as merely another living system, as a form of compound organism which appeared late in phylogeny and in which the metazoan individual is no longer the whole but a part. The organism analogy at one time played its heuristic role in the study of social insects. We shall use it here because it permits us to start out from familiar biological dimensions. We shall ask the questions that every biologist asks when he faces a new kind of organism, namely those concerning the anatomy, the physiology, the ontogeny, the ecology, and the evolution of the "group organism." In answering each of these questions, we shall arrive at a point where the analogy with the organism no longer holds and where the vertebrate group as a form of life reveals its own characteristics. To the biologist working in other fields, these points will best demonstrate the problems of studies on primate societies.

The primate species of the open country of East and South Africa serve as examples throughout this paper. Their social organizations show two basic types of groups in various combinations: the multi-male group, in which several adult males live with a number of females and their offspring, and the one-male group, in which females and young are associated with only one male. The multi-male group is typical of the savanna baboons *(Papio anubis, P. cynocephalus, P. ursinus)*. In these groups, each male potentially has access to each female (Hall and DeVore, 1965). The patas monkeys *(Erythrocebus patas)* of Uganda represent the other extreme; their organizational units are one-male groups which live far apart from each other (Hall, 1965). Between these two extremes there are two species that show a combination of the two types of groups. In *Papio hamadryas,* the "desert baboon" of Ethiopia, a number of one-male groups together form a larger association, the "band," which travels and fights as a unit. The band resembles the multi-male group of the savanna baboons except that each female is the exclusive partner of one and only one male (Kummer, 1967). A similar two-level organization is found in the gelada baboons *(Theropithecus gelada)* of the Ethiopian highlands. But the gelada one-male groups are more independent of each other; they spearate when food is scarce; and, although they join to form large troops, there is no evidence that several one-male groups form a stable well-organized association with the pattern of the hamadryas band (Crook, 1966).

GROUP ANATOMY

Like an amoeba, a group constantly changes its shape in space, but certain arrangements of the members of the group occur more frequently than others. Some of them hit the eye immediately. In baboons and macaques, females tend to hold the center of the group with a few dominant males, whereas younger males are more peripheral. This general arrangement, however, can be modified according to the situation. In a troop of geladas walking along the edge of a vertical cliff, the females walk close to the edge, shielded only on the farther side by a belt of large males. When two one-male groups of hamadryas baboons forage in the savanna, their females will form a line between the males. But if the two males start to threaten each other, each set of females swings outward to line up behind its respective male and away from the other group. The obvious advantage of flexible anatomy is that the group can cope with certain situations simply by altering its shape.

The exact quantitative analysis of a group's spacing pattern is rather difficult. My own preliminary attempts have failed because the animals under experimental conditions did not keep one particular arrangement for more than seconds or minutes. Maps of spatial arrangements of hamadryas baboons in the field nevertheless showed that certain simple characteristics survive most changes in formation. For example, the animals of a particular sex-age class are usually surrounded by neighbors of a typical sex-age distribution, and this reveals much about the affinities between the classes.

Although we know so little yet about the spatial dimensions of groups, the question "What is a group?" is in practice answered most often and with reasonable success on the basis of a spatial criterion. In general, a spatial aggregation of primates that travel and rest together and at the same time avoid the proximity of other such aggregations is, at closer inspection, also a functional and reproductive unit.

GROUP PHYSIOLOGY

The members of a group, like the cells of an organism, exchange signals that affect the activity as well as the development of the members that receive them. The effect is a more or less coordinated activity of the group as a whole. From what has been said about the loose spatial structure of the group, it is obvious that group physiology faces a particular task in merely maintaining the group's identity within the population. The individual primate, unlike the metazoan cell, can physically leave the body of the group and survive on his own, at least for some time. In addition, since he is not biochemically earmarked as a stranger, he can enter another group and become its member. Why, then, are certain primate groups as stable in membership as we have found them in the field? What is the "immunological" process by which the

stranger is recognized and rejected? Here again, we know next to nothing. One might hypothesize that the members of each group share certain behavioral or morphological traits by which they are recognized, and this may most likely be true in species where the groups respond to each other with "territorial" calls. The alternative is that primates know the members of their group as individuals and recognize a stranger by exclusion, as an unfamiliar individual.

Beyond the necessity of differentiating between strangers and group members, the closed group must have mechanisms of actual inclusion and exclusion if it is to maintain its integrity. Some members of the same species must attract or tolerate each other while avoiding or chasing away others. Groups of savanna baboons avoid each other, and occasional strangers lingering about the group are chased away, although with persistence they may finally enter the group. A patas male spotting another male near his own group will simply chase the stranger away. The integrity of the group is in these cases maintained by the use of distance as an isolating agent. This widespread and relatively primitive technique, however, is obviously replaced by others in species such as the gelada or the hamadryas, where several small groups join to form larger social units without losing their identity. Although the one-male groups of a hamadryas band travel and rest so close together that it can take hours to tell the groups apart, the members of each one-male group mate and groom only among themselves. The spatial proximity of these groups does not destroy their isolation where social interactions are involved. In hamadryas, the mechanisms that maintain this segregation are not the same for females and males. By themselves, the females do not refrain from interacting with other band members, and they actually manage to do so when their male is not watching. Their isolation is imposed on them by the male, who threatens and even bites them when they move too far away from him or when they try to mate or groom with members of other one-male groups. The male hamadryas, in contrast, refrains from mating or grooming with outsiders for reasons not apparent to an external observer. Even a male to whom other animals submit in other contexts will not interact with the females of subordinate males. Of the nature of this inhibition we know nothing except that it is probably limited to the members of the same band: one-male groups artificially transplanted into a distant area are attacked by the local males, and their females are distributed among the resident males without any fighting among the new "owners." Such experimental transplantations may soon teach us more about the mechanisms of exclusion and the permeability of group boundaries.

A closed primate group not only maintains its composition but also travels as a closed body, in a coordinated fashion. How do its members determine the direction of their common travel? In a gorilla group, the members attend to and follow their leader, the single silver-backed male (Schaller, 1963). But in a large hamadryas troop ready for departure from a resting place there are several such old males, and the younger males, in addition, reveal clear directional intention of their own. The ultimate direction is determined by a process in which younger males walk away from the troop in the direction of their choice, thus forming troop "pseudopods" in various directions. The troop, however, does not follow them until an older male accepts one of the proposed directions by walking toward one of the pseudopods. At this signal, the younger males in the pseudoped start out in the indicated direction, and the troop follows with the older males in the rear. In this case, the functioning order reveals two male "roles": the role of initiative, typical of younger males, and the role of decision, taken in turn by one of the older males of the troop.

Functioning orders of vertebrate groups are most frequently described by the term "dominance." In its classical definition, a dominance order is the relatively stable sequence in which the animals of an established group have access to an "incentive," such as a piece of food or a desired social partner. The emphasis that this concept puts on the competitive aspect of group life betrays its origin, the laboratory. In the captive group, competition is indeed a prominent feature of social order, more so, it seems, than in the wild. Field studies show that group function is based on a number of additional orders, which have little to do with

sequences of access. Drawing again on the hamadryas data, we find that the number of females belonging to a male (a classical criterion of dominance) is not correlated with his influence on the troop's travel direction: younger males have more females than older males, but it is the older males that determine where the troop will go. The dominance concept, often used so broadly as to be ambiguous and misleading, must be complemented by other concepts. Among the social "roles" (cf. Bernstein and Sharpe, 1966), which may or may not be correlated with classical dominance, the following may be mentioned:

1. Leadership can be provisionally defined as the probability with which an animal's movements in space are taken over by others. The hamadryas example shows that leadership must not be correlated with classical dominance.
2. The role of protection may or may not rest with the dominant animal. The spatial arrangement of baboon troops suggests that the less dominant males on the troop's periphery may be more active in encounters with humans and predators.
3. An animal may be so persistent in asserting his exclusive access to a particular partner that the latter becomes his social "property." The hamadryas male achieves this by interfering with his females' interactions with all other males. In a comparable way, baboon mothers are more possessive about their infants than are the mothers of langurs. Logically, this exclusiveness is the extreme expression of dominance. However, since even a mother or a male of otherwise low dominance status can establish and assert the exclusive access to a particular partner, the phenomenon of exclusiveness must be distinguished from the dominance concept and be investigated as a separate aspect of a group's functioning order.

In short, a dominant primate may be the leader or protector of his group as well as the exclusive owner of his females, but correlations between roles cannot be taken for granted. On the other hand, classical dominance can be correlated with apparently unrelated behavioral traits. In a zoo colony of hamadryas baboons, the four adult females stirred during sleep at night with frequencies that conformed exactly with their dominance order. The most dominant female stirred most rarely, the most subordinate most frequently (Kummer, 1956). When the dominance order was rearranged, the frequencies of sleeping movements changed accordingly.

In all these aspects of a group's functioning order, a basic contrast to the functioning order of an organism is apparent. In a developing metazoan organism, the parts gradually differentiate as to structure and function, and at a certain stage of development this differentiation of a part becomes irreversible. The functional role of a part is then determined for the rest of the organism's life. In contrast, the only roles in a primate group that are irrevocably prescribed by morphological and functional differentiation are those of the two sexes. Within the sexes, the roles of the dominant animal, of the leader, or of the peripheral defender are not the permanent roles of clearly differentiated castes. The individual qualities of a dominant animal, for example, occur on a continuous scale throughout a group, and the actual role taken by an individual therefore depends on where his qualities place him in his particular group. The low-ranking male of this year can become the high-ranking male of next year since the relevant qualities change with age; changing alliances in the group add to the lability of role distribution. Even the roles of the two sexes are not exclusively differentiated. One female in a captive hamadryas colony showed complete male herding behavior toward the other females of her group, and the most dominant female of each of our captive gelada groups adopted male roles toward the rest of each group's females. In comparison with the tissues of an organism, the members of a vertebrate group are so similarly equipped that the distribution of roles is never quite stable, and distribution is often achieved with difficulty. In the case of dominance, the ultimate decision may only be reached by overt, aggressive competition. It is this competition for roles among similarly equipped parts in which the functioning order of the vertebrate group most clearly differs from the physiology of organisms. Human history has seen many attempts to abandon this competitive order and violent struggles to reestablish it.

CAUSES OF DIFFERENCES IN GROUP TYPE

In this section we are concerned only with the immediate causes of group organization. The question is not: why did this species evolve its present social organization? Instead, we ask, of what kind are the *immediate* motivational or behavioral causes which, in a given generation, bring about monogamous groups in one species, polygynous groups in another, and multi-male groups in still another?

Our first attempt to answer these questions consists of a close look at the social behavior of the individual group member. It has become a tradition, inherited from ethology, that a preliminary field study should include a catalogue of the gestural and vocal signals exchanged by the individuals of the respective species. In studying the signals used among the members of a species we may have hoped to discover some key signals that have a direct effect on the composition of the group. If we had any such hopes, they have failed so far. From the very similar behavioral catalogues of *Papio anubis* and *P. hamadryas* nobody could predict that anubis baboons live in basically promiscuous groups, whereas hamadryas are organized in bands composed of polygynous one-male groups. The behavior that one would expect to be an exclusive hamadryas pattern is the male's particular bite on the nape of the female's neck. This bite brings straying females back to their male and thus is the enforcer of group cohesion. But even this pattern is common to both species. The anubis baboons simply do not use it to herd females. Our captive gelada males also bit their females on the neck, but without relating this action to the female's being too far away. On the other hand, the behavioral repertoires of patas monkeys and geladas are very different, although they both are organized in one-male groups. The field studies to date suggest that the patterns of social *behavior* of a species are related to the taxonomic position of the species. Social *organizations*, however, seem to appear here and there in the order Primates without apparent relationship to taxonomy or to patterns of social behavior. Improbable as it sounds, social behavior as we have so far described it cannot be the cause of differences in social organization. We obviously must separate the two phenomena more clearly in our research than we have done so far. We must also expect to find that apparently similar, convergent organizations in distant species have different causes.

One reason for our failure to explain various types of social organizations is obvious. In the field as in the laboratory, social behavior has almost exclusively been studied on dyads, i.e., on interactions of only two animals. But to study the exclusion of a stranger from a group or the mechanisms responsible for the formation of a monogamous pair, one has to analyze the interactions of at least three animals. If this is done, the causes of differences in type of group may be found to be different affinities among sex-age classes and active interferences of one class with the interactions among two other classes. A comparison of the species forming one-male groups may give us a glimpse of the kind of causal factors we may find. The patas monkeys of Uganda and a population of Hanuman langurs near Dharwar in India (Sugiyama, 1966) both live in groups of one adult male and a number of females. Apparently, the adult males of these populations do not tolerate one another in the same group. Surprisingly, however, these populations also include groups of several males without females. This suggests that there is an attraction among the males but that it breaks down in the presence of females. An observation by Sugiyama confirms this hypothesis for the langur. He has sometimes seen an all-male langur group that cooperates in expelling the single male of a one-male group and takes over its females. Immediately after that, however, the new males fight each other until one of them has expelled all the others and becomes the sole leader of the female group. In contrast with these species, the one-male groups of hamadryas and gelada baboons live together in large troops. Here, the attraction among the males seems to outweigh the disruptive effect of the females, but this effect is nevertheless apparent: hamadryas males who have no females often sit close to each other and groom each other, but those who have females keep farther apart and are never seen to groom each other. Our unpublished experiments on captive geladas have shown that the bond

between two males regresses to an earlier, more hostile stage as soon as females are added: grooming disappears and aggressive behavior is resumed. Observations of the four species mentioned suggest that there are at least two causal factors determining their social organization: the degree of attraction among adult males and the degree of its reduction in the presence of females. The organizational differences between langurs, patas, geladas, and hamadryas may be an effect of different ratios of these two factors. This interpretation admittedly lacks nothing in crudeness, but it can be experimentally tested, and it seems at least to aim at the kind of phenomena that will ultimately lead to an understanding of the causes of social organizations.

GROUP ONTOGENY

We would certainly understand more about what causes various kinds of groups if we could study their development. But here, unfortunately, the organism analogy seems to fail right away. The ontogeny of an organism is the result of an ordered sequence of gene actions which initiate developmental steps and create temporary states in which the organism is especially sensitive to certain developmental stimuli. In contrast, groups appear to have no distinct life cycle; they do not go through an irreversible ageing process. Potentially the group's capacity to regenerate appears unlimited.

There is, however, a sort of "false exception." A group may be organized around one key animal whose death it cannot survive. In the extreme case, the composition and organization of the group may be so strongly affected by the key individual that the group itself assumes a life cycle, which is the effect of the behavioral ontogeny of that one critical member.

The hamadryas one-male group presents such a case. Subadult hamadryas males have a tendency to "kidnap" and mother infants and young juveniles temporarily. Single infants and juveniles that we released into hamadryas troops were adopted by single, young adult males, who behaved as typical hamadryas mothers. Left to themselves, such young adults will eventually adopt a one-year-old female of their own troop. Thus, the typical one-male group of a young adult male consists of himself and one sexually immature female. There is no overt sexual behavior in these initial groups; instead, the male handles and carries his female as if he were her mother. A number of intermediate stages between this immature form and the groups of old males suggests that the young female eventually becomes the male's sexual consort. Toward the male's early prime, the number of his females increases, for he probably adopts one or two more juvenile females and takes over adult females from older males. During early prime, the male's herding behavior is most intense, and the group's spatial cohesion is strongest. As the male approaches his late prime, however, he becomes more tolerant. His females may now stray away from him as far as 40 meters, and even then the male is unlikely to threaten them. Accordingly, the group of the ageing male decreases in size, but at the same time he becomes more influential in matters of band and troop movements. This influence can still be found in old males who have lost or given up all their females.

This development shows first that certain roles in a primate group may be specifically attributed to certain age classes, even within the time span of adulthood. Secondly, it suggests a hypothesis about the causation of the hamadryas social system: the adult hamadryas female remains a life-long follower of a particular male *because* she was so early in life adopted, mothered, and restricted by a single adult male. Whereas her mother would soon have released her from control, the male who adopted her will keep "maternal" control over her until she is fully adult. Thus, the hamadryas female never develops the independent social habits of female anubis baboons.

A strong "parental" motivation of the males may be only one way by which a species develops a system of one-male groups. Neither Crook (1966) nor Hall (1965) has found evidence of the hamadryas solution in their gelada and patas populations. Since one-male groups appeared independently in one species of each of four genera, it would not be a surprise if they arrived at their similar organizations by different pathways and by exploitation of different behavioral and motivational raw materials. These one-

male units would then be typical examples of convergence.

ENVIRONMENTAL MODIFICATIONS OF GROUP STRUCTURE

When Zuckerman (1932) formulated his theory of primate social organization, he appeared to assume that all higher primates were organized in the same basic grouping pattern. Later, Carpenter's (1964) work and the field studies of the last decade suggested that each primate species has its own organization. Only the most recent studies, in which a species was observed in various parts of its distributional range, have shown that there is also a considerable intraspecific variability of social life (e.g., Gartlan and Brain, in press). Unless we assume that these intraspecific variations are genetical, we may interpret them as modifications induced by the particular physical environments. The issue could be settled experimentally by transferring random samples of the same population into diffferent habitats where they could then be studied for at least two generations. The rhesus population introduced by Carpenter and other workers to several islands off Puerto Rico offers research opportunities in this direction, although the value must decrease with every generation that is subjected to the particular selective factors of the new environment before the comparisons are made. Modifications induced by the *social* environment can be more easily studied. It would be sufficient to raise, for example, anubis baboons in a hamadryas troop to explore the capacity of anubis to be modified toward hamadryas group life.

Another opportunity for evaluating the modifying effects of environment, although unsatisfactory, is the study of colonies established in zoological gardens and laboratory enclosures. Since these artificial environments differ in nearly all variables from the original habitat of the transferred animals, they serve merely as a test of the resistance of a social organization to a drastic, general change. Furthermore, captive groups are usually composed of individuals that have not grown up together in the same wild group. Instead of growing into an existing group, they have to build one with unfamiliar partners. If the new organization turns out to be different from that of the original population, it will not be possible to attribute the change to any particular environmental factor. But if the original grouping pattern reappears and survives into the next generation, we may assume that it is highly resistant to a wide range of environmental changes. Some species indeed have shown this stability. A colony of geladas, imported from the wild as subadults, formed one-male groups within ten days after being admitted to the 100 by 400 foot enclosure of the Delta Center. Zuckerman (1932) found that the hamadryas colonies of three different zoos were organized in one-male groups (Kummer and Kurt, 1965), and the hamadryas baboons of the Sukhumi research station in Russia show the same pattern even after several generations in captivity (Bowden, 1966).

Studies of groups under changed environments can, however, produce results that are more interesting than a mere demonstration of organizational stability. The hamadryas colony of the Zurich Zoo regularly displayed a behavior pattern that we never observed in wild hamadryas troops. In this pattern, called "protected threat," an animal enlists the support of a stronger individual against his opponent by a specific set of gestures. Surprisingly, the protected threat is not found in wild hamadryas, but wild anubis baboons (De Vore, 1962) and rhesus monkeys (Altmann, 1962) show it. This and parallel examples support the assumption (probable already on theoretical grounds) that the genetic potential of a species for social behavior and organization is broader than the overt behavior observed in the wild. Parts of the repertoire of a species must be latent, and among these latent behaviors there may be some that are overt in related species. An investigation into these latent repertoires would certainly add to our understanding of comparative social life in primates.

In interpreting the effects of a change in environment on social structure, one has to consider a possibility that can be disregarded in analogous studies on single organisms, namely the transmission of non-genetical information from one generation to the next by means of "tradition." The work at the Japanese Monkey Center on the spreading of

food habits within a group is too well known to be reviewed here. What we must realize, however, is that traditions of group life (i.e., social behavior appearing in younger animals as an enduring response to behavior of their elders) might counteract modifying effects of the physical, non-social environment. Geladas may form one-male groups in captivity because they have been socialized to do so as juveniles in the wild, and their captive-born offspring might be socialized in the same way. Only a partial reduction of the socialization process could reveal the modifications of the physical environment within one generation.

EVOLUTION AND ADAPTIVE FUNCTIONS OF TYPES OF GROUPS

A social organization must have an evolutionary history if it is determined by genes. As we just observed, however, we have as yet no idea of the extent to which a social organization is genetically determined. We know that skeletal and many biochemical characters are under relatively precise genetic control, and we may therefore attribute changes in them during evolution to changes of genotypes. But if we find that two related species differ in their grouping patterns, we cannot decide whether the difference was caused by a change in the constituents of the gene pool or by a modification of the expression of the genotype. It is uncertain whether hamadryas baboon behavior is merely an overt display of an environmental modification which the savanna baboons would show as well if they were subjected to the hamadryas environment or whether the hamadryas organization is the result of an evolutionary change. The latter appears more likely because both the savanna baboons and the hamadryas baboons maintain their type of group in captivity, but the answer must wait for the appropriate experiments.

Regardless of the degree to which modifications and mutations contribute to a particular organization, we should eventually investigate the adaptive functions of the organization in various types of habitat. The question of adaptation has been the foremost concern of the anthropologists studying primates in the field, and therefore I should like to illustrate the kinds of speculations that we may derive from the available preliminary studies.

All three African monkey species that have been found to organize themselves in one-male groups are highly terrestrial, and all live in open habitats where food is sparse and where sleeping trees are scarce or unsafe. Since widely scattered food resources are better exploited by small groups than by large troops, independent one-male groups of the patas type may be an adaptation to the distribution of food supply. In accordance with this hypothesis, Crook (1966) found that geladas live in isolated one-male groups in areas where food is scarce. In richer areas, the one-male groups join to form large troops.

The density and quality of sleeping lairs for the night seem to be the second major factor determining the organization of the open-country species. The best sleeping trees in the habitats of patas monkeys are small and offer little protection against predators. Patas monkeys reduce the risk of predation by dispersal at nightfall: each tree is occupied by only one individual. In a hamadryas habitat, the best sleeping lairs are vertical cliffs. These cliffs, however, are often far apart, and therefore the baboons must form large sleeping parties at night. The hamadryas thus have to cope with two contradictory ecological factors; they form small foraging groups of four to eight animals during the day, but at night they congregate by hundreds on the few available cliffs. No single type of group can satisfy these contrasting needs. Accordingly, the hamadryas has developed a unique multi-level organization, in which small one-male groups, without losing their identity, are organized in large troops or sleeping parties. This interpretation does not explain the intermediate level of hamadryas organization, the band. The similarity of the band to the multi-male group of savanna baboons has already been mentioned. If, as is likely, the hamadryas has evolved from savanna baboons as a specialist of the semidesert, the hamadryas band is probably the surviving homologue of the savanna baboon group. By splitting the original group into small foraging one-male groups for the day and by developing an intergroup tolerance at night, the hamadryas may have arrived at his present three-level stage of organization

which permits reversible fusion and fission according to conditions.

CONCLUSION

By subjecting the primate group to the standard questions of biological research, we have tried to point out to the biologist working in other fields some of the special characters of the group organism. The flexibility of a group's anatomy permits the group to assume various shapes, each of which may be adaptive in a special situation. On the other hand, this loose structure leaves the group with the constant task of maintaining its identity, i.e., attracting its members and excluding strangers. The functioning order of the group is further marked by the minimal morphological and functional differentiation of its members. Assumption of some of the roles or functions within the group are therefore subject to competition from a number of similarly equipped individuals. The distribution of roles has only temporary stability, for the established order is for some time recognized rather than challenged by the group members.

The immediate causes of a particular social organization apparently are not related to the repertoire of social signals but probably to the relative strength of affinities among sex-age classes and to the degree to which relationships among certain classes are tolerated or prevented by other animals in the group. The example of hamadryas baboons suggests that phylogenetically old motivations, such as maternal motivations, may assume new functions in group life. Groups in general appear to lack a genetically programmed life cycle except when they are focused on the life cycle of one key individual.

What can a comparative science of primate social organization contribute to anthropology? It may show us the repertoire of motivations and organizational elements present in the order Primates: it may show us what forms of societies have evolved on the basis of this raw material; and it may show us what kinds of inhibitions and functional readjustments of phylogenetically old motivations could lead to the types of societies presently found in nonhuman primates. What, for instance, are the motivational syndromes that can produce monogamous groups or purely male groups? Is primate monogamy, for instance, always based on the same constellation of motivational factors, regardless of whether it appears in the gibbon or in the South American *Callicebus*, or are there several ways in which primates can realize the monogamous pattern? The answers to such questions would establish a body of comparative theory and data against which the specific solutions found by human societies could be evaluated. Which factors of the group-building repertoire does man share with other primates and in which has he specialized? In short, where in the order Primates is man to be placed on the basis of the specific factors underlying social organizations?

A second group of questions concerns the modifiability of social organization. We have seen that a species may in captivity reveal organizational elements that it does not show in the wild but which are found in closely related species under natural conditions. Such observations suggest that a species has a repertoire of social organizations which is only partly realized in any single environment. How large is this latent repertoire? Man may serve as an example. His technical capacities have allowed him to occupy an enormous variety of physical environments, and this variety probably brought out at some epoch and in some place all social modifications of which he is capable. The question of tremendous practical importance is: to how many and to what new kinds of environments can man yet respond with adaptive social organizations without changing his present gene pool? Under what conditions does this capacity to modify fail, and which elements of social behavior and organization are most likely to fail under a particular condition? No nonhuman primate has had man's enormous technical ability to adapt to a large variety of habitats. Each species is more or less confined to one type of habitat, which in turn produces social organizations that vary little within each species. The full genetic potential of such species would only come to the fore if they were experimentally exposed to other environments. The results would not only reveal much more about the evolution of social life than we can presently know, but they could also yield some answers on the critical limits of our own social adaptability.

LITERATURE CITED

Altmann, S. 1962. A field study of the socio-biology of rhesus monkeys, *Mucaca mulatta*. Ann. N.Y. Acad. Sci., *102*: 338–345.

Bernstein, I.S., and L.G. Sharpe 1966. Social roles in a rhesus monkey group. Behaviour, *26*: 91–104.

Bowden, D. 1966. Primate behavioral research in the USSR—The Sukhumi medico-biological station. Folia primat., *4*: 346–360.

Carpenter, C.R. 1964. Naturalistic Behavior of Nonhuman Primates. Pennsylvania State University Press, University Park.

Crook, J. 1966. Gelada baboon herd structure and movement. A comparative report. Symp. Zool. Soc. Lond., *18*: 237–258.

DeVore, I. 1962. The social behavior and organization of baboon troops. Ph.D. Thesis, Department of Anthropology, University of Chicago.

Gartlan, J.S., and C.K. Brain In press. Ecology and social variability in *Cercopithecus aethiops* and *C. mitis*. In: Primates: Studies in Adaptation and Variability. P. Jay (ed.), Holt, Rinehart and Winston, New York.

Hall, K.R.L. 1965. Behaviour and ecology of the wild patas monkey, *Erythrocebus patas*, in Uganda. J. Zool., *148*: 15–87.

Hall, K.R.L., and I. DeVore 1965. Baboon social behavior. In: Primate Behavior, I. De Vore (ed.), Holt, Rinehart and Winston, New York.

Kummer, H. 1956. Rangkriterien bei Mantelpavianen (Criteria of dominance in hamadryas baboons). Revue Suisse de Zool., *63*: 288–297.

———. 1967. Social organization of hamadryas baboons. Bibl. Primatol. 6. Karger, Basel.

Kummer, H., and F. Kurt 1965. A comparison of social behavior in captive and wild hamadryas baboons. In: The Baboon in Medical Research, H. Vagtborg (ed.), University of Texas Press, Austin.

Menzel, E.W. 1967. Naturalistic and experimental research on primates. Human Development, *10*: 170–186.

Schaller, G.B. 1963. The Mountain Gorilla. University of Chicago Press, Chicago.

Sugiyama, Y. 1966. An artificial social change in a Hanuman langur troop *(Presbytis entellus)*. Primates, *7*: 41–72.

Zuckerman, S. 1932. The Social Life of Monkeys and Apes. Kegan Paul, London.

11

SOCIAL ORGANIZATION AND THE ENVIRONMENT: ASPECTS OF CONTEMPORARY SOCIAL ETHOLOGY
John Hurrell Crook

A generation ago, scientists assumed that the social organization of a particular kind of animal was genetically determined. Heredity, it was thought, determined that the leopard should be a solitary creature while sheep should live in herds. Much more is now known about the development and maintainance of social organization and, as Crook's article shows, both ecological factors and the varying experiences of growing organisms contribute to the shaping of social organization.

For example, in a single kind of baboon, groups in dry terrain will tend to be smaller in number, consisting of a single adult male plus several mature females with their immature offspring. In better watered country, the same species will exist in much larger groups with an organized heirarchy of mature males, satellite groups of immature males, a core of mature females with infants, and various juvenile play groups (Kummer 1968). Efficiency of ecological exploitation rather than rigid genetic conditioning evidently contributes to the difference.

Within a group, differences in experience can contribute to aspects of organization. The much talked about dominance heirarchy is more than just a gradient of strength and aggressiveness. Growing female monkeys, for instance, tend to enter the adult heirarchy with the same relative ranks as their mothers (Koford 1963; Sade 1965). Where male monkeys are concerned, Crook cites Wilson's doctoral work (as yet unpublished), which demonstrates that at adolescence, they tend to leave the natal group to play their emerging adult roles elsewhere. But they do not join just any other group. Rather, their entrance to the new group is sponsored by an older male member who had previously been a participant in the same juvenile play group of the natal troop. In fact in many instances it would appear that the sponsor is an older brother of the entering member who then takes the same relative rank.

With ecological factors, and the matter of previous experience that members have had with each other, both playing a part in determining group structure, it is no wonder that zoos have had so much trouble when they have simply dumped quantities of individual monkeys from various sources into single cages and assumed that everything would work out.

Koford, C.B. 1963. Rank of mothers and sons in bands of rhesus monkeys. *Science* 141:356–357.

Kummer, Hans. 1968. *Social Organization of Hamadryas Baboons: A Field Study.* University of Chicago Press, Chicago. 189 pp.

Sade, Donald S. 1965. Some aspects of parent-offspring and sibling relationships in a group of rhesus monkeys, with a discussion of grooming. *American Journal of Physical Anthropology* 23:1–18.

INTRODUCTION

During the rapid development of ethology in the last decade two diverging lines of research have become particularly apparent. In the first and more voluminous development the classical ethology of Lorenz and

From *Animal Behaviour* 18:197–209. Reprinted with the permission of the author and publisher.

Tinbergen has flowered into a rigorous and lively area of study depending fundamentally upon physiological research and the approaches of experimental biology. The main fields of investigation continue to be motivation analysis, developmental studies and the evolution of species specific behaviour. A number of major textbooks presenting this material have appeared. Preeminent among them is Hinde's (1966) remarkable coverage of the subject including an important attempt to synthesize approaches derived from behaviourist psychology with those of ethology.

The second development comprises a rapidly growing interest in the relations between ecology, population dynamics and social behaviour (e.g. Klopfer 1962). The social emphasis here is not so much upon the traditional ethographic study of behaviour patterns shown between conspecific individuals usually studied in dyadic interaction, but upon the relations between individuals and the natural group considered as the social environment within which they live and to which they are adapted. This second development is the subject of the present paper and the field of study will be termed Social Ethology. The links between the socially and the physiologically oriented wings of ethology remain very close, particularly in such areas as the endocrinology of social interaction and developmental studies. These connections illustrate the continuing interdependence of the branches of the subject.

Curiously enough, in spite of an early emphasis by such workers as Espinas (1878), Kropotkin (1914) and Allee (1938), social ethology has not flowered in the clear cut manner of physiological ethology. Indeed, the recent popular accounts of the subject, avidly read both inside and outside the academic world, far from presenting a stable front of established knowledge, have revealed fundamental contrasts in theoretical orientation and interpretation and have given rise to noisy speculation regarding the inferences that may be made from animal to human social behaviour.

One of the major reasons for this lack of clarity lies, I think, in the failure of ethologists generally to consider social behaviour as a group process. Social behaviour has been treated mainly in terms of reciprocal interactions between individuals presenting stereotyped signals to one another, signals moreover that were commonly species specific and which could be broadly considered as innate. Given such material, it is not difficult to interpret such behaviour as the relatively straightforward outcome of neo-Darwinian selection. It would then follow that society, treated as a matrix of such behavioural interactions, is likewise a direct product of natural selection and adapted to the particular circumstances that have moulded it. A number of recent studies of social structure, admirable in other respects, have begun with this a priori supposition. If this were indeed true one could compare societies in the same way as the classical ethologists compared the behaviour of individuals. Unfortunately, societies, being inadequately characterized by such an approach, are unlikely to be programmed entirely in this way as indeed studies of intraspecific variation make very clear.

Although the emphasis on fixed action patterns in communication has been one focus of mainstream ethology an alternative and minority viewpoint has taken a very different stand, one moreover of increasing significance today. The sociologists Emile Waxweiler (1906) and Raphael Petrucci (1906) working in Brussels between 1900 and the First World War developed a well defined social ethology of which sociology referring to man was itself considered a part (Crook 1970a). Petrucci studied social structures as such: spatial dispersion, numbers in groups, group composition, etc., and he pointed out that there were few correlations between a taxonomy of social organizations and the classification of species. At each phyletic level, he saw a marked tendency for similar societies to emerge in parallel adaptation to similar conditions. He concluded that spatial dispersion, group composition and relations between individuals were directly responsive to the environment and that the factors programming the system included such features as food supply, predation and the requirements for sexual reproduction in differing habitats. The limitation on the range of social structures was determined only by the limited variability of the determining conditions. Petrucci concluded that since societies were determined directly by extrinsic factors they cannot be compared in the way that biologists compared morphological characteristics. And it followed, of course, that the social evolution of man was not to be explained purely in Darwinian terms.

Petrucci had taken an extreme position, but the almost total historical neglect of his work is quite unjustified. Recent studies of social organization, particularly in ungulates (Estes 1966) and primates (Crook 1970b), have revealed important intra-specific variations in group composition and inter-individual relations which for the most part appear to conform well with constrasts in the ecology of the demes concerned. Such social characteristics, furthermore, are more labile than the patterns of signalling which formerly comprised the main descriptions of social behaviour.

It seems therefore that any statement about contemporary social ethology must begin with at least the following propositions.

(i) Social structure as a group characteristic cannot be conceived as a species specific attribute or property in quite the same way as has commonly been done with, for example, wing colour or leg length. Instead, social structure is a dynamic system expressing the interaction of a number of factors within both the ecological and the social milieux that influence the spatial dispersion and grouping tendencies of populations within a range of lability allowed by the behavioral tolerance of the species.

(ii) Historical change in a social structure consists of several laminated and interacting processes with different rates of operation. Thus while the direct effect of environment may mould a social structure quickly, the indirect effects of this on learned traditions of social interaction come about more slowly and genetic selection within the society even more slowly still.

(iii) Because a major requirement for biological success is for the individual to adapt to the social norms of the group in which it will survive and reproduce it follows that a major source of genetic selection will be social, individuals maladapted to the prevailing group structure being rapidly eliminated. Social selection is thus a major source of biological modification. In advanced mammals it is perhaps of as great an importance as natural selection by the physical environment.

(iv) Lastly a methodological point. It seems desirable in considering group characteristics to shift the research emphasis away from questions concerning informational sources (i.e. relative significance of genetics, traditions, environmental programming, etc.) to direct analysis at the level of the social process itself. This shift would do much to bypass the never ending sterility and unreality of the nature-nurture controversy when

applied to social life. An understanding of a social process will in itself help to define the nature of the factors involved in its programming.

From this basis we may attempt a brief conspectus of contemporary social ethology focusing upon three interdependent perspectives.

(a) *Socio-ecology.* The comparative study of social structure in relation to ecology. The main focus here is upon correlations between social organizations and contrasts in ecology.

(b) *Socio-demography.* The relations between social organization and population dynamics including the role of social behaviour as a mortality factor and hence as an important source of genetic selection.

(c) *Social systems research.* The study of the actual behavioural processes that maintain group structure, bring about social change, and which may cause the social elimination of some individuals rather than others.

SOCIO-ECOLOGY

Within the last eight years a number of ornithological studies have shown quite clearly that the social structures of species populations correlate closely with ecology. Social structure in fact is one aspect of a whole syndrome of characteristics that are in the broadest sense adaptive. Huxley (1959) used the term "grade" to refer to the characteristic life styles of species adapted to a particular biotype. The species belonging to the same grade commonly show similar social organization. Such correlations have been well demonstrated by research on gulls and terns, penguins, Ploceine weaver birds, Estrildidae, Icterids, Sulidae, and a number of other groups that have been intensively studied comparatively in the field. The work of Tinbergen (1964, 1967), E. Cullen (1957), J.M. Cullen (1960), Stonehouse (1960), Crook (1964, 1965), Immelmann (1962, 1967), Orians (1961), Nelson (e.g. 1967), and Pitelka (1942 and unpublished) comes particularly to mind and Lack (1968) has recently published a major review.

The comparative approach of the ornithologists has now been applied to mammalian groups and has shown especial utility in studies of primates and ungulates. Both these groups are also relatively easy to study in the field, at least when compared with such cryptic beasts as insectivores, bats, rodents and many small carnivores. Furthermore, certain common themes occur in both primates and ungulates suggesting that we may soon have some important integrative principles by the tail.

The primate story due to Altmann, Carpenter, Gartlan, DeVore, Hall, Imanishi, Itani, Kummer, Rowell, Struhsaker, Washburn and other recent workers is perhaps most clearly illustrated by reference to the old-world Cercopithecoidea now extensively studied across a wide range of habitats. Both interspecific and intraspecific population comparisons have been made (reviewed by Crook 1970b).

A survey of current studies suggests a tentative model of socio-ecological relations in these animals. Generally speaking, population demes consisting of one-male groups or "harems," together with peripheral males or all-male groups, occur in a variety of spatial arrangements, in the least ecologically stable savannah and saheal areas having long harsh dry seasons and relatively low predation frequency. In ecologically more stable woodland savannah and light forest with less extreme annual climatic fluctuation and presumed to have higher potential predation frequency multi-male troops are common. Finally, in tropical and semi-tropical forests an increasing number of species have been found once more to live in small one-male groups often confined to small territories. Peripheral non-social males also occur and recent studies suggest a high rate of male interchange between groups, the female membership of which remains relatively constant.

It has been argued that this range of social contrasts is adapted to differences in the food resources and their seasonal availability in the differing habitats. In the more arid areas food resources are limited in the long dry season at which period dispersion in small groups, the reduction of males to a singleton in reproductive groups and the separate foraging of all-male groups allows optimum food availability to females which are commonly pregnant or lactating. The most effective evidence, although not con-

clusive, comes at present from the Gelada baboon in Ethiopia. These data are furthermore unconfounded by grouping tendencies influenced by the shortages of safe sleeping sites (Crook 1966; Crook & Aldrich-Blake 1968).

Geladas live near canyons and sleep on the gorge cliffs. During the day they wander either in harems or in congregations of independent harems and all-male groups that may together number several hundred. In the rains the animals move slowly in large herds over rich food resources. As the dry season progresses and food shortage becomes visibly apparent, Geladas travel rapidly in small groups often of single harem or all-male group size and the greater part of each day (e.g. up to 70 per cent of all afternoon activity) is spent in feeding. At this season all-male groups tend to disperse away from the canyon more markedly than do the harems. This appears to reduce the food competition between the two types of group. As we shall see such behaviour also occurs in certain ungulates and leads to a differential mortality between the sexes, females being far more fortunate than the non-reproductive males.

In richer savannah the large troops of baboons or macaques live in areas where food resources normally appear to be sufficient to withstand sustained exploitation by sizeable groups and furthermore such groups offer increased protection against the many potential predators.

The discovery of one-male groups in forests poses difficult theoretical problems but we may perhaps employ in this primate context Ashmole's (1961, 1963) argument applying his explanation of sea-bird breeding biology to the reduced clutch sizes of forest bird species when compared with those of open country relatives (see Lack 1966, pp. 266–270). From Ashmole's viewpoint we may argue that the relatively unchanging forest environment together with the high density of individuals present due to the great productivity of the biotope, produces conditions in which the population is very close to food shortage throughout the year. Under such circumstances it would be advantageous for individuals to live in small spatially circumscribed groups with low male representation. This would once more permit an optimum allocation of resources to reproductive females.

As Aldrich-Blake (1970) has remarked this view is certainly a simplification. While productivity in tropical forests may vary relatively little, this is not true within the home ranges of individual groups. In any one range there are relatively few food resources, say fruit trees, and these are in fruit only periodically. Feeding conditions, even given a wide variety of plant foods, are likely to vary greatly from week to week. Nevertheless he considers that feeding ecology seems very likely to be involved in an explanation of the contrasting spatial dispersions of forest monkey species. Current studies of the autecology of certain species and the synecology of the monkey populations of given forests will go far to explain these differences.

It remains plausible, however, that social forces alone may play a greater role in the determination of primate social behaviour than is at present known. The Gelada and the Hamadryas baboons (Kummer 1968) live under quite comparable conditions and have social structures that at first sight resemble one another closely. Yet the fine details of group dynamics and the individual qualities that make for reproductive success differ greatly. Adaptation to contrasting group processes within groups of comparable structure may lead to the selection of animals of very different behavioural character. Contrasts in social processes within similar social structures may thus be based on differences in behaviour that are the results of marked and long-term social selection.

Recent work on a wide range of African ungulates by Jarman (1968) reveals a fascinating range of social structures that partially parallels those of primates. In forest and forest fringes most species such as duikers and dik-dik are small in size, show little sex dimorphism, show no sexual segregation, have territories and live in pairs or alone. These animals are browsers. Other forest and savannah forms, oribi and bushbuck, for example, and also a number of montane animals not treated by Jarman live in small groups of up to about twelve. Males are a little larger than females. Some show territorialism and all are grazer-browsers. In savannah and open savannah the social units

are various, usually consisting of one-male breeding groups, all-male groups and sometimes lone males. The one-male breeding groups may be territorial or move as parts of herds. In some species such as the wildebeeste (Estes 1966) some populations are migratory and gregarious, others nearby in a more stable ecology being stationary and territorial. These animals are browser-grazers and grazer-browsers. Out on open grassland plains occur vast herds of mixed sexes and ages (eland, buffalo) in which several varieties of one male group or multimale reproductive units occur. These are mostly of nomadic grazers.

Jarman interprets the survival value of these various grouping tendencies mainly in terms of food availability, particularly in relation to seasonal differences in resources. For example, he argues that the dispersed condition of many forest browsing ungulates is related to the spatial and temporal scattering of suitable food plants. The large nomadic herds of grass plains by contrast are a function of the need for protection from predators in an environment offering little cover and which allows large congregations to form. Nomadism is related to the danger of over-exploitation of resources in a given locality, the large expanse of available habitat and the seasonality of the richness of the grass cover.

Jarman's (1968) study of species with one-male reproductive units living along the Kariba river is especially important for he shows that in the dry season the one-male groups occupy the food-rich riverine areas while the excess males are dispersed further inland where they get less food and are subject to higher predation. He demonstrates that such a dispersal also means that a predator has a higher probability of encountering a male than a female prey animal. Clearly the one-male group structure is highly advantageous to the individual females and single males living in the breeding unit and is a direct cause of much nonbreeding male mortality.

We cannot yet tell whether all mating systems of one-male group living ungulates necessarily have these effects. Jarman has nevertheless contributed important evidence for the involvement of a social factor in population dynamics, which goes a long way to vindicate arguments used in explaining the similar social structures in primates.

SOCIO-DEMOGRAPHY

The dispute in socio-demography has centred upon two alternative viewpoints. Lack (1954, 1966) originally interpreted population dynamics in birds as largely the outcome of interacting density-dependent environmental factors. He argues that spatial dispersion is a consequence of the natural selection of individuals and that it allows maximum recruitment from breeding units. By contrast Wynne-Edwards (1962) has argued that social behaviour influences dispersion to maintain optimum numbers in relation to resources, that dispersion patterns are a consequence of group selection and that socially mediated mortality is the prime factor in population dynamics.

In the hands of the main protagonists these approaches have perhaps both tended to acquire somewhat scholastic attributes. There is in fact a serious dearth of critical studies and Chitty (1967) has called for a more open-ended theoretical and a more experimental approach to the whole problem.

Wynne-Edwards' work has focussed attention upon the question whether social attributes promoting dispersion do in fact play a major role in population dynamics as mortality factors and therefore also as important social selection pressures in evolution. A demonstration that this may often be the case would not however necessarily support Wynne-Edwards' theory as a whole. Indeed it would allow (see below) the construction of "open adaptive" models (Buckley 1967) of the socio-demographic process, perhaps representing quite closely Lack's more recent position (1968).

TERRITORY AS A SOCIAL MORTALITY FACTOR

Some six studies on a variety of birds appear to demonstrate the significance of territory in this respect. Jenkins, Watson & Miller (1963) working on grouse and ptarmigan, Delius (1965) on skylarks, Tompa (1964) on song sparrows and also Patterson (1965) and Coulson (1968) on certain colonial seabirds have all published material strongly support-

ing Kluyver & Tinbergen's (1953) original views concerning the great tit.

The studies of grouse, song sparrows, skylarks and Dutch tits all indicate that either the autumnal or spring occupation of territories causes a dispersion of the population in excess of the carrying capacity of the local habitat. The excluded birds may either leave the location and suffer increased mortality through various causes in the peripheral and sub-optimal environments or they may remain as a non-breeding population overlapping with the breeding population and to some extent perhaps competing for food and ready to occupy vacated territory as soon as it appears.

The work on gulls has shown that there is survival value in terms of reproductive success in occupying the preferred territories in the centre of a colony rather than peripheral sites. Coulson in particular showed that intense competition for central sites in a kittiwake colony resulted in their occupation by heavyweight birds. Both sexes surviving at least 5 years from the time of first breeding were heavier there than were neighbours that died within this time. In the centre of the colony there was also a larger mean clutch size, higher hatching success and more fledged young than at the periphery.

It appears that spatial dispersion whether in conventionally territorial or colonial-territorial mating systems involves higher individual survival and better reproductive success for the occupiers of prime sites than for those animals forced to a periphery.

However, while the breeding stock of these species was commonly determined by dispersal, this was not always invariably the case. For example, on food-poor grouse moors, numbers varied more annually than on food-rich ones, suggesting a more direct control there by extrinsic environmental factors involving food shortage. Similarly with the skylarks, in one spring following a harsh winter the population was well below the carrying capacity of the local preferred habitat and no dispersal effects were operative that year.[1]

[1]Conceivably this may always be the case in more northerly populations, subject to hard winters, annually.

These findings recall Kluyver & Tinbergen's (1953) report that the numbers of great tits vary annually more in less preferred woods than in the most preferred areas nearby. Working at Oxford Krebs (personal communication) reports that there is now evidence that the territorial factor may be more significant in the control of tit numbers than had been earlier supposed.

SOCIAL MORTALITY IN FLOCKS

Some years ago Lockie (1956), working then with Corvids, argued that individual distance and dominance-subordination phenomena in bird flocks had survival value in that in an encounter over a food item the loser could avoid its opponent without damage and the winner would win without a fight. Either way energy valuable to the individual is conserved. Under conditions of food shortage, however, the loser will progressively starve. The accumulative loss to a population mounts gradually, the relatively subordinate dying first. Were all birds equal presumably the cutback would be sharp and sudden with little mortality differential.

The work of Murton, Isaacson & Westwood (1964) has shown very clearly the importance of such socially mediated mortality in British woodpigeon populations. In flocks the feeding rates of these birds are greater in the middle and to the rear than in the van. Only a proportion of the pigeons can gain entry to the preferred flock centre. Others are pushed to the periphery. Those in front, harried by those behind them, eat less and commonly flee from flock to flock, usually again landing in front and being hustled. Under limiting conditions the effect of such behaviour leads to differential mortality.

Murton et al. (1964) note that the social effects allocating individuals to starving or non-starving sections of a population do in fact adjust flock size within limits to food availability and do maintain the highest survival rate relative to supplies. However the system sometimes breaks down. One year persistent heavy snowfall forced the pigeons into sudden conflict for limited Brassica plants. Then almost the whole population suffered a severe weight reduction at the same time. The effectiveness of

social factors in limiting mortality thus depends on food type, item size and dispersion.

Comparable findings emerge from studies of the African savannah weaver bird, *Quelea quelea*, studied in the field by Ward (1965) and in the laboratory by Crook & Butterfield (1970). Ward, an ecologist, had shown that during the dry season period of reduced food availability these weavers show a rapid drop in weight, particularly marked in females. At the same time the proportion of males in the population increased. Ward concluded that competition for food led to a elimination of females. Laboratory work shows that males are dominant over females in mixed sex groups and experimental studies suggest that oestrogen inhibition of the LH effects otherwise maintaining a low threshold for aggression in males is responsible for this sex difference. An effect of male dominance appears to be a major reduction in the number of females ready for reproduction at the onset of the breeding season. Unlike many species of weaver, the *Quelea* is obligatorily monogamous yet, even so, many nests in colonies are never occupied. It seems that in the rather harsh sahael environment where *Quelea* lives the practice of monogamy allows a male to assist the female more in rearing the brood than would be the case had he several mates. Both his and the female's reproductive success may indeed be maximized by the procedure. The natural selection of the behavioural features determining this monogamy is likely to have arisen within the context of the shortage of available females for breeding. And this, as we have seen, is a consequence of differential socially-mediated mortality between the sexes in the dry season.

In general, the available studies show that the control of numbers is brought about by numerous factors, some environmental and some social. At any one period the key factor involved may be extrinsic, for example, food shortage, while under other conditions social factors such as territorial behaviour may be the prime regulator through their effects on dispersal. Sometimes, one may suppose, that several factors interact to produce a given outcome and that no clear-cut key factor is operating. In addition the effects of an extrinsic factor may be mediated or buffered by a social process such as the intra-flock spacing mechanism to produce gradual and selective mortality rather than an abrupt fall.

Such a process of population control may be relatively easily modelled using a computer and allocating arithmetic values to hypothetical "Availability to Demand ratios" for each of the several commodities likely to act as controlling factors. Such a model is open and adaptive. A relative steady state is maintained by virtue of the limited variance of each factor. However, should one or more factor move by stepwise change to another range of variance, such a population may be conceived as adjusting to the new levels or new ecological "legislation," as Solomon (1964) calls it.

Such a control model, inherent in the views, for example, of Chitty and his associates differs markedly from the closed homeostatic model used by Wynne-Edwards. In the latter, the animals' perpetual calculating of the relation between its own numbers and its resources, even including those it has yet to exploit, functions as a Sollwert giving the fixed point about which the homeostat functions. There is in fact little evidence for such a model and the one proposed here appears to concord best with reality.

THE SOCIAL PROCESS

The traditional approach of ethology to social interaction has consisted in the study of reciprocal behaviour usually between members of dyads and the signal patterns used in such behaviour. The dyadic relations are classified in terms of context, courtship, mating, etc., and the sum of such features (an ethogram) often treated as an adequate account of the social process. At least with advanced mammals, this now appears most unlikely to be the case.

Imagine attempting to understand a game of football by means of a study of the dyadic interactions between individual players. As Ray Birdwhistell has repeatedly emphasized, such an approach is sterile. To understand the game, the social location of each individual as a role player in relation to each and every other player needs description. Then, with the ball in motion, the relations between these relationships become apparent and the rules may be determined. To gain

comparable information for behaviour within mammal societies is an exacting task but one in which considerable progress has been made recently, using both wild and captive groups of primates, mostly macaques. To conclude this paper a brief account of the current perspectives in social primatology will be presented, drawing mainly on the recent work of Japanese, American and European workers.

For many years the structure of primate groups was analysed primarily in terms of dominance. The existence of a status hierarchy was generally thought to stabilize relationships through the reduction of social tension, each animal knowing its place. Often animals are found to cooperate either in the enforcement of existing rank relations or, by contrast, in upsetting them. Cooperation in social control emerges as an important problem area in primate social research. Recently it has become apparent that the simple dominance concept was not only inadequately defined and carrying many unwarranted motivational overtones but that the description of group structure in dominance terminology was in many species not only a difficult task but also an inappropriate procedure (Gartlan 1968).

In an important discussion of dominance in a captive baboon group Rowell (1966) infers that relative rank depends upon a continuous learning process in relation to rewards in inter-individual competition for environmental or social goals. This occurs, moreover, against a background of differential kniship status and the observational learning of the behavioural styles of companions. Relative rank is much affected by health. Dominance ranking is based upon the approach-retreat ratio in encounters between two individuals in a group. Measures of rank by differing criteria do not however necessarily correlate and Rowell found no single criterion for high rank.

Rowell (1966) shows that apparent rank is a function of the behaviour of the relatively subordinate. Higher rankers, at least in Cercopithecoid primates, evidently feel free to initiate interactions. These initiations commonly lead to some suppression in an ongoing activity by a subordinate or to an outright conflict. Subordinates learn to avoid such situations. Avoidance learning leads to behavioural restraint that leaves higher rankers even greater freedom of movement, easy access to commodities and freedom to initiate behaviour with others. In competition for commodities in short supply, low rankers are likely to suffer deprivation and in social relations repeated constraint may involve physiological "stress" and concomitant behavioural abnormality.

Hall & DeVore (1965) describe the "dynamics of threat behaviour" in wild baboon troops. A male's dominance status relative to others is a function not only of his fighting ability but also his ability to enlist the support of other males. In one group studied two adult males formed a central hierarchy, the pivot around which the social behaviour of the group was organized. When one of these two died the remaining one was unable to prevent the third ranking male in cooperation with a newcomer (a subordinate male that had left another troop) from establishing themselves as central. The third male and the newcomer had evidently become affiliated when both had been relatively peripheral in the group structure. Common mutually supportive behaviour seems to have been the pre-condition for their "success" in assuming high rank later. By so doing they gained the freedom to express behaviour in the absence of previous constraints and to initiate behaviour as and when they wished.

Wilson (1968) provides further information on mutual support in a study of the rhesus troops on Cayo Santiago Island. Young males tend to leave the smaller groups and move into the all-male peripheral areas of larger ones. When they do this they are commonly attacked unless they gain the protection of another male already established there. It so happens that males that give support are usually relatives, even brothers, who originated from the same natal group as the "protege."

The inadequacies of the dominance terminology have led Bernstein & Sharpe (1966), Rowell (1966) and Gartlan (1968) to describe the social positions of individuals in a group in terms of roles. Roles are defined in terms of the relative frequencies (e.g. per cent of group occurrence) with which individuals perform certain behavioural sequences. When the behaviour set of an individual or class of individual is distinct the animal is said to show a "role."

Bernstein (1966) emphasizes particularly the importance of the role of "control animal" in primate groups and shows that such a role may occur in a group of capuchins, for example, in which no clear status hierarchies can be established. The prime responses of a control animal are assuming a position between the group and a source of external disturbance or danger, attacking, and thereby stopping, the behaviour of a group member that is distressing another, and generally approaching and terminating cases of intragroup disturbance. Whether or not a control animal is also recognizably the "dominant" or a "leader" (in the sense of determining direction of march) depends upon the social structure in which he or she is situated.

Social position in primate groups may be well described in terms of roles but little attention has been given as yet to an appropriate set of descriptive terms. It is one thing to say an animal shows a "role," another to say precisely what is meant. Using concepts derived from writers such as Nadel (1957) and Sarbin (1959) we may describe a primate's social behaviour in terms of the individual's age and sex status, social position and group type affiliation. In any given group each individual shows characteristic patterns of response in relation to others in the group, to older animals, to dominant animals, to subordinates, to peers of comparable kinship, rank, etc. The range of an animal's behaviour patterns in relation to others in the group comprise its social behaviour repertoire, as shown with its companions in the group. The sum of the proportions of group scores of such characteristics shown by an individual defines its social position in the group. An observer may prepare a social position matrix by allocating the relative frequency of interaction patterns shown by each member to a particular cell. In a more general statement each individual may be defined by its proportion of the total of the various interaction patterns shown within the group.

It so happens that macaque social positions may be categorized into consistent types that recur repeatedly in new groups formed from the division of the old or in separately analysed independent groups. Such categories are termed "roles." There is, for example, the control male role, the central sub-group secondary male role (competitive with another in the sub-group, dominant to peripheral males but subordinate to the central animal and commonly supportive of him), the peripheral male role, the isolate male, the central and peripheral male role, the isolate male, the central and peripheral female roles. We may also bracket together certain types of behaviour to describe roles of animals of high status kinship and low status kinship respectively. Now, these styles of behaviour may be called roles because they are not fixed and immutable aspects of the life of a given individual. On the disappearance of a control animal another male typically adopts the same role. A male rising or falling in a dominance hierarchy changes his behaviour. Fallen males may, however, march out of the group with affiliated females and establish a new group in which they may adopt the role of a central animal. Isolate males may enter a group and form a central sub-group, one of them perhaps being the control.

While not every conceivable role is necessarily present in any given group there is an overall consistency that makes this approach meaningful. Certain roles are usually characteristic of some kinds of groups and not of others—the harem "overlord" occurs in Hamadryas, Patas and Gelada groups but not in other baboons or among macaques.

The behaviour characteristic of a particular role is not the "property" of the individual playing it. Such behaviour is not fixed by conditioning so that the individual remains forever the same. Physiological and social changes impel behavioural shifts so that in a lifetime individuals may play many roles in their social structures. Social mobility in the sense of role changing is an important attribute of primate groups. It seems more characteristic of males than of females. Young and subadult males go solitarily, live peripherally or in all-male groups or shift from one reproductive unit to another. Females are more loyal to their natal group providing the more fixed social positions around which males revolve. This mobility is an expression of a set of tensions or forces characteristic of group life. At least three sets of factors interact in this social sorting process (Crook 1970c). These are: (i) the maturing and ageing of individual group members, (ii) the growth and splitting of groups, and (iii) intra-group competition for environmental and social commodities together with the affiliative cooperation and subterfuge that this entails.

The third set is the most critical at any one time, the other factors acting over longer periodicities. There appear then at any one time to be two opposed social processes operating within a baboon or macaque troop. One consists of the assertive freely expressed utilization of available physical and social commodities by high status animals which has the effect of constraining the behaviour of juveniles and subordinates. The other consists of the adoption of behavioural subterfuge by certain subordinates whereby such behavioural constraint can be avoided (e.g. by temporary solitary living or by splitting up the group into branch groups permitting a greater freedom of expression to the new leaders).

This "subterfuge" is presumably not conscious or deliberate. It appears to arise from the need of certain subordinates to free themselves from the behavioural constraints to which they have been exposed. There are in fact relatively few known "routes" along which such an aspirant may move. These are: (a) temporary solitarization, followed by take-over of a small branch group; (b) the use of an affiliated companion to ensure the rise of a dominant animal into a higher or even a centrally located position; and (c) the care given by "aunts" and "uncles" to infants and babies as a means of entering high-status sub-groups and so to affiliate with them.

Examples of the last case are particularly interesting. Itani (1959) showed that adult male macaques become interested in juvenile animals when the latter are 1 year old. At this time females are in the birth season and cease protecting the young of a previous year. The males appear to show interest in young animals only in this period. Their behaviour consists of hugging and sitting with the infant, accompanying it on the move, protecting it from other monkeys and dangerous situations and grooming it. Although Itani found no relationship between dominance as such and the frequency of child care he did find the behaviour to be especially developed in middle-classed animals of the caste structured troops. The behaviour indeed seemed pronounced in animals that were sociable, not aggressive and oriented towards high caste animals.

Itani suggests that certain monkeys by showing care to high caste children succeed in being tolerated by leaders and their affiliated females. Such animals may therefore rise in rank. Protectors usually behave in a mild manner which may facilitate both their association with infants and their rise in rank. It is not clear, however, whether the effect on rank lasts for more than the birth season. Itani gives no details of permanent changes in social structure so produced. The adult males appear to protect 1-year-old males and females equally but more second-year females than males are protected owing to the social periphalization of young males. Protected 2-year-olds are moreover often poorly grown individuals that were protected by the same male in the previous year. Protection has a further interesting effect in that adults more readily learn to investigate the new foods a progressive infant has discovered than would otherwise be the case.

Itani found cases of male care common only in three of eighteen troops investigated. It occurred very rarely in seven others and was not observed in the remaining eight. The behaviour thus appears to be a local cultural phenomenon. It undoubtedly provides additional chances of survival for young animals likely to be relatives, increases the rate of spread of new patterns of behaviour in the group and, since its frequency differs between troops, may increase the reproductive success of some monkey groups over others.

Recent observations on the Barbary Macaque (Macaca sylvana) in the Moyen Atlas of Morocco show that adult males in wild groups show an extraordinary amount of interest in young babies of the year. An interest in babies so young was relatively uncommon in Itani's study. Furthermore, the male Barbary Macaque does not seem, on present evidence, to limit his interest to a particular infant. He appears to appropriate babies from females in the group and to groom and care for them for short periods usually under 15 min duration. Babies may, moreover, move away from their mothers to accompany males, commonly riding off on their backs. Babies also move from one male to another. Males carrying babies frequently approach males without them in such a way as to encourage the approached animal to engage in a mutual grooming session with the baby as target. In some of these sequences babies are presented while on the back of the approacher, the animal turning its rear towards the other male (as it would do in sexual presenting) as it does so. In one case the approached male was seen to mount and thrust an animal that had done this. It appears too, that most males approaching with babies are relatively juvenile animals. It looks as if relatively subordinate animals are using the babies in some way to improve their relations with higher ranking males (Deag & Crook, 1970).

So far too little is known about the social structure of the Barbary Macaque to show whether there is a caste system comparable to that described from Japan. Whether males are using the babies as a means to increase their social standing and, hence, their freedom to behave without the constraints imposed by low rank, remains unknown. It does seem, however, that in both species not only does the male's behaviour increase the chances of survival for young animals but it appears to be closely related to the structure of the monkey group and the patterns of constraints regulating social mobility of individuals within it. We do not know yet whether the behaviour of the Barbary Macaque male is restricted, as it is with the Japanese Macaques, to certain troops and localities or whether it is a general phenomenon found throughout the species.

In all these cases individuals closely affiliated to others can combine cooperatively to bring about the liberating effect, an effect which, furthermore, in times of shortage (food, females) would ensure an increased probability of survival and/or reproductive success in addition to the psychological freedom from the effects of "stress" that undoubtedly accompany in some degree a continuing social restraint on individual behavioural expression. Similarly, by enlisting the cooperation of affiliated animals, often relatives, in their "control" behaviour, animals that are already established in social positions of high rank will be able to maintain such positions, and the access to commodities it provides.

It seems, then, that cooperative behaviour of the high order found in macaque and baboon groups has arisen within the context of competition for access to both physical and social commodities (Crook 1970c discusses). Both direct affiliative behaviour and indirect affiliation, for example through a common interest in child-care, provide the basis for common action. As we have seen such cooperation provides numerous advantages for the participants, and not only for the most dominant animals among them. It also provides the behavioural basis for the complex class-structured society of these animals with its tolerance of individual mobility between roles.

Finally, the stable social structure maintained by a powerful clique around a control animal seems to provide the optimum circumstances for maternal security and child rearing. Females form the more cohesive elements of primate groups and, as a consequence of their affiliative relations and kinships links, may play a much greater role in determining who emerges as "control" than is at present known. Males by contrast, subject to the full force of social competition, are the more mobile animals transferring themselves, as recent research shows, quite frequently from one group to another.

CONCLUSIONS: SIGNIFICANCE FOR HUMAN ETHOLOGY

In this paper I have tried to present a conspectus of the current state of social studies in ethology. Much more could of course have been added and not all would adopt the particular orientation I have used. It is my belief that an effective ethology of man must be based primarily on social considerations. Such a basis may possibly be supplied by a viewpoint such as I have adopted here. Often inherent in this approach is the use of social psychological ideas as a useful adjunct to ethological analysis. This mutuality between two disciplines is likely to develop quickly probably to the benefit of both.

There seems to be a problem in differentiating "human ethology" from the already existing behavioural sciences of man although Waxweiler had in 1906 already made clear that ethology was a broad biopsychological discipline which included sociology and its derivatives as a special branch subject focussing upon the problems of man. Today it seems that by human ethology we designate not so much a subject as a way of approaching human behaviour viewing the species as a member of the animal kingdom rather than as a separate and peculiar phenomenon. This I believe to be most healthy so long as one remembers that man is indeed a peculiar phenomenon and that mere biological reductionism, a "nothing butism" as Julian Huxley used to say, will get us nowhere.

An attempt to apply classical ethology to man would suggest that an ethological version of kinesics and proxemics was in the offing together with an elaboration of evolutionary theories regarding the adaptive significance of breasts and beards. Although interesting this would seem too curtailed an approach.

My feeling is that human ethology should comprise the whole behavioural biology of man. Such a science, it seems to me must focus its attention on at least the following problems.

1. The evolution and cultural history of the basic human grouping structures, families, all-male congregations, etc., and their origins in non-human primate grouping patterns (Reynolds 1966, 1968).
2. The relations between human individual behaviour, group composition and population density. How far do the problems of rodent stress-physiology apply also to man?
3. Non-verbal communication through facial and postural expression. The evolution of emotional expression in man.
4. The functioning of non-verbal communication in the control of affect in small groups, the rules of interpersonal ethology in companionship and courtship, the uses of ethology in sensitivity training, control of interpersonal aggression, etc. (Goffman 1963; Argyle 1967).

A programme as broad as this needs a basis within the framework of a biological social ethology such as I have tried to outline in this paper and which must include at least the three perspectives discussed. The scope is clearly very wide with links to anthropology, demography, stress physiology, ecology and particularly social psychology and psychiatry. To obtain workers equipped for research in this area requires an emphasis on training and a focus on such problems within the university syllabus. The day of routine study patterned by the ethological traditions of the past is over. We need fresh orientations and to find them social ethologists must go looking in new places along unexplored paths.

SUMMARY

1. A major development within the ethology of the last decade focusses attention upon the relations between social behaviour, ecology and population dynamics. This field may be termed "social ethology" following an early but neglected usage of the term by Waxweiler at the start of the century.
2. Contemporary social ethology comprises three interdependent perspectives, socio-ecology, socio-demography and the study of social processes within natural and experimental groups.
3. In socio-ecology recent studies reveal that close correlations exist between the forms of avian and mammalian social organizations and their respective ecological niches. In particular the adaptive significance of certain mammalian societies comprising, on the one hand, multi-male reproductive units and, on the other, those made up of one-male and all-male units is discussed and explanatory hypotheses derived from primate and ungulate data briefly considered.
4. In socio-demography research suggests that socially mediated mortality is of greater significance in the density-dependent control of bird and mammal numbers than had formerly been thought. The relations between ecological factors extrinsic to and social factors intrinsic to a social organization may be modelled in the form of open adaptive cybernetic systems rather than expressed in terms of analogies to closed mechanical or physiological systems.
5. Studies of social processes in non-human primate groups suggest that some form of role analysis may prove heuristic. The relations between dominance status, affiliative and kinship relations, social subterfuge and competition-contingent cooperation are discussed in an attempt to outline the dynamics of social change within relatively stable group structures.
6. "Human ethology" seems at present to lack adequate definition as an academic discipline. Social ethology may provide the essential biological basis for future research in this area.

ACKNOWLEDGMENTS

Revised text of an address to the plenary session on Social Organization, XIth International Ethology Conference, Rennes, France, 1969. Text prepared during the tenure of a Fellowship at the Center for Advanced Study in the Behavioral Sciences, Stanford, California, 1968 to 1969.

I am most grateful for advice and comment on the text of this paper, whether in whole or part, kindly given me by Ray Birdwhistell, L. Poser, Kai Erikson, John Goss-Custard, Robert Hinde and Henri Tajfel.

REFERENCES

Aldrich-Blake, F.P.G. (1970). Problems of social structure in forest monkeys. In: *Social Behaviour in Birds and Mammals* (Ed. by J.H. Crook). London: Academic Press.

Allee, W.C. (1938). *Cooperation Among Animals.* New York: H. Schuman.

Argyle, M. (1967). *The Psychology of Interpersonal Behaviour.* London: Pelican.

Ashmole, N.P. (1961). The biology of certain terns. D. Phil. Thesis, Oxford.

Ashmole, N.P. (1963). The regulation of numbers of tropical oceanic birds. *Ibis,* 103b, 458–473.

Bernstein, I.S. (1966). Analysis of a key role in a capuchin *(Cebus albifrons)* group. *Tulane Stud. Zool.,* 13, 49–54.

Bernstein, I.S. & Sharpe, L.G. (1966). Social roles in a rhesus monkey group. *Behaviour,* 26, 91–104.

Buckley, W. (1967). *Sociology and Modern Systems Theory.* New York: Prentice Hall.

Chitty, D. (1967). What regulates bird populations? *Ecology,* 48, 698–701.

Coulson, J.C. (1968). Differences in the quality of birds nesting in centre and on the edges of a colony. *Nature, Lond.,* 217, 478–479.

Crook, J.H. (1964). The evolution of social organization and visual communication in the weaver bird (Ploceinae). *Behaviour,* Suppl. 10.

Crook, J.H. (1965). The adaptive significance of avian social organizations. *Symp. zool. Soc. Lond.,* 14, 181–218.

Crook, J.H. (1966). Gelada baboon herd structure and movement, a comparative report. *Symp. zool. Soc. Lond.,* 18, 237–258.

Crook, J.H. (1970a). Social behaviour and ethology. In: *Social Behaviour in Birds and Mammals* (Ed. by J.H. Crook). London: Academic Press.

Crook, J.H. (1970b). The socio-ecology of primates. In: *Social Behaviour in Birds and Mammals* (Ed. by J.H. Crook). London: Academic Press.

Crook, J.H. (1970c). Sources of cooperation in animals and man: In: *Man and Beast, Comparative Social Behaviour*. IIIrd International Symposium. Smithsonian Institution, 1969.

Crook, J.H. & Aldrich-Blake, P. (1968). Ecological and behavioural contrasts between sympatric ground dwelling primates in Ethiopia. *Folia primat.*, 8, 192–227.

Crook, J.H. & Butterfield, P.A. (1970). Gender role in the social system of Quelea. In: *Social Behaviour in Birds and Mammals* (Ed. by J.H. Crook). London: Academic Press.

Cullen, E. (1957). Adaptations in the Kittiwake to cliffnesting. *Ibis*, 99, 275–302.

Cullen, J.M. (1960). Some adaptations in the nesting behaviour of terns. *Proc. XII Int. Orn. Congr. Helsinki*, 1958, pp. 153–157.

Deag, J. & Crook, J.H. (1970). Social behaviour and ecology of the wild Barbary Macaque (*Macaca sylvana* (L.)). (In preparation).

Delius, J.D. (1965). A population study of skylarks, *Alauda arvensis*. *Ibis*, 107, 465–492.

Espinas, A. (1878). *Des Sociétés Animales*. Paris: Baillière.

Estes, R.D. (1966). Behaviour and life history of the Wildebeest (*Connochaetes taurinus* Burchell). *Nature, Lond.*, 212, 999–1000.

Gartlan, J.S. (1968). Structure and function in primate society. *Folia primat.*, 8, 89–120.

Goffman, E. (1963). *Behavior in Public Places*. New York: Free Press.

Hall, K.R.L. & DeVore, I. (1965). Baboon social behavior. In: *Primate Behavior* (Ed. by I. DeVore). pp. 53–100. New York: Holt, Rinehart & Winston.

Hinde, R.A. (1966). Animal behaviour. In: *A Synthesis of Ethology and Comparative Psychology*. New York: McGraw-Hill.

Huxley, J.S. (1959). Grades and grades. Systematics Ass. Publ. No. 3. *Function and Taxonomic Importance*, pp. 21–22.

Immelmann, K. (1962). Beiträge zur Biologie und Ethologie australischer prachtfinken (Spermestidae). *Zool. Jb. (Syst.)*, 90, 1–196.

Immelmann, K. (1967). Verhaltensökalogische Studien an afrikanischen und australischen Estildidae. *Zool. Jb. (Syst.)*, 94, 1–67.

Itani, J. (1959). Paternal care in the Wild Japanese Monkey, *Macaca fuscata*. *J. Primat.*, 2, 61–93.

Jarman, P. (1968). The effect of the creation of Lake Kariba upon the terrestrial ecology of the Middle Zambezi valley, with particular reference to the large mammals. Ph.D. Thesis, Manchester University.

Jenkins, D., Watson, A. & Miller, G.R. (1963). Population studies on Red Grouse, *Lagopus l. scoticus*. *J. anim. Ecol.*, 36, 97–122.

Klopfer, P.H. (1962). *Behavioral Aspects of Ecology*. New Jersey: Prentice Hall, Englewood Cliffs.

Kluyver, H.N. & Tinbergen, L. (1953). Territory and the regulation of density in titmice. *Arch. neerl. Zool.*, 10, 266–287.

Kropotkin, P. (1914). *Mutual Aid, a Factor in Evolution*. New York: A.A. Knopf, Inc.

Kummer, H. (1968). Social organization of Hamadryas baboons. *Bibliotheca Primatologica*, No. 6.

Lack, D. (1954). *The Natural Regulation of Animal Numbers*. Oxford: Clarendon Press.

Lack, D. (1966). *Population Studies of Birds*. Oxford: Clarendon Press.

Lack, D. (1968). *Ecological Adaptations for Breeding in Birds*. London: Methuen.

Lockie, J. (1956). Winter fighting in feeding flocks of Rooks, Jackdaws and Carrion Crows. *Bird Study*, 3, 180–190.

Murton, R.K., Isaacson, A.T. & Westwood, K.T. (1964). The relationships between woodpigeons and their clover food supply and the mechanism of population control. *J. appl. Ecol.*, 3, 55–96.

Nadel, S.F. (1957). *The Theory of Social Structure*. Glencoe, Illinois: Free Press.

Nelson, J.B. (1967). Etho-ecological adaptations in the Great Frigate-bird. *Nature, Lond.*, 214, 318.

Orians, G.H. (1961). The ecology of blackbird (*Agelaius*) social systems. *Ecol. Monogr.*, 31, 285–312.

Patterson, I.J. (1965). Timing and spacing of broods in the Black Headed Gull (*Larus ridibundus*). *Ibis*. 107, 433–459.

Petrucci, R. (1906). Origine polyphyletique, homotypie et non-comparabilité direct des sociétés animales. *Travaux de l'Institut de Sociologie. Notes et Memoires*, 7. Bruxelles. Instituts Solvay.

Pitelka, T.A. (1942). Territoriality and related problems in North American humming birds. *Condor*, 44, 189–204.

Reynolds, V. (1966). Open groups in hominid evolution. *Man*, 1, 441–452.

Reynolds, V. (1968). Kinship and the family in monkeys apes and man. *Man*, 2, 209–223.

Rowell, T.E. (1966). Hierarchy in the organization of a captive baboon group. *Anim. Behav.*, 14, 420–443.

Sarbin, T.R. (1959). Role theory. In: *Handbook of Social Psychology* (Ed. by G. Lindzey). Cambridge, Massachusetts: Addison-Wesley.

Solomon, M.E. (1964). Analysis of procedures involved in the natural control of insects. In: *Advances in Ecological Research* (Ed. by J.B. Crag), Vol. 2. London and New York: Academic Press.

Stonehouse, B. (1960). The King Penguin *Aptenodytes pategonica* of South Georgia. I. Breeding behaviour and development. *Sci. Rep. Falkland Is. Depend. Surv.*, 23, 1–181.

Tinbergen, N. (1964). On adaptive radiation in Gulls (Tribe Larini). *Zool. Meded.*, 39, 209–223.

Tinbergen, N. (1967). Adaptive features of the Black Headed Gull (*Larus ridibundus* L.). *Proc.*

XIV Int. Orn. Congr., Oxford, 1966, pp. 43–49. Oxford: Blackwell.

Tompa, F.S. (1964). Factors determining the numbers of Song Sparrows *Melospiza melodia* (Wilson) on Mandarte Island, B.C. Canada. *Acta Zool. fenn.*, 109, 1–68.

Ward, P. (1965). Seasonal changes in the sex ratio of *Quelea quelea* (Ploceinae). *Ibis.* 107, 397–399.

Waxweiler, E. (1906). Esquisse d'une Sociologie *Travaux l'Institut de Sociologie. Notes et Memoires,* 3. Bruxelles: Instituts Solvay.

Wilson, A.P. (1968). Social Behaviour of free-raning rhesus monkeys with an emphasis on aggression. Ph.D. Thesis, University of California, Berkeley.

Wynne-Edwards, V.C. (1962). *Animal Dispersion in Relation to Social Behaviour.* Edinburgh: Oliver & Boyd.

12

A FIELD STUDY OF THE KENYA BABOON
Peter E. Maxim and John Buettner-Janusch

The modern study of animal behavior owes an enormous debt to the resourceful and controversial Austrian zoologist Konrad Lorenz. Starting in the late 1920s he created the field of ethology virtually single-handed. Right from the beginning he urged the study of animals in their undisturbed natural habitats, but he quickly realized that some of his most original insights came when he had failed to provide completely natural conditions for the creatures he was trying to observe. In effect, he produced experimental situations in which one or another condition of the natural wild environment was modified.

Of all the recent field studies of primate behavior, the article by Maxim and Buettner-Janusch comes closest to the accidental but insight-producing natural experiments that characterized the early work of Konrad Lorenz. While Crook's article showed the impact that ecology can have on social organization, this article shows what happens when a whole group is removed from an area it previously controlled. It also shows the plight of a single animal when released far from its group and its familiar territory.

Lorenz, Konrad. 1935 (1937). Companionship in bird life (Der Kumpan in der Umwelt des Vogels) translated in C. H. Schiller (ed.) *Instinctive Behavior.* International Universities Press, New York. pp. 83–128.

———. 1952. *King Soloman's Ring.* Methuen, New York. 202 pp.

The immediate aims of our research are to collect data about population genetics of Primates and to study in detail certain traits such as the inherited variation in hemoglobin and serum transferrin. As our laboratory studies of the baboon and other Primates progress, it is clear that more information than we have at present about the composition of troops, the social behavior, breeding habits, range of territory, and interaction between troops is necessary. The way in which genetic traits are distributed among baboons, for instance, is closely related to the way in which the segments, i.e., troops, interact. In Kenya, during June, July, and August, 1960, we captured a number of baboons *(Papio doguera)* for genetic studies and for use as experimental animals in the United States. At that time we were able to make many observations about the animals in the wild bush country of southeastern Kenya, between Kibwezi and Mtito Andei along the Athi River. We emphasize, in this

paper, the social aspects of baboon population dynamics, derived from our observations in the field.

The bush country where we worked is a natural habitat of the baboon quite different from the more open country of two of the game reserves of Kenya where baboons were studied by other workers. The different habitat influences the behavior of the animals as much as it does the behavior of the observers. It is for this reason, we believe, that our observations from this rather brief period will have some value, particularly since they seem to confirm many of Bolwig's (1958) observations made in similar bush country and illustrate Hall's (1960) discussion of vigilance patterns.

Most of the work of Zuckerman (1932) and the more recent reports of others were derived from close study of the animals in zoos or in game reserves (Washburn and DeVore, 1961). Although the animals in game reserves are wild, they are accustomed to visitors. Indeed, certain troops in the Royal Nairobi National Park, Kenya, have developed patterns of behavior toward visitors in automobiles that remind one of the bears of Yellowstone Park, Wyoming. Some allowance, we believe, must be made for a "social adjustment" or "human adjustment" factor. Similarly, the behavior of some of the baboons which we report here was conditioned by the fact that our camp and baboonery and traps became part of their environment. Nonetheless, our situation in a fairly remote location in southeastern Kenya provided an excellent opportunity for study of the animals in the wild state, as such.

Many of our observations agree with those made by Bolwig (1958) on the Chacma baboon, *Papio ursinus*, or, through priority, according to Fiedler (1956), *P. comatus*. Certain observations we made have not been recorded before, to our knowledge. Some have been matters of discussion, dispute and/or conjecture. Zuckerman (1932), for example, denies the concept of a "troop sentinel," while Elliot (1913) and Alee (1931) believe it is a reasonable one. Bolwig reports (1958) that he did not observe any fighting between troops over territorial rights, although he had reports of such actions. We did see a fight between two troops that seemed to be over territorial domination. We observed what we could interpret as true leadership behavior in older, dominant animals as they protected young ones. However, it is clearly more reasonable to discuss it as a form of individual vigilance behavior (Hall, 1960). We shall be the first to admit that it is sometimes difficult to record without anthropocentric overtones observed behavior of baboons in the field.

ACKNOWLEDGMENTS

This research was supported by grants from the National Institutes of Health (RG-6053), the National Science Foundation (G-12331), and the Department of Anthropology, Yale University. Assistance to one of us (P.E.M.) from Dean William C. DeVane, Yale College, and the Department of Zoology, Yale University, is gratefully acknowledged. The splendid cooperation of Dr. N.T. Werthessen and the Southwest Foundation for Research and Education, San Antonio, Texas, made possible our extended stay in the bush country of Kenya. Doctors George Nelson and Henry Foy, Medical Research Laboratories, Nairobi, Kenya, provided valuable advice and material help. Doctor R.J. Andrew, Yale University, read the manuscript and provided invaluable advice about terminology to describe baboon behavior.

SOME GENERAL CONSIDERATIONS

This report is based on personal observations, most of them made by the senior author. The animals were collected at two separate sites, Masalani and Darajani Station, near the Athi River in southeastern Kenya. Both sites are about 150 miles from Nairobi and are 40 miles apart (Fig. 1). Daily observations were made under as many different conditions as possible.

The countryside is predominantly scrub bush with scattered patches of open plains which are seldom more than a mile square. Most of the trees are species of *Acacia*, the few notable exceptions are the baobab and candelabra trees. Rainfall is at a minimum here. Rain occurs normally in two wet seasons, one from late March through May and one from November to early January. At the time of this study, June, July and August, most of the rivers in the region, including the nearby Kibwezi and Darajani rivers, had stopped flowing. For a radial distance of over 60 miles from Masalani, only the Athi River contained water in any quantity. Consequently along the edge of the river, the vegetation, small thorny trees and bushes, was in fairly thick stands which thinned out to open savannahs about amile from the banks of the river. This savannah-scrub ecotone persisted for many miles in all directions (Fig. 2).

Because the Athi River was the sole water supply, the density of baboons in the region was relatively high—a factor to be considered here in evaluating what may be the abnormal behavior of the baboons in regard to conflict over territory.[1] We made most of our observations in the vicinity of Masalani,

[1]East Africa was suffering from a severe, two year drought at the time we made these observations. The rains in the March-May period had been meager and no rain fell for almost two years. When the rains returned they were more than double the usual amount, and, after the disastrous flooding subsided, the vegetation was remarkably luxuriant and thick. Recently, in December 1961 and again in November 1962, visits were paid to the Darajani area (J.B.J.) and it was clear that the luxuriant vegetation, the vast amount of available food, and the fact that every watercourse draining into the Athi was running with water had radically altered the pattern of daily activity of the baboon troops in this area. It is hoped at least a brief study of this area will be possible under these conditions.

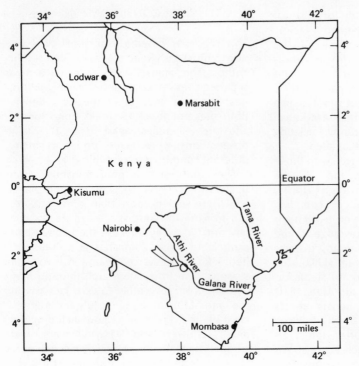

Figure 1. Map of Kenya. Area in circle noted by arrow is approximate location of Masalani and Darajani.

and we also include events observed at Darajani.

THE MASALANI AREA

The Masalani area (Fig. 2) was, principally, our camp situated in the midst of two abandoned sisal plantations. The main road between Nairobi and Mombasa is 11 miles away and the nearest native village, where Wakamba people lived, is about seven miles away. The Athi River flows alternately through gorges and flats to emerge onto a broad flat in front of our camp. Across the river, the Yatta Plateau rises some 500 feet in a steep ascent. The area supported many elephants which used a river-crossing a quarter of a mile downstream from the camp. Rhinoceros, warthogs, giraffes, waterbucks, gazelles, bush bucks, dik-diks, and many species of birds inhabited the area along with the baboons.

Three baboon troops were studied intensively here: T troop, containing 60 individuals, ranged along the nearby Kibwezi river bed where it joined the Athi and along which a trap-line had been set. S troop, eight individuals, was composed of remnants of the troop which had been trapped at the campsite itself; it was easily identified through one of its members, "Stubtail," a

female with an amputated tail. V troop, 25 individuals, ranged on both sides of the Athi River, upstream from the camp, and its range extended into the camp itself. Of the three, we considered V troop as the most typical and studied it the most. S troop was a fragment and T troop was being trapped continuously. S and V troops were stalked and observed both without glasses and with the aid of binoculars (8 X). T troop was studied without binoculars during frequent encounters, or perhaps "interactions," with it in and around the trapping area.[2]

[2]It is difficult to be certain that one's count of the individuals in a particular troop of baboons inhabiting the scrub bush country is correct when the troop has more than 10 or 15 members. We believe the composition of T troop was four large males (dominants), six females in estrus, ten females each with a single infant (20), eight young males, i.e., almost fully mature, seven females in the anestrus condition, and 15 juveniles whose sex we could not positively determine. S troop was made up of three young females, two young, but mature, males, two juveniles whose sex we did not determine, and one large, fully mature, "stubtail" female. V troop was made up of two large males (dominants), five young males, two females in estrus, six anestrus females, three females each with a single infant (6), and four juveniles whose sex we could not positively determine.

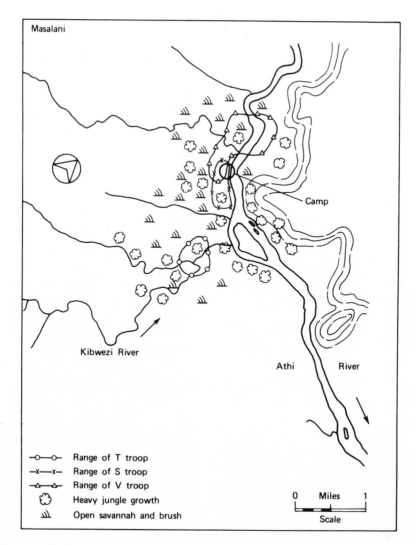

Masalani

Camp

Kibwezi River

Athi   River

—○——○— Range of T troop
—x——x— Range of S troop
—△——△— Range of V troop
🔘 Heavy jungle growth
𝓈𝓁 Open savannah and brush

0   Miles   1

Scale

Figure 2. Detail map of area around camp in Masalani area. Redrawn from Sheet 175/III (South A-37/0-1-SW) published by the Directorate of Overseas Surveys, Tolworth, Surrey, England, and the Survey of Kenya, 1969. Large arrow indicates North in this and subsequent figures.

In addition we observed, in connection with some laboratory studies, a troop, O troop, at Darajani Station. During the last two weeks of observation we centered our interest around Darajani Station. This small native community is 15 miles from the Athi River and is located on the usual savannah-scrub plains. Baboon troop O, numbering 20 individuals ranged widely over this area, drinking at a nearby spring or temporary waterhole and periodically raiding native maize fields during the morning hours.[3]

[3]Conditions made it difficult to do more than count the number of individuals in O troop. Therefore, no specific troop composition is given.

Observations of this troop were limited to the times they crossed wide stretches of grassland.

TROOP STRUCTURE AND ACTIVITY

A troop may range over a considerable amount of territory, up to six miles in diameter (Bolwig, 1958), but at the concentrated food and water resources of the Athi, where territorial competition was apparently fierce, the average troop ranged over an area of only two or three square miles.

A normal troop is composed of one or several dominant males, eight to ten other males of various ages, several family units of mother and offspring, and five to eight other females. No harems or chosen pairs were observed; dominant males took as many females as they could handle, constantly losing and gaining them in "bluff fights." The females, when in estrus,[4] were receptive to all of the males. Dominance showed itself also in feeding habits. The baboonery in which our trapped animals were kept and the garbage heap near the camp were subject to

[4]Estrus is the period of receptivity in female monkeys. It is during this period that a female baboon will, apparently, engage in behavior that may be interpreted as provoking or soliciting mounting by males. Baboon estrus reflects the changes in anatomy, endocrinology, and behavior which occur in every normal menstrual cycle. Female baboons develop a red and highly visible swelling of the sexual skin around the tail, the turgescent perineum, during the height of estrus. We have never seen any evidence that a biologically innate breeding season exists, even though there seem to be periods of the year when a greater number of newborn animals appear. DeVore considers this a likely result of ecological conditions (DeVore and Jay, in press). Recent work on the spermatozoa cycle of rhesus macaques opens the question of whether a cyclical fertility is also present in baboons.

Female baboons that are not pregnant develop the swollen, red estrus signs about every 30–40 days. Gillman and Gilbert (1946) found that, after exclusion of abnormal cycles, of 404 cycles the mean was 35.6 days, the range was 20 to 42 days.

Since Gillman and Gilbert refer to this cycle as a menstrual rather than an estrus cycle we might well be stricter in our terminology and reserve estrus for those periods of "heat" which occur in animals such as dogs or seals. However, female baboons do go into "heat" about every 30–40 days as is shown by their behavior and by the remarkable changes in the sexual skin. They concomittantly have a menstrual cycle. In observations of wild, free-ranging baboons one cannot include data about menses. Bleeding is often seen, but female baboons are often scratched by thorns and bushes, bitten by male baboons about the tail, etc., so that certainty about menses was almost impossible in our study. Only the periods of perineal turgescence, one of the anatomical changes that occurs during the menstrual cycle, are observed. Since Gillman and Gilbert noted abnormal cycles in which turgescence was not associated with menses, we cannot assume menses occurred when the estrus signs, i.e., red, swollen perineum, provocative behavior, enhanced female aggressiveness, appeared.

constant picking over for food by S troop. Choice places were always taken by the large males who chased off the young ones, often running them down to obtain a particular morsel the youngsters were carrying. Dominance among females was limited to feeding; the more irascible females in estrus would chase anestrus females from this same scrap heap. But no clear reversal of dominance roles among females was observed during estrus. The males of V and T troops, when observed away from the campsite where food in the form of grasses and berries was evenly distributed over a large area, exhibited less tendency to chase youngsters from choice food spots.

Behavior with regard to other baboons can be studied best by dividing it into several subclasses: fighting within the troop, fighting with other troops and inter-troop rivalry, and behavior near the traps.

Fighting within the troop: among males this centered, generally, around the struggle to acquire a female in estrus. The males always outnumbered the receptive females at any one time. A dominant male, unless continually with a particular female, shared the latter with the younger, more furtive males who mounted females whenever the dominant male was not present to drive them away. A graphic example of this was seen in V troop when a particularly young male had mounted a female in estrus while the dominant male was feeding a short distance away. Upon catching sight of the performance the big male darted upon the pair, growling and screaming. The young male shrieked and rushed for a tree with the older one in pursuit. In his headlong rush the older male bowled over another young one, grabbed it and "dusted" its howling form on the ground, while continuing his pursuit. The young male fled to the topmost branch of an acacia tree and edged out to the ends of the branches as the big male followed. The branches swayed as the big male, roaring, tried to shake the youngster loose. Finally, the big male edged out too far, the branch broke with a crash, carrying him to the ground, while the young male leaped to another branch. During this time, the female in question had received three other males. The dusting behavior noted above, also seen by Bolwig (1958), is characteristic of intra-troop squabbles. The dominant male grabs the fleeing smaller animal by the neck, shakes him from side to side, scrapes him along the ground, then releases him.

Fighting behavior with other troops: this was observed when V troop, near the campsite, made a sudden mid-morning raid upon the S band which was routinely feeding on the scrap heap and taking food from some caged baboons, the latter ex-members of S troop. S band at this time was composed of two almost fully grown males, two females in estrus, and several other females. The dominant males as well as the family units and younger baboons of S troop had been trapped and were being kept in the outdoor baboonery. It was interesting to note the continued affiliations that the remnant baboons of S troop kept with the trapped animals. The trapped ones passively let the former steal food and upset their water dishes. The remnant baboons also came onto the platform of the baboonery and groomed the trapped males and played with the babies of the trapped family units. On this particular morning, 20 to 25 baboons of V troop suddenly raced into the clearing from the tall grass, the males in the lead, bowling over and chasing down all the remnant members of S troop. Meanwhile, the trapped males of the S troop roared and snarled, throwing themselves against the screening in an effort to get out and join the fight. They slashed savagely at the wire and wooden frame-work of the cages. The male invaders from V troop raced up and down the baboonery aisles and tried to grab the younger animals while the trapped big males in turn futilely tried to grab them. V troop remained at the baboonery and nearby scrap heap for several days and the trapped animals continually showed signs of arousal. Stealing food from caged animals became a violent skirmish. Normally a V baboon would approach a cage snarling at the occupant who in turn vainly tried to grapple with him. Meanwhile another V baboon would quietly steal up behind the pair, and, reaching through the wire mesh, grab all the food within reach. On one occasion, this maneuver backfired: the second V baboon grabbed the trapped one from behind in a hammerlock, pinning him backwards against the mesh. The first reached inside the cage to steal the food

from the struggling, squawling animal. But the tail of the second V baboon also came to rest close to the cage behind him and that S baboon reached out, grabbed the tail, yanked the animal against the mesh of his cage, thus forcing him to break his hold on the trapped male. The trapped male then grabbed the arm of the first V baboon before he could withdraw and slashed at it with his canines just as the other trapped S baboon sank his teeth into the tail of the second V baboon. The reactions were vigorous.

Generally inter-troop conflict seems to be rare. On several occasions troops were seen feeding and moving about quite close to one another while showing no aggressive tendencies. The unusually abundant food supply available locally in a larger area of parched natural food sources evidently induced the extreme rivalry which we observed between the S and V troops.

Behavior around traps: The most noteworthy aspects of this involved certain males or very large females who, on many occasions, were seen stationed in front of baited traps, sitting back, and chasing off or grabbing any young animals who tried to get at the bait. S troop remnants were wary of the traps set for them around the baboonery, but when the V troop entered the territory it was not at all shy. In a very few hours three of the five largest males in the V troop were trapped. The ensuing movement of people necessary for handling and transferring the trapped animals and the accompanying squeals and roars of the freshly trapped males made the rest of the troop shy away from the traps, although they roamed all around them. When the traps were cleared and reset a young baboon became trapped at once; but almost immediately a large female ran over, seated herself in front of the trap's door, worked her nails into the wood joints and lifted the door. The young one darted free and the female dropped the door. A short time later when young animals advanced towards a trap to get at fresh bait (in this case, papaya), a male ran over and pushed them away, seating himself at the trap's entrance and chasing off, for an hour or more, any young baboons that ventured near.

T troop also became adept at springing its members from traps. On many occasions we came upon a baboon working on the door of the trap from outside while the trapped animal was trying to lift it from the inside. As time went on T troop became so adept at this that we obtained only one out of every two animals that sprang a trap. The situation was partially remedied, for us, by covering the doors on both sides with smooth sheets of tin which afforded no purchase for baboon nails.

On another occasion, an attempt was made by untrapped members of a troop to rescue one six-week old infant from its cage in the baboonery. Two adult animals tried to pull the infant through the wire mesh of the cage; the attempt was unsuccessful, but the infant's hand was torn off at the wrist. We can add, parenthetically, that the infant survived. This sort of behavior seems to indicate a relationship between troop members which goes from simple dominance or sexual vigilance leading to a high degree of group cohesion.

The intense reactions which are elicited by threats to very young baboons may be illustrated by the deliberate attempt by one of us (J.B.J.) to test the behavior of adult baboons when an infant is threatened. A very young baboon, estimated age ten days, was taken from its mother by the observer. The infant's shrieks and howls rose in volume and pitch. All the caged animals of T troop began to bark and shake their cages. The rest of T troop, feeding at the garbage heap, noticed the observer with the infant. While barking, snarling, and threatening, they surrounded the observer. No animal approached closer than eight feet. The largest males and females were stationed closest to the observer, the rest seemed to circle aimlessly and agitatedly outside the ring of larger animals. The threats of the animals grew in intensity; the barks and snarls, directed towards the experimenter, grew in intensity and "hysteria." As these threats reached the observer's threshold of tolerance, he responded by stamping his foot forcibly on the ground and by shouting at the circle of animals. The baboons retreated a bit and resumed their threats. The experimenter increased the violence of his stamping and shouting and began to imitate the "bluff threats" of the baboons. The entire troop began a retreat, breaking the circle around the observer. Two or three more "bluffs" by the observer and the troop retreated uneasily

to the vicinity of the garbage heap. The observer climbed to the baboonery with the infant. As he climbed the stairs to the cages two large males rushed forward and stood at the base of the stairs, barking and threatening. The infant was returned to its mother who instantly seized it; the mother stopped screaming; she squeezed the infant tightly. As the observer retreated, she took the infant from her breast and began to examine it and groom it. Several adult animals, who earlier were threatening the observer, climbed up in front of the cage and held a "colloquy" with the mother. These uncaged adults reached into the cage to stroke the infant while warily eyeing the experimenter.

VIGILANCE BEHAVIOR

The term sentinel behavior has attracted much controversy and many opinions are held about this phenomenon. Eliot (1913) and Allee (1931) both hold the view that one or more members of a troop act as lookouts. Elliot claims this on the basis of observation of baboons crossing roads; Allee derives his opinion second hand from a description by Phillips (1926). Zuckerman (1932), on the other hand, refutes the idea of a single selected animal acting as a sentinel, but claims that different troop members take turns as such. Our observations agree with this, but our interpretation is in agreement with Hall (1960). The general manner in which we saw baboons crossing the Mombasa-Nairobi road could hardly be called anything but mass flight or mass hysteria, despite Fitzsimmons (1911). Even when we approached quietly we never saw troops crossing this major road in anything but an hysterical fashion. A troop when disturbed, for example by an automobile, rushed helter-skelter, barking and squealing from one side of the road to the other. The strongest and swiftest animals seemed to be in the lead, while the females burdened with infants crossed last.

It appeared to us that animals which could be called sentinels or lookouts occurred as flankers in a troop only when an area of known danger was approached—a road, a waterhole, a river, a disputed feeding area, etc. Often in the early morning and late afternoon, baboons of V troop and T troop would be encountered on their respective ranges moving in a single file along animal trails. Carpenter (1934) noted that howler monkeys seem to move towards and away from centers of activity, morning and evening, respectively. The same holds for baboons. V troop left their sleeping area in the early morning to cross the river in search of food; in the late afternoon, they were back at the river, on schedule almost to the minute, to drink and to go off into the bush to sleep.

We examined their footprints on their regular trails. These showed that they moved, when undisturbed, in a more or less long, relatively straight, line. At Darajani, O troop's tracks were followed each morning in the course of our attempts to collect various members. Their tracks from the area of the Darajani River to the campsite showed that they moved in a long, narrow file, which was 20 feet across at its widest point.

When the baboons were approaching a "danger" point, or when they were surprised, a pattern of vigilance (Hall, 1960) was set up. A particular pattern of social vigilance was organized in all instances we observed. V troop, when approaching the Athi River with its open banks and lack of shelter, would gradually cluster into a triangle—the foremost members of the file forming the apex and slowing until the members in the rear had closed in (Fig. 3). The animals

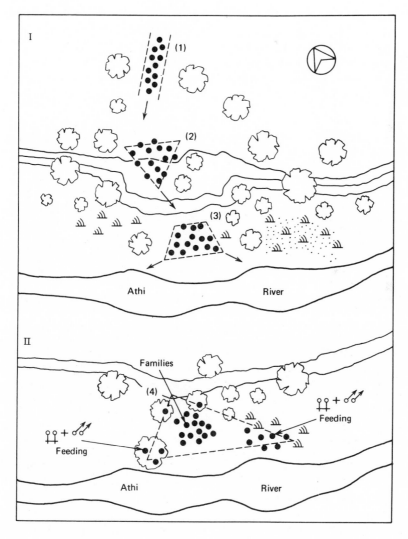

Figure 3. Triangular formation used by baboon troops approaching Athi River bank. I, 1. normal single file movement, 2. triangle formed with one or more leaders at apex, 3. "inversion" of triangle taking place, II, 4. feeding triangle formed.

forming the base of the triangle advanced slowly while some members climbed trees and others squatted on the ground, shading their eyes with a paw to scan the opposite shore. After four or five minutes of scanning and sitting in absolute quiet, the triangle elongated, the animals at the periphery began to feed, and the youngsters in the family groups began to tumble and play. The family units always remained within the triangle. When feeding and drinking were over, the animals regrouped by shortening the triangular points toward the center of the figure, the distal triangular point then led off the troop single file back in the direction from which it had come (see Fig. 4).

This same triangular pattern of vigilance was seen when V troop moved toward the

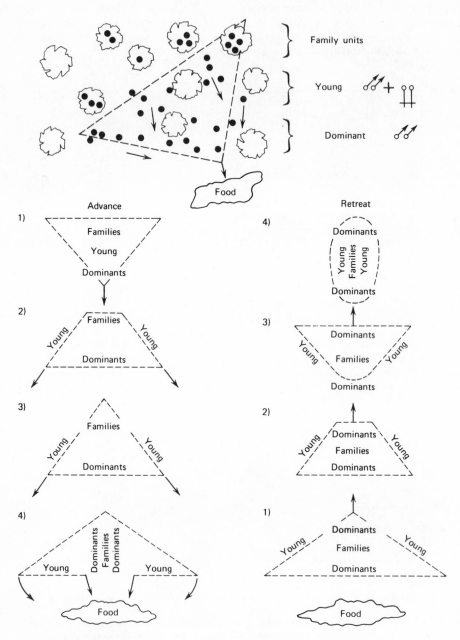

Figure 4.   Morning maneuver of V troop as it approached food, scrap-heap in camp area.

scrap heap near our camp each morning. This scrap heap, on the edge of a cleared area, was always approached with caution. Here again the triangle started with the apex first, the dominant males being the first to advance to the food. Any young animals which tried to run ahead of the slow advance were headed off by the dominants and chased into the rear. Again this triangle spread, flowed, and reversed itself so that its broad side was dispersed along the perimeter of the food pile (Fig. 4). The family units tended to remain in the background and females with young apparently got the less desirable food. When assured that no danger was present animals around the perimeter of the triangle then shifted freely into this triangular area to obtain choice bits of food.

The same triangular formation was seen when S troop was feeding while aware of the observer. As we followed the S troop through rocky terrain while it fed, special vigilance behavior (Hall, 1960) was observed in actions of the troop in relation to the observer. Scanning sites for specially vigilant animals were momentarily occupied, one generally on a rock ledge and another in a tree or low bush, as the remaining six members of the troop fed at the apex of the triangle most distant from the observer (Fig. 5). The feeding members were frequently out of sight of the observer and every few minutes a feeding member changed places with the vigilant one. On one occasion we climbed a small tree to view the feeders out of their sight. Apparently they were unaware of the onlooker, for they fed, then looked up

from time to time to watch the animals at the periphery. Not seeing the observer, they based their reactions on signals given by these peripheral, lagging animals.

Vigilance patterns changed with variations in the actions of the observer. When the observer approached slowly the peripheral animal responded with an alert tensing of the back and bouncing on the forepaws with forward thrusting head movements. The animal would sway from side to side with his eyes fixed on the observer, then bounce up and down with back and hindquarters tensed. This slightly aggressive action became marked on those occasions when the observer approached the roosting trees of the S troop early in the evening. At those times the troop seemed particularly anxious for one to leave. The two males, making aggressive head movements, charged silently forward a few feet. These aggressive movements were also seen in captive S troop baboons when members of V troop were sighted.

When the observer remained motionless after chasing the troop a short distance from its feeding area, the foremost individuals and especially the young animals grew progressively bolder and more curious. T troop was observed often in this connection. The animals constantly shifted positions, coming gradually closer by means of an oblique approach—the movement towards the observer was not direct but accomplished by a lateral or "sidling" approach. Small "brave" males ventured into a more open spot to be replaced by larger dominant males. These

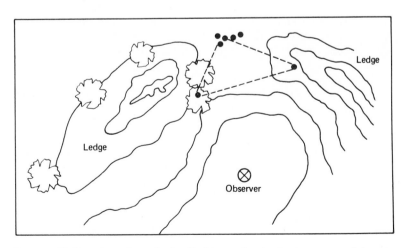

Figure 5.   Vigilance formation maintained by S troop when feeding in presence of observer.

seated themselves and watched the observer. They yawned elaborately and gazed up and to the sides, then got up to shift position slightly, sat again, gazing at the observer while shielding the eyes with one forepaw. When the observer moved, the animal immediately sprang up tensely and, if slowly approached, went into the aggressive pattern.

In low brush and grass the vigilance pattern was quite different. When pursued here the animals moved off at a rate relative to the rate of pursuit. When moving on all fours, the animals could not see over the grass, thus every 20 feet or so one or two of the animals at the side and rear of the group rose up briefly on hind legs to view the observer. Hunting on foot with a gun was impossible—we wanted to collect animals to study stomach contents. However, the troops were not particularly shy of trucks. Therefore, whenever we sighted a troop on open grassland, negotiable in a Land Rover, the driver approached slowly and came as close to the troop as possible. The observer jumped from the truck into the grass, using the truck as a screen. Usually the troop would move but a little way off. After raising one's head just enough to see the animals, and for them to see the observer, the head was lowered. An animal at the rear of the troop or at the edge would rise on two legs in an attempt to see us from the tall grass and brush. By rising and firing quickly before these individuals dropped down into the grass again, we were eventually able to collect a few animals.

Yawning and scratching behavior has been reported during violent threat and has been related to expressions of anxiety (Bolwig, 1958). Generally, we saw yawning in feeding members of V troop when observed from a great distance. Females with offspring have been observed scratching themselves while simultaneously grooming their own or other young. Essentially, we saw scratching and yawning in its "normal" contexts, with the exception noted earlier.

SEXUAL AND PARENTAL BEHAVIOR

The estrus cycle[5] in baboons is about 34 days, and during the period of estrus the females

[5]See footnote 4.

are much more aggressive than usual in their dominance behavior and are attended by most of the males in the troop. The genitalia and sex skin are greatly swollen and easily seen from a long distance, since they are a bright flesh red in contrast to the dun-color coat of hair. In S troop where the number of males was small compared to the number of females, the females in estrus were shared and covered by both dominant males. In V troop where females were more in demand in relation to the number of males, dominance and fighting, as described earlier was prevalent. Sometimes the female would pair with a male for several hours, feeding and moving with him. But the ties were very temporary and easily broken under a variety of circumstances.

Mating was generally initiated by the female presenting herself to the male, although on occasion the male was seen to walk up behind the female while the latter watched his approach. The female generally lifted her tail making the anal-genital region and the sex skin more visible to the male, while watching him over her shoulder. Baring of teeth while emitting low grunts, which increased in frequency and intensity, accompanied the actual mounting. Copulation was short and intense.

Actions that we can term reverse sexual behavior were occasionally noticed. Estrus females were seen mounting anestrus females, and pelvic "copulatory" movements were seen. We also saw rather desultory mounting of males upon males occasionally. All these cases occurred immediately before or after copulation between a male and female in estrus. Intense excitation and general arousal may have accounted for these actions. We had expected to see many more examples of reverse sexuality than we did. Since it has been held to be an important and, indeed, essential, social bond among baboons (Zuckerman, 1932) we feel our data do not lend support to this opinion. Our relatively few examples are not due, we are certain, to lack of opportunity to observe their possible occurrence.

Lipsmacking in courtship, reported by Bolwig (1958), was not observed in wild baboons, although we have seen it among members of the inbred colony maintained in San Antonio, Texas.

We saw grooming occur in two basic social

relationships among baboons: those of mother-offspring and of male-female. In the latter case grooming was a preliminary to copulation. When the female presented herself, the male frequently groomed her flanks and sacral region, often while the female stretched a leg out behind, touching the seated male on the chest or shoulder. Grooming was intermittent here and was accompanied by stroking and rubbing of the swollen sex skin. Often the animals would stop grooming, separate a short distance, begin to feed, then abruptly come together and copulate. The most intensive grooming was performed by females, either on males or on their offspring. Frequently females in estrus were seen grooming males carefully about the head and back, as well as around the flank.

Grooming of the young offspring by its mother was frequently observed in the captive S troop baboons and in the V troop families. The babies submitted to being rolled on their backs, stomachs, and sides while the mothers diligently scratched, plucked, searched, and patted them. Babies, until about seven weeks of age, were carefully guarded by mothers. When the V troop moved to the river to drink and feed, the mothers sat and allowed the babies to play within a radius of a few paces from where they sat. The young baboons delighted in wrestling with larger, immature animals, pulling their tails, biting and teasing their suffering older relatives, who, under the watchful eye of the mother, dared to do nothing to stop the torment. At one point when a dominant male was in headlong pursuit of a smaller male, he bowled over a young baboon which had wandered into his path. Before the big male could turn to slash at the small one, the mother, a much smaller animal, was upon him with a roar, and he fled. Babies were occasionally seen being punished in the troops when they strayed too far; the mother generally rushed and grabbed the young one to her, smacking it as she did so.

Captive mothers were often savage in punishing their offspring, especially when danger was near, or when the mother became greatly agitated. When mothers of V troop ventured near the S troop family captives, the caged mother hastily scooped up her youngster and clutched it to her as she fled to the safest part of the cage. Should it try to get loose, it received a sharp cuff. When attempts were made by us to handle captive mothers, the mother often stumbled over her youngster and agitatedly flung him against the cage with one sweep of her paw.

When a troop is moving, the babies are generally carried slung under the stomachs of the mothers where they hold on by grasping the long belly hair. It was a rare sight to see youngsters in the scrub terrain riding on the backs of their mothers. Only in the comparatively open savannah-plain country of the Royal Nairobi National Park and at certain open areas near Darajani Station was the latter a common sight.

TERRITORIALITY

As we noted earlier, the troops along the Athi River tended to range over a smaller distance than O troop at Darajani. The concept of territoriality is ambiguous here, however. Each band that we observed seemed to range over an exclusive region, yet these ranges overlapped in some places. In at least one case this overlap produced a conflict. In this case, the aggressor, V troop, was moving in on a troop, S troop, which recently had most of its members trapped. It would appear that V troop suddenly found itself as the dominant band in the vicinity and accordingly moved to extend its range into the territory which S troop, accustomed to similar strength, had apparently held through its large numbers. The sudden depletion in numbers had not made S troop aware of its new vulnerability. It made no attempt, furthermore, to retake part of the campsite, even when V troop dispersed over a large feeding area.

Some idea of territorial rights exclusive to each band does seem to exist, for on four occasions solitary animals were found sitting in trees or feeding a good distance from the known position of the troop. This raises the question of how one of these animals came to venture far from the main troop during the day. Is the animal so conditioned to exclusive rights to territory in which it would be unmolested by other baboons? In three cases large males were the solitary animals seen, all of them at Darajani Station, where we did not find any other troop near O troop. Does this mean that these animals were certain of their safety in the established range of their own O troop? Such conclusions seem reasonable, yet they really depend upon presupposing a human-like set of reactions. It is unwise to use terms with specifically human reference—leadership, loyalty, lookout, sentinel, guard—to describe what one sees baboons doing.

On the fourth occasion the solitary animal was a female from S troop. The observer was attracted by her insistent barking and, on approaching, found her sitting low in an acacia tree on the bank of the Athi River. She paid little attention, but was very restless, moving all about the tree, bouncing and tensing, barking at intervals, and staring fixedly down the river. She raised her snout at intervals, as if sniffing the air, then agitatedly moved her head from side to side. As it grew darker she moved to another tree 50 yards down river and repeated her actions until darkness. The next morning S troop was found roosting where the lone female had been seen the night before, their customary spot. The following night when the observer approached the roost, the aggressive attitudes described earlier occurred. This seems to indicate that the female who apparently had moved alone during the day was extremely anxious at nightfall to rejoin the troop. This tendency to huddle safely with other troop members was also noted in the case of two young captive baboons, females,

who slept embracing one another tightly every night.

The roosting site of only one troop was known, that of S troop noted above. This was apparently a fairly permanent one, situated on a flat spit where the Athi River broadened. The low sandrock bank afforded a view in all directions for several hundred feet, and the breezes blew straight across the roosts (Fig. 6). The animals roosted in adjacent trees in a line parallel to the direction of the wind.

Two other episodes illustrate the intensity with which territory, or troop integrity, may be defended against strangers. A female in estrus, that had been trapped about seven miles from the camp, escaped. She ran from the baboonery toward the Athi River. Several baboons from the troop feeding at the garbage heap rushed in pursuit. The screams, howls, snarls, and thrashings in the bush which ensued indicated a violent conflict. About an hour later the cadaver of this female, apparently killed by members of the local troop, was found in a thicket near the Athi River.

A few weeks later two young males, marked with a brilliant orange dye, were released from the baboonery. Each had been captured about ten miles from the camp. One was pursued by the largest animals from the local troop, the other took refuge in a trap near the baboonery. The first was never seen again, the second refused to leave his

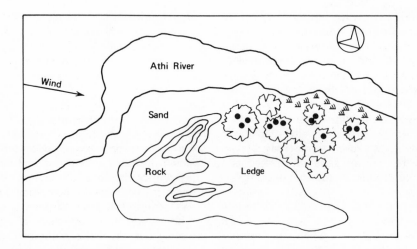

Figure 6. Semi-permanent roost on river bank, S troop. The roost was used throughout each of our visits in 1959 and 1960. The number of baboons is indicated by dots in the figure; it is based upon the first, "pretrapping," count of 1960—11 animals.

cage when another attempt was made to release him.

DISCUSSION

The pattern of vigilance behavior we observed seems to be more organized, regular, repetitive, and consistent than that reported by Hall (1960). It is certainly very clear to us why the expressions "sentinel," "guard," "leader," and "lookout" have been used by people writing about baboons. Hall's characterization of most of the behavior we are reporting as belonging to the category of vigilance behavior is excellent. We can, using his strictures and terms, avoid making human social structure the model for baboon behavior.

We attribute differences in observed vigilance patterns of the baboons we watched from those reported by Hall largely to ecological factors. The country in which we worked was covered by a heavy growth of scrub bush. In certain sections near the Athi River rocky gorges and high bluffs were frequent. The triangular pattern is certainly an efficient defensive formation under such conditions. When visibility is limited, as it is in bush country, it seems likely to be a positive factor in survival of a troop. Since we observed it frequently and consistently in similar situations, we believe our explanation of it will hold up.

Hall refers most aspects of vigilance behavior to dominance patterns within a baboon troop. This is not so clear in the observations we made. Dominance patterns are certainly important and basic to most of the behavior we observed. The variation in vigilance patterns Hall describes he attributes to circumstances within the group and to the relation of the baboon troop to the observers. We found little variation in the triangular vigilance pattern. We did find that there was no apparent consistency in choice of individual animals to play specific roles in the vigilance patterns. The defensive triangle pattern we observed is likely a case of selection operating. The most efficient pattern of vigilance is partly dictated by the terrain and vegetation.

Territoriality is another matter. We cannot argue strongly that our observations are direct evidence for it. We find it easy to interpret many of our observations to imply a high degree of territorial exclusiveness. The animals apparently recognize and know their range as intimately as do birds. Certainly some of our cited examples imply strong defense of territory against "foreign" or intruder baboons.

Throughout our discussion we have tried to emphasize that aspect of our observations which relates to our problems of baboon population dynamics and population genetics. We have said nothing about the vocalizations involved in much of vigilance behavior. We are under the impression that the troops we followed in heavy bush country were *normally* very quiet. Barking and other vocal displays were most noteworthy in very special, exceptionally alarming situations.

Recently Bolwig (1961) described the surprising extent to which a female baboon can learn to handle objects more or less like tools, when placed in a new and strange environment. Bolwig's observations make us confident that the behavior we observed around the traps is part of the normal range of adjustment and learning of which the genus *Papio* is capable.

The apparent territorial exclusiveness and the various forms of vigilance behavior which we have observed among *Papio* seem to be adequate and important mechanisms for maintaining a high level of genetic homogeneity within a specific troop. Of great interest to us are the effects of the group behavior on the population genetics of *Papio*. The most important would be increased inbreeding, and hence greater homogeneity and homozygosity than in man or other Primates. We have unpublished evidence that this is indeed the case for certain genetic traits, *Papio* exhibits far greater homozygosity than do members of the genus *Cercopithecus*. We have very few data about the social behavior of the various species of that genus. From our laboratory studies that show greater apparent genetic variability among them, we would predict that members of the genus *Cercopithecus* have almost no territorial behavior of the sort exhibited by *Papio* and relatively weak troop integrity.

Everything we observed indicates a very powerful tendency to maintain troop versus individual identity. Solitary baboons, as others have said, do not survive. The implications of this behavior for the population genetics of *Papio* have been indicated above. The implications for analysis of the evolution of primate behavior we leave to others.

LITERATURE CITED

Allee, W.C. 1931. Animal aggregations; a study in general sociology. University of Chicago Press, Chicago, Illinois.

Bolwig, N. 1958. Behaviour of the Chacma baboon. Behaviour, 13–14: 136–161.

———. 1961. An intelligent tool-using baboon. So. Af. J. Sci., 57: 147–152.

Carpenter, C.R. 1934. A field study of behavior and social relations of howling monkeys. Comp. Psychol. Monogr., 10(2): 1–168.

DeVore, I., and P. Jay (In press) Mother-infant relations in baboons and langurs. ms. chapter for Maternal Care in Mammals, edited by H.L. Rheingold, John Wiley and Sons, New York.

Elliot, D.G. 1913. A review of the Primates. II. Amer. Mus. Nat. Hist., New York.

Fiedler, W. 1956. Ubersicht über das System der Primaten. In Primatologia, I. 1–266. S. Karger, Basel.

Fitzsimmons, F.W. 1911. The monkey-folk of South Africa. Longmans, London.

Gillman, J., and C. Gilbert. 1946. The reproductive cycle of the Chacma baboon (Papio ursinus) with special reference to the problems of menstrual irregularities as assessed by the behaviour of the sex skin. So. Afr. J. Med. Sci., 11: Biological supplement 1–54.

Hall, K.R.L. 1960. Social vigilance behaviour of the Chacma baboon. Behaviour, 16: 261–294.

Phillips, J.F. 1926. "Wild pig" at the Knysua: notes by a naturalist. So. Af. J. Sci., 23: 655–660.

Washburn, S.L., and I. DeVore. 1961. The social life of baboons. Sci. Amer., 204:62–71.

Zuckerman, S. 1932. The social life of monkeys and apes. Routledge, London.

13

PSYCHOBIOLOGICAL STUDIES OF AGGRESSIVE BEHAVIOR
David A. Hamburg

Some of the previous papers have focused on primates that are not particularly close to man, or even on creatures that are not primates at all. Hamburg brings the matter closer to home. If man did not actually descend from a chimpanzee, certainly chimpanzees, more than any other living primate, must be closer approximations to what man's real ancestors were like. Hamburg ties together observations on the development of behavior that illustrate a continuity from monkey to ape to man.

In this regard, it is interesting to note that adult behavior is not totally conditioned by specific learning experiences. Some things are learned much more easily than others, and there are basic male-female differences in the ease with which particular kinds of behavior are learned. There have been two opposed views dealing with the genesis of observed human behavior. One school, including the early behaviorists and the extremists in the current woman's liberation movement, has stressed the tabula rasa or blank-slate view that attributes all observed behavior to learning. The other extreme, including some of the early intelligence testers and modern educational psychologists, has stressed the preeminence of heredity. We shall return to this matter at the end of Section Four, but we should note that effective and eloquent attempts have been made to strike a balance between the extremes (Hirsch 1967, 1970). Hamburg's approach belongs with the balancers and adds the perspective of comparable observations on nonhuman as well as human populations.

Hirsch, Jerry (ed.). 1967. *Behavior-Genetic Analysis*. Mc-Graw-Hill, New York. 522 pp.

————. 1970. Behavior-genetic analysis and its bio-social consequences. Invited address presented to to the XIXth International Congress of Psychology, London, England, July 30, 1969, and dedicated to T. Dobzhansky on his seventieth birthday. *Seminars in Psychiatry* 2:89–105.

Although there are obvious reasons for scientific interest in the evolutionary and developmental origins of human aggressive tendencies,[1-4] there has been little work on this subject. For example, in the upsurge of primate field studies during the past decade, very few studies have paid primary attention to aggressive behaviour.[5-9] For this reason, Eric Hamburg and I have recently conducted an investigation of aggressive behaviour in chimpanzees and baboons in East Africa. For more than 200 hours we observed animals within ten yards of us, and with help from Jane van Lawick-Goodall in Tanzania and Phyllis Jay in Kenya, we collected considerable data on aggression in these two species.

By "aggressive behaviour" I mean actions in

From *Nature* 230:19–23. Copyright 1971, Macmillan Journals Ltd. Reprinted with the permission of author and publisher.

which an animal inflicts, or tries or threatens to inflict, damage on another animal—in other words, threat and attack patterns. I shall try to describe such patterns, to determine the conditions in which they occur, and the circumstances in which they are likely to be diminished or terminated, particularly by means of inter-animal communication.

We chose chimpanzees for our study because they are probably man's closest living relative. There are many similarities between man and chimpanzee in the number and form of chromosomes, in blood proteins, in immune responses, in DNA, in brain structure and behaviour.[13] The more we see of their behaviour, the more we are impressed with the resemblance between some of their communicative repertoire and that of the human species.

Goodall's research at the Gombe Stream Reserve in Tanzania[10–12] has the special assets of detailed, systematic, close range, longitudinal observation with full recognition of individual animals and their habituation to human observers. And her husband, Hugo van Lawick, has made an extensive film record of threat and attack patterns in chimpanzees, and the various contexts which elicit such patterns. He has filmed several types of threat behaviour, ranging from the low intensive threat (a slight tipping back of the head accompanied by a soft coughing sound) to high intensity threat (such as swaying back and forth in an upright position, or charging towards the animal which has elicited the aggressive behaviour). His films also show various attack patterns, ranging from a slap of the extended hand to a vigorous stamping on the back of the victim. Stones and sticks are used as simple but effective weapons.[14] Attacks are usually of short duration—on a time scale of seconds or minutes—and, immediately afterwards, the victim often approaches the aggressor with submissive gestures and is then apparently reassured with gestures such as an embrace or pat on the back. Indeed, Goodall has described a remarkable repertoire of submissive and reassurance behaviour patterns.

Goodall's observations and our own suggest that aggressive interactions are likely in connection with (1) competition over food, especially if highly desirable foods are spatially concentrated or in short supply; (2) defence of an infant by its mother; (3) a contest over the dominance prerogatives of two individuals of similar social rank; (4) redirection of aggression (such as when a low ranking male has been attacked by a high ranking male and immediately turns to attack an individual subordinate to him); (5) a failure of one animal to comply with a signal given by the aggressor (for example, when one chimpanzee does not respond to another's invitation to groom); (6) strange appearance of another chimpanzee (such as a chimpanzee whose lower extremities became paralysed by poliomyelitis); (7) changes in dominance status, especially among males; (8) the formation of consort pairs at the peak of oestrus (this is quite a recent discovery among wild chimpanzees and requires further study).

Longitudinal study is essential to clarify the nature and extent of aggressive behaviour in the context of changes in dominance relations. These relations may be stable for long periods, but when they change, the level of violence is likely to increase. For example, van Lawick filmed a transition period in which a male first acquired a top ranking status. He was very aggressive, constantly threatening and often attacking his subordinates, but as months passed and his position apparently became more secure, he became increasingly tolerant of other chimps. During the several ensuring years, he has been the highest ranking chimp in this community, and is accorded much deference by the others.

EARLY AGGRESSION

Goodall has also reported the development of aggressive patterns during the early years of life. For example, a ten month old male infant was filmed making typical threatening gestures, in a context similar to those of adult threat. These early aggressive patterns are much more characteristic of males than of females. Kinship is also important in the development of such behaviour; for example, a juvenile may threaten or attack chimpanzees older than itself if its mother is near and if her rank is higher than that of the victim. Adolescent males are often aggressive towards females when no higher ranking males are in the group, but apparently restrain such behaviour toward females when dominant males are present. As adolescent males mature, they tend to threaten the lowest ranking mature males and so gain admittance to the hierarchy of adult males. In general, adolescence is a turbulent, aggressive period among these chimpanzees.

Why study baboons? There are several reasons: (1) the adaptive success of the baboon-macaque group, having spread widely through Asia and Africa in various habitats; (2) the baboons are the largest monkeys; and (3) the relatively large extent of their ground-living capability, in a type of habitat (savannah) that was probably crucial in the emergence of early man.

Based chiefly on the extensive field work of Hall, DeVore, Washburn, Altmann, Rowell, and Ransom, plus our own observation of baboons in two contrasting habitats, it is possible to summarize briefly the conditions in which baboons threat and attack patterns are likely to occur.[15–21] The species under consideration here is the common olive baboon of East Africa.

In certain circumstances the probability of overt threat behaviour and of fighting is higher than in the other contexts of baboon life. These include protection of the troop by adult males against predators such as lions and cheetahs; resolution of disputes within the troop by adult males; formation and maintenance of consort pairs at the peak of oestrus; attainment of preferred sleeping sites in the trees, particularly in the presence of predators; acquisition of premium foods such as figs, nuts, and bananas, especially when spatially concentrated rather than widely distributed. Dominance interactions, especially in the presence of premium foods, scarcity of sleeping sites, and females in full oestrus; exploration of strange or manifestly dangerous areas, a function largely of adult males; and contact between different troops, especially if such contact is infrequent.

TIME FOR AGGRESSION

Baboons, like chimpanzees, spend much of the day in peaceful activities, and there is abundant evidence of affectional systems, similar to those analysed by Harlow in rhesus macaques.[22] And so what circumstances precipitate aggressive behaviour? In trying to answer this question I shall deliberately discuss aggressive behaviour within the species and against other species.

The circumstances which I have mentioned as conducive to aggression in chimpanzees and baboons reveal that much of the behaviour occurs in two general categories: in defence and in obtaining access to valued resources. Within these general categories, various animals, objects or activities may be involved.

My list of situations eliciting threat-attack patterns in chimpanzees and baboons does not include the defence of a fixed territory; our observations are consistent with those of Crook:[23] "Comparative studies of forest fringe, and savannah *Cercopithecus* and *Macaca* monkeys, the baboons of the general *Papio* and *Theropithecus*, the chimpanzee and gorilla do not provide evidence of rigorously defended territories."

Although most higher primates do not live in permanently fixed territories which they defend rigorously, there is a behavioural distinction between currently familiar and relatively unfamiliar territory. A savannah baboon troop may live in an area of 10–15 square miles for some weeks or months before moving to another nearby area. While it is living in a given area, the behaviour of its members tends to take on distinctive features at the fringes of this currently familiar space: they are highly vigilant, threaten readily, and some males move out a considerable distance beyond females and young in exploring the relatively unfamiliar area. An important topic for future research is the contact between groups in such circumstances. The limited data available suggest that there is considerable caution, vigilance, and agonistic behaviour when groups meet, although usually they seem to avoid serious fighting. In some conditions serious intergroup fighting does occur, for example, among rhesus macaque groups in cities in conditions of crowding, food shortage, and inter-species harassment.[24]

EVOLUTONARY ADVANTAGES

The observations of aggressive behaviour in higher primates deserve consideration in the framework of an adaptive evolutionary view of aggressive behaviour. Although we cannot be sure of the ways in which aggressive behaviour has functioned adaptively during the course of evolution, the following possibilities deserve serious consideration: (1) increasing the means of defence; (2) providing access to valued resources such as food, water and females in reproductive condition; (3) contributing to effective utilization of the habitat by distributing animals in relation to available resources—a spacing function of inter-group tension; (4) resolving serious disputes within the group; (5) providing a predictable social environment; (6) providing leadership for the group, particularly in dangerous circumstances; and (7) differential reproduction—it is compatible with present knowledge (though not proved) that relatively aggressive males are more likely to pass on their genes to subsequent generations than less aggressive males, because of the consort pairing at the peak of oestrus in which male aggressiveness plays some role.

Some of these factors may have given selective advantage to aggressive primates, if they could effectively regulate their aggressive behaviour. They have well defined cues that usually terminate aggressive sequences, and an elaborate repertoire of submissive behaviour. They have a stable and agreed dominance hierarchy that contributes to the predictability of the social environment, and they have clear, vivid sequences of aggression-submission-reassurance that have elements in common with the behaviour of man. Future research will profit from paying as much attention to the regulation and control of aggressive tendencies as to their sources and instigation.

If evolution is given serious consideration, it is difficult to overlook the likelihood that man has a vertebrate-mammalian-primate heritage predisposing him to aggressive behaviour. But what is known of the processes that govern the expression of such predispositions? To try to answer this question I shall consider the development of aggressive behaviour within the individual life cycle. Hormonal influences on brain organization early in life affect later aggressive and sexual behaviour.[25-27] Even brief treatment of newborn female rats with testosterone produces lifelong abolition of female sexual behaviour and a tendency to male patterns of aggressive behaviour. Pregnant rhesus macaques given large doses of testosterone during the second quarter of gestation produced female offspring which were abnormal[28] with some anatomical and behavioural characteristics of the male type. One of the well documented behavioural characteristics of this species is a sex difference in the behaviour of infant monkeys, the males being more aggressive. This difference can be measured reliably in the first few months of life in the laboratory. Similar sex differences in aggressive behaviour have been observed in wild macaques and baboons.

Female infants of mothers given testosterone during pregnancy are more aggressive than normal females. They threaten other infant monkeys more often, initiate play more often, and engage in rough and tumble play more often than do normal females.

During growth and development, many influences can modify the expression of these aggressive patterns. For example, undue infant aggressiveness may be severely punished by larger and more powerful animals, leading to fearful inhibition later in life. In view of these possibilities for environmental influences during development, it is interesting that there is some tendency toward persistence of hyper-aggressive characteristics into adult life in females whose mothers are exposed to testosterone in pregnancy.

HUMAN DEVELOPMENT

Is there any evidence that testosterone has similar effects on the development of behaviour in humans? We have been able to study a few cases of girls who had been exposed to androgens *in utero*. At the Pediatric Endocrine Clinic at Johns Hopkins University, John Money has been conducting a long term programme of research, and a report has been published on twenty-two girls, mostly studied in late childhood and early adolescence.[29] Those with striking anatomical abnormalities had undergone surgical treatment shortly after birth. By means of interviews and projective tests, information was obtained from each girl and from at least one parent in each of several behavioural categories. The research design undertook to control for observer bias. Results indicated that the early androgenized girls, in contrast with a control group, tended to be described by themselves and others as tomboys, to engage in outdoor sports requiring much energy and vigour, to prefer rough play, and to prefer toys ordinarily chosen by boys (such as guns). This initial study requires replication, even though replication will necessarily be difficult. This line of inquiry has led from basic research on the biology of sex differentiation to an important human problem. The results are at least compatible with the concept that testosterone is one of many influences which shape the development of aggressive behaviour in the human species.[30]

Does the exposure of foetal brain to testosterone have a distinctive influence on the differentiation of circuits that will later mediate aggressive responses? This seems likely in the light of current research on biochemical mechanisms of brain differentiation.[31] This does not, however, suggest that testosterone establishes fixed patterns of complex behaviour, unmodifiable by subsequent events. More likely, the hormone affects the brain in such a way as to facilitate the learning of aggressive patterns later in life. For any species, some patterns of behaviour are easy to learn, some fairly difficult, and some exceedingly difficult.[32] In general, patterns that have been valuable in species survival are easy to learn;[33] and hormonal influences on brain development may have important mediating roles, especially where sex differentiation is concerned.[34] One way this can occur is through differences in the development of attention, for attention is crucial in learning processes. A hormonal influence during a sensitive period of brain development may render a certain class of stimuli more interesting to the organism at a later stage. This line of inquiry is amenable to experimental analysis in primates.

VISUAL STIMULI

Do some types of visual input elicit more sustained attention from infant monkeys than others? In one experiment, monkeys were raised in a total isolation chamber for the first nine months of life, during which they were exposed to various types of visual input from coloured slides.[35] These slides depicted monkeys in various activities and also depicted various non-monkey stimuli. Monkey pictures elicited much more interest than non-monkey pictures, and moreover, pictures of monkeys showing a species-typical threat expression were especially potent in eliciting behavioural responses. Between two and a half and four months of age, threat pictures yielded a particularly high frequency of disturbance. Similar results were obtained with films in the same experimental design (personal communication from G.P. Sackett). As with most studies in this new area of scientific inquiry, this calls for replication. It suggests that the infant rhesus has a built-in, special responsiveness to the threatening facial expression which is characteristic of its species. Given a responsiveness of this sort, it is not difficult to imagine how the infant in the natural environment would learn a great deal about threat and attack behaviour. Once the infant monkey's attention was powerfully drawn to threat stimuli, he would rapidly learn the conditions in which threat and

attack patterns were likely to occur, and the actions likely to terminate aggressive sequences.

This brings me to a consideration of observational learning in primate adaptation.[36] Traditionally, discussions of aggressive behaviour have associated unlearned responses with non-human creatures and learned responses with humans. Curiously, this linkage has persisted in spite of the enormous research literature on learning in non-human animals.

One of the most interesting findings of the primate field studies in the past decade has been the recurring theme of observational learning in a social context.[37] In many species and diverse habitats, the following sequence has been described: close observation of one animal by another; imitation by the observing animal of the behaviour of the observed animal; practice of the observed behaviour, often for some hours after its occurrence, especially in the play group of young animals. This sequence of observation, imitation, and practice has been described in relation to several adaptive situations: food gathering, tool-using and tool-making (in chimpanzees), nest building, infant care, copulation and aggressive interactions. In essence, the young have access to virtually the full range of adult behaviour, and take advantage of it to learn patterns of behaviour that have been effective in adaptation. The motivation for such observational learning seems to be well established in the young primate. Observational learning in monkeys has also been studied experimentally. It has been demonstrated that one monkey readily learns from watching another in food choice situations. Moreover, the observing animal learns from incorrect as well as correct responses of the animal he is watching.[38] In other words, he learns from the consequences of the operating animal's behaviour.

SEX DIFFERENCES

In this context, our field observations are consistent with two concepts: (1) aggressive patterns are learned early in life through observation–imitation–practice sequences; (2) there is a sex difference in the attractiveness of some aggressive patterns from infancy onward. In baboons and chimpanzees, aggressive play is prominent during growth and development, with males spending considerably more time than females in such activities. Chimpanzee males (and also gorillas) make elaborate aggressive displays in adult life, and the young males, even in infancy, show more interest in such behaviour than do females. Young males are keen observers of older males in such matters.

This line of inquiry is important for an understanding of the influence of the social environment on the development of aggressive behaviour. It provides another link between evolutionary and developmental views of the organism. Lately, developmental psychologists have been calling attention to the importance of observational learning in young children.[39] The child between one and two years of age is a devoted watcher. At this age, observation and imitation may well provide his principal mode of learning.

A remarkable set of findings has highlighted the susceptibility of children to learn aggressive patterns by viewing models which act aggressively. For example, in one experiment pre-school children were exposed to an aggressive model attacking a target object for ten minutes in a laboratory situation without an aggressive model. When the children were tested in the same situation six months later, the former were much more aggressive towards the target object than the latter—that is, a ten-minute exposure enhanced physical aggressiveness in the same situation six months later. This experiment is one of a series carried out by Bandura and his colleagues at Stanford during the past few years,[40–41] showing vividly how children can learn aggressive patterns by watching film or television and enact these patterns in their later play. He has shown that pre-school, middle class children tend to imitate the aggressive behaviour of adults whether they observe it in people in their presence or depicted on film; moreover, the effect is obtained even with cartoon films. In short, aggressive patterns are imitated whether the dramatic presentation is realistic or fantasy-like. Imitation is increased if the aggressive model is rewarded in the drama, decreased if the aggressive model is punished. In general, these imitative acts are displayed spontaneously in the play of these young children, sometimes in remarkable fidelity to the model's original behaviour. But recent work

goes beyond this, showing that the children are capable of performing imitatively many more aggressive acts than they show spontaneously—provided they are given an incentive for doing so. Thus, there is a tendency to restrain expression of aggressive patterns in spontaneous play; this is particularly true for girls and for patterns in which the model has been punished. But the patterns have been learned, and their performance can readily be elicited by a suitable incentive. It is worth emphasizing that these studies rely on direct observation of the child's behaviour in the experimental setting.

Thus, it seems that biological predispositions to learning aggressive patterns and exposure to specific social learning situations may interact to produce great individual differences in aggressiveness during later life.[42–43] In analysing such problems scientifically, the effective conjunction of biological and psychosocial disciplines—so far rarely achieved—holds much promise for future understanding. It hardly seems necesssary to point out the aggressive tendencies of the human species today. Whatever adaptive functions such behaviour may have served in man's evolutionary past, there is serious question about its utility in contemporary society.[44] The risks inherent in such behaviour have been greatly amplified within our lifetime. Yet these problems at present attract only a modest amount of attention in the scientific community. It is difficult to imagine a more important area for research in the future.

REFERENCES

[1]Hamburg, D.A. (ed.), *Psychiatry as a Behavioral Science*, 103 (Prentice-Hall, New Jersey, 1970).

[2]Garattini, S., and Sigg, E.B. (eds.), *Aggressive Behaviour*, 369 (Wiley, New York, 1969).

[3]Daniels, D.N., Gilula, M.F., and Ochberg, F.M. (eds.), *Violence and the Struggle for Existence*, 441 (Little, Brown, Boston, 1970).

[4]Washburn, S.L., and Hamburg, D.A., in *Primates: Studies in Adaptation and Variability* (edit. by Jay, P.C.), 458 (Holt, Rinehart and Winston, New York, 1968).

[5]Washburn, S.L., and Jay, P.C., *Perspectives on Human Evolution*, 1, 287 (Holt, Rinehart and Winston, New York, 1968).

[6]DeVore, I. (ed.), *Primate Behavior: Field Studies of Monkeys and Apes*, 629 (Holt, Rinehart and Winston, New York, 1965).

[7]Jay, P.C. (ed.), *Primates: Studies in Adaptation*

and Variability, 503 (Holt, Rinehart and Winston, New York, 1968).

[8]Rowell, T.E., in Primate Ethology (edit. by Morris, D.), 219 (Aldine, Chicago, 1967).

[9]Washburn, S.L., and Hamburg, D.A., in Primate Behavior: Field Studies of Monkeys and Apes (edit. by DeVore, I.), 607 (Holt, Rinehart and Winston, New York, 1965).

[10]van Lawick-Goodall, J., in Animal Behaviour Monographs (edit. by Cullen, J.M., and Beer, C.G.), 165 (Bailliere, Tindall and Cassell, London, 1968).

[11]van Lawick-Goodall, J., in Primates: Studies in Adaptation and Variability (edit. by Jay, P.C.), 313 (Holt, Rinehart and Winston, New Yor, 1968).

[12]Goodall, J., in Primate Behavior: Field Studies of Monkeys and Apes (edit. by DeVore, I.), 425 (Holt, Rinehart and Winston, New York, 1965).

[13]Sarich, V.M., in Perspectives on Human Evolution, 1 (edit. by Washburn, S.L., and Jay, P.C.), 194 (Holt, Rinehart and Winston, New York, 1968).

[14]Goodall, J., Nature, 201, 1264 (1964).

[15]Hall, K.R.L., and DeVore, I., Primate Behavior: Field Studies of Monkeys and Apes (edit. by DeVore, I.), 53 (Holt, Rinehart and Winston, New York, 1965).

[16]DeVore, I., and Hall, K.R.L., in Primate Behavior: Field Studies of Monkeys and Apes (edit. by DeVore, I.), 20 (Holt, Rinehart and Winston, New York, 1965).

[17]DeVore, I., in Sex and Behavior (edit. by Beach, F.A.), 266 (Wiley, New York, 1965).

[18]Hall, K.R.L., in The Natural History of Aggression (edit. by Carthy, J.D., and Ebling, F.J.), 51 (Academic Press, New York, 1964).

[19]Rowell, T.E., Anim. Behav., 15, 499 (1967).

[20]Altmann, S.A., Social Communication Among Primates, 392 (University of Chicago Press, 1967).

[21]Ransom, Observations of Baboons at the Gombe Stream Reserve, Presentations at Stanford University and University of California, Berkeley (1969).

[22]Harlow, H.F., and Harlow, M.K., in Behavior of Nonhuman Primates (edit. by Schrier, A.M., Harlow, H.F., and Stollnitz, F.), 2, 287 (Academic Press, New York, 1965).

[23]Crook, J.H., in Man and Aggression (edit. by Montagu, M.F.A.), 141 (Oxford University Press, New York, 1968).

[24]Southwick, C.H., Beg, M.A., and Siddigi, M.R., in Primate Behavior: Field Studies of Monkeys and Apes (edit. by DeVore, I.), 111 (Holt, Rinehart and Winston, New York, 1965).

[25]Harris, G., Endocrinology, 75, 627 (1964).

[26]Levine, S., and Mullins, jun., R. F., Science, 152, 1585 (1966).

[27]Young, W., Goy, R., and Phoenix, C., Science, 143, 212 (1964).

[28]Goy, R.W., Endocrinology and Human Behaviour (edit. by Michael, R.P.), 12 (Oxford University Press, New York, 1968).

[29]Money, J., and Ehrhardt, A.A., Endocrinology and Human Behaviour (edit. by Michael, R.P.), 32 (Oxford University Press, New York, 1968).

[30]Hamburg, D.A., in Stimulation in Early Infancy (edit. by Ambrose, A.), 269 (Academic Press, New York, 1969).

[31]Clayton, R.B., Kogura, J., and Kraemer, H.C., Nature, 226, 810 (1970).

[32]Seligman, M.E.P., Psychol. Rev. (in the press).

[33]Hamburg, D.A., Expression of the Emotions in Man (edit. by Knapp, P.), 300 (International Universities Press, New York, 1963).

[34]Hamburg, D.A., and Lunde, D.T., The Development of Sex Differences (edit. by Macoby, E.), 1 (Stanford University Press, 1966).

[35]Sackett, G.P., Science, 154, 1468 (1966).

[36]Hall, K.R.L., in Primates: Studies in Adaptation and Variability (edit. by Jay, P.C.) (Holt, Rinehart and Winston, New York, 1968).

[37]Hamburg, D.A., in Determinants of Infant Behaviour, 4 (edit. by Foss, B.M.), 3 (Methuen, London, 1969).

[38]Riopelle, A., in Principles of Comparative Psychology (edit. by Waters, R., Rethingshafer, D., and Caldwell, W.) (McGraw-Hill, New York, 1960).

[39]Siegel, A.E., in Violence and the Struggle for Existence (edit. by Daniels, D.N., Gilula, M.F., and Ochberg, F.M.), 193 (Little, Brown, Boston, 1970).

[40]Bandura, A., in Advances in Experimental Social Psychology (edit. by Berkowitz, L.), 3 (Academic Press, New York, 1965).

[41]Bandura, A., Aggression: A Social Learning Interpretation (in the press).

[42]Boelkins, R.C., and Heiser, J.F., in Violence and the Struggle for Existence (edit. by Daniels, D.N., Gilula, M.F., and Ochberg, F.M.), 15 (Little, Brown, Boston, 1970).

[43]Daniels, D.N., and Gilula, M.F., Violence and the Struggle for Existence (edit. by Daniels, D.N., Gilula, M.F., and Ochberg, F.M.), 405 (Little, Brown, Boston, 1970).

[44]Hinde, R.A., Intern. J. Social Sci. (in the press).

14

SOME BEHAVIORAL COMPARISONS BETWEEN THE CHIMPANZEE AND THE MOUNTAIN GORILLA IN THE WILD
V. Reynolds

For the last reading in Section Two, we have chosen an essay that compares the life-ways of the two primates generally considered to be most closely related to man, the gorilla and the chimpanzee. Since Reynolds' account was written, a good deal more information on gorilla ecology and distribution has appeared in print (Groves 1967, 1970, 1971), and a detailed account of the ecology of both chimpanzees and gorillas at the overlapped western end of their distribution has been published (Jones and Pi 1971). These recent studies reinforce Reynolds' points—and provide more evidence for his voicing of Schaller's feeling that gorilla populations had formed an east-west continuum in the recent past, rather than the discrete and widely separated picture they now present.

For well-written and authoritative accounts of gorillas and chimpanzees in the wild, consult the popular books by Schaller (1965) and van Lawick-Goodall (1971). And for a comparative overview of all the great apes (including the orang and the gibbon), Reynolds' own book The Apes *(1967) remains the most instructive.*

Groves, Colin P. 1967. Ecology and taxonomy of the gorilla. *Nature 213*:890–893.

————. 1970. *Gigantopithecus* and the mountain gorilla. *Nature 226*:973–974.

————. 1971. Distribution and place of origin of the gorilla. *Man 6*:44–51.

Jones, Clyde, and J. S. Pi. 1971. *Comparative Ecology of Gorilla gorilla (Savage and Wyman) and Pan Troglodytes (Blumenbach) in Rio Muni, West Africa.* Bibliotheca Primatologica, No. 13, Karger, New York. 96 pp.

Reynolds, Vernon. 1967. *The Apes: The Gorilla, Chimpanzee, Orangutan and Gibbon—Their History and Their World.* E. P. Dutton, New York. 296 pp.

Schaller, George B. 1965. *The Year of the Gorilla.* Ballantine Books, New York. 285 pp.

van Lawick-Goodall, Jane. 1971. *In the Shadow of Man.* Houghton-Mifflin, New York. 297 pp.

INTRODUCTION

Two types of behavioral information may be distinguished in the literature on chimpanzees and gorillas: 1) that obtained in the wild, which may be subdivided into the reports of unarmed naturalists such as Garner (1896) or the Akeleys (1923), and the reports of collectors or hunters such as Aschemeier (1921); and 2) that obtained in captivity, in zoos (e.g. Budd et al. 1943), laboratories (e.g. Yerkes 1943), and by people who kept these apes as pets (e.g. Hayes 1951, Lang 1961).

Reproduced by permission of the American Anthropological Association from *American Anthropologist*, Vol. 67, 1965. Reprinted with permission of the author and publisher.

Following in the tradition of the unarmed naturalists, a series of field-workers (Schaller 1963, Goodall 1962, 1963, Kortlandt 1962, Reynolds 1963, 1964, 1965 and in press) has recently contributed greatly to our knowledge of the natural behavior of these anthropoids.

The aim of this paper is to make some behavioral comparisons between the population of chimpanzees (*Pan troglodytes schweinfurthii*) studied by the author in the Budongo Forest, W. Uganda, and the population of mountain gorillas (*Gorilla gorilla beringei*) studied by Schaller (1963), chiefly at Kabara in E. Congo and also in S. W. Uganda. Unless otherwise stated, data referring to the mountain gorilla are taken from Schaller (1963) and those for the chimpanzee from the author's observations (Reynolds 1963, 1964, 1965, and in press).

DISTRIBUTION

The mountain gorilla occupies a smaller range than the chimpanzee. The total area inside which *Gorilla g. beringei* occurs is about 35,000 sq. miles, from the equator to latitude 4°20'S and from longitude 26°30'E to 29°45'E. The total area within which *Pan troglodytes schweinfurthii* occurs is around 400,000 sq. miles, from latitude 5°N to 8°S and longitude 17°E to 32°E. While it is known that the gorilla occurs in isolated populations within its total range (Emlen and Schaller 1960), no evidence is available concerning the existence of isolated populations in the chimpanzees of the E. Congo forest, although it is probable that in some areas they do exist (Schaller, personal communication). In Uganda, at the eastern edge of the range, chimpanzee distribution coincides with the isolated patches of rainforest; likewise, isolated population units occur in the Sudan and in Tanganyika. The altitude of the gorilla's range is from around 1,500 feet to 13,500 feet, while that of the chimpanzee is from around 1,000 feet in the Congo basin to over 9,000 feet in the Ruwenzori Mountains (Wollaston 1908 and personal observation). In areas where the chimpanzee and gorilla occur together, there is some evidence that they do not mix freely. In the Kayonza Forest, Uganda, Pitman (1935 and personal communication) has observed that as gorillas moved into an area containing chimpanzees, the latter moved away.

HABITAT

Gorillas are confined to humid forests. Around three-quarters of all mountain gorillas occur in lowland rain forest, the remaining quarter occupying mountain rain forest. The latter quarter additionally occupy bamboo forest, and sporadically the Senecio zone occurring above 11,500 feet. Like mountain gorillas, chimpanzees are typically found in humid forests, but a smaller proportion of them occupies mountain rain forest. A small proportion of all chimpanzees, however, lives permanently in forest-savannah mosaic (Keay 1959) around the periphery of the rain forest zone. These areas are humid for part of the year, but have a

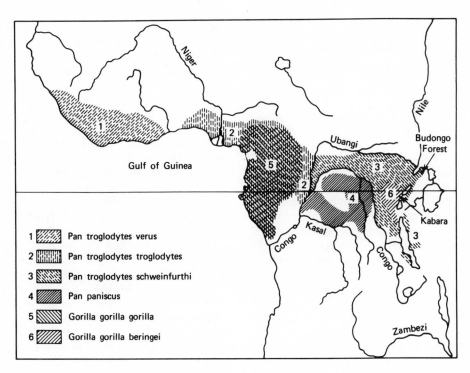

Distribution of chimpanzees and gorillas, showing relevant study areas. (Based on Vandebroek, 1958).

1 Pan troglodytes verus
2 Pan troglodytes troglodytes
3 Pan troglodytes schweinfurthi
4 Pan paniscus
5 Gorilla gorilla gorilla
6 Gorilla gorilla beringei

definite dry season. Nissen (1931) and Good-all (1962) studied chimpanzees in this type of habitat, which typically consists of grassland, woodland, and gallery forest. Thus, while both chimpanzees and gorillas live in lowland and mountain rain forest, chimpanzees additionally live outside such forests and therefore show greater habitat diversity than gorillas. The temporary exploitation of high altitude zones by mountain gorillas is a specialization not found in chimpanzees.

FOOD HABITS

Both species are vegetarians, but while the gorilla feeds mainly on stems, leaves, and shoots, the chimpanzee is primarily a fruit-eater. Schaller estimated that around Kabara, in the Virunga Volcanoes, Albert Park, 1 vine and 3 herbs furnished at least 80% of the daily food supply, while in the Budongo Forest, fruits of four tree species dominated the chimpanzees' diet during the periods when those species were ripe. Both gorillas and chimpanzees show a marked adaptability to different foods in different parts of their range, and this is true whether the same foods are available in different areas or not; thus, Schaller found no overlap of actual foods consumed between the Utu region and the Virunga Volcanoes, although 55 food species were available in both areas, and in chimpanzees, none of the four major food species of the Budongo Forest occurs in the nearby Kibale Forest, which harbors a large chimpanzee population.

LOCOMOTION

Both gorillas and chimpanzees are quad-rupedal. Their food requirements take them long distances on the ground and into the trees. But whereas the gorilla is essentially terrestrial, climbing trees with caution, chimpanzees are best characterized as arbo-terrestrial, being equally at home and skillful in the trees as on the ground; and, in fact, in the Budongo Forest they were observed to spend about 75% of their time in the trees. Brachiation is found in chimpanzees but not in gorillas. Swinging and leaping from branch to branch is a feature of chimpanzee behavior but not of gorilla. Hanging from thin branches by one or more limbs, with the body dangling down, is a typical feeding position of the chimpanzee, which is forced

to exploit the outer periphery of trees where the fruit often grows; these postures were not seen in adult gorillas. On the ground both species support the front of the body upon the knuckles and the rear of the body on the flat soles of the feet; in trees the hallux is abducted to grip the branch or trunk in both species, on stouter branches the knuckles are used for support, while on thin ones and when climbing vertically, the long hand is used to grasp.

POPULATION DYNAMICS

The total population of mountain gorillas is between 5,000 and 15,000; for the chimpanzee, no census has been made and it is impossible to guess what the population may be, but from the available evidence it seems that the population is very much greater. In the Budongo Forest, there are between 1,000 and 2,000 chimpanzees.

Population density of the mountain gorilla varies from around 1 per sq. mile in the Congo basin to 6.6 per sq. mile in the Kabara area. In an area of intensive study in the Budongo Forest there were 10 chimpanzees per sq. mile. The Budongo Forest seems, however, to have a denser population than most of the other Uganda forests and certain areas of the E. Congo (personal observation and Schaller, personal communication).

Mountain gorilla females give birth about every three and a half to four and a half years if the infant survives. In chimpanzees the commonest birth interval is slightly less, being about three years most often, commonly four years, while anything from one year onwards occurred.

Both gorillas and chimpanzees seem to be relatively free from predators. Leopards do not appear to constitute a serious threat to either species. The worst enemy of both is man.

Diseases—especially viruses, bacteria, and various blood and intestinal parasites—are probably the major cause of death in gorillas, and the same is probably true of chimpanzees. In the wild, both species appeared robust and healthy for the most part. Blindness in one eye was observed in both studies (one adult animal in each case), but whether this occurred through disease or accident is not known. Symptoms resembling the common cold were observed in some gorillas, and prolonged bronchial coughing was observed in an adult chimpanzee.

In gorillas, injuries of a superficial kind are fairly common and internal injuries such as bone fractures and breakages are occasional (see discussion in Schaller 1963). Bites account for some of the wounds. None of the Budongo chimpanzees showed any superficial injuries or bite scars, but one broken wrist was observed, and on two occasions chimpanzees fell from trees when branches broke. Schultz (1940) has drawn attention to the high frequency of fractured and repaired bones in old wild chimpanzees. Fighting is rare among gorillas, although it seems possible that on the occasions when fighting does occur, serious wounds may be inflicted. Possibly the teeth are used more than in the chimpanzee, which uses its limbs extensively in quarrels. However, perhaps a major factor limiting physical combat between the chimpanzees is the fact that they spend most of their time in the trees, where fighting cannot be fierce without the risk of a fall.

The oldest gorilla of known age in captivity was 34 1/2 years old when he died. In captive chimpanzees, a male aged 35 years was in fine condition when he died accidentally (Mason, personal communication) and a 42-year old female survives at the Yerkes Laboratories (Riopelle and Daumy 1962). In both species senility was rarely seen in the wild, and it was impossible to judge the ages of the oldest animals seen; it seems possible that in both life expectancy is about 30 years in the wild.

In adult gorillas the ratio of females to males was 1.5:1.0, while in chimpanzees this ratio was probably about 1:1. In gorillas the proportion of animals in the population aged about 6 years or below was 45%, in chimpanzees the proportion observed was a little under 26%. However, the fact that in chimpanzees the mothers with infants and juveniles are the shyest of all groups and consequently the hardest to observe, may have contributed to the small percentage of infants and juveniles seen.

SOCIAL ORGANIZATION

A major difference exists between the social organization of gorillas and chimpanzees. Whereas in the gorilla, groups are fairly permanent in that most of the members of any given group keep together most of the time, giving the group temporal and spatial distinctness, no permanent groups which conform to the above conditions are found in chimpanzees. The gorilla social group has a scatter of 200 feet or less and consists of both sexes and all ages, the average constitution of a gorilla group at Kabara being as follows:

Adult male	3.2 animals
Adult female	6.2 animals
Juvenile	2.9 animals
Infant	4.6 animals

No comparable data can be obtained for the chimpanzee. In this species, most bands are so fluid and volatile that their constitution changes daily or hourly, as new animals join the band and others leave; or the band may split into two or more units which go their own ways and do not rejoin for a period of days, weeks, or months, if indeed they ever rejoin. Within the framework of this loose social organization, four types of bands may be distinguished: Mother-groups, Adult male groups, Adult groups (both sexes), and Mixed groups (both sexes and all age groups). Of these, the former two have the highest degree of permanence; nevertheless, all are temporary. The diameter of chimpanzee groups at any time depends entirely on the degree of dispersion of the forage.

Changes in group composition, the daily norm in chimpanzees, are rare in some gorilla groups, occasional in others. Adult males show the greatest mobility between gorilla groups. In chimpanzees, Male-groups (bands of about four adult males) travel more widely than other groups. Thus it seems that in both gorillas and chimpanzees, certain adult males cover more ground than females and young. In both species, however, there are less mobile adult males; in gorillas these are the ones which stay with the group, including the leader males, while in the chimpanzee these are the more timid and older males, which are most often found with Adult groups and Mixed groups.

Lone males, that is males leading a solitary life for a period of a month or more, are common in gorillas, but lone females were not observed. In chimpanzees it is probable that no animal spent as long as a month without joining up with other chimpanzees, although animals of both sexes and all age groups down to Juvenile 2 (average age=4 yrs.) were seen alone from time to time in the Budongo Forest.

Intergroup interactions in gorillas are usually peaceful. Two groups will approach to within 100 or 150 feet of each other, then part, or will rest side by side, or occasionally mix briefly, or sleep together at one site, and on one occasion only was antagonism observed between the dominant males of two groups. Small bands of chimpanzees mingle freely; however, there is often excitement exhibited by leaping and noisy vocalization when bands meet, before they settle down feeding together.

GROUP RANGES AND MOVEMENTS

Neither gorillas nor chimpanzees have defended territories. Gorilla groups had an estimated average home range of 10–15 sq. miles, and there was great overlap between the ranges of neighboring groups. Owing to the lack of a cohesive social unit in chimpanzees, it is difficult to apply the term "home range." However, regions measuring 6–8 sq. miles each were found in the study area, within which there was a higher percentage of chimpanzee movements and interaction than there was between them. These regions may perhaps be considered as the home ranges of the 70-odd chimpanzees which apparently spent most of their time within them.

Seasonal movements, controlled by changes in the distribution of the food supply, were not important in gorillas, in which the only example of this was the more extensive feeding in bamboo zones during the rains, when tender young bamboo shoots provided an attractive source of forage. For most of the year, however, gorilla groups travel around the range without a definite pattern, forage being equally abundant almost everywhere. In this respect, the contrast with chimpanzees is very great, where the seasonal ripening of fruits in different forest types at different times of the year is the major factor determining the whereabouts of the animals. In the Budongo Forest, during the fig season, chimpanzees were found at sunny spots in Mixed Forest where fig trees grow; during the periods of food shortage, they were widely scattered over the whole forest; during the *Pseudospondias* season they were concentrated in Swamp Forest where this species grows, and during the *Maesopsis* season they were concentrated in *Maesopsis* Forest. There is, however, no clear evidence that trees in equatorial forest ripen at a given time each year, so that there is probably no annual cycle of chimpanzee movements.

The daily pattern of feeding activity of gorillas is as follows. Within an hour of dawn they move away from the sleeping site, travelling slowly and feeding intensively as they go. There is a mid-day rest period, followed by renewed feeding activity in the afternoon, less intense and with faster movement than in the morning. The normal daily total distance covered by gorillas is 300 feet to 6,000 feet (average about 1,700 feet), although they occasionally travel 15,000 feet on one day. Chimpanzees have a less clear-cut daily cycle in the Budongo Forest. After rising at daybreak, there is an hour or two of high-intensity feeding, after which feeding is slower. At this point some animals move on to a new feeding area, perhaps a mile or two away, while others, especially mothers and their offspring, stay put and settle down to very slow feeding and grooming or play activities. The mobile animals feed again on arrival at the new area, and can often be found feeding around midday. This general patern continues all day. In the late afternoon feeding becomes more intensive, and at dusk it reaches a peak comparable to the early morning peak. The total daily distance covered by the mobile Male and Adult groups may be 5,000 feet to 25,000 feet, while Mother groups probably travel less than 1,500 feet a day on many days. Daily travel distance is, however, greatly affected by the scarcity or abundance of food, being greater if food is scarce.

SOCIAL BEHAVIOR

In both gorillas and chimpanzees, posturing has communicative significance in the behavior of dominant males. Dominant male gorilla leaders move forcefully, and "stand and face" when they want the group to move off. Most chimpanzee groups have no leaders, but some male groups have an especially dominant male which leads the way across

	Gorilla		Chimpanzee	
	Total No. observations	Frequency obs/hr.	Total No. observations	Frequency obs/hr.
Dominance	110	0.23	25	0.98
Grooming	134	0.28	57	0.19
Social play	96	0.11	47	0.16

Sequence of Events in Displays of Gorilla and Chimpanzee

Gorilla	Chimpanzee
1. 2–40 clear hoots 2. "symbolic feeding" 3. Throws vegetation 4. Bipedal stance 5. 2–20 chest beats 6. Leg kicking 7. Running sideways 8. Branch shaking and breaking 9. Thumps ground with one or both palms	1. Panting hoots by one animal, slowly, low pitch 2. Panting hoots by nearby animals, with increasing pitch, tempo and volume 3. (on ground only) Drumming on tree buttresses 4. Shaking of saplings or branches, running, and leaping.

roads and leaves feeding trees first; dominant males were seen in other types of group as well, being distinguished by forceful movements and fine physique. The role of facial expressions was difficult to determine in both species; each, however, exhibited teeth and gums in strongly disturbing situations.

Vocalizations present an area of extreme contrast between gorillas and chimpanzees. while gorillas are normally rather quiet animals, chimpanzees are among the noisiest animals in the Budongo Forest. Most gorilla sounds are abrupt and of a low intensity when they are undisturbed; their most intense vocalization, the roar, is given to man, or when otherwise greatly excited. Twenty-one more or less distinct vocalizations were distinguished in free-living gorillas, of which eight were fairly common. In the chimpanzee, 11 more or less distinct vocalizations were common. Of these, one type—calls which are prolonged and high pitched and may be called hoots—are emitted by several animals together, a phenomenon which does not occur in gorillas. The resulting chorus is extraordinarily loud and has a carrying power of up to two miles. In response to man, chimpanzees individually emit a short loud bark. In both species, vocalizations exhibit great variability in pitch,

pattern of delivery, and intensity, and in both species infants are the least vocal group, their vocalizations being confined to distress screeches.

A complex display is found in adult gorillas, comprising a total of 9 acts often in a definite dequence. In adult chimpanzees, a less stereotyped but similar display is found, and for comparison the two are outlined above.

In chimpanzees, the display is primarily a communal activity; thus, if there is no response to stage 1 by other animals, the hoots of the initiating chimpanzee may trail off; although occasionally individual animals go from panting hoots to drumming, this is more commonly the case when many animals are vocalizing. This contrasts with the gorilla, where a single animal normally gives the display, irrespective of the response of other animals. A point of similarity is that chimpanzees frequently drum without accompanying vocalization, and chest-beating (perhaps the gorilla equivalent of drumming) may occur on its own unaccompanied by the display sequence. In both species the display results from excitement, caused by a wide variety of things.

Overt social interactions were few in both studies, as the following figures for certain kinds of interactions show:

These figures indicate a somewhat greater proportion of dominance interactions in the gorilla than in the chimpanzee. In both cases it most often consisted of moving away by the subordinate at the approach of the dominant or pushing away of the subordinate by the dominant. Each gorilla group observed had a dominant silverbacked male who was dominant over every other member of the group. In chimpanzees, dominant males when they occurred were fully grown and black haired with greying rumps; other, apparently older, males with grey backs were not seen to be dominant. Between males, a linear hierarchy was present in the gorilla, not in the chimpanzee. In the gorilla, while silverbacked males were dominant over adult females, variable dominance relations were observed between black-backed males and adult females; in the chimpanzees, all adult males were found to be dominant over adult females. In both species, females had no stable dominance hierarchy.

Three-quarters of all grooming interactions observed in the gorilla were between females and their offspring, and the remaining quarter were mainly grooming by juveniles of females, other juveniles, and infants. It was extremely rare for an adult male to groom, and no adult female was seen to groom an adult male. In chimpanzees, on the other hand, only a quarter of all grooming interactions observed were of a female grooming her offspring, while adult male:adult female grooming accounted for a little over 30% of the total. In two thirds of the cases of male:female grooming, the female was in oestrus.

In both gorillas and chimpanzees, juveniles and infants play. In gorillas, 43% of all play was solo, while in chimpanzees the proportion was 36%. Of play groups, 81% consisted of two youngsters in the gorilla, 83% in the chimpanzee.

Mother-infant ties are close in both gorillas and chimpanzees during the first three years of the infant's life. Thereafter, they persist in the chimpanzee for a further year or two, but not in the gorilla, which is usually independent by the age of three years, although associations with the female may continue to 4–4 1/2 years. During the first three months of life, the gorilla baby clings to its mother's belly, and she supports it usually with one arm as she walks along; at around three months the infant begins to ride on its mother's back, at 6–7 months it occasionally walks and even climbs on its own, after the first year independent locomotion becomes more common until at 2 1/2–3 years riding on the mother stops except in emergencies. In chimpanzees, no supporting of infants by the mothers was observed. The infant clings to its mother's belly ceaselessly for about six months, especially while she is moving around in the treetops. From 6 months to two years it makes forays of increasing length outwards from the mother, riding under her belly when she moves any great distance, say to a new tree. At 2–3 years juveniles are carried on the mother's back when she moves along the ground, but in trees, if they are carried, it is under the belly. This continues for a further 2–3 years, during which time juveniles are still carried during normal rapid group progression through the forest, although they trot behind the mother if progress is slow. On several occasions mothers were seen carrying an infant under the belly and a juvenile on the back. Thus in chimpanzees the pattern of mother:infant responses is more prolonged than in the gorilla. Possibly the stresses of arboreal life and the need for movement over long distances in order to exploit the fruit supply necessitate this prolongation of maternal care.

Sexual behavior was infrequently seen in both studies. Only two gorilla copulations were observed, while four chimpanzee copulations were seen. The only other form of sexual behavior seen was invitation to copulate, which occurred rarely in both species. All the wild copulations were dorsoventral, but the exact position adopted was rather variable; they included copulation of the series and single types.

The estrous cycle in captive gorillas is 30–31 days long, and the female exhibits no sexual swelling. There is a period of sexual receptivity during each cycle, lasting 3–4 days, when she may initiate sexual behavior. The estrous cycle in captive chimpanzees is 37($\pm$0.14) days long (Young and Yerkes 1943), the female exhibits a very large and prominent pink or grey swelling, and, during the 10–day period when it is maximal, she initiates sexual behavior (Yerkes and Elder

1936). Thus both the sexual cycle and the period of sexual receptivity are longer in the chimpanzee than in the gorilla.

Observations on both species indicated the absence of any clear-cut breeding season or birth periodicity.

NESTING BEHAVIOR

Both species normally make a nest to sleep in every night. In chimpanzees, such nests were very rarely on the ground (2 out of 259), being found most often between 30 and 40 feet up (30% of all nests), while 15% were above 90 feet. In gorillas, nest heights vary according to locality, but ground nests are common: the lowest proportion of ground nests was found in lowland rain forest (21.8%), while the highest was 97.1% in Hagenia woodland, Kabara. In most areas, nests were lower than 20 feet, except in lowland rain forest, where 38% were above this height. The basic construction of nests by both species is similar, but the chimpanzee often finishes its nest by adding a lining of leaves and branchlets while the gorilla does not. The same fact has been reported by Reichenow (1920) concerning the chimpanzees and gorillas of Upper Njong, Cameroons.

Both gorillas and chimpanzees are wholly diurnal, resting throughout the hours of darkness. In gorillas the dominant male appears to select the nesting site and is the first to nest, but this sequence was not observed in chimpanzees. Gorillas often spend an hour or more in their nests after first light, but chimpanzees normally get up at dawn and after urinating and/or defecating, commence feeding. This fact has also been reported of the gorillas and chimpanzees of Gaboon (Aschemeier 1922). Gorillas nearly always soil their nests, whereas chimpanzees nearly always do not; infants normally sleep in the same nest as mother in both species; alarmed chimpanzees may hide in nests (Schaller, personal communication, and personal observation) while this has not been reported for the gorilla.

RELATIONS WITH OTHER SPECIES

In relations with man, gorillas are known to be more dangerous than chimpanzees; their bluff charges may, on rare occasions, lead to attack. Chimpanzees rarely charge a human. However, adult males, black- or grey-backed, often stay behind when the group they were with has fled as a result of the appearance of a human. They sit in a low branch, staring at the human, barking sometimes, and looking around. If the observer stays put, it may be many minutes before the male leaves, and during this time he may lie down along the branch with his back to the observer.

Gorillas were not observed to respond to golden monkeys (Cercopithecus mitis kandti) within 10 feet of them. In the Budongo Forest, chimpanzees came into contact regularly with four monkey species: redtail monkeys (Ceropithecus ascanius), blue monkeys (C. mitis stuhlmanni), black and white colobus monkeys (Colobus abyssinicus), and baboons (Papio anubis). Relations were normally peaceful, but on one occasion when a blue monkey came within three yards of an adult male chimpanzee, the later jerked towards it and the monkey ran off. Chimpanzees did not react to the presence of baboons in the vicinity; however, on the only observed occasion when a party of baboons climbed into the crown of a tree in which chimpanzees were feeding, the latter moved away into neighboring trees. Our findings suggest that while chimpanzees are dominant over redtail, blue, and colobus monkeys, they are not dominant over baboons if the latter are in large numbers.

Relations with non-primate species, such as buffalo and elephant, appear to be neutral. No evidence of predation on either chimpanzees or gorillas was obtained in either of the present studies, but it may occasionally occur. With smaller mammals, such as duikers, no clear-cut interactions were observed in either study; however, Goodall (1963) has observed the eating of such animals by chimpanzees in a reserve in Tanganyika. There is no evidence that gorillas ever resort to meat-eating.

These apes live at peace with various bird species, they are not known to eat reptiles, and while chimpanzees regularly eat insects this is not known for the gorilla.

DISCUSSION

The chief morphological difference between

gorilla and chimpanzee is one of size; their appearance, apart from the sagittal crest of the male gorilla, the longer coat and smaller ears in gorillas, and the pink skin colour of chimpanzees when it occurs, is rather similar. Their body proportions are very similar.

The manner of locomotion of these apes is largely similar, both on the ground and in trees; however, the chimpanzee brachiates while the gorilla does not, and shows greater skill and ease in moving about in trees than the latter, spending far more time in them.

They are closely related species, possibly being descended from a Miocene or Pliocene ancestor. Schultz (1927) has suggested, on the basis of foot structure, that gorillas have evolved from an ancestor with more arboreal specializations. One item of behavior supports this suggestion. Schaller noted that the gorillas "exhibit and retain vestigial nest-building behavior in an environment where nests seem superfluous—an anachronism which suggests arboreal ancestry" (1963:198).

The present day adaptation of the gorilla to terrestrial life, and its primarily herbivorous diet, compared with the more arboreal, frugivorous chimpanzee, may help us understand the present-day distribution of these species. The two extant gorilla types are widely separated from each other, occurring at the eastern and western ends of the equatorial forest but not between. Chimpanzees, on the other hand, are known to be distributed throughout this forest zone. Schaller speculates that in the past the gorilla population may have been continuous along a belt north of the present limit of rain forest, and that, in a dry period this population died out. In view of the dietary needs of the gorilla, depending as it does on the lush vegetation of humid zones, it is probable that the species cannot survive in woodland areas with a pronounced dry season and general desiccation at that time. Chimpanzees, however, are known to be able to exploit such areas (Nissen 1931 and Goodall 1962); Nissen made his study in French Guinea during the dry season, and throughout this period there was an abundance of fruits available to the chimpazees. Thus one advantage of a fruit-eater over a shoot-eater is that its food supply is less seriously affected by the transition from forest into woodland caused by general climatic desiccation, and by the occurrence of a dry season in the annual cycle.

Secondly, assuming that the more open conditions of woodland increase the danger of predation by ground-living carnivores such as lion, the more arboreal chimpanzee would have a further advantage over the gorilla.

The extreme contrast between the social organization of the chimpanzee and the gorilla calls for explanation. Perhaps the most important factor underlying this difference is the distribution of food. For gorillas, the problem of finding sufficient food is negligible in areas such as Kabara. They are constantly surrounded by a variety of edible matter, and feeding decisions revolve, perhaps, more around the question of which of the available foods to consume than where to find food. This may be less true in Congo lowland rain forest, where large areas of primary forest provide little food for gorillas, which prefer secondary forest. In both regions, which in some ways represent the extremes of gorilla habitat, food is located in the same areas throughout the year, i.e. everywhere at Kabara, and in secondary forest in the Congo basin.

In the case of chimpanzees, the distribution of food is radically different. In the Budongo Forest, the successive ripening of food-fruits in different parts of the forest makes the finding of food a prime factor in chimpanzee survival. There are no small areas in the forest where food is available all year round, the minimum size of such an area being several square miles. At certain times of the year, food is highly concentrated in particular zones, while at others it is widely scattered over the forest.

In gorillas, permanent social groups may have an advantage over a looser form of social organization. For in this essentially ground-living and ground-feeding form, they may provide better defence against predators. The specialized role of the dominant male as protector of the group is seen in his spectacular display against enemies.

It is also possible to explain the difference in social organization by examining the advantage to the chimpanzee of having a very loose form. In the ecological setting of the Budongo Forest, this type of social organization enables a greater number of animals to survive because they are better able to exploit the food supply than they would be if they moved about in permanent groups. During the period of the year when food is scarcest, it is widely scattered over the forest, and clearly the most efficient way of exploiting such a food supply is to scatter widely, foraging in pairs and threes. Conversely, when food is extremely abundant but concentrated in, say, one hundredth of the total forest area, it can be exploited most efficiently only if the animals are all within this small area.

The problem of why the gorilla is a fairly quiet animal while the chimpanzee is exceedingly and noisily vocal may be related to the difference in social organization. Observations in the Budongo Forest showed that (a) during the period when food was scarce and widely distributed, the chimpanzees were not very vocal, hooting occasionally and chorusing rarely or not at all, while during each of the periods of concentrated food, they made the maximum noise, sometimes chorusing for stretches of minutes without interruption, at intervals of less than an hour throughout the day; and (b) that the response of chimpanzees in one area to strong chorusing from another part of the forest was to move towards the calling and join them. It thus seemed that the loud hooting choruses served to alert nearby chimpanzees to areas of plentiful food.

In the gorilla this entire signalling system is absent. Absent too are both the widespread, highly volatile population which could concentrate on sources of loud vocalizations, and areas which for a brief period have a superabundance of food. The conditions in rain forest, where the position of the best foods cannot be located visually, may have laid emphasis on the development of vocal cues in the system of food-finding of chimpanzees, while in the gorilla it seems reasonable to suppose that visual cues suffice in enabling animals to locate all the food they require.

If this interpretation is correct, the marked difference in development of vocalizations in the two species indicates that the difference in social organization has been present for a long time. Additionally, the larger size of the ears in chimpanzees than in gorillas is correlated with a more extensive reliance on vocal signals in the former.

A distinctive morphological difference between these two species is the occurrence in the chimpanzee of a large sexual swelling of the perineal area, which reaches its maximum development for a ten-day period during every estrous cycle. Concurrent with her swelling, the female is sexually receptive and initiates mating with males by sexual presentation. During this period she ovulates, and thus matings may be fertile. In the gorilla such swelling of the female's sexual skin is totally absent. Here again, an adaptive advantage of the swelling in chimpanzees can be most clearly seen in the light of our knowledge concerning social organization. In the gorilla, the existence of permanent social groups means that females are near males at all times. There is thus no lack of opportunity for copulation. In chimpanzees there may be a greater need for some form of distance signal by females in estrous, in order to increase the chances of matings occurring at the optimal time, and in order to attract and hold the attention of males which might otherwise move out of reach. Several males will follow a female with a prominent swelling, and may copulate with her one after the other. The swelling thus operates as a distance signal, visible by the male as soon as the female herself is visible, and acting as a source of attraction, drawing the male to her and causing him to follow her about. Gorillas neither have nor need such a signal.

In their displays, the gorilla's locomotor behavior is more stereotyped than that of the chimpanzee, and an explanation for this may be that gorillas display on the ground only, while all the parts of the chimpanzee's display may be exhibited in the trees except drumming. While a ground display gives the animal freedom to move its body in any direction it wishes, so that there is no inherent danger in such acts as standing bipedally, leg kicking, and running sideways, such acts could be dangerous if performed in a tree. Thus, the lack of interference of considerations of posture and balance have made it possible for the gorilla to evolve a stereotyped sequence of locomotor activities into its display sequence, while in the chimpanzee, such behavior has had to take constant consideration of the problem of support and balance, and has thus not developed much locomotor stereotypy.

The habitual soiling of its nest by the gorilla is in sharp contrast with the chimpanzee's habit of keeping its nest clean and defecating over the edge. Gorilla feces are firm and well knit, composed mainly of indigestible fibrous matter: "the usual consistency of the dung is such that it retains its shape when falling to the ground and that the animal's fur is not soiled when it sits on it" (Schaller 1963:88). Bingham (1932, Plate 14) has shown clearly that gorilla feces do not disintegrate when lain on. In contrast, the consistency of chimpanzee dung is normally soft, the feces being composed of the waste of a diet consisting in large part of soft fruits. A chimpanzee lying in its dung would soil its coat, and the resultant adhering feces might well attract insects and in other ways act as a source of infection. Thus it may be that, in the evolution of defecating behavior in these species, natural selection has favored defecation outside the nest in chimpanzees, while in gorillas this has not been the case.

Finally, we may briefly consider the contrast in temperaments between these two anthropoid species. Comparative behavior studies in the past often stressed this difference. Tevis (1921), instance, wrote "In mental characteristics there is the widest difference between the two apes that we are considering. The chimpanzee is lively, and at least when young, teachable and tameable. The gorilla, on the other hand, is gloomy and ferocious, and quite untameable" (1921:122). It is possible to suggest an explanation for this contrast between the morose, sullen, placid gorilla, and the lively, excitable chimpanzee. The difference seems to be most clearly related to the difference in social organization and foraging behavior. The herbivorous gorilla is surrounded by food; the more intensively it feeds, the slower it travels; its survival needs are easily met, and it is protected from predators by the presence of powerful males. Here there is no advantage to any form of hyper-activity, except in threat displays and the charge of the big male, which is a hyper-aggressive behavior form. Chimpanzee survival, on the other hand, depends heavily on the fluidity of social groups and the ability to communicate the whereabouts of food by intense forms of activity (wild vocalizing and strong drumming). Moving rapidly about the forest, meeting up with new chimpanzees every day, vocalizing and drumming, and locating other chimpanzees by following their calls, are the basic facts of chimpanzee existence. Here an advantage may be seen in having a responsive, expressive and adaptable temperament. Hyper-activity is the chimpanzee norm in the wild, and with this goes a volatile temperament.

SUMMARY

Some behavioral comparisons are made between the population of chimpanzees (Pan troglodytes schweinfurthii) studied by the author in W. Uganda, and the population of mountain gorillas (Gorilla gorilla beringei) studied by Schaller (1963) in E. Congo and S. W. Uganda. The gorilla is less arboreal and less frugivorous than the chimpanzee; it lives in permanent groups while the chimpanzee does not, does not exhibit the vocal chorusing typical of chimpanzees, has a more stereotyped display than the chimpanzee. Chimpanzees are better able to exploit dry-season zones than gorillas. Their food supply is located in different places at different times of the year while the gorilla's is not, so that food-finding is a greater problem for the chimpanzee than it is for the gorilla. The looser social organization and development of group chorusing in chimpanzees may be a response to the difference in the pattern of food distribution. The sexual swelling of chimpanzees, absent in gorillas, may be a distance signal. The relative absence of display stereotypy in chimpanzees may be associated with their greater arboreality. The gorilla's habit of defecating in the nest, not found in the chimpanzee, may be related to the constitution of its defecate, in contrast with that of the chimpanzee. The more volatile temperament of chimpanzees than of gorillas is examined in the context of their ways of life in the wild.

NOTE

This paper was written while the author was a Fellow of the Center for Advanced Study in the Behavioral Sciences, Stanford, California, and grateful acknowledgment is made for the research facilities provided by the Center. Dr. G. Schaller was also at the Center, and I wish to thank him for many helpful suggestions. Finally, I wish to thank Dr. C. Jolly for many useful criticisms.

REFERENCES CITED

Akeley, C. 1923. In brightest Africa. Garden City.

Aschemeier, C. R. 1921 On the gorilla and the chimpanzee. Journal of Mammalogy 2:90–92.

———. 1922 Beds of the gorilla and chimpanzee. Journal of Mammalogy 3:176–78.

H. C. Bingham 1932. Gorillas in a native habitat. Carnegie Institute, Washington, Pub., 426.

Budd, A., L. G. Smith, and F. W. Shelley 1943 On the birth and upbringing of the female chimpanzee "Jacqueline." Proceedings of the Zoological Society of London 113:1–20.

Emlen, J. T. and G. B. Schaller 1960 Distribution and status of the mountain gorilla (Gorilla gorilla beringei). Zoologica 45:41–52.

Garner, R. L. 1896 Gorillas and chimpanzees. London, Osgood, McIlvaine & Co.

Goodall, J. 1962 Nest building behaviour in the free-ranging chimpanzee. Annals of the N. Y. Academy of Science, 102,455.

———. 1963 Feeding behaviour of wild chimpanzees, a preliminary report. Symposium of the Zoological Society of London 10:39–47.

Hayes, C. 1951 The Ape in our house. New York, Harper.

Keay, R. W. 1959. Vegetation map of Africa south of the Tropic of Cancer. Oxford.

Kortlandt, A. 1962 Chimpanzees in the wild. Scientific American 206:128–138.

Lang, E. M. 1961 Goma—das Korillakind. Zurich.

Nissen, H. W. 1931 A field study of the chimpanzee. Comparative Psychology Monographs, 8 (1): 1–122.

Pitman, C. R. S. 1935 The Gorillas of the Kayonsa Region, Western Kigezi, S. W. Uganda. Proceedings of the Zoological Society of London 105, 2:477–499.

Reichenow, E. 1920 Biologische Beobachtungen an Gorilla und Schimpanse. Sitzber. Ges. naturf. Fr. Berlin, 1–40.

Reynolds, V. 1963 An outline of the behaviour and social organisation of forest-living chimpanzees. Folia Primatologica 1:95–102.

———. 1964 The "Man of the Woods." Natural History 73, no. 1:44–51.

———. 1965 Budongo: an African forest and its chimpanzees. Natural History Press, New York.

Reynolds, V. and F. Reynolds (in press) Chimpanzees in the Budongo Forest. In Primate behavior: field studies of monkeys and apes, Ed. I. DeVore, N. Ý., Holt, Rinehart, and Winston.

Riopelle, A. J. and O. J. Daumy 1962 Care of chimpanzees for radiation studies. Proceedings of the International Symposium on Bone Marrow Therapy 205–227.

Schaller, G. B. 1963 The mountain gorilla, ecology and behavior. Chicago, University of Chicago Press.

Schultz, A. H. 1927 Studies on the growth of gorilla and of other higher primates . . . Memoir of Carnegie Museum 11, 1:1–87.

———. 1940 Growth and development of the chimpanzee. Contributions to Embryology, Carnegie Institute, 29:1–63.

Tevis, M. 1921 Gorilla, chimpanzees, and orang utans. Scientific American Monthly 4:121–125.

Vanderbroek, G. 1958 Notes ecologiques sur les Anthropoides. Society Royal Zoological Society, Belgium, 89:203–211.

Wollaston, A. F. R. 1908 From Ruwenzori to the Congo. London, John Murray.

Yerkes, R. M. 1943 Chimpanzees, a laboratory colony. New Haven, Yale University Press.

Yerkes, R. M. and J. H. Elder 1936 The sexual and reproductive cycles of chimpanzee. Proceedings of the National Academy of Science, Washington 22:276–283.

Young, W. C. and R. M. Yerkes 1943 Factors influencing the reproductive cycle in the chimpanzee: the period of adolescent sterility and related problems. Endocrinology 33:121–154.

3
MAN'S FOSSIL ANTECEDENTS

15

THE SIGNIFICANCE OF PRIMATE PALEONTOLOGY FOR ANTHROPOLOGICAL STUDIES
E. L. Simons

Fossil primates, whether hominid or nonhominid, are extremely rare. The discovery of key specimens is often the result of prolonged and expensive effort (as well as luck), by which time the finder has invested so much of himself in the endeavor that he can no longer be objective about its significance. More often than not, the finder of an important fossil feels that it is uniquely significant, deserving of a special name, and that it overturns all previous views of primate or hominid evolution. With the finder so frequently expressing what nearly amounts to a parental bias, many an evolutionary scholar, attempting to referee the conflicting claims, has expressed the feeling that there would be far less confusion if the discoverers would restrict themselves to the digging and leave the interpretations to those properly trained in evolutionary biology and less emotionally involved.

No single person has discovered more crucial specimens than Dr. L. S. B. Leakey of Nairobi, Kenya, whose persistence and luck are legendary. Along with his discoveries, Leakey has produced a stream of preliminary reports which are short on description and long on speculation. As a result of Leakey's long and extraordinarily productive career, the quantities of crucial fossils we now possess are exceeded only by the interpretive confusions that surround them. The indefensible designations "Zinjan-thropus," "Kenyapithecus," and "Homo habilis," and others, as well as the idea that a relatively modern form of hominid existing in the remote past was the true ancestor of modern man—have drawn repeated opposition (e.g., Brace, Mahler, and Rosen 1971 and the Simons article reprinted here). And even though Leakey can meet none of the criteria of modern taxonomic practice, he continues undaunted (Leakey, Prost, and Prost 1971).

Simons, whose training and field work provide him with unmatched qualifications, offered his first critical assessment a decade ago (Simons 1963). Later he expanded on this critique in the article reprinted here. To his cogent caveat, we can only add amen!

Brace, C. L., P. E. Mahler, and R. B. Rosen. 1971. "Homo habilis" tested by tooth measurements. *Michigan Papers in Anthropology* No. 1. pp. 1–22. Published by the Department of Anthropology, University of Michigan, Ann Arbor. (In 1973 a revised version of this will appear in the *Yearbook of Physical Anthropology*, J. Buettner-Janusch ed.).

Leakey, L. S. B., Jack and Stephanie Prost (eds.). 1971. *Adam or Ape: A Sourcebook of Discoveries About Early Man.* With the assistance of Ronald Goodman. Schenkman, Cambridge, Mass. 452 pp.

Simons, E. L. 1963. Some fallacies in the study of hominid phylogeny. *Science* 141:879–889.

———. 1972 *Primate Evolution: Introduction to Man's Place in Nature.* Macmillan, New York. 322 pp.

ABSTRACT. *The correct use of taxonomic names must become widespread if a clear understanding of primate paleontology is to exist among anthropologists. Physical an-*

From *AJPA* 27:307–332 (1967). Reprinted with the permission of the author and publisher.

thropologists are urged to acquire genuine competence in the paleontology, systematics, and taxonomy of mammals. Examples are given of improper taxonomic procedure and of the perpetuation of invalid names. The need for a stable and correct nomenclature of the primates is emphasized. The importance of examining actual fossil specimens is stressed. The taxonomy of the Hominoidea is discussed and a summary of invalid names in current use is given. Recently discovered fossils from Oligocene strata in the Egyptian Fayum are figured and the pertinence of these to the origins of higher primates is suggested.

The general intent of this symposium seems to warrant some recommendations from a primate paleontologist to physical anthropologists. It should be emphasized that not all my recommendations are new, for many of the points expressed here arise from the new systematics and modern paleontology, recent discussions of which can be found in such works as Rensch (1959), Simpson (1961), Dobzhansky (1962), and Mayr (1963). Although there is nothing novel in urging that modern taxonomy be utilized in the naming of man and his relatives, the point deserves emphasis because badly founded names continue to be proposed. Those who teach about human origins would probably agree that this has brought about a most confused situation which is difficult to understand and harder to explain.

There are two primary reasons for this confusion: first, some of those who find and describe human and prehuman fossils have not studied taxonomy and comparative morphology sufficiently; second, there is almost no audience of professionally trained students of anthropogenesis who can serve as a critical opposition. This is due primarily to the fact that few educational institutions have programs that provide a new generation of scholars with an adequate training in mammalogy, anatomy, stratigraphy, geochronology, and taxonomy. The significance of primate fossils cannot be assessed without competence in and adequate understanding of these subjects. Least understood of these, and least studied, has been taxonomy.

Thus, my primary recommendation is that anthropologists and primatologists should no longer neglect primate taxonomy. It should be made clear that, even now, abandoned or unsubstantiated names are being used for at least some fossil apes and men. It seems advisable that some training in systematics of primates and other mammals should be part of the curriculum offered in graduate training programs in physical anthropology. The day of the description of fossil primates by persons with only an amateur's knowledge of taxonomy is, or should be, over. Even those anthropologists who do not expect to describe fossil species should know the right and wrong ways of doing this. The origins and history of man and the higher primates are broadly popular subjects. Interest in them is increasing. More physical anthropologists should evaluate theories of the origins of man and other primates critically by acquiring professional competence in paleontology and mammalian systematics. Scholars cannot talk intelligently about fossil apes and fossil men until some agreement is reached as to their valid names.

More important to physical anthropology is that clear understanding will come only when the use of correct names becomes widespread in teaching and publication. Nomenclature is an historical subject, so that names and their sequential relationships are important. One could not talk about written history, either, if one were plagued by lack of agreement on the simplest facts, such as whether Charlemagne and William the Conqueror were or were not the same person, or whether the families descended from them were the same or different families. Some of the disagreements about the correct names for species ancestral to or related to man are as fundamental as this.

THE CONTINUED CIRCULATION OF UNNECESSARY NAMES

As an example that unnecessarily proposed names continue in circulation, one can cite Napier (1967) who publishes in italics the mistakenly founded names *Zinjanthropus boisei, Homo habilis,* and *Proconsul.* Such usage means that the user supposes that these terms are valid Linnaean nomina. Since all three nomina have now been treated as synonyms of prior names by more than one author, perhaps it would have been more appropriate for Napier to have pointed out his disagreement explicitly. That is, he could not agree that these terms are all unnecessary synonyms, if that was indeed his viewpoint. Otherwise one must assume that he supports the validity of all three names. On the other hand, it may be that Napier was utilizing these terms in the sense of common nouns rather than as formal Linnaean terms. If this were the case the terms should not have been set in italics. Italics imply to taxonomists that the author supposes the nomina set in this typeface to be valid Linnaean names, corresponding to actual species, populations which do or did exist as real and distinct entities in ages past. Valid Linnaean names are not descriptive labels for individuals.

Zinjanthropus has never received much credence as a valid generic name. Robinson (1960) showed that it was not distinct from *Australopithecus* (subgenus *Paranthropus*), and Leakey (1963), although himself the author of this name, abandoned the term as a genus, relegating it to subgeneric status under *Australopithecus*. *Zinjanthropus* should not have subgeneric status apart from *Paranthropus*. Tobias (1967) retains *Zinjanthropus* as a subgenus under *Australopithecus* distinct from *Paranthropus*, in the title and in the text until page 232 where he remarks:

"It may be inferred that Zinjanthropus *is not even subgenerically distinct from* Australopithecus, *sensu stricto, or* Paranthropus. *I therefore propose formally that the subgenus* Zinjanthropus *be sunk and that the australopithecine taxon from Olduvai Bed I be considered no more than specifically distinct."*[1]

The best materials of robust *Australopithecus* from East and South Africa taken together do not seem to me to exhibit greater variation than that shown in one species of hominid, *Homo erectus*, as currently understood (see Howells, 1966). Tobias (1967:235) has attempted definitions of *A. robustus* and *A. boisei* in which he lists sixteen comparable characters. Not all are different from *A. africanus*. Half of these characters are listed as occurring in both *A. robustus* and *A. boisei*. Two features of the dentition, degree of cingular development and relative size of M^3, are different. These features are minor and their meaning ob-

[1]It is to be regretted that this author has in the title and throughout most of the text perpetuated the name *Zinjanthropus* which he believed to be meaningless. Not only has a meaningless name gained further circulation by this but the paper violates the professional practice of maintaining internal nomenclatural consistency.

scured because *A. boisei* is based on a sample of one, and thus nothing about variation in the population it represents is known. In these definitions Tobias left out the point that the dimensions, particularly the breadth of all the cheek teeth, in *A. boisei* are much greater than the average for *A. robustus*. This does constitute a real separation, but perhaps only at subspecies level. Nevertheless, measurements on the cheek teeth of all East and South African robust *Australopithecus* show no greater extremes in range than occur within *Gorilla gorilla*. All the other characters listed by Tobias are correlated with the great robustness of the Olduvai skull, as was stressed by Robinson (1960). The taxonomic significance of this remains poorly understood. Very small samples of robust *Australopithecus* are known at present; these do not provide much evidence that different species are represented. At least the evidence does not carry much weight for a mammalian taxonomist.

Naturally there are morphological differences between the East and South African populations of robust *Australopithecus*. The significance of these differences depends on the geographic and temporal separation of the two populations represented. We know that approximately 1,700 miles separates these finds, but in spite of all that has been published on the relative dating of the South African finds we still do not know whether the East and South African populations of robust *Australopithecus* lived at the same time or a million years apart. But even should they differ in age by a million years the morphological difference is not great, as can be seen in Figure 1.

The binomen *Homo habilis* has repeatedly been termed invalid by a whole range of authorities including Campbell (1964b), Clark (1964b), Robinson (1965, 1966, 1967), Pilbeam and Simons (1965), and Simons (1967a). All of these scientists have said in one way or another that the type mandible and name bearer of *Homo habilis* cannot be shown to differ significantly from mandibular specimens of *Australopithecus*. Moreover in the opinion of Robinson (1967:70) the diagnosis of *Homo habilis* is technically invalid.

"Another form of failure to comply with the Code is illustrated by a case to be found in

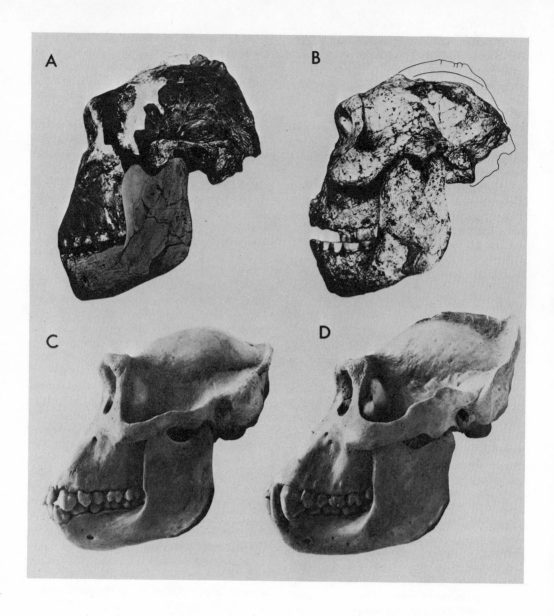

Figure 1. Comparison of East and South African crania and mandibles of robust *Australopithecus* with skulls of two lowland gorillas. A, Olduvai skull, hominid no. 5 and Peninj jaw, East Africa (both reversed); B, Cranium SK48 and mandible SK23 from Swartkrans, South Africa; the photographs of the lower jaws are brought to a size to articulate with the crania. C and D, skulls of lowland gorillas, Yale Peabody Museum collections. The photographs have been printed so as to bring the four skulls to the same facial height (nasion to alveolare).

the original taxonomic description of the supposed new taxon Homo habilis. *This 1964 description contains a direct statement to the effect that the new taxon may be the same as another that was described in 1949. According to the Code no taxon that is proposed conditionally after 1960 is valid."*

Robinson means that whatever the remains from Bed I Olduvai are, they should no longer be referred to as "Homo habilis." These remains were supposed to be different from *Australopithecus africanus* at both the generic and specific levels (Leakey et al., 1964).

Proconsul Hopwood 1933a was relegated to subgeneric status within *Dryopithecus* by Simons and Pilbeam (1965). We (Simons and Pilbeam, 1965) stated what remains our conviction, that the subgeneric divisions within *Dryopithecus* are at best tenuous and nominal and probably will not be sustained by further research. This means that such words as *Sivapithecus*, *Sugrivapithecus*, and *Proconsul* no longer mean much. The supposedly distinctive features of the genus *Proconsul*, frequently cited by Leakey (most recently in Leakey, 1967), are not unique to the African forms among *Dryopithecus*. For instance, the characteristics thought most typical of *Proconsul* as a distinct genus —triangular symphyseal cross-section, diastema between canine and front premolar, and absence of a posteriorly directed simian shelf—are all to be noted in the second mandible of the type species of *Dryopithecus*, *D. fontani* from the type-locality at Saint Gaudens, France. As a consequence of this, the term *Proconsul* now has little meaning or value in primate taxonomy apart from its use as a tie-in with earlier literature.

Use of numerous binomina in another non-taxonomic sense was implied by Leakey (1963: 45) when he remarked that there is a

". . . need for a descriptive label so that we can make it clear to others what specimen (or group of similar and associated specimens), we are referring to."

He goes on to say that Linnaean binomina are also intended to show a degree of relationship, whether of the same species, different species or different genera, etc. But it is clear from this passage that Leakey is influenced in naming fossils by the notion that individual fossils need names which serve as "labels" or "handles" by which one can refer to the specimens. Vertebrate paleontologists give individual specimen numbers to individual fossils.[2] Thus, Y.P.M. 13799 is the specimen on which the genus

[2]Abbreviations used: A.M.N.H., American Museum of Natural History, New York; B.M.N.H., British Museum (Natural History), London; C.M.H., Coryndon Museum (now National Museum), Nairobi; G.S.I., Geological Survey of India, Calcutta; U.M.P., Uganda Natural History Museum, Kampala; Y.P.M., Peabody Museum, New Haven (O.C. osteological collection).

Ramapithecus is based, because it is the holotype of the type species of *Ramapithecus*: *R. brevirostris*. This species in turn is a junior subjective synonym of the species *R. punjabicus*, of which the holotype specimen is G.S.I. D.118/119. SK48 is the "descriptive label" of the best South African skull of *Australopithecus robustus*, from Swartkrans. The same error was committed, and even admitted, by Pilgrim (1927: 12) when naming the Indian fossil ape "*Hylopithecus hysudricus*." In the initial description of this supposed species he remarked:

"In preference to leaving the tooth now described without a generic name and so increasing the difficulty of reference I am giving it the name of Hylopithecus, *although I am conscious that my material is quite insufficient for [formal Linnaean][3] diagnosis."*

Taxonomic names should never be given to individual specimens as labels. Taxonomic names can only be assigned to an individual type specimen when it can be shown that the type specimen represents a newly discovered species population. The "labels" or "handles" for individual fossils, other than type specimens, are of course specimen numbers, field numbers, or locality names (like Maiko Gully skull, Olduvai Bed II), not new Linnaean binomina.

The fact that Linnaean binomina may be unconsciously mistaken for individual names has probably exerted a subtle influence on the naming of taxa of human and other fossils. Most western scholars live in an environment in which a system of binomina, given names and surnames, is applied to individuals. Therefore, application of binomina to new individual specimens may sometimes occur. In actual fact a Linnaean binomen refers to a species, (a population) of which the type specimen is the name-bearer only. Such populations, among fossil mammals at least, would have contained tens of thousands of individuals or more. The type specimen need not even be a typical individual (Simpson, 1940). The name "*Zinjanthropus boisei*" is a case in point. There is only one skull. Although many students would agree that this is really a skull of

[3]Author's insertion.

Australopithecus robustus or at most of a closely allied species, the term continues to show up in professional papers such as Napier's article cited above. Although I am of the opinion that the hominid fossil from Olduvai Bed I is an *Australopithecus robustus*, I personally can report that it is most difficult to stop speaking of *"Zinjanthropus boisei."* In conversation a preferable handle for this one skull would be its specimen number, Olduvai hominid 5. It is extremely difficult to eradicate from one's thinking a poorly founded name, even when one knows it is invalid. The evil of ill-founded names lives after them, and, by this, the good of caution in naming them is often obscured.

TAXONOMIC RULES AND PROCEDURES

The first international agreement on taxonomic rules for the Linnaean binomial system was reached 66 years ago at the Fifth International Congress of Zoology in Berlin, 1901. Consequently there has been ample time for these rules to be noted by students and teachers alike. A set of rules had previously been drawn up by an International Commission of five scientists appointed in Leyden (Third Congress) in 1895. In Berlin the parts of their report that were agreed upon unanimously by commission members were adopted as the *Règles* or Rules. The *Règles international de la Nomenclature zoologique* were published in Paris (1905). The latest edition of the revised rules or code came out as recently as 1964 and is the result of continuous modification and refinement of taxonomic procedure and recommended practice which has been going on since the time of Linnaeus' tenth edition of *Systema Naturae* (1758). These rules, therefore, have been undergoing continual evolution since their adoption, and they now constitute a sensible code deserving universal attention and adherence. To suggest not following them, as Tobias (1967) has recently done,[4] would be at best divisionist and at worst scientific anarchy.

For many reasons besides convenience, biological and medical researchers need a

[4]He is apparently serious in proposing that paleoanthropologists use "bigeneric" designations for fossil hominids.

stable system of names with which to refer to their experimental animals. From time to time in recent years concern has been expressed that the taxonomic names of the living Old World monkey species are in a state of confusion. This is touched on in an accompanying paper by S. L. Washburn. If stability is desired for the generic and specific names of certain cercopithecoid monkeys, the course is clear; official clarification by the Commission should be sought. Any *ad hoc* committee of scientists wishing to clarify monkey taxonomy could reach agreement as to prior and preferred generic and specific names and submit such an agreed upon list to the International Commission of Zoological Nomenclature for clarification or adoption. The listing so arrived at could be accepted unofficially by primatologists until the Commission acted. As an example, a summary of a similar opinion previously rendered by the International Commission of Zoological Nomenclature and reproduced in Schenk and McMasters (1962) is as follows:

"122. Seven Generic Names in Primates Adopted in the Official List of Generic Names.—The following generic names in Primates are hereby placed in the Official List of Generic Names, with type species as cited: Colobus (polycomos), Galago (galago), Gorilla (gorilla), Hylobates (lar), Lemur (catta), Pithecia (pithecia), Tarsius (spectrum)."

In addition to rulings such as this about genera, the Commission may act to validate or suppress species names where there is a conflict of priority or of understanding as to what is the valid type.

THE CURRENT STATUS OF HOMINOID TAXONOMY

Twenty-five years have elapsed since Huxley, Mayr and others formulated the new systematics, and it has been 17 years since Ernst Mayr pointed out at a Cold Spring Harbor Symposium (1950) that perhaps all known Pleistocene species of man should be placed in the genus *Homo*. Still, the new systematics have not made much impact on the process of naming hominoid fossils.

The most satisfactory, up to date, and modern approach to taxonomy of early hominids is that of J. T. Robinson (1962, 1963, 1965, 1967). Unfortunately, even Robinson (1967) advocates a return to Mayr's 1950 suggestion that *Australopithecus africanus* should be called *Homo transvaalensis*. Nevertheless one can go too far in synonymizing proposed genera of fossil men. In my opinion this has been done by Robinson (1967), who, following Mayr (1950), referred *Australopithecus africanus* to the genus *Homo*. Mayr concluded that the prior species name would have to be *Australopithecus* (=*Plesianthropus*) *transvaalensis* Broom 1938 because he considered the juvenile from Taung inadequate to be a species type. Moreover, Robinson (1967) erred in stating that *Homo africanus* is not available because Broom (1918) had previously applied this name to the Boskop skull. Actually, neither case invalidates *A. africanus*. The Taung child has adult first molars, and even so juvenile types stand as valid under the Code. Broom (1918) named the Boskop skull *Home capensis* not *africanus*. Thus if placed in *Homo* the species name would remain "*africanus*."

Robinson (1967) has also stated that since *Australopithecus africanus* now appears more likely as a human ancestor it should be placed in the same genus as its descendants. He remarks (1967: 97, 98):

"It seems to me that human paleontology has been characterized by tendencies to overlook . . . the fact that species belonging to different lineages differ from each other in a manner different from that in which species of the same [ancestor-descendant][5] lineage differ. This cannot be emphasized too strongly . . . This line includes what currently is regarded as Australopithecus *(sensu stricto) and* Homo. *Since it is a line occupying one adaptive zone, I consider it reasonable to use a single generic name for it, and this would have to be* Homo *according to the Code."*

In taking this stand Robinson has sidestepped the most serious problem in the taxonomy of fossils, that is, since all lineages of organisms represent genetic continua from generation to generation, only arbitrary, not real, distinctions between ancestor and descendant can be made. If animal

[5]Author's insertion.

species are always to be placed in the same genus as their descendants, what is to prevent one from placing earlier and yet earlier forms in an extant genus? Should we place 14 million year old *Ramapithecus punjabicus* in genus *Homo*? Should we jump farther back and place 30 million year old forms such as *Aegyptopithecus zeuxis* or *Propliopithecus haeckeli* in genus Homo? Although we cannot definitely say so at present, these three Tertiary species may prove to be in man's direct ancestral line. Ancestor-descendant lineages certainly should not be placed in the same genus on the basis of their phyletic relationship alone or because of inferences about identity in their adaptive zones. If this were done, we would have all mammalian lineages, as they became paleontologically documented, falling into genera with species extending back to the early Tertiary. No one has ever seriously advocated such a thing for fossil mammals.

However, if Robinson means to suggest in the above quotation that time-successive genera should be so delimited as to include only succeeding species in the same "adaptive zone," we are then making "adaptive zone" a new measure for defining genera. Other taxonomists have seldom considered this a factor in generic definition, and, inasmuch as full knowledge of the way in which extinct species occupied their adaptive zones can seldom be obtained, the criterion is vague and is simply not applicable to most fossils.

McAlester (1962) has discussed Simpson's (1961) somewhat similar definition of an evolutionary lineage at the species level in fossils. Simpson (1961: 153) defined an evolutionary species as:

"a lineage (an ancestral-descendant sequence of populations) evolving separately from others and with its own unitary evolutionary role and tendencies."

On this definiton McAlester (1962: 1380) comments:

"Such definitions seem to me to be one step removed from the genetic factors which are the basis of evolutionary isolation and species limits. Because genetic barriers are the ultimate cause of the separate evolutionary

tendencies which are stressed in these definitions, I feel that genetically based species concepts are more fundamental. In practice, I also find reproductive isolation to be a more easily visualized basis for species limits than a vague 'unitary evolutionary role.' Particularly in the case of the model just discussed (i.e. successive species in a separate, nonbranching lineage), such evolutionary concepts seem to provide no useful guide for species limits comparable to that derived from a genetic species interval."

Another aspect of the problem of dividing up continua of time-successive populations has been partly lost sight of by Robinson (1967) and clearly avoided altogether by Leakey (1966). Leakey (1966) compares members of a primitive species of Homo, H. erectus, with "advanced" individuals of a preceding species occurring in stratigraphic horizons below the oldest Homo erectus at Olduvai.[6] He attempts to show that both of these also belong in Homo, as members of the species "Homo habilis." Naturally, in any time-successive continuum of mammalian species, some of the youngest specimens of one species are similar to the oldest specimens of a succeeding species even though the two species might be classified in different genera. This criterion, however, should not be used to draw older and yet older species into a genus such as Homo, for this genus is based on the extant type-species Homo sapiens. Logically, one could always bring in the next older species by comparing it favorably with what had been previously accepted as the oldest species of a genus. The morphological "space" between genus Homo and genus Australopithecus should, therefore, be considered as falling between the present-day species of Homo and the type specimens of Australopithecus species. Naturally the intermediate forms link individual specimens exhibiting the two generic extremes. This problem does not occur often with living forms because intermediates between species placed today in different genera are usually extinct, and the end-product species in given generic radiations cannot or normally do not exchange genetic information. If the implied degree of

[6]The so-called Chellean skull from the top of Bed II, Olduvai Gorge, Tanzania, is generally accepted as Homo erectus (see Howells, 1966).

genetic difference between samples of modern Homo sapiens and the hypodigm of Australopithecus africanus (from Taung, Sterkfontein, and Makapansgat, South Africa) is as great as that which separates two species of related genera today, then there is reason for keeping Australopithecus and Homo separate.

The problem raised by Leakey (1966) includes more than his differing from the usual approach to taxonomy discussed above. His argument in support of continued retention of the supposed species "habilis" in Homo is unfortunately specious. In his extensively illustrated article (Leakey, 1966) he does not figure or mention any of the characters or attributes of the holotype specimen, the mandible of "Homo habilis" from Olduvai Bed I. However, the paratypes from Bed II are not actually the basis on which the concept "Homo habilis" rests, for they are only part of the hypodigm which has been and may continue to be referred by some to "Homo habilis." Tobias and von Koenigswald (1964) showed that some of the hominid material found in Bed II is similar to Home erectus. These materials from Bed II may well be referred to Homo erectus and not to the same taxon as the type mandible of "Homo habilis" from Bed I. What "Homo habilis" is, even if it were anything different from Australopithecus africanus, must rest upon the characteristics of the type mandible and referred specimens (parietals, foot, etc.) from the same site or stratigraphically related sites in Bed I and not upon referred materials from Bed II. The latter may be a million years younger than the tool makers of Bed I and could well belong to a different species, as Robinson (1965) and Pilbeam and Simons (1965) have pointed out. The specimens from Bed II are the only specimens of "Homo habilis" mentioned by Leakey (1966). They do resemble other members of Homo, particularly Homo erectus, and they are probably closer in time to Homo erectus found in Java than they are to the type jaw from Bed I. The dental morphology of the Olduvai Bed II hominid materials is more similar to that of H. erectus than to the type mandible of "Homo habilis" from Bed I. Tobias and von Koenigswald (1964) clearly illustrated this point. The unmistakable action implied, although not actually taken, by them, is to refer many if not all of the paratypes from Bed II to *Homo erectus*. Howells (1967) has done this recently.

Inasmuch as there is no justification on morphological grounds for placing *Australopithecus africanus* in *Homo* we can avoid another serious problem. Should one follow Robinson (1967) and place *Australopithecus robustus* in a separate genus *Paranthropus*, no type-species for the genus *Australopithecus* remains, and the term would have to be dropped as a binomen. It seems far more advisable to me to fix terminology in agreement with the great majority of authors (Leakey, 1963; Campbell, 1965; Tobias, 1967; Clark, 1959, 1962, 1966 and elsewhere; Simons and Pilbeam, 1965), i.e., there is but one genus, *Australopithecus*. I do not generally support consensus thinking in taxonomy, but, since these authors all agree on this point when some of them agree about little else, this does seem an acceptable synonomy. If *Paranthropus* is to stand as a valid genus, it will have to be justified by the demonstration that the postcranial skeleton is reasonably different from species of *Australopithecus* and *Homo*. Napier (1964) suggested that marked postcranial distinctions exist, as did Patterson (1965). But in my opinion sufficient proof of marked postcranial distinctions in *Australopithecus robustus* has not so far been published. The relevant specimens, postcranial bones of *Australopithecus robustus*, are extremely rare. What little there is has not been fully described. Essentially nothing is known about the limits of variation in the postcranial anatomy of *Australopithecus robustus*. The dental and cranial anatomy of *Australopithecus africanus* and *A. robustus* do not, in fact, provide grounds for separating them at the generic level. The differences in overall cranial morphology of the skulls (see Tobias, 1967, Figure 21) are no greater than the differences found between skulls of male and female gorillas.

THE CONCEPT OF MORPHOLOGIC SPACE

For some years paleontologists have been advocating an arbitrary solution to the problem of dividing phyletic continua. Although not all paleontologists are able to agree on the best methods, anthropologists

should not lose sight of the fact that discussion of the problem continues and much thought has gone into the "species problem" as it applies to fossils. Apart from the works of Mayr (1957), Simpson (1961), and others already cited, comprehensive discussions of the problems raised in dividing lineages taxonomically are included in Sylvester-Bradley (1957) and Weller (1961). More recently these paleontological viewpoints were reviewed by McAlester (1962).

What the modern view about such fossil species comes down to is well stated by McAlester (1962: 1381):

"In summary, then, I regard genetic species definitions to be the most useful and practical for all kinds of life because species originate and are maintained by genetic barriers. . . .
Biologically meaningful limits can be applied to successive species by considering that there is a natural genetic interval for placing species boundaries in an evolutionary continuum.
In both living and fossil organisms the basic genetic factors which limit species can seldom be investigated directly. All systematists are forced to rely heavily on indirect evidence, primarily morphological discontinuities supplemented by distributional, ecological and behavioral data, in recognizing the genetically controlled limits of species in time and space. Students of the systematics of both living and fossil organisms therefore commonly face the same problems and use many of the same kinds of evidence in solving them."

In formulating binomina for extinct organisms one should generally ask: are the character complexes for proposed extinct species and genera at the same level of magnitude as those that separate related, living species and genera of mammals? In other words, is the "morphological space" between time-successive species and genera about the same as that which separates related living species and genera? I believe the most rational approach to classification of vertical or time-successive species and genera evolving through time is to use the same "yardsticks" or measures as are applied to horizontal species, that is, the contemporary end-product species which now exist in what one might call the horizontal time-plane. No new taxon of fossil primates is justified if the variation noted in the supporting description is at the level of intraspecific variation among living primates related to these fossils. Certainly, those who name fossils are convinced that they have found some combination of features sufficiently distinctive at the specific, or even the generic, level to warrant a new taxon. The intent to delimit a new taxon of fossil hominid is almost universally honest and sincere even among extreme splitters. Scholars differ when naming and interpreting fossil forms because they are ignorant of, or unable to agree upon, taxonomic procedures. This in turn is due to inadequate knowledge of the range of intraspecific variation or lack of understanding of the anatomical structure of the particular organisms concerned. Another source of error which plays a role in naming extinct organisms is our limited knowledge of the whole anatomy of fossils. Error can creep in because we misunderstand the shape and orientation of skeletal fragments from once-living organisms. These are the principal sources of confusion in the proper description of extinct species.

Since the time of Linnaeus the best practitioners of mammalian taxonomy recognized that genera bring into association groups of closely related species. Species names are reserved to indicate separate, discrete, and typically non-interbreeding populations. In other words, it is with species that one shows distinctions.

A new hominid genus is not needed unless the type-species of a proposed hominid genus is as different morphologically from any other mammal as a fox is from a dog, a sheep from a goat, a house cat from a cheetah, and so forth. Among hominids such degrees of difference have seldom if ever been proven. In naming a living species one delineates a population of organisms that cannot readily exchange genetic material with any other population and seldom if ever does so in the wild. When we turn to fossils all we can do is try to adopt standards similar to those used in establishing the taxonomic arrangements of living vertebrates. If we are going to classify fossil apes, near-men, and men, we must classify them according to the criteria used among better-understood ex-

tant mammals, such as the modern cats (Felidae), the living apes (Pongidae), or the present-day bears (Ursidae).

One must have up to date knowledge of taxonomy, mammalogy, and an understanding of the various techniques for analyzing limited fossil evidence, if one is to understand or to practice coining names for and synonymizing fossil mammals. There has been a tendency among some physical anthropologists to attribute controversy in the study of fossil man and fossil apes to the fragmentary nature of the evidence. Some error, of course, does result because the data are scarce and different scientists interpret fragmentary evidence differently. Nevertheless many well-known fossils have become bones of contention primarily because they were never very well studied. Information of major significance can still be found by examining fossils discovered 30 or 40 years ago, for these fossils have never been fully reported in the literature. Clearly, many anthropologists were not prepared to make a thorough investigation of each fossil fragment. More blood could be wrung from these stones than was generally realized. The short canine socket in the upper jaw of *Ramapithecus punjabicus* at Calcutta (see Pilgrim, 1915) is an example which will be discussed below. I repeat again that it is the original fossils in museum collections which provide the data for analysis of the evolution of the higher primates. It is to these specimens and not to incorrect traditions or assertions in the literature of anthropology that the inquiring students in this field should turn.

It is also necessary to study polytypic species of living vertebrates when one wishes to understand hominoid taxa properly (Rensch, 1959; Mayr, 1967). The populations at the extremes of the range of polytypic species are usually most different. The populations at the extremes of the range are joined by a series of intermediate populations so that continuous genetic exchange takes place throughout the whole range from one adjacent population to the next. Polytypic, variable species are now better understood to be such, than used to be the case, and this increased understanding makes the modern taxonomist of mammals even more conservative about splitting up fossil forms. Similarly, extinct species could have varied within even broader morphological limits than do living species. Extinct species were distributed in time as well as space. A series of variant local populations existed, at any one time, in a geographic area, and they lived throughout a time range as well.

When considering what are valid fossil hominoid species, one must understand the morphological range typically contained within single modern mammalian species. Particular attention should be given to intraspecific variation among the closest living relatives of the fossil forms, in this case living apes and men. Such variation within one species is well known to physical anthropologists because all are acquainted with the very great and obvious extremes of form and color variation within populations of modern man. This is just one example of the range of variation in a member species of Hominoidea. Modern human variation demonstrates that this group may typically include highly variable member species. Since the 1920's Schultz, Remane, and others have been producing a corpus of literature that has clearly established how markedly individual apes of one species vary in size and form of teeth, in cranial and, indeed, in all skeletal structures. This point of view is summarized in Schultz (1963) and Remane (1965) and in earlier papers cited therein. It has been well demonstrated in all of the living apes, as well as among the varieties of living man, that dental morphology within species is highly variable. That this was equally true of higher primates in the distant past is demonstrated by the remarkable dental variability seen in the considerable samples of mandibles of *Apidium phiomense* from the African Oligocene recently collected under my direction. Many things about teeth vary, for instance, cuspsize, degree of expression of ridges and grooves, and extent and character of enamel wrinkling. Numerous students have tried to work out the meaning of the complex patterns of wrinkling in teeth of *Dryopithecus* and other hominoids. Patterns of wrinkling have been thought by some, beginning with Schlosser (1887), to have significance for determination of taxonomic affinity and phylogenetic relationship among hominoids. Such patterns of wrinkling, in my opinion, are not particularly meaningful for this purpose. These wrinkles are highly variable among individuals of a given living hominoid species. One could almost say they vary in degree of expression and distribution as wrinkles on prunes. Because of the extreme variation of such structures between individuals, their taxonomic value is low. Nevertheless, highly specific individual patterns occur, a fact best revealed by the detailed concordance in ridges, grooves, and wrinkles in teeth of identical twins. This and related problems are discussed by Kraus and Oka (1967) who have recently summarized some new ideas about hominoid molar wrinkling.

LUMPING AND SPLITTING

We should understand that many, not just a few, basic problems are involved in the naming of extinct organisms. The solution for those who are interested in knowing what are the correct names of fossil species of apes, near-men and men, is not as simple as taking sides with a "lumper" or a "splitter," or perhaps with a fence-straddler. Terms like lumping and splitting have been loosely used and, in my opinion, no longer mean much. Leakey has recently referred to an American school of extreme lumpers of fossil men. He presumably had in mind those who follow Mayr (1950) who suggested as mentioned above that all Pleistocene fossil hominid species be placed in the genus *Homo*.

Nevertheless, since structural differences in bones and teeth of individual mammals can be found in essentially all cases, anyone who can both observe and write is able to draw up a list of slight morphological distinctions that can be said to characterize either a species or a genus. When this is done, the basis for correctly naming extinct species is lost. W. E. Le Gros Clark (1967) in *Man-apes or Ape-men?* discusses lumping and splitting of early relatives of man. This careful analysis documents far more thoroughly than I can here the very great range of within-species morphological variation that is known to characterize mammalian species, particularly hominids. About the taxonomic splitters of Hominidae he comments (p. 9):

"It might be supposed that they expect individuals of the same species to be the equivalent of identical twins!
"Probably nothing has done more to in-

troduce confusion into the story of human evolution than the reckless propensity for inventing new . . . names for fragmentary fossil relics that turn out eventually to belong to genera or species previously known."

SOME EXAMPLES OF TAXONOMIC SPLITTING

Not all the cases of possible synonomy among hominoid species and/or genera present the same kind of problem. I should now like to outline three rather different cases which have recently entered the literature. These cases will serve as examples of the entirely different kinds of taxonomic disagreements which have arisen over certain primate fossils.

Kenyapithecus: a junior synonym for Ramapithecus

"Kenyapithecus" Leakey 1962, from 14-million-year-old deposits near Fort Ternan, Kenya, is not a valid new genus (Simons, 1963). The type specimen of the type-species and the only individual specimen belonging to this supposed new genus does not exhibit any significant structural features different from the material of Ramapithecus punjabicus from North India. The very words of Leakey's diagnosis (1962) of "K. wickeri" describe fully the characteristic features of R. punjabicus from India. Thus no new name was justified in this case. If further collecting were done in East Africa, more parts of these 14-million-year-old primates might be found. These parts might allow one to show a difference at the generic level from the creature we know from Haritalyangar, India. However, on the present evidence one cannot show this kind of difference. Thus, if one follows proper taxonomic usage, no distinct new taxon should have been diagnosed. The East African and Indian Ramapithecus material presently available cannot be shown to differ at any taxonomic level, whether racial, specific, or generic. We would not have this redundant name "Kenyapithecus wickeri" to deal with if proper comparison of other relevant material had been made before taxonomic description of the Fort Ternan discovery. The International Code makes clear that all descriptions of new taxa should show why the binomen or

species being proposed deserves a distinct diagnosis. Specifically, this requires that one examine all relevant known and named type specimens and referred material in order to make sure the new form really represents a new taxon. This is why conditional diagnoses have not been acceptable under the Code since 1960. Moreover, the diagnosis should discuss other possible taxonomic placements of a new find and list the distinctive characters, whether at the specific or generic level, which make such alternative placements inadvisable. Naturally, considerations of travel expense and lack of knowledge of where relevant comparative material is may bring a scientist to the point of just going ahead and naming a species even when he is not sure it is really new. The consequences of such unguarded actions are numerous invalid nomina.

I initially pointed out in 1963 that Kenyapithecus is a junior synonym for Ramapithecus, and I have continued to publish to this effect (Simons, 1964b, 1965, 1966, 1967b, 1968b; Simons and Pilbeam, 1965). No one need have missed the detailed accounts of why this was done. Perhaps at present the name has only nuisance value, but the continued use of this unsubstantiated generic label (Leakey, 1967) does not render much professional service to anthropologists. Naturally, I could be more precise in dealing with this problem if more skeletal material of these animals from Fort Ternan and Haritalyangar had been discovered. In fact, further field work in both sites is of prime importance. Even if we find out a great deal more about skeletal structure of the populations of Ramapithecus represented at these two late Miocene Old World sites, we might only discover that these ancient populations of relatives of man were wonderfully similar in the two regions. It is pointless to say now that they might prove to differ when the known parts show no difference of specific or generic weight. The facts remain, as I have stated elsewhere, that between the Kenyan and Indian Ramapithecus maxillae "greater differences than are to be noted here typically occur among members of a single family social group within nearly all species of present-day hominoids" (Simons, 1963: 886). Consequently, as I recently remarked (Simons, 1968b) about the so-called species "Kenyapithecus wickeri" . . . "it was premature to describe the East African form as a new binomen, for the known parts show no significant distinction from Indian *Ramapithecus.*"

Zinjanthropus equals Paranthropus equals Australopithecus

A different problem of synonymy occurs from considerations that led to the establishment of the genus "*Zinjanthropus*" as distinct from the genus *Paranthropus* (itself usually considered a subgenus of *Australopithecus*). In this case the type specimens of the type-species of the proposed nomina, that is *Australopithecus africanus, Paranthropus robustus,* and "*Zinjanthropus boisei,*" do show differences. In addition, comparison between the type specimens of the three species of *Australopithecus* that have most often been urged as valid is not fully possible since the type of *A. africanus* is a much younger individual than the type of "*Z. boisei.*" In this case scholars have more recently associated a number of parts of adults from Makapansgat and Sterkfontein with the juvenile type from Taung. The type and referred specimens of *A. (P.) robustus* also consist of a series of specimens, many of which are adult, from the Kromdraai and Swartkrans sites. These two sets of material represent in each case the hypodigm or referred material of the two generally accepted South African species. There are several minor differences between the adults of *A. robustus* from South Africa and the skull that Leakey (1959) reported from Bed I Olduvai Gorge, Tanzania. So the contention that they were different genera and species was based on a series of observed differences—unlike the situation with the supposed distinctions of "*Kenyapithecus.*" Nevertheless, Robinson (1960) carefully pointed out that the degree and kinds of differences seen between the robust forms from East and South African localities are not significant at the generic and, perhaps, not at the specific level. He considered that such differences as were seen were largely due to the greater individual robustness of the specimen from Olduvai Bed I and to its relative completeness as a specimen. Figure 1, in which comparative photographs of the actual specimens from the two regions are included, should adequately demonstrate Robinson's point. For

greater convenience in comparison of the entire skull and its presumed myology, the Tanzanian and South African crania have been supplied with mandibles from the same site or region. In fact, the only notable differences to be seen in these two skulls are the crushed vault and the slightly more gracile construction of the skull in the South African individual (Fig. 1B). It has sometimes been presumed that this is a skull of a female, and the East African that of a male. It is easy to see in figure 1 many features of obvious similarity that can be taken to establish generic and probably specific identity. These include the relatively larger or megadont molars and pre-molars, the long, massive ascending ramus of the mandible, the vertically deep maxilla, the heavy cheekbone, the dished-in face and projecting brow ridge above and between the orbits, the low hafting of the cranial vault onto the face—all characteristics of *Australopithecus robustus* initially discerned in the South African material such as SK 48 (Fig. 1B).

The presumed distinctiveness of Proconsul

Other problems that represent a different aspect of "lumping and splitting" are the considerations that led Hopwood to separate *Proconsul* as a genus different from *Dryopithecus.* Hopwood (1933b), in the initial description of *Proconsul* as a distinct genus, wrote of the type-species *Proconsul africanus:* "Indeed, if this species were represented only by the lower jaw, to separate it from *Dryopithecus* would be difficult." In fact, Simons (1964a, 1965) and Simons and Pilbeam (1965) showed that mandibles of the two type-species, *Proconsul africanus* Hopwood (1933a) and *Dryopithecus fontani* Lartet (1856) cannot be separated at the generic level.

Since no maxillae clearly referable to the type-species of the genus *Dryopithecus, D. fontani,* have ever been found in Europe, it was not a correct procedure for Hopwood to allow the generic distinctions of *Proconsul* to rest on characters of the upper dentition. Without any known maxillary dentition of *Dryopithecus fontani* and thus with no information about maxillary dentition of the type-species, how could he, or indeed anyone, demonstrate generic difference in upper tooth structure? This oversight allowed Hopwood to fall into further error because he then proceeded to draw the supposed generic distinctions in the upper dentition of *Proconsul africanus* against a partial maxilla from Haritalyangar, North India, Pilgrim (1910, 1915) had referred this latter maxilla to a then new species of *Dryopithecus* which he had named (1910) *Dryopithecus punjabicus*. Pilgrim (1915) stressed his conviction that this, maxilla G.S.I. D-185, should be referred to the species represented by the type mandibular fragments of "*Dryopithecus*" (now *Ramapithecus) punjabicus*. However, he did make his discussion about the reference of the upper jaw conditional, remarking (1915: 19) that the allocation should stand "unless fairly conclusive evidence were forthcoming of a close affinity to another genus, or of the existence of features in the maxilla, which told against an affinity with *Dryopithecus . . .*" In the latter suggestive clause Pilgrim may have had the very small canine socket and expanded molar trigons of this specimen in mind (both then known as features resembling those of *Homo sapiens*), but he failed to be more specific about what features might tell 'against an affinity with *Dryopithecus.*' Of course, he must also have been aware that there was no known upper dentition undoubtedly belonging to *Dryopithecus*. Moreover, Pilgrim (1915) clearly did not understand the dental anatomy of the type-species of *Dryopithecus, D. fontani* (see Simons, 1968c). It is no wonder then that this upper jaw subsequently proved not to belong with *Dryopithecus*. In 1962, in Calcutta, I determined that the paratype maxilla of *D. punjabicus* is actually of *Ramapithecus*, not *Dryopithecus* (Simons, 1963, 1965). Consequently, when Hopwood in 1933b undertook the detailed description of the supposed new genus *Proconsul*, what he actually did in dwelling almost entirely on the Haritalyangar maxilla of *Ramapithecus* (as typical of *Dryopithecus*) was to discuss and to explain the generic differences that do exist between *Ramapithecus* and an African species of *Dryopithecus*. These materials, of course, do belong to different genera, one being a pongid and the other a hominid.

The question of whether the East African form was generically different from the type-species *D. fontani* was hardly dealt with by Hopwood other than to imply, in the above quoted remark, that in the parts actually comparable it would be difficult to show generic difference. This situation was not modified by further anatomical and taxonomic observations published on *Proconsul* by Clark and Leakey (1950, 1951). They in fact remarked (1951: 107):

"The distinctive features of the dentition of Proconsul are to be found in the maxillary rather than the mandibular teeth, and the main characteristic of the former is undoubtedly the strong development in the molars of the internal cingulum. . . ."

Simons and Pilbeam (1965: 105–111) discuss all the reported characters of genus *Proconsul*. After comparison of lower jaws it is clear that none of the reportedly unique mandibular features of *Proconsul* actually constitute anything distinct from features seen in the type mandible of *Dryopithecus fontani* from St. Gaudens, France, or in the other two relatively complete mandibles from the type locality. Moreover, a few upper molars that have sometimes been referred to *D. fontani* are known from Europe. These all show the reasonably tightly clustered trigon cusp and the broad upward and outward slope of the internal and external upper molar faces. They also show the large hypocones with development of lingual upper molar cingulum varying from present to absent. All of these features also exist in the East African and Indian species of *Dryopithecus*. Simons and Pilbeam (1965: 111) state in concluding the discussion of the supposed generic distinctions of *Proconsul*:

". . . none of the characters ever listed as distinguishing Proconsul africanus [type species] from Dryopithecus fontani [type species of the genus] demonstrates the existence of a separate genus Proconsul, a statement with which Le Gros Clark is now in agreement (personal communication, 1964)."

These authors, with this statement, thereby rendered *Proconsul* a junior subjective synonym of *Dryopithecus*. Consequently, the term should not be used to indicate a valid taxon at the generic level, unless in connection with presentation of new evidence about *D. fontani* or "*Proconsul*" *africanus* which might conceivably allow reinstatement of *Proconsul* as a valid genus.

This is the kind of problem which, in part, cannot be resolved because no upper jaw of *Dryopithecus fontani* has ever been found at the type locality in France. People can argue all they wish, because all they have to do is to say, "If we found the upper jaws of *D. fontani* we would discover them to be unlike the upper jaws of *Proconsul africanus*." If one wanted to argue in such an unscientific way perhaps one could defend the genus, but without being able to substantiate it with actual evidence.

NEW KNOWLEDGE OF EARLY DENTAL PATTERNS AMONG HIGHER PRIMATES[7]

Now I would like to present some evidence on the newer finds pertinent to understanding origins of higher primates. Figure 2 shows a newly recovered juvenile pongid jaw from the Egyptian Fayum beds of Oligocene age. This specimen is a juvenile with permanent canine, premolars, and M_2 unerupted. It should provide further information on the phyletic affinities of the earliest apes. A triangular symphyseal cross-section exists in at least this one Oligocene ape. This feature is reminiscent of the symphyseal cross-section of some members of subgenus *Proconsul*. It is a primitive feature of the symphyseal region of higher primates. Nevertheless, the outline of symphyseal cross-section varies greatly in individual Hominoidea, and it is highly dubious as a useful character in classification of higher primates. We also see among Oligocene apes symphyseal cross-

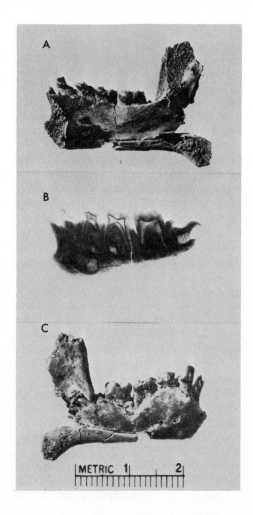

Figure 2. Right mandibular ramus (Y.P.M. 23804), as yet undescribed, of a juvenile pongid from Yale Quarry I, upper level, Jebel el Qatrani Formation, Oligocene, Egypt, U.A.R.

[7]Speaking of the relevance of correct taxonomy and of the importance of direct study of dental and skeletal anatomy among fossil apes, I should like to interject a personal experience. As a curator of fossil ape specimens, I am surprised by the lack of interest among anthropologists in study of the actual fossils. I can report that McKenna of the American Museum and I, who together curate most of the fossil ape specimens in the New World, have compared notes and discovered that only six American physical anthropologists had actually asked to study any of these fossils during the last eight years. Perhaps curators have been remiss in the past in not urging more strongly that scientists study these actualities. It is, however, a part of the business of curators to show visiting scientists such materials, and answer questions about them. The Egyptian fossils illustrated here in figures 2, 3, 4 and 5 are some of the important new material now available.

sections of more conventional type—with a simian shelf. We see the same range in modern gorillas—most gorillas have a simian shelf, a geniohyal pit above this, and a superior transverse torus above that. But some gorillas do not have a posteriorly directed simian shelf; some are more like the juvenile pongid jaw shown in Figure 2. Such variation is also typical of *Dryopithecus*. The symphyseal cross-sections of apes have varied enormously within species for the past 30 million years of evolutionary history. The variation ranges from complete absence of the simian shelf to its presence, and the cross-sections vary in other proportions and outlines as well. Evidently a triangular symphyseal cross-section is the condition more common among primitive Hominoidea. Consequently it is typical of some of the early Miocene apes of East Africa and few apes thereafter. This consideration is important because a number of scholars have said that, since this triangular symphyseal cross-section and some other primitive features are seldom present in modern apes but common in *Proconsul*, members of the *Proconsul* group could not have anything to do with the ancestry of the living African apes. This type of logic might cause a man to reject his own relationship to his great-grandfather. Naturally, ancestral forms will differ from their descendants in various ways. We must be prepared to expect that some of these primitive differences when found out will be surprising or unforeseen, since many of the broadest aspects of the main course of hominoid evolution are unknown. The variation in morphology of the simian shelf is presumably due to an increasingly sophisticated construction of the symphysis brought about through millions of years of selection for a different type of buttress of which the backward projecting, ventrally located simian shelf of present day apes is an example. Other structural variants which similarly buttress the front of the lower jaws are a greatly thickened symphysis in the region of the superior transverse torus or a slight thickening in the inferior portion of the symphysis (some *Gorilla*, some *Dryopithecus*).

Another recent find from Yale Quarry I in the Fayum are parts of about a dozen mandibles of a new species of *Parapithecus* (Fig. 3). The new species is not very different from the type-species, *Parapithecus fraasi*, but in most dimensions is 15 to 20% larger. It is also probably several million years younger. There are three major faunal horizons in the Fayum and the type-species probably came from much lower strata than those at Quarry I.

These new finds of *Parapithecus* suggest that it is considerably more like an Old World monkey in dental characteristics than are other Oligocene primates. The resemblance is particularly close to the modern talapoin monkeys, *Cercopithecus talapoin* (Fig. 3). In the fossil on the right the two anterior teeth are deciduous, and only the permanent M_1 and M_2 have erupted. These molars in this particular specimen are important, for the

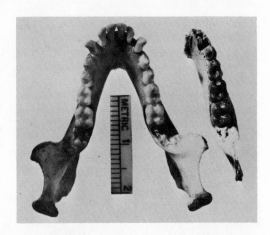

Figure 3. Right mandibular ramus of *Parapithecus* sp. nov. (Y.P.M. 23796), from Yale Quarry I, compared with complete mandibular dentition of a subadult Recent African talapoin monkey (Y.P.M.O.C. 913).

tooth crowns show no wear. The teeth of *Parapithecus* tend to wear off flat, and in old individuals cusp patterns are hard to discern.

The precise relationships of some of the Fayum primates are still somewhat in doubt. In order to gain more certainty about affinities with later forms, the material we now have must be exhaustively compared with later and modern Anthropoidea, a project currently underway at Yale. It is safe to say that preliminary work suggests that some of these creatures (*Apidium* and *Parapithecus* species) may be related to the Old World monkeys. Affinities with monkeys have been urged before for certain Fayum primates, but material found before 1960 provided very limited evidence and this was often misinterpreted. Comments as to the "monkey-ness" of forms like *Moeripithecus markgrafi* were more fashion than fact. The type-species of *Moeripithecus*, actually, has proved to be assignable to *Propliopithecus* (Simons, 1968a), which is not even a monkey but an ape.

A specimen of one of the newly discovered Fayum primate species *Aegyptopithecus zeuxis* is shown in Figure 4. Something characteristic of the Miocene/Pliocene apes and, for example, modern gorilla is that lower molar size usually increases posteriorly—notice that by far the largest tooth in *A. zeuxis* is M_3. This type of molar construction is extraordinarily like that seen in members of the subgenus *Proconsul*. I think we can be

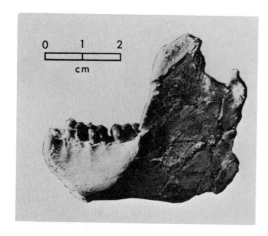

Figure 4. Lateral view of the mandible of *Aegyptopithecus zeuxis*, from Yale Quarry I (Y.P.M. 21032).

fairly certain that *Aegyptopithecus* is the forerunner of the subunit of *Dryopithecus* that we provisionally call *Proconsul*. Some of the broad dental similarities in upper teeth between specimens of *Aegyptopithecus* and *Proconsul* are shown in Figure 5. All but the lateral incisor (Fig. 5A) seem definitely to be of *Aegyptopithecus*. The lateral incisor may be of *Aegyptopithecus*, but could be a central incisor of *Apidium*. Since this drawing was prepared, associated upper teeth of this animal have been found. The important thing to notice here is the extent of the lingual or internal upper molar cingulum or shelf and the relatively small and compact trigon. In many specimens the cingulum runs across the hypocone which perhaps indicates that the hypocone was a much earlier derivative of the cingulum in this group of primates. This heavy shelf-like structure seen in *Aegyptopithecus* is also characteristic of East African *Dryopithecus*. The heavy cingulum in the upper molars is characteristic of late Oligocene and early Miocene apes, but its degree of expression varies considerably in individual teeth.

The teeth and face of *Dryopithecus* (Fig. 7B) from the early Miocene of East Africa show quite clearly all of the features that are important in determining whether an animal is an ape or not. Such a determination, of necessity, must be made from the dental-facial region because virtually all the fossils are from that part of the skeleton only. Most of the features that we find in the jaws of apes and we do not see in hominids are, of course, well known: canines that are large relative to the size of the other teeth; the antero-lateral extension of the anterior premolar; the elongation or sectorality of the anterior lower premolar; the relatively large size of incisors; and the molar increase in size posteriorly (particularly characteristic of Tertiary apes). Figure 7B shows the pronounced anterior extension of the anterior upper premolar, a typical feature of P_3 in apes. In the molars of *Dryopithecus* the primitive mammalian trigon cusps are closely placed and cover a small area of the crown compared to the area of the crown at the base of the enamel. Such constriction is not typical of the upper molars of Hominidae. Indeed, in many living apes the trigon is expanded relatively more. Moreover, this is a feature that is profoundly affected by abrasive wear of the teeth. As the trigon cusps wear down, an increase in the worn surface area of the teeth takes place. This can easily be mistaken for the more widely spaced unworn trigon cusps of typical individuals of *Homo*, *Australopithecus*, and *Ramapithecus*. Usually in newly erupted and unworn upper molars in individuals of *Gorilla* and *Pan* the constricted "ape" type of trigon can be seen, but molar trigons in these modern African apes are sometimes expanded more than is typical of Miocene apes.

Another primitive feature among apes is the lingual cingulum in the upper molars. From the later Oligocene, as represented by Fayum finds, up to the present date we find a tendency to an overall decrease in the expression or development of this ridge among Hominoidea, both in the pongid and hominid lines. In most hominoids today we seldom find a groove in this position. In *Gorilla* and some *Pan* a lingual cingulum is often expressed in the upper molars but is usually not as long or as prominent as in Miocene forms. Otherwise, this feature is not usually well-expressed in molars of Pliocene-Recent Hominoidea. The manner of expression of these cingula is not bilaterally symmetrical in many individual apes. This is often the case in both fossil and modern apes. Such variability of a feature within one individual shows why degree of development of the cingulum is not a good taxonomic character. Features whose expression varies from side to side (bilaterally) among individual Hominoidea are not good criteria

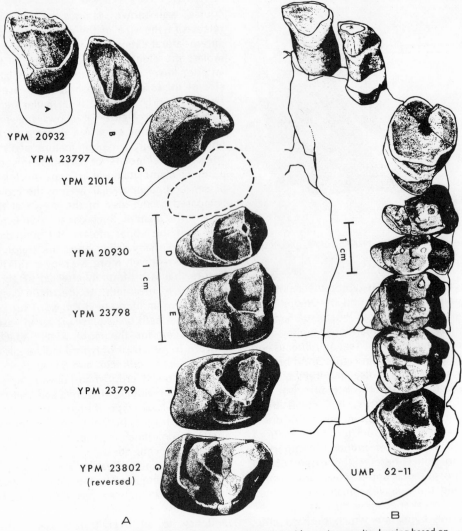

YPM 20932

YPM 23797

YPM 21014

YPM 20930

YPM 23798

YPM 23799

YPM 23802
(reversed)

UMP 62-11

A

B

Figure 5. Upper molar series of A, an Oligocene ape *Aegyptopithecus* (composite drawing based on isolated teeth found in Yale Quarries G and I) and B, *Dryopithecus major* from the Miocene of Moroto, Uganda. See text for details.

for the establishment of species or genera of fossils.

HOW HOMINIDAE AND PONGIDAE DIFFER

When one looks at an X-ray of human teeth (Fig. 6A) one can see that the angle of eruption of the canine is 80 to 85° from the horizontal axis of the tooth row, and the root does not overlap the roots of the adjacent premolars. The question of root size and placement is important in studying fossil fragments. What is underneath the surface of the bone is, taxonomically, just as important as the cusps of the teeth.

In a juvenile ape, *Pongo pygmaeus* (Fig.

6B), one can see in the X-ray the enormous crown and root of the unerupted permanent canine. This structure is not showing on the surface of this specimen at all. In an old individual of *Pan troglodytes* (Fig. 6C) the large canine root curves back over the roots of the premolars. This curvature is never as great in hominid canine roots.

Many fossils are broken off at odd angles and these specimens reveal things about internal structures which anatomists, habituated to the study of whole skeletons, are not used to seeing. One can often find evidence in a fossil fragment of a large canine root. This evidence is as good proof of the animal's having been ape-like in canine

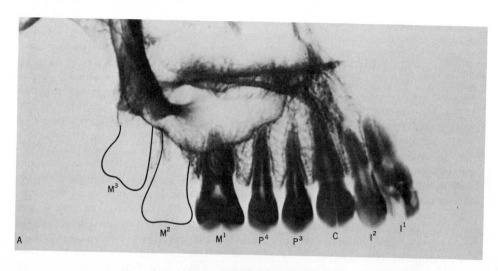

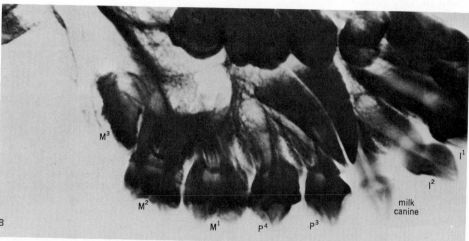

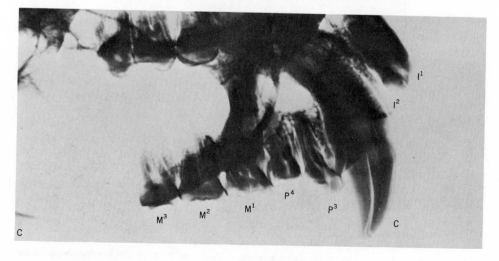

Figure 6. Positive prints of X-ray films of the anterior upper tooth row in A, *Homo sapiens* (Y.P.M.O.C. 2353); B, *Pongo pygmaeus* (Y.P.M.O.C. 2547); and C, *Pan troglodytes* (Y.P.M.O.C. 2704).

formation as if the large canine crown were still projecting from the fossil jaw fragment concerned. This is the case, for instance, in the type specimen of "Kenyapithecus africanus," recently proposed by Leakey as a hominid.

The paratype maxilla which Pilgrim (1915) referred to *Dryopithecus punjabicus* Pilgrim 1910 is another case in point. From the same site in India (Haritalyangar) Lewis (1934) named another similar find *Ramapithecus brevirostris*. Now we call the species *Ramapithecus punjabicus* because the species name was preoccupied by Pilgrim (1910) but the generic name was not. The anterior part of the premolar of *R. punjabicus* is not particularly elongated. Naturally, since these might well be very primitive relatives of man, the degree of expression of this feature is

important. It is clear from Figure 7A that the antero-lateral enlargement of the external face of P$_3$, characteristic of apes, is not present. This enlargement does not appear in Pleistocene and Recent hominids. Although the specimen was found before 1915, nobody reported in print that this Calcutta facial fragment of *Ramapithecus* preserves enough of the canine alveolus to show the full length of the root. From this one can tell how large and long the root was and at what angle the tooth was implanted. This fact was first mentioned in Simons (1963).

In Figure 7A the close-up of the external face of the Yale facial fragment of *Ramapithecus* shows sub-equal sized premolars. The canine socket has been cleaned out and X-rayed so that the size and direction of placement of the root is known. Its size and

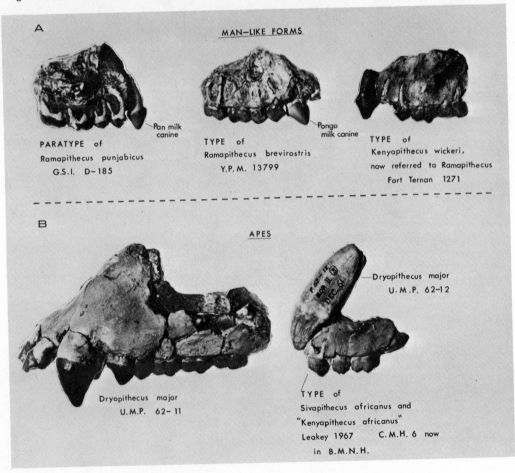

Figure 7. Comparison of maxillary fragments. A, three man-like fragments of Miocene age; B, two fragments of apes from the Miocene of Africa. "*Kenyapithecus africanus*" has recently been mistakenly called a hominid.

angle of placement are not like those of an ape but just as in hominids.

A comparison of the dentitions of *Ramapithecus* from Haritalyangar and Fort Ternan (Fig. 8) is instructive, for it shows that each exhibits the expanded trigon more character-

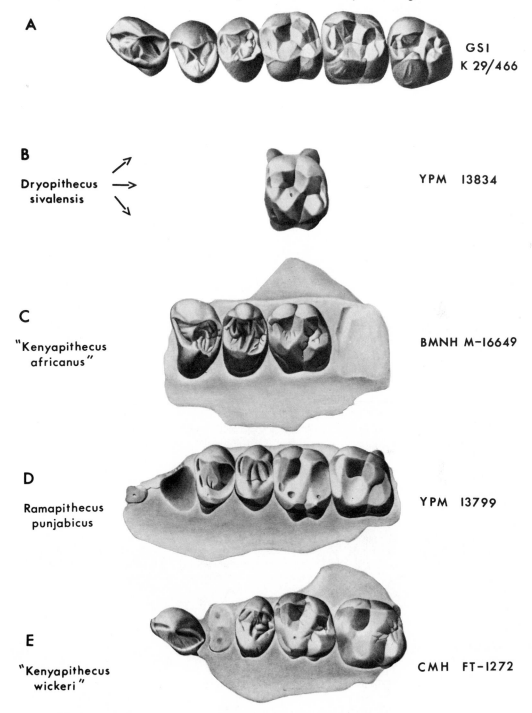

A
GSI K 29/466

B
Dryopithecus sivalensis
YPM 13834

C
"Kenyapithecus africanus"
BMNH M-16649

D
Ramapithecus punjabicus
YPM 13799

E
"Kenyapithecus wickeri"
CMH FT-1272

Figure 8. Upper dentitions of *Dryopithecus* and *Ramapithecus*. Drawings based either on originals at Yale or on sharp casts checked by published photographs (Cut E, C.M.H. FT-107, *erratum* for FT-1271).

istic of Hominidae than of early apes. These detailed drawings are based either on originals at Yale or on sharp casts checked by photographs. I have personally examined all originals. It is important to stress that the lingual faces of the upper molars of *Ramapithecus* are unlike the apes discussed above as they show a steeply rising, almost vertical internal face rather than a gentle upward curvature. Moreover, unlike most early apes there is no trace of a cingulum. Consequently this feature is already lost or rare in some lines by about 14 million years ago. The external cusp in the anterior upper premolar is somewhat larger than that in the posterior premolar. In this *Ramapithecus* is intermediate between most Pleistocene-Recent hominids and most apes. The Calcutta and Yale facial fragments of *Ramapithecus* also resemble man in their extremely small canine sockets. The upper dentitions from both the Haritalyangar and the Fort Ternan *Ramapithecus* show exactly the same things—the broad trigon, flat teeth with no lingual cingulum, and a canine comparatively smaller than in any ape. Crown shape and angle of placement are more or less intermediate between an ape canine and a human canine. The size of the upper canine or of the tooth sockets of *Ramapithecus* are within the range for *Homo sapiens*. In other words, milk canines of female apes are usually too large to fit the canine sockets of *Ramapithecus*, even though the permanent cheek-teeth of *Ramapithecus* are equivalent in size to those of female chimpanzees and orangutans. These numerous similarities confirm the view that the Fort Ternan find is really another *Ramapithecus* from East Africa and not a new or different genus, "*Kenyapithecus*," as Leakey named it before he had made any direct comparison with similar finds housed in New Haven and Calcutta.

One might fairly question whether one genus and species of advanced hominoid primate might have had a geographic range stretching between the two continents concerned, but vertebrate paleontologists know that during much of the Miocene a very great degree of similarity existed between the mammalian land faunas of India and Africa (Simons, 1963). This similarity requires some kind of broad corridor for faunal exchange or migration between the two regions. There is unpublished evidence that during the Miocene several higher primate genera and species other than *Ramapithecus* had ranges which crossed between Eurasia and Africa.

RECENT PRIMATE SYNONOMIES

Finally I wish to stress again that, since the process of naming new species and genera of fossil primates is now so complex and the implications of naming so important, only the most competent taxonomists should attempt it. Those who do not learn the principles involved are likely to embarrass themselves by being the promulgators of error. In conclusion I shall survey briefly

Table 1

SOME SYNONOMIES AMONG RECENTLY PROPOSED HIGHER PRIMATE TAXA

A. Recently proposed Linnaean binomina that do not constitute valid names for hominid taxa		B. Binomina that could be used if the type specimens of the names in column A could be convincingly shown to differ at the species level from the types and hypodigm material of the taxa in column C	C. Binomina with types and hypodigm from which the taxa in column A have not convincingly been distinguished at present at the generic or the specific level	
Ankarapithecus meteai	1957	Dryopithecus meteai	Dryopithecus indicus	(1910)
Zinjanthropus boisei	1959	Australopithecus boisei	Australopithecus robustus	(1938)
Sivapithecus aiyengari	1962	Dryopithecus aiyengari	Dryopithecus indicus	(1910)
Kenyapithecus wickeri	1962	Ramapithecus wickeri	Ramapithecus punjabicus	(1910)
Homo habilis	1964	Australopithecus habilis	Australopithecus africanus	1925
Tchadanthropus uxoris	1965	Indeterminate	Indeterminate	
Kenyapithecus africanus (new combination)	1967	Dryopithecus major, nyanzae or sp. nov.	Dryopithecus sivalensis	(1879)

some of the erroneous taxa that have been proposed in the last ten years in addition to those already dealt with in order to emphasize that the process of proposing invalid names has continued unabated during recent years. These synonymies are listed in Table 1.

"*Sivapithecus aiyengari*" Prasad 1962 was described recently, but it is only different from other Indian specimens of *Dryopithecus indicus* in that it is quite an old

individual from which the canine had been lost and the alveolus filled with cancellous bone. Another recent invalid genus and species of fossil ape is "*Ankarapithecus meteai*" Ozansoy (1957). In Figure 9A and B one can see the types of these two invalid species compared with other specimens from India. All of these belong to one of the related species *Dryopithecus indicus* and *D. sivalensis*. With the exception of the find of "*Ankarapithecus*" near Ankara, Turkey, all of

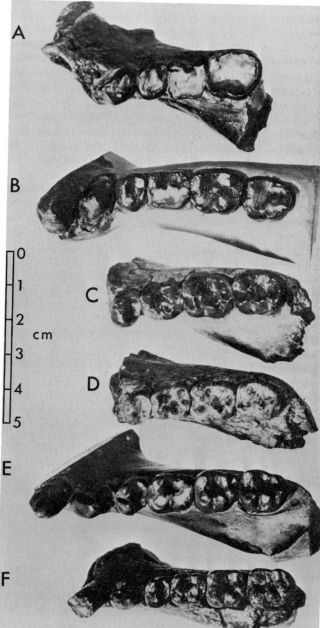

Figure 9. Comparison of mandibular dentition of *Dryopithecus* and *Gorilla*. A, type specimen of "*Sivapithecus aiyengari*" (G.S.I. 16919); B, type specimen of "*Ankarapithecus meteai*"; C, a referred specimen of *Dryopithecus indicus* (Y.P.M. 13828); D, type specimen of *Dryopithecus* "*frickae*" (A.M.N.H. 19413); E, female lowland gorilla (cast of Y.P.M.O.C. 2546); F, type specimen of *Dryopithecus* "*cautleyi*" (A.M.N.H. 19412). The cast of E has been colored to resemble a fossil.

these specimens come from the same geographic region of North India, and all lived at nearly the same time period, during the process of deposition of the Chinji and Nagri Formations in the Siwalik Hills and Salt Range of North India. There is no more variation among these mandibles than one would find in the same parts of a small sample of any of the living great apes; the jaw in figure 9E happens to be cast from a mandible of a female lowland gorilla. The cast has been colored to resemble a fossil in order to heighten comparability between this Recent and these Mio-Pliocene ape mandibles, all of which are very similar.

Another case in point is the recent naming of "Tchadanthropus uxoris," Coppens (1965). The type of this binomen is an indeterminate frontal fragment so permineralized and wind-worn that internal cancellous bone has been exposed over much of its surface. This fragment is quite indeterminate and could be anything from *Australopithecus africanus* to *Homo sapiens*. It is preposterous to indicate, by giving it a Linnaean binomen, that it represents a population distinct on both the specific and generic level from any other hominid population. There is not one unusual feature of distinction in this facial fragment to lend credence to such a procedure. What the proper nature of a type specimen should be is certainly no secret. Almost 70 years ago Marsh (1898: 401, 402) remarked:

"The value of a type depends first of all upon whether it is a characteristic specimen, worthy of being the representative of a new group of individuals. Without this distinctive quality, its importance is greatly diminished. . . .

"Type specimens that do not show characteristic features are, of course, of little value to science, and many such prove a delusion and a snare to the investigator, however faithfully he may endeavor to study them. The imperfect types require still more labor to decipher them. Not a few specimens today are types, for the simple reason that they are imperfect. If they had been entire when described, their true nature would have been recognized, and much confusion in nomenclature have been avoided."

Advice of the sort Marsh had to give on choosing type specimens has long been available in the literature. There is now really no excuse for propounding binomina such as "Tchadanthropus uxoris." Inasmuch as the other cases summarized in Table 1 have already been discussed it is only necessary, in conclusion, to turn to this table as an example of what has been and what should be done in the recent taxonomy of higher primates.

ACKNOWLEDGMENTS

The research reported here was supported in part by grants from the Boise Fund, Oxford University; the Wenner-Gren Foundation New York; N.S.F. grants GP-3547 and GA-723; and Smithsonian Foreign Currency grants 5 and 23.

Acknowledgments for figures: Figure 1A composite (reversed) from Leakey and Leakey 1964 and from Tobias 1967; 1B courtesy A. W. Crompton; photographs for Figures 2, 3, 6, 7, 10, J. Howard; layout for figures Miss M. W. Whittington and Mrs. V. A. McGinnis; drawings, Fig. 5, E. F. Koerlin, Fig. 8, C. R. Wester.

LITERATURE CITED

Broom, R. 1918 The evidence afforded by the Boskop skull of a new species of primitive man (*Homo capensis*). Anthrop. Pap. Amer. Mus. Nat. Hist., 23: 63–79.

——. 1938 The Pleistocene anthropoid apes of South Africa. Nature, 142: 377–379.

Campbell, B.G. 1964a Science and Human evolution. Nature, 203: 448–451.

——. 1964b Just another 'man-ape'? Discovery, 25 (6): 37–38.

——. 1966 Human Evolution. Aldine, Chicago.

Clark, W. E. LeGros 1959 The Antecedents of Man. Edinburgh Univ. Press, Edinburgh.

——. 1964a The Fossil Evidence for Human Evolution (Second edition). Univ. of Chicago Press, Chicago.

——. 1964b The evolution of man. Discovery, London, 25: 49.

——. 1967 Man-Apes or Ape-Men? The Story of Discoveries in Africa. Holt Rinehart and Winston, New York.

Clark, W. E. LeGros, and L. S. B. Leakey 1950 Diagnoses of East African Miocene Hominoidea. Quart. J. geol. Soc. Lond., 105: 260–262.

——. 1951 The Miocene Hominoidea of East Africa. Fossil Mammals of Africa, No. 1. Brit. Mus. (N.H.) London: 1–117.

Coppens, Y. 1965 L'hominien du Tchad. C. R. Acad. Sci., *260*: 2869–2871.

Dobzhansky, T. 1962 Mankind Evolving. Yale Univ. Press, New Haven.

Hopwood, A. T. 1933a Miocene primates from British East Africa. Ann. Mag. Nat. Hist. (Ser. 10), *11*: 96–98.

———. 1933b Miocene primates from Kenya. J. Linn. Soc. Lond., Zool., *38* (260): 437–464.

Howells, W. W. 1966 Homo erectus. Sci. Amer., *215* (5): 46–53.

Huxley, J. 1942 Evolution, The Modern Synthesis. George Allen and Unwin, London.

Kraus, B. S., and S. W. Oka 1967 Wrinkling of molar crowns: new evidence. Science, *157*: 328–329.

Lartet, E. 1856 Note sur un grand singe fossile qui se rattache au groupe des singes supérieurs. C. R. Acad. Sci., *43*: 219–223.

Leakey, L. S. B. 1959 A new fossil skull from Olduvai. Nature, *184*: 491–493.

———. 1960 Adam's Ancestors (Fourth edition). Harper and Row, New York.

———. 1962 A new lower Pliocene fossil primate from Kenya. Ann. Mag. Nat. Hist. (Ser. 13), *4*: 689–696.

———. 1963 East African Fossil Hominoidea and the classification within this super-family. In: Classification and Human Evolution, S. L. Washburn (ed.), Aldine, Chicago.

———. 1966 Homo habilis, Homo erectus and the australopithecines. Nature, *209*: 1279–1281.

———. 1967 An early Miocene member of Hominidae. Nature, *213*: 155–163.

Leakey, L. S. B., and M. D. Leakey 1964 Recent discoveries of fossil hominids in Tanganyika: at Olduvai and near lake Natron. Nature, *202*: 5–7.

Leakey, L. S. B., P. V. Tobias and J. R. Napier 1964 A new species of the genus Homo from Olduvai Gorge. Nature, *202*: 7–9.

Lewis, G. E. 1934 Preliminary notice of new man-like apes from India. Amer. J. Sci., *27*: 161–179.

Linnaeus, C. 1758 Systema naturae per regna tria naturae secundum classes, ordines genera, species cum characteribus differentris, synonymis, locis. Editis decima, reformata. Stockholm, Laurentii Salvii, *1*: 1–824.

Marsh, O. C. 1898 The value of type specimens and importance of their preservation. Amer. J. Sci. (Ser. 4), *6*: 401–405.

Mayr, E. 1942 Systematics and the Origin of Species. Columbia Univ. Press, New York.

———. 1950 Taxonomic categories in fossil hominids. Cold Spring Harbor Symp. Quant. Biol., *15*: 109–118.

———. 1963 Animal Species and Evolution. Harvard Univ. Press, Cambridge.

McAlester, A. L. 1962 Some comments on the species problem. J. Paleont, *36*: 1377–1381.

Napier, J. R. 1964 The evolution of bipedal walking in the hominids. Arch. Biol. Liège, *75* (Suppl.): 673–708.

———. 1967 The antiquity of human walking. Sci. Amer., *216* (4): 56–66.

Ozansoy, F. 1957 Faunes des mammifères du Tertiaire de Turquie et leurs revisions stratigraphiques. Bull. min. Res. Exp. Inst. Turkey, *49*: 29–48.

Patterson, B. 1965 [Remarks on hominid evolution]. In: The Origin of Man (Transcript of a symposium), P. L. DeVore (ed.), Wenner-Gren Foundation, New York.

Pilbeam, D. R., and E. L. Simons 1965 Some problems of hominid classification. Amer. Sci., *53*: 237–259.

Pilgrim, G. E. 1910 Notices of new mammalian genera and species from the Tertiaries. Rec. Geol. Surv. India, *40* (1): 63–71.

———. 1915 New Siwalik primates and their bearing on the questions of evolution of man and the Anthropoidea. Rec. Geol. Surv. India, *45* (1): 1–74.

———. 1927 A *Sivapithecus* palate and other primate fossils from India. Palaeont. Ind. (N.S.), *14*: 1–24.

Prasad, K. N. 1962 Fossil primates from the Siwalik beds near Haritalyangar, Himachal Pradesh, India. J. Soc. Ind., *3*: 86–96.

Remane, A. 1965 Die geschichte der Menschenaffen. In: Menschliche Abstammungslehre: Fortschritte der Anthropogenie 1863–1964, G. Heberer (ed.), Fischer Verlag, Stuttgart.

Rensch, B. 1959 Evolution above the Species Level (English translation). Columbia Univ. Press, New York.

Robinson, J. T. 1960 The affinities of the new Olduvai australopithecine. Nature, *186*: 456–458.

———. 1965 Homo 'habilis' and the australopithecines. Nature, *205*: 121–124.

———. 1966 Comments on the distinctiveness of Homo habilis. Nature, *209*: 957–960.

———. 1967 Variation and the taxonomy of the early hominids. In: Evolutionary Biology, vol. I, T. Dobzhansky, M. K. Hecht, W. C. Steere (ed.), Appleton-Century-Crofts, New York.

Schenk, E. T., and J. H. McMasters 1959 Procedure in Taxonomy (Third edition, revised). Stanford Univ. Press, Palo Alto.

Schlosser, M. 1887 Die Affen, Lemuren, Chiropteren usw. des europaischen Tertiärs. Beitr. Palaont. Geol. Öst.-Ung., *6*: 1–162.

Schultz, A. H. 1963 Age changes, sex differences, and variability as factors in the classification of primates. In: Classification and Human Evolution, S. L. Washburn (ed.), Aldine, Chicago.

Simons, E. L. 1961 The phyletic position of *Ramapithecus*. Postilla, *57*: 1–9.

———. 1963 Some fallacies in the study of hominid phylogeny. Science, *141:* 879–889.

———. 1964a. The early relatives of man. Sci. Amer., *211:* 51–62.

———. 1964b On the mandible of *Ramapithecus*. Proc. Nat. Acad. Sci., *51:* 528–535.

———. 1965 The hunt for Darwin's third ape. Med. Opin. and Review, *1* (11): 74–81.

———. 1967a Unraveling the age of earth and man. Nat. Hist., Feb.: 53–59.

———. 1967b Fossil primates and the evolution of some primate locomotor systems. Am. J. Phys. Anthrop., *26:* 241–253.

———. 1967c New evidence on the anatomy of earliest catarrhine primates. In: Neue Ergebnisse der Primatologie: Progress in Primatology. July 26–30, 1966, D. Starck, R. Schneider, H.-J. Kuhn (ed.), Fischer Verlag, Stuttgart.

———. 1968a Review of the phyletic interrelationships of Oligocene and Miocene Old World Anthropoidea. In: Evolution des vertébrés. Colloques Internationaux du Centre National de la Recherche Scientific, Paris, June 1966.

———. 1968b On the mandible of *Ramapithecus* [revised text of Simons 1964b] In: Evolution and Hominization (Second edition), G. Kurth (ed.), Fischer Verlag, Stuttgart.

———. 1968c A brief source for dental comparison of *Ramapithecus* with *Australopithecus* and *Homo*. R. A. Dart *Festshrift* volume, ed. P. V. Tobias.

Simons, E. L., and D. R. Pilbeam 1965 Preliminary revision of the Dryopithecinae (Pongidae, Anthropoidea). Folia Primat., *3:* 81–152.

Simpson, G. G. 1940 Types in modern taxonomy. Am. J. Sci., *238:* 413–431.

———. 1961 Principles of Animal Taxonomy. Columbia Univ. Press, New York.

Sylvester-Bradley, P. C. (ed.) 1956 The Species Concept in Paleontology. Systematics Assoc., London, *2:* 1–145.

Tobias, P. V. 1967 Olduvai Gorge, vol II, The cranium of *Australopithecus (Zinjanthropus) boisei.* Cambridge Univ. Press, Cambridge.

Tobias; P. V., and G. H. R. von Koenigswald 1964 A comparison between the Olduvai hominines and those of Java and some implications for hominid phylogeny. Nature, *204:* 515–518.

Weller, J. M. 1961 The species problem. J. Paleont., 35: 1181–1192.

16

THE SEED-EATERS: A NEW MODEL OF HOMINID DIFFERENTIATION BASED ON A BABOON ANALOGY
Clifford J. Jolly

As has been recognized repeatedly in previous articles, man's closest primate relatives are the great apes, the gorilla, and the chimpanzee. For over a century, the question uppermost in the mind of students of human origins was "How did men evolve from apes?" It was assumed that the apes from which men evolved were, if not actual gorillas or chimpanzees, earlier counterparts of the same kind of adaptation. Periodically scholars have stressed the possibility that modern apes have diverged as much from the common man-and-ape ancestor as modern man himself has done (Jones 1929; Straus 1949), but, in spite of this, the general feeling has persisted that man's immediate ancestor was a tropical-forest-dwelling fruit-and-plant-eating primate and that the gorilla and the chimpanzee provide the best models available for our consideration.

Over the last thirty years or so, however, as the evidence for the immediate pre-Homo ancestors—the Australopithecines—has accumulated, it has been increasingly apparent that the earliest hominids were not denizens of the tropical rain forest. Instead, they inhabited the drier savanna and adjacent gallery-forest areas of East and South Africa. Furthermore, in the portion of the skeleton that best reflects the dietary adaptation—the teeth—the earliest hominids differed considerably from the known pongids. Relative to body size, their molar teeth were enormous. In absolute dimensions, molars are as large as gorilla molars, while body size was at most no more than half gorilla size and in some instances evidently only one-quarter as large. Front teeth, however, were as small as those of modern man. Evidently the adaptation was quite different from that of the known apes.

Jolly comes to grips with these issues and others, including the matter of erect posture. While we do not think his "somatic budget effect" is an improvement over the PME as an explanation for the reduction of the size of the incisors and canines, the other aspects of his presentation strike us as the most fruitful yet offered.

Jones, F. Wood. 1929. *Man's Place Among the Mammals.* Longmans, Green and Co., New York. 372 pp.

Straus, W. L., Jr. 1949. The riddle of man's ancestry. *Quarterly Review of Biology* 24:200–223.

Wolpoff, M. H. 1973. Tooth size, body size, and diet in gracile Australopithecines. *American Journal of Physical Anthropology*, in press.

Despite years of theorising, and a rapidly accumulating body of fossil evidence, physical anthropology still lacks a convincing causal model of hominid origins. Diverse lines of evidence point to a later common ancestry with the African pongids than with any other living primate, and studies of hominid fossils of the Basal and Early Lower Pleistocene (Howell 1967) have elucidated the complex of characters which at that time distinguished the family from African and other Pongidae (Le Gros Clark 1964). It is also possible to argue that the elements of the complex form a mutually reinforcing positive feedback system. Bipedalism frees the forelimb to make and use artefacts; regular use of tools and weapons permits (or causes) reduction of the anterior teeth by taking over their functions; the elaboration of material culture and associated learning is correlated with a cerebral reorganisation of which increase in relative cranial capacity is one aspect. Bipedalism is needed to permit

From *Man*, N. S. 5:5–27. (1970). Reprinted with the permission of the author and publisher.

handling of the relatively helpless young through the long period of cultural conditioning, and so on.

Preoccupied with the apparent elegance of the feedback model, we tend to forget that to demonstrate the mutual relationship between the elements is not to account for their origin, and hence does not explain *why* the hominids became differentiated from the pongids, or why this was achieved in the hominid way. From their very circularity, feedback models cannot explain their own beginnings, except by tautology, which is no explanation at all. In fact, the more closely the elements of the hominid complex are shown to interlock, the more difficult it becomes to say what was responsible for setting the feedback spiral in motion, and for accumulating the elements of the cycle in the first place. Most authors seem either to avoid the problem of origins and causes altogether (beyond vague references to "open country" life), or to fall back upon reasoning that tends to be teleological and often also illogical. This article is an attempt to reopen the problem of origins by examining critically some of the existing models of hominid differentiation, and to suggest a new one based on a fresh approach.

PREVIOUS MODELS OF HOMINID DIFFERENTIATION

Direct fossil evidence for the use of 'raw' tools or weapons is necessarily tenuous, and that for the use of fabricated stone artefacts appears relatively late (Howell 1967). Nevertheless, as Holloway has pointed out (1967), the currently orthodox theory regards these elements as pivotal in the evolution of the hominid adaptive complex, probably antedating and determining the evolution of upright posture, and certainly in some way determining the reduction of the anterior teeth, the loss of sexual dimorphism in the canines, and the expansion of the cerebral cortex (Bartholomew & Birdsell 1953; Washburn 1963; DeVore 1964). A variant of this theory, proposed by Robinson (1962), sees bipedalism as the primary adaptation (of unknown origin), from which tool-using developed and hence anterior dental reduction.

Holloway (1967) rejects the orthodox, tool-and-weapon-determinant model, partly on the grounds that it postulates no genetic or selectional mechanism for anterior dental reduction, and thus implies Darwin's 'Lamarckian' notion of the gradual loss of structures through the inherited effects of disuse. It seems a little carping to accuse Washburn and his colleagues of Lamarckism because they omit to make explicit their view of the selective factors involved. These are in fact stated by Washburn in his reply to Holloway (Washburn 1968): natural selection favours the reduction of canines after their function has been subsumed by artificial weapons since this reduces the chance of accidental injury in intra-specific altercations. Since, as we shall see, orthodox natural selection is adequate to explain the reduction of teeth to an appropriate size following a change of function, it is hard to see why Washburn should avoid the Scylla of Lamarckism only to fall into the Charybdis of altruistic selection. Why should natural selection favour the evolution of a structure that is of no benefit to its bearer, for the benefit of other, unrelated, conspecifics? Even if we swallow altruistic selection, a basic illogicality remains. If the males use artificial weapons to fight other species, why should they bite one another in intra-specific combat? If they do not, then the size of their canines is irrelevant to the infliction of any injury, accidental or otherwise. In any case, the best way to avoid accidental and unnecessary intra-specific injury, of any kind, is to evolve unambiguous signals expressing threat and appeasement without resort to violence. The ability to make and recognise such signals is of advantage to *both* parties to the dispute, and therefore can be favoured by orthodox natural selection, is independent of the nature of the weapons used, and is found in the majority of social species, including both artefact-using and non-artefact-using higher primates.

We may now consider the underlying proposition that it was artefact use, which, by making the canine redundant as a weapon, and the incisors as tools, led to their reduction. It is known that hominoids with front teeth smaller than those of living or fossil Pongidae were widespread at the close of the Miocene period: *Oreopithecus* in southern Europe and Africa (Hürzeler 1954, etc.; Leakey 1967), and *Ramapithecus* (probably including *Kenyapithecus*) in India,

Africa, and perhaps southern Europe and China (Simons & Pilbeam 1965). If the theory of artefactual determinism is to be applied consistently, regular tool- and weapon-making has to be extended back into the Miocene, and also attributed to Hominoidea other than the direct ancestor of the Hominidae, whether one considers this to be *Ramapithecus*, *Oreopithecus*, or neither. Simons (1965) regards *Ramapithecus* as too early to be a tool-*maker*, but he and Pilbeam (1965) suggest that it was a regular tool-*user*, like the savannah chimpanzee (Goodall 1964; Kortlandt 1967). This is eminently likely, but is no explanation for anterior dental reduction since the chimpanzee has relatively the largest canines and incisors of any pongid, much larger than those of the gorilla, which has never been observed to use artefacts in the wild. To explain hominid dental reduction on these grounds, therefore, we presumably have to postulate that the basal hominids were much more dependent upon artefacts than the chimpanzee, without any obvious explanation of why this should be so. One would also expect signs of regular toolmaking to appear in the fossil record at least as early as the first signs of dental reduction, rather than twelve million years later. The more artefactually sophisticated the wild chimpanzee is shown to be, of course, the weaker the logic of the tool/weapon determinant theory becomes, rather than the other way about, as its proponents seem to feel.

Clearly, some other explanation is needed for anterior tooth reduction, at least at its inception. Recognising this, Pilbeam and Simons (1965) and Simons (1965) regard tool-use by *Ramapithecus* as compensation rather than cause for anterior tooth reduction, adopting as a causal factor Mills's (1963) suggestion that upright posture leads to facial shortening, and that canine reduction would then follow to avoid "locking" when the jaw is rotated in chewing. The main objection to this scheme (Holloway 1967) is that there is no logical reason why facial shortening should follow upright posture. Indeed, if brachiation is counted as upright posture, then it clearly does not. (Among extinct Madagascan lemurs, for instance, the long-faced *Palaeopropithecus* was a brachiator, the very short-faced *Hadropithecus* a terrestrial quadruped (Walker 1967).) Nor

does a reduced canine accompany a short face in, for instance, *Hylobates* or *Presbytis*. Furthermore, the explanation extends only to the canines, and does not account for the fact that incisal rather than canine reduction distinguishes the known specimens of *Ramapithecus* from small female Pongidae.

The same criticism applies to the model proposed by Holloway (1967), who finds an explanation of canine reduction in hormonal factors associated with the adoption of a hominid way of life:

. . . *Natural selection favoured an intragroup organisation based on social cooperation, a higher threshold to intragroup aggression, and a reduction of dominance displays . . . a shift in endocrine function took place so that natural selection for reduced secondary sexual characters (such as the canines) meant a concomitant selection for reduced aggressiveness within the group* (1967: 65).

Thus, reduced canine dimorphism is apparently attributed to a pleiotropic effect of genetically-controlled reduction in hormonal dimorphism, itself favoured by the "co-operative life" of hunting.

This argument is vulnerable on several counts. First, there is no obvious reason why even *Homo sapiens* should be thought less hormonally dimorphic than other catarrhines; in structural dimorphism the "feminised" canine of the male is a human peculiarity, but humans are rather more dimorphic in body-mass than chimpanzees, and much more dimorphic than any other hominoid in the development of epigamic characters, especially on the breast and about the head and neck, which can only be paralleled, in Primates, in some baboons. Equally, there seems little to suggest that human males are any less competitive and aggressive among themselves than those of other species; the difference rather lies in the fact that these attributes are expressed in culturally-determined channels (such as vituperative correspondence in the *American Anthropologist*) rather than by species-specific threat gestures or physical assault, so that expression of rage is postponed and channelled, not abolished at source. It seems unlikely that the basal hominids had departed further than modern man from the catarrhine norm. In fact, an elaboration of dominance/subordination behaviour, and thus an intensification of the social bond between males, is often attributed to a shift to "open-country" life (Chance 1955; 1967).

Second, the hypothesis that the canines which are disclosed when a male primate yawns are functioning as "organs of threat" is not unchallenged; Hall (1962) found that in Chacma baboons yawning appeared in ambivalent situations where it could more plausibly be interpreted as displacement. The size of the canines 'displayed' by a male in a displacement yawn would be of no consequence to his social relations or his Darwinian fitness.

Third, and most trenchant, we must critically examine the assumptions, accepted by "orthodox" opinions as well as by Holloway, that an increase in meat-eating beyond that usual in primates would follow "open-country" adaptation, and that the peculiarities of the hominids ultimately represent adaptations to hunting. The first of these assumptions is perhaps supported by the fact that chimpanzees living in savannah woodland have been seen catching and eating mammals (Goodall 1965), while those living in rain-forest have not. The flaw lies in the second part of the argument, and is like that in the artefact-determinant theory; the more proficient a hunter the non-bipedal, large-canined, large-incisored chimpanzee is found to be, the less plausible it becomes to attribute the origin of converse hominid traits to hunting. Moreover, the hunting and meat-eating behaviour of the chimpanzee does not, to the unbiased eye, suggest the selective forces that could lead to the evolution of hominid characters. Neither weapon-use nor bipedalism is prominent. Prey is captured and killed with the bare hands, and is dismembered, like other fleshy foods, with the incisors. Thus, if a population of chimpanzee-like apes becomes adapted to a hunting life in savannah, there is absolutely no reason to predict incisal reduction, weapon-use, or bipedalism. On the contrary, it is most difficult to interpret the hominid characters of the australopithecines functionally as adaptations to life as a carnivorous chimpanzee. Incisal reduction would make for less efficient processing of all fleshy foods, including meat. A change from knuckle-walking, which can be a speedy and

efficient form of terrestrial locomotion, to a mechanically imperfect bipedalism (Washburn 1950; Napier 1964) would scarcely improve hunting ability, especially since a knuckle-walking animal can, if it wishes, carry an artefact in its fist while running (cf. illustration in Reynolds & Reynolds 1965: 382). Once these characters existed as pre-adaptations in the basal hominids, they may well have determined that when hunting was adopted as a regular activity, it was hunting of the type that we now recognise as distinctively human, but to use this as an explanation of their first appearance is inadmissibly teleological.

This view is supported by the absence of fossil evidence for efficient hunting before the latter part of the Lower Pleistocene. It seems most unlikely that the hominid line would become partially and inefficiently adapted to hunting in the Miocene, only to persist in this transitional phase until the Lower Pleistocene (becoming, meanwhile, very specialised dentally, but no better at hunting or tool-making!), when a period of rapid adaptation to hunting efficiency took place. Perhaps recognising this, adherents of the "predatory chimpanzee" model tend to situate the hominid-pongid divergence in the late Pliocene, and regard all known fossils of basal Pleistocene Hominidae as representative of a short-lived transitional phase of imperfect hunting adaptation (Washburn 1963). This is a view that is intrinsically unlikely, and difficult to reconcile with the fossil evidence of Tertiary hominids. The obvious way out of the dilemma is to set aside the current obsession with hunting and carnivorousness, and to look for an alternative activity which is associated with "open-country" life but which is functionally consistent with the anatomy of basal hominids.

Impressed by the bipedal charge of the mountain gorilla, and his tendency to toss foliage around when excited, two authors (Livingstone 1962; Wescott 1967) have suggested that therein might lie the origin of human bipedalism and the other elements of the hominid complex. The objection to this notion is again that it is illogical to invoke the behaviour of living apes to explain the origin of something that they themselves have not developed; if upright display leads to habitual bipedalism, why are gorillas still walking on their knuckles? Conversely, if hominid bipedalism were initially used solely in display, why should they have taken to standing erect between episodes? Even if we grant that the savannah is more predator-ridden than the forest (a view often stated but seldom substantiated, even for the recent, let alone the Tertiary), it is difficult to believe that attacks were so frequent as to make defensive display a way of life.

The occasional bipedalism, tool- and weapon-use, and meat-eating of the pongids are useful indicators of the elements that were probably part of the hominid repertoire, ready for elaboration under particular circumstances. To explain this elaboration, however, we must look *outside* the normal behaviour of apes for a factor which agrees functionally with the known attributes of early hominids. As we have seen, "hunting" is singularly implausible as such a factor. The object of this article is to suggest an alternative, based initially on the observation that many of the characters distinctive of basal hominids, as opposed to pongids, also distinguish the grassland baboon *Theropithecus* from its woodland-savannah and forest relatives *Papio* and *Mandrillus*, and are functionally correlated with different, but no less vegetarian, dietary habits.

THEROPITHECUS-HOMINID PARALLELISMS

The assumption is made here that both hominids and living African pongids are descended from Dryopithecinae, a group intermediate between the two in most of its known characters (most of which are dental), though rather closer to Pongidae than to Hominidae. The chimpanzee can then be seen as manifesting evolutionary trends away from the ancestral condition more or less opposite to those of the Hominidae, while the gorillas retain a more conservative condition, at least dentally. This model would work as well on the less likely assumption that the chimpanzee represents the primitive condition. It is also assumed that the Cercopithecine genera *Theropithecus* and *Papio* either diverged from an intermediate common ancestor, or, more probably, that *Theropithecus* and *Mandrillus* have become differentiated in opposite directions from a *Papio*-like form (Jolly 1969). This process can be documented for

Theropithecus during the course of the Pleistocene (Jolly 1965; in press).

Table 1 summarises characters by which *either* early Pleistocene Hominidae differ from *Pan*, *or Theropithecus* from *Papio* and *Mandrillus*, listed without regard to their functional interrelationships or significance. Those which distinguish early Hominidae from Pongidae constitute the "Hominid adaptive complex," and are indicated in column A, while those which form part of the 'Theropithecus' adaptive complex' are indicated in column B. Rectangles show those features common to the two complexes, of which there are twenty-two out of forty-eight, reasonable *prima facie* evidence for parallelism between them. This hypothesis can be tested by checking the elements of the complexes for cross-occurrence in *Papio* and *Pan*. If the high number of common characters were simply due to chance, rather than to parallelism, we should not expect significantly fewer of the Hominid characters to appear in *Papio* (as opposed to *Theropithecus*), or significantly fewer of the *Theropithecus* complex characters to occur in *Pan*. In fact, none of these cross-correspondences occurs. There are some grounds, therefore, for assuming the existence of evolutionary parallelism, and perhaps some degree of functional equivalence between the differentiation of *Theropithecus* and that of the basal hominids, and the common features may be used to construct a model of hominid divergence from pongids. To do this, we must examine the functional implications of the "AB" characters.

Of these, only one certain one appears in the "behaviour" category, largely because of the impossibility of observing the behaviour of fossil forms. Inferences of behaviour from structure are, of course, not permissible at this stage of analysis. The single common character is the basic one of true "open-country" habitat, inferred largely from the death-assemblages in which early *Theropithecus* and Hominidae are found, as well as the habitat of *T. gelada*.

Three skeletal "AB" characters are post-cranial. The abbreviated fingers and unreduced thumb makes a pollex-index grip possible for the terrestrial monkeys (Napier & Napier 1967). Bishop (1963) showed that *Erythrocebus patas* made more consistent use of such a grip than its more arboreal

Table 1
ADAPTIVE CHARACTERS OF THE VILLAFRANCHIAN HOMINIDAE AND *THEROPITHECUS*.

Column A. Characters distinguishing early Hominidae from *Pan* and other Pongidae.

B. Characters distinguishing *Theropithecus* from *Papio* and *Mandrillus*.

C. Features of the Hominid complex not seen in *Theropithecus*.

D. Features of the *Theropithecus* complex not seen in Hominidae.

	A	B	C	D	Note no.
I. *Behaviour*					
a. Open-country habitat, not forest or woodland	X	X	—	—	
b. Trees rarely or never climbed when feeding	(X)	(X)	—	—	1
c. One-male breeding unit	(X)	(X)	—	—	1, 2
d. Foraging mainly in sitting position	?	(X)	—	—	1
e. Small daily range	?	(X)	—	—	1
f. More regular use of artefacts in agonistic situations	X	—	X	—	3
g. Regular use of stone cutting-tools	X	—	X	—	4
h. Most food collected by index-pollex precision grip	?	(X)	—	—	1
2. *Postcranial structure*					
a. Hand more adept, Opposability Index higher	X	X	—	—	5, 6
b. Index finger abbreviated	?	X	—	—	7
c. Hallux short and weak	—	X	—	X	7
d. Hallux relatively non-abductible	X	X	—	—	7, 8
e. Foot double-arched	X	—	X	—	8
f. Phalanges of pedal digits 2–5 shorter	(X)	X	—	—	7
g. Ilium short and reflexed	X	—	X	—	9
h. Sacroiliac articulation extensive	X	—	X	—	9
i. Anterior-inferior iliac spine strong	X	—	X	—	9
j. Ischium without flaring tuberosities	X	—	X	—	9
k. Accessory sitting pads (fat deposits on buttocks) present	(X)	(X)	—	—	7
l. Femur short compared with humerus	?	X	—	—	7
m. Distal end femur indicates straight-knee 'locking'	X	—	X	—	9
n. Epigamic hair about face and neck strongly dimorphic	(X)	(X)	—	—	1, 7
o. Female epigamic features pectoral as well as perineal	(X)	(X)	—	—	1, 10
3. *Cranium and mandible*					
a. Foramen magnum basally displaced	X	—	X	—	11
b. Articular fossa deep, articular eminence present	X	—	X	—	9
c. Fossa narrow, post-glenoid process appressed to tympanic	X	X	—	—	9, 7
d. Post-glenoid process often absent, superseded by tympanic	X	—	X	—	9
e. Post-glenoid process long and stout	—	X	—	X	7, 12
f. Basi-occipital short and broad	X	X	—	—	9, 7
g. Mastoid process regularly present	X	X	—	—	9, 7, 13
h. Temporal origins set forward on cranium	X	X	—	—	9, 7
i. Ascending ramus vertical, even in largest forms	X	X	—	—	9, 7, 12
j. Mandibular corpus very robust in molar region	X	X	—	—	9, 7, 12
k. Premaxilla reduced	X	X	—	—	9, 7
l. Dental arcade narrows anteriorly	X	X	—	—	9, 7
m. Dental arcade of mandible parabolic, 'simian' shelf absent	X	—	X	—	9

n. Dental arcade (especially in larger forms) V-shaped; shelf massive	—	X	—	X	7
4. *Teeth*					
a. Incisors relatively small and allometrically reducing	X	X	—	—	9, 7
b. Canine relatively small, especially in larger forms	X	X	—	—	9, 7
c. Canine incisiform	X	—	X	—	9
d. Male canine 'feminised', little sexual dimorphism in canines	X	—	X	—	9
e. Third lower premolar bicuspid	X	—	X	—	9
f. Sectorial face of male P_3 relatively small and allometrically decreasing	—	X	—	X	7
g. Molar crowns more parallel-sided, cusps set towards edge	X	X	—	—	14, 7
h. Cheek-teeth markedly crowded mesio-distally	X	X	—	—	14, 7
i. Cheek-teeth with deep and complex enamel invagination	—	X	—	X	7
j. Cheek-teeth with thick enamel	X	—	X	—	—
k. Canine eruption early relative to that of molars	X	X	—	—	7, 9
l. Wear-plane on cheek-teeth flat, not inclined bucco-lingually	X	—	X	—	9
m. Wear on cheek-teeth rapid, producing steep M_1–M_3 'wear-gradient'	X	X	—	—	14, 7

Notes to Table 1.

1. Crook 1966; 1967; Crook & Aldrich-Blake 1968. Parentheses indicate behavioural and soft-part features which are present in the living representative of the group *Theropithecus gelada* or *Homo sapiens*), but which cannot be demonstrated on fossil material.

2. In all but a very few human societies, where polyandry sometimes occurs (Murdock 1949).

3. The 'bashed baboons' of the South African cave sites (Barbour 1949; Dart 1949, etc.) are the most direct evidence for this.

4. Not, apparently, in the earliest Pleistocene hominid sites (Howell 1967).

5. Napier 1962.

6. J. R. Napier, personal communication.

7. Pocock 1925; Jolly 1965; 1969a; 1969b.

8. Day & Napier 1964.

9. Clark 1964.

10. Matthews 1956.

11. The functional interpretation of this character is disputed (cf. Clark 1964; Biegert 1963).

12. Leakey & Whitworth 1958.

13. Not in *T. gelada*, but regular in larger Pleistocene forms.

14. Simons & Pilbeam 1965.

relatives, the guenons. Recent work by Crook (e.g. 1966), including filmed close-ups of hand-use in the wild, has made it clear that the gelada (in contrast to, for instance, *Papio*) uses a precision-grip for most of its food-collecting. Food consists mainly of grass-blades, seeds and rhizomes which are picked up singly between thumb and index, and collected in the fist until a mouthful is accumulated. The index is thus continually used independently of the other digits. This feeding method is facilitated by the well-developed pollex and the very short index finger (Pocock 1925; Jolly 1965), a combination giving the gelada the highest "opposability index" (Napier & Napier 1967) of any catarrhine, not excluding *Homo sapiens* (J. R. Napier, personal communication). It is significant that the precision-grip of the gelada, which like other Cercopithecinae has not been seen making or using artefacts in the wild, should far outclass that of the tool- and weapon-using chimpanzee (Napier 1960).

The two common features of the foot are attributable to terrestrial adaptation which requires pedal compactness rather than hallucal gripping-power (Pocock 1925; Jolly 1965); the rest of the foot structure is different in the two forms and reflects the fact that their move to terrestrialism was quite independent and analogous. Most of the postcranial elements of the hominid complex are absent in *Theropithecus*, being related to upright bipedalism (Clark 1964). The post-cranial features of the *Theropithecus* complex are much fewer, expressing the fact that apart from the absence of tree-climbing its locomotor repertoire scarcely differs qualitatively from that seen in its woodland and forest relatives, although the frequency of the elements differs considerably (Crook & Aldrich-Blake 1968).

The mastoid process of the large Pleistocene *Theropithecus* is perhaps unexpected, since in Hominidae it can be related to erect posture (Krantz 1963). However, unlike the hindlimb characters which *Theropithecus* does not share, the mastoid is related to poising the head on the erect trunk, not the trunk upon a hyperextended hindlimb. The gelada spends most of the day in an upright *sitting* position, as, probably, did its Pleistocene relatives, and, when foraging, even moves in the truncally erect position, shuffling slowly on its haunches, hindlimbs flexed under it. Thus, *truncal* erectness is more habitual than in any non-bipedal catarrhine, and the mastoid process becomes explicable. Also, the forelimb is more "liberated" from locomotor function in *Theropithecus* than in any other non-biped, simply because the animal rarely locomotes. Sitting upright allows both hands to be used simultaneously for rapid gathering of small food-objects, a pattern seen more rarely in *Papio* where a tri-pedal stance leaving one hand free is associated with a diet mainly of larger items (Crook & Aldrich-Blake 1968).

The majority of "AB" characters are in the jaws and teeth. The temporal muscles (which are large in *Theropithecus* and some, at least, of the early Hominidae) are set well forward, so that their line of action lies almost parallel to that of the masseters, and their moment-arm about the temporo-mandibular joint is relatively long, as compared to that of the resistance of food-objects between the teeth, thus exerting a high grinding or crushing force per unit of muscular exertion. On the other hand, the gap between the opposing occlusal surfaces is small per unit of muscular extension, limiting the size of objects that can be tackled. Also, the horizontal component of temporal action is reduced, lessening its effectiveness in bilateral retraction of the mandible against resistance ("nibbling"), and in resisting forces tending to displace the mandible forwards, as when objects are held in the hand and stripped through the front teeth. Thus efficiency of incisal action, which is used by catarrhines in fruit-peeling, nibbling flesh of fruits from rinds, stripping cortex from esculent vines and tubers, and, occasionally but very significantly, tearing mammal-meat from bones or skin (DeVore & Washburn 1963; Goodall 1965), is sacrificed to adding the power of the temporals to that of the masseters and pterygoids, used mainly for cheek-tooth chewing.

In the larger forms (of both taxa), with their allometrically longer faces, the forward position of the temporals is preserved by making the ascending ramus of the mandible high but vertical, deepening the posterior maxilla. The tooth row scarcely lengthens, although the face is long from prosthion to nasion, and the cheek-teeth become mesio-distally crowded. In the fruit-eaters the horizontal component of temporal action is maintained by keeping the ascending ramus low as the face lengthens; the corpus becomes elongated and marked diastemata tend to appear in the tooth row. The short basi-occiput, and anterio-posteriorly narrowed articular fossa of both *Theropithecus* and Hominidae can be seen as part of the same functionally-determined developmental pattern. The proportions of the molars and incisors fit the same functional complex. Both *Theropithecus* and the hominids have narrower, smaller incisors than their woodland and forest relatives. Molar area is greater per unit of body-mass, and incisal width less, in *Theropithecus* than *Papio* or *Mandrillus*, and absolute incisal breadth is no greater in *T. oswaldi mariae*, as big as a female gorilla, than it is in *T. gelada*. In *Papio* both incisors and molars increase proportionately to body-mass in larger forms, and in the forest-dwelling *Mandrillus* it is the molars which in males are scarcely larger than those of females half their weight (Jolly 1969; in press). Among the Hominoidea, the Villafranchian Hominidae are *Theropithecus*-like in their dental proportions, and perhaps in their allometric ratio; the large form "Zinjanthropus" has the most extreme relative incisal reduction, while *Pan* is *Mandrillus*-like in proportions and ratios (Jolly & Chimene in preparation).

In the monkeys, the evidence for molar dominance in *Theropithecus* agrees well with data on diet in the natural habitat. In the few areas where the Pleistocene sympatry of *Theropithecus* and *Papio* still exists in the Ethiopian highlands, *Theropithecus* eats small food objects requiring little incisal preparation, but prolonged chewing, while *Papio* (which elsewhere in its wide range is a most catholic feeder) here concentrates on fleshy fruits and other tree products, most of which require peeling or nibbling with the incisors (Crook & Aldrich-Blake 1968). There seems no good reason against attributing the *Theropithecus*-like incisal proportions and jaw characters of the early hominids to a similar adaptation to a diet of small, tough objects. There is no need to postulate a compensatory use of cutting-tools for food preparation, until it can be shown archaeologically that such tools were being made (cf. Pilbeam & Simons 1965).

To avoid the charge of Lamarckism, I should perhaps suggest some selectional mechanisms leading to incisal reduction in molar-dominant forms. One is a general explanation of the reduction of structures to a size related to their function. Every structure is at once a liability, in that it can become the site of an injury or infection and requires energy and raw materials for its formation and maintenance, and an asset in so far as it performs a homeostatic function. Natural selection will favour the genotype producing a structure of such size and complexity as to confer the greatest *net* advantage. In a monkey or hominoid adapting to a gelada-like diet, each unit of tooth-material allotted genetically to a molar will bring a greater return in food processed than a unit allotted to an incisor. Thus selection should favour the genotype which determines the incisors at the smallest size consistent with their residual function. This "somatic budget effect" differs from Brace's (1963) "random mutation effect" (criticised by Holloway (1966) among others) chiefly in that it proposes a positive advantage in reduction.

A second mechanism is specific to teeth. While dental size is genetically (or at least

antenatally) determined, the development of the alveolus depends partly upon the stresses placed upon it during its working life (Oppenheimer 1964). An under-exercised jaw may thus be too small to accommodate its dental series, which tends to become disadvantageously crowded and maloccluded. Natural selection will then favour the genotype which reduces the teeth to a size fitting the reduced alveolus. The "Oppenheimer effect," originally proposed to explain the reduction of complete dentitions (as in the case of *Homo sapiens* after the introduction of cooking and food-preparation), could equally operate on particular dental regions, as in the case of *Theropithecus* and the early hominids, where the incisors were reduced but the molars were, if anything, larger than those of their forest- and woodland-dwelling relatives.

One of the more surprising findings is that canine reduction is one of the shared characters. This is contrary to the weapon-determinant hypothesis which states that "open-country," terrestrial primates, being more exposed to predation, should have *larger* canine teeth, unless they use artificial weapons. The situation in *Theropithecus* is somewhat complicated by the existence of both allometric and evolutionary trends towards canine reduction (Jolly in press). The canines decrease in relative size from the Basal to the Upper Pleistocene, when compared between forms of approximately equal body-size. And within each palaeospecies, there is evidence that the canine is smallest, relative to the molars and to the general size of the animal, in the largest forms, where the males were about the same size as a female gorilla. The allometric trend is exactly opposite to that seen in present-day *Papio*, in which the males of the largest forms have relatively and absolutely the largest canines. (*Theropithecus gelada*, a very small form of highly-evolved *Theropithecus*, has a male canine size that is relatively large for the genus, but entirely predictable from the allometric ratios between molars and canines characteristic of the whole genus.)

Both the allometric and the evolutionary trends are incompatible with the theory that canine size in males is positively correlated with terrestrial life in non-artefactual primates, but at least two alternative explanations for canine reduction are possible. It may be favoured as an adaptation to increased efficiency in rotary chewing, by avoiding canine "locking" and producing more even molar wear; this would be consistent with the evidence for "molar dominance." An early stage of adaptation might involve the canines' being worn flat as they erupted. This would obviously be a wasteful situation which might be expected to be corrected by the "somatic budget" effect, and natural selection.

The other possible explanation relates canine reduction to reduction of the incisors. The fact that the two trends parallel each other so closely in both *Theropithecus* and the Hominidae, both evolutionarily and allometrically, suggests, a *priori*, a relationship between these processes. Since incisal reduction can be plausibly interpreted as an adaptation to small-object feeding, it seems reasonable to treat canine reduction as the secondary, dependent, character. The dependence can be attributed to either, or both, of two mechanisms. First, the direct effects of incisal disuse upon the anterior alveolar region might produce an extended "Oppenheimer effect," acting primarily on the incisors, and, secondarily and less intensely, on the neighbouring canines. This might explain the fact that while incisal reduction seems fully evolved already in the rather primitive, probably early, Makapan *Theropithecus*, canine reduction proceeds through the Pleistocene. Alternatively, the dependence might be at the genetic level, with canine reduction being a simple pleiotropic effect of a genotype which primarily determined incisal reduction. There is some evidence for a canine-incisal genetic "field" in both Cercopithecoidea (Swindler et al. 1967) and Hominoidea (Jolly & Chimene, unpublished data). It may well be that both selective factors are operative in canine reduction; adaptation to rotary chewing favouring crown height reduction, and effects stemming from incisal reduction acting upon crown-area dimensions. Since the genetic factors determining these two parameters of canine size are most unlikely to be independent of each other, the two processes would be mutually reinforcing.

This scheme for canine reduction in *Theropithecus* is distinct from that of Simons and Pilbeam (1965) who also attempted to explain both incisal and canine reduction (in *Ramapithecus*) in terms of diet. They proposed that canine size was related to its own function in food preparation, thus exposing themselves to Washburn's objection that if this were so canine sexual dimorphism would imply a sexual dietary difference in non-human catarrhines which is not borne out by field observations. The scheme proposed here recognises the essentially agonistic function of the canine but suggests that its reduction in *Theropithecus* is unrelated to this function, and is a secondary effect of dietary influences on incisors and molars. If as a consequence of a dietary aspect of terrestrial adaptation, and in the complete absence of either bipedalism or use of artificial weapons, a trend towards canine reduction can be initiated in *Theropithecus* (a highly terrestrial catarrhine), then there is no need to postulate that these characters either preceded or accompanied the earliest stages (at least) of canine reduction in Hominidae, which could similarly be attributed to dietary factors.

Having, I hope, established that adaptation to terrestrial life and small-object feeding constitutes at least a reasonable working model for the initial hominid divergence from Pongidae, I should now like to speculate about the characters of soft tissues and social organisation, although admittedly these can never be tested against the fossil record.

Unlike the savannah-woodland species, all three truly "open-country" Cercopithecinae (*Theropithecus*, *Erythrocebus* and *Papio hamadryas*) have a social organisation involving exclusive mating-groups with only one adult male. Of the three, the patas is peculiar in that a female-holding male maintains his exclusive sexual rights by vigilant and agonistic behaviour directed against other adult males, whose presence he will not tolerate (Hall et al. 1965). Patas "harems" do not, therefore, co-exist as parts of a higher-order organisation. In the hamadryas and gelada, however, the male maintains cohesion of his group by threatening and chastising his own females when necessary, and many one-male groups co-exist within semi-permanent troops or bands (Kummer 1967; Crook 1967). In both species, cooperation between males is not excluded, and is frequently seen in situations of extra-troop threat. It would not be unreasonable to expect a similar social organisation, with permanent, monogamous or polygamous one-male groups set within the matrix of a larger society, to be developed by a hominoid adapting to a gelada-like way of life. This pattern is also, one might add, still distinctive of the vast majority of *Homo sapiens* (Murdock 1949).

In both hamadryas and gelada the attention-binding quality of the adult male is enhanced by the conspicuous cape of fur about his shoulders, which is groomed by his harem. It is likely that this feature has been favoured by Darwinian sexual selection (Jolly 1963). Only one other living catarrhine has such striking sexual dimorphism in epigamic hair about the face and neck: *Homo sapiens*. Similarly, bearing the female epigamic features pectorally and ventrally, rather than perineally, is a feature which can be correlated, in geladas, with a way of life in which the majority of the foraging time is spent sitting down (Crook & Gartlan 1966). It is unique to *Theropithecus* among non-human primates, but also occurs in *Homo sapiens*.

Fatty pads on the buttocks, adjacent to the true ischial callosities, are another *Theropithecus* peculiarity (Pocock 1925) which can be plausibly related to the habit of sitting while feeding, and also occur uniquely in *Homo sapiens* among the Hominoidea.

DIVERGENCES BETWEEN THE THEROPITHECUS AND HOMINID ADAPTATIONS

So far I have concentrated on the parallelisms between the *Theropithecus* and hominid adaptive complexes. Their divergences are, however, equally instructive. Columns C and D of table 1 have been added to extract those characters which occur as part of one of the complexes, but not of the other. Since characters were initially selected because they fitted either A or B (that is, they discriminate *within* superfamilies), I omit the large number of attributes which simply indicate that *Theropithecus* is a monkey but the Hominidae are Hominoidea, a point that is not at issue. The last two columns therefore indicate features adaptive to different aspects of the "open-country" habitat, and analogous adaptations to the same aspect. Again, we must examine their functional implications.

The "AB" characters of the jaws and teeth seem to comprise a functional complex related to a diet of small, tough objects. In *Theropithecus*, these are known to be mostly grass blades and rhizomes, accounting for the tendency towards cheek-tooth crown complexity which is convergent upon similar structures in grass-eating animals as diverse as voles, warthogs and elephants. This character is not part of the hominid complex, which instead includes cheek-teeth with relatively low cusps but thick enamel which wear to an even, flat, and uniform surface. Also, the temporo-mandibular joint of the hominids is unique among catarrhines in the possession of an articular eminence upon which the mandibular condyle rides in rotary chewing. Thus, the molar surfaces do not simply grind across one another in chewing, they also swing towards and away from one another. Such molars and jaw action are clearly not adapted to mincing grass blades, but rather to breaking up small, hard, solid objects of more or less spherical shape, by a combination of crushing and rolling such as is employed in milling machines. The efficiency of the combined action lies in its seeking out, by continuous internal deformation, the weaknesses in the structure of the object to be crushed.

The possession of a parabolic dental arcade (rather than the V-shape seen in large *Theropithecus*), and the absence of the "simian" symphyseal shelf, are also explicable on the basis of such a diet. The features cannot be related to tooth-function in any obvious way, nor can they be attributed simply to a Hominoid rather than Cercopithecoid inheritance, since the Hominoid *Gigantopithecus bilaspurensis* has a *Theropithecus*-like arcade and symphysis. A possible functional explanation involves the tongue. Experiments with grain-chewing in *Homo sapiens* suggest that objects not crushed by one masticatory stroke tend to be pushed by the rolling action into the oral cavity, whence they are guided back to the teeth by the tongue. This demands much more constant, agile, lingual motion than is needed in masticating a fibrous bolus of fruit (or turf). Thus, a chewing apparatus of the hominid type might be expected to include a thick, muscular, mobile tongue, accommodated in a large oral cavity. The highly-arched palate, capacious interramal space, and absence of symphyseal shelf may all be interpreted as elements of the large oral cavity, also, incidentally, providing preadaptations to articulate speech.

We can thus distinguish a sub-complex of unique hominid characters which suggests that the "small objects" of the basal hominid diet were solid, spherical, and hard. Many potential foods fit the description, but only one is widespread enough in open country to be a likely staple. This is the seeds of grasses and annual herbs, which still provide the bulk of the calories of most hominids. This is not to say that other resources were not exploited when available, but that the diet of basal hominids was probably centred upon cereal grains as that of the chimpanzee is upon fruit and that of the gorilla on herbage.

Although canine reduction is one of the AB features, the incisiform shape of the canine, and its "feminisation" in the male are unique, among catarrhines, to hominids of australopithecine and later grades. Presumably these features represent an extreme stage of reduction in adaptation to rotary chewing, reflected in the flat wear-plane of the cheek-teeth. One might therefore ask why a similar degree of reduction has not appeared in the Theropithecus line. Several explanations are possible. First, the chewing motion involved in grass-mincing might not be as demanding as that used for seed-milling. Second, a relatively high canine/incisor ratio and high sexual dimorphism are probably Cercopithecoid heritage characters, which would tend to blunt the effect of 'genetic fall-out' from incisal reduction. A reduction in anterior tooth size which leaves the cercopithecoid Theropithecus with a canine reduced in size, but still a useful weapon, might reduce the canine of a hominoid beyond the point of usefulness. Perhaps because the canines of all Pongidae are shorter and blunter than those of Cercopithecoidea, a tendency to use artefacts as weapons was probably another hominoid heritage character, thus permitting the Hominidae to compensate for the loss of biting canines favoured by rotary chewing, and allowing the extreme degree of reduction represented by incisification and feminisation. Alternatively, it may be that Theropithecus, a much more recent lineage than the hominids, has not yet had time to achieve full canine reduction.

A second group of C and D characters is postcranial and reflects the fact that while Theropithecus is a quadruped, at least when moving more than a few paces, the Villafranchian hominids were evidently bipeds of a sort. Again, we can evoke a combination of adaptational and heritage features in explanation. A gelada-like foraging pattern leads to constant truncal erectness in the sitting position, with the trunk "balanced" on the pelvis, and the forelimbs free. In Theropithecus, this behavioural trait (and its associated adaptive features) are superimposed upon a thoroughgoing, cercopithecoid quadrupedalism, producing a locomotor repertoire in which the animal abandons "bipedal" bottom-shuffling for quadrupedal locomotion when it moves fast, or for more than a few paces. The hominoid ancestor of the Hominidae, on the other hand, is most unlikely to have been postcranially baboonlike. The smallest, and best known, dryopithecine (D. (Proconsul) africanus), described as a "semi-brachiator" (Napier & Davis 1959), shows limb proportions and other features recalling generalised arboreal climbers like some of the Cebidae, but no distinctively cercopithecoid features. Its larger relatives had probably moved in the direction of truncal erectness, forelimb independence and abductibility, and the other characters distinctive of the Pongidae as a group, which are generally attributed to brachiation and can be seen as the consequences of large size in an arboreal habitat (Napier 1968).

Recently Walker and Rose (1968) and Walker (personal communication) have detected signs of locomotor adaptations very like those of the living African pongids in the fragmentary (and largely undescribed) postcranial remains of the larger African Dryopithecinae. In the basal hominid, therefore, the "gelada" specialisations would be superimposed upon a behavioural repertoire and post-cranial structure already attuned to some degree of truncal erectness. This combination of heritage and adaptation may have been the elusive determinant of terrestrial bipedalism, a gait that is inherently "unlikely," and which would thus have begun as a gelada-like shuffle. Locomotion of any kind is infrequent during gelada-like foraging, so that (unlike hunting!) it is an ideal apprenticeship for an adapting biped. Furthermore, as a final bonus, if the hominids were derived from a "brachiator" or knuckle-walker stock, they would have carried, in preadaptation, the high intermembral index which *Theropithecus* has had to acquire as part of his adaptation.

A NEW MODEL OF HOMINID DIFFERENTIATION: PHASE I, THE SEED-EATERS

The anatomical evidence seems to suggest that at some time during the Tertiary, the populations of Dryopithecinae destined to become hominids began to exploit more and more exclusively a habitat in which grass and other seeds constituted most of the available resources, while trees were scarce or absent. However, the great majority of contemporary tropical grasslands and open savannahs (especially those immediately surrounding patches of evergreen rainforest in all-year rainfall areas), are believed to be recent artefacts of burning and clearance by agricultural man (Rattray 1960; Richards 1952; Hopkins 1965; White *et al.* 1954). Under climatic climax conditions the vegetation of the seasonal rainfall tropics would almost always include at least one well-developed tree stratum, ranging from semi-deciduous forests through woodlands to *sahel* where paucity of rainfall inhibits both herb and tree strata (Hopkins 1965).

What, then, would have been the biotope of the grain-eating, basal hominids? The obvious answer is provided by the areas of treeless edaphic grassland which exist, even under natural conditions, within woodland or seasonal forest zones, wherever local drainage conditions cause periodic flooding, and hence lead to perpetual sub-climax conditions by inhibiting the growth of trees and shrubs (Richards 1952; Sillans 1958). These areas range in extent from hundreds of acres, like the bed of the seasonal Lake Amboseli, to a network of strips interlaced with woodlands (*dambos;* Ansell 1960; Michelmore 1939; Sillans 1958). Edaphic grasslands produce no tree-foods, but support a rich, all-year growth of grasses and other herbs, and are the feeding-grounds for many grass-eating animals (Ansell 1960). The remains of Villafranchian hominids are often found in deposits formed in such seasonal waters, as is Pleistocene *Theropithecus* (Jolly in press), adding some circumstantial evidence that this was their preferred habitat.

Seasonality in rainfall, producing a fluctuating water-level, is important to the development of edaphic grasslands, since perennial flooding leads to a swamp-forest climax. While there is little evidence for catastrophic desiccation in the tropics of the kind demanded by some models of hominid differentiation, there are indications that a trend towards seasonality persisted through the Tertiary, especially in Africa (Moreau 1951).

The first stages of grain-feeding adaptation probably took place in a *dambo*-like environment, later shifting to wider floodplains. The change from a fruit (or herbage)-centred diet to one based upon cereals would lead, by the evolutionary processes discussed, to the complex of small-object-feeding, seed-eating, terrestrial adaptations (see Fig. I). Other grassland resources obtainable by individual foraging or simple, *ad hoc* co-operation like that seen in the woodland chimpanzee, would also be utilised. Such items as small animals, vertebrate and invertebrate, leafy parts of herbs and shrubs, and occasional fruits and tubers would be qualitatively vital, if only to supply vitamins (especially ascorbic acid and B_{12}), and minerals, and could easily be accommodated by jaws adapted to grain-milling.

The ability to exploit grass-seeds as a staple is not seen in other mammals of comparable size, though it is seen in birds and rodents, presumably because the agile hand and hand-eye co-ordination of a higher primate is a necessary pre-adaptation to picking up such small objects fast enough to support a large animal. With these preadaptations, and the adaptive characters of jaws, teeth and limbs, the basal hominids would have faced little competition in the exploitation of a concentrated, high-energy food (a situation which would hardly have existed had they, as the "hunting" model demands, started to eat the meat of ungulates in direct competition with the Felidae, Canidae, Viverridae, and Hyaenidae). They would thus have attained a stable, adaptive plateau upon which they could have persisted for millions of years, peacefully accumulating the physiological adaptations of a terrestrial, "open-country" species. There is no reason to suppose that they would show radical advances in intellect, social organisation, material and non-material culture, or communication, beyond

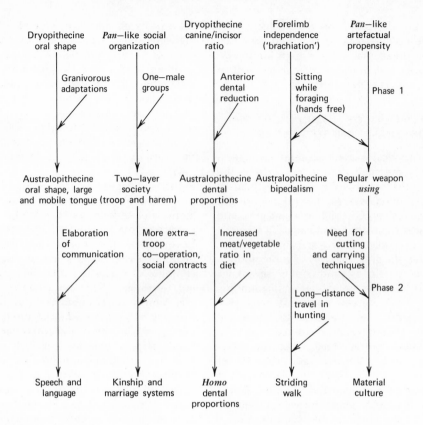

Figure 1. A model of the development of some of the major hominid characters. During Phase I a series of Dryopithecine-heritage characters (top line) is modified by the functionally-determined requirements of the sedentary seed-eating complex (second line), producing the characters of evolved Phase I hominids (line three). These are the preadaptive heritage characters of Phase 2, which determine the fact that adaptation to the demands of a hunting way of life (fourth line) takes the form of the human traits listed in the bottom line. The illogicalities of previous models tend to arise from omitting the vital second line inserting the elements of the hunting complex in its place, and invoking feedback.

that seen in one or other of the extant higher primates. The "third ape," in Simons's phrase, remained an ape, albeit a hominid ape.

PHASE 2, "HUMAN" HOMINIDS

We do not therefore need to invoke late, "human" characteristics in teleological explanation of initial hominid divergence. However, Phase 1 hominids would be uniquely preadapted to develop such features following a further, comparatively minor, ecological shift. The latter may have involved the increasing assumption by the adult males of the role of providers of mammal meat, with the equally important (but often neglected) corollary that the females and juveniles thereby became re-

sponsible for collecting enough vegetable food for themselves *and* the hunters. The adult males would perhaps be behaviourally predisposed to hunting by an existing role as "scouts" (Reynolds 1966). This is as inherently likely in a species adapted to exploiting patches of seeding grasses as it is in the fruit-eating chimpanzee which Reynolds uses as a model of a pre-hominid hominoid. The environmental change prompting the inception of hunting need have been only slight; perhaps an intensification of seasonality in a marginal tropical area which would put a premium on exploiting meat as an additional staple instead of an occasional treat. The dietary change would be small; an increase in the ratio of one high-energy, concentrated food (meat) to another (grain), which would be reflected dentally in a moderate reversal of the Phase 1 back-tooth dominance in favour of the incisal breadth needed to tear meat. The major impact of the change would be upon culture and society rather than upon diet itself. To a female, collecting vegetable food for herself and her mate, there would be great advantage in developing techniques for more rapid harvesting, for carrying the day's booty, and for preparing it by a less laborious means than chewing. On the male side, there would be a premium on the development of cutting-tools for preparing the kill for transport back to the band. The skilful hands, upright posture, and reduced anterior dentition acquired as part of the Phase 1 complex would predispose the hominids to solve these problems of adaptation by the development of their hominoid artefactual propensity into true material culture, a solution which could not be predicted on the basis of the "hunting chimp" model (see Fig. 1). In both sexes the division of labour would involve constantly postponing feeding for the sake of contributing to the communal bag, and, in males, the impulse to dominate would likewise have to be controlled in the interests of the hunt. The need for co-operation between local bands may have led to the elaboration of truly human kinship systems, in which rights to females are exchanged.

All these factors, and others, were probably related to the evolution of complex forms of symbolic communication (largely, thanks to the seed-eating mouth, in the form of speech rather than gesture), language, ritual, and intellect. Thus the beginning of true hunting and the division of labour would initiate a second period of quantum evolution in hominid history, which we are still experiencing. The effects of this step upon human physical and behavioural evolution have been examined at length by others (e.g. Washburn & Lancaster, 1968), and are beyond the scope of this article. The point to be emphasised here is that this second, distinctively human phase is most comprehensible when it is built upon a firm base of preadaptations which had their initial significance in the seed-eating complex, not upon a chimpanzee-like or semi-human condition. By distinguishing the elements of the Phase 1 adaptive plateau, those of the Phase 2 "hominisation process" are thrown into relief.

After some populations had shifted into the Phase 2 cycle, there is no reason why they should not have existed sympatrically with other hominid species which continued to specialise in the Phase 1 niche.

THE FOSSIL RECORD IN THE LIGHT OF THE NEW MODEL

The new model must now be compared with the fossil record, both to test its compatibility and to relate its events to a timescale.

A medium-sized *Dryopithecus* of the Miocene is a reasonable starting-point for hominid differentiation, and increased seasonality in the Middle-to-Upper Miocene and Lower Pliocene makes it likely that Phase 1 differentiation began at that time. The fragmentary Upper Miocene specimens referred to *Ramapithecus* (Simons 1965), though representing only jaws and teeth, are of precisely the form to be expected in an early Phase 1 hominid: narrow, uprightly-placed and weak incisors, broad, large and mesio-distally crowded cheek-teeth, set in a short but very robust mandibular corpus. Recent work has shown (D. Pilbeam, personal communication) that the molar enamel is thicker than that of contemporary Dryopithecinae, though thinner than that of later hominids, and that the wear-gradient from anterior to posterior molars is steeper. In the Fort Ternan specimen the canine crown is small, but still conical, like that of a Mid-Pleistocene *Theropithecus* female of comparable size. The material is as yet insufficient to show whether or not the male canine was yet "feminised"; this is immaterial to the argument that by Fort Ternan times the Hominidae had entered a granivorous niche in edaphic grasslands. Tattersall's recent (1969) appraisal of the habitat of the Siwalik *Ramapithecus* is consistent with this hypothesis. He describes forested country crossed by watercourses which at the latitude of the Siwaliks must have fluctuated with a seasonal rainfall, resulting in *dambo*-like conditions. The very incompleteness of the *Ramapithecus* material enables predictions to be made to test the seed-eating model. We may predict that the mandibular ascending ramus of *Ramapithecus* will be found to be relatively vertical, its postorbital constriction narrow, supraorbital ridge projecting and face concave in profile; the postcranial skeleton should show a short ilium and short, stout phalanges, but also rather long arms and short, stout legs.

Among the Early Pleistocene hominids, the "robust" australopithecines show exactly the combination of characters to be expected from long-term Phase 1 adaptation. Indeed, a major advantage of the two-phase model is that it makes sense of the apparent paradox of these hominids. Their specialisations (such as "superhuman" incisal and canine reduction) are related to the seed-eating complex, while their apparent primitiveness (represented by characters like relatively small cranial capacity and comparatively inefficient bipedalism (Napier 1964; Day 1969; Tobias 1969) is simply *absence* of Phase 2 specialisations.

Robinson (1962; 1963) is one of the few to see the robust australopithecines as representative of a primitive stage of hominid evolution, rather than a late and "aberrant" line, and to recognise that basal hominids are unlikely to have been more carnivorous than pongids. He therefore comes closest to the present scheme, but does not solve the paradox of *robustus* by recognising the significance of *small-object* vegetarianism to the characters of Phase 1 adaptation. Recent discoveries suggest that robust australopithecines have a time-span in Africa running into millions of years; this would be compatible with our model of Phase 1 differentiation leading to an adaptive plateau, but not with schemes which see all australopithecines as incompetent and transient hunters, nor those that see the robust group as a late "offshoot."

The population represented by the specimens called *Homo habilis* (Leakey *et al.* 1964) fit the model as early, but clearly differentiated Phase 2 hominids, as their describers contend, with a dentition in which the trend to back-tooth dominance has been partially reversed, a cutting-tool culture, and increased cranial capacity. At several African sites there is evidence of contemporary and sympatric Phase 1 (*robustus*) hominids, as predicted by the model.

If this interpretation is correct, there would seem ample justification for referring *habilis* to the genus *Homo*, on the grounds of its departure along the path of Phase 2 adaptation.

The "gracile" australopithecines (excluding *habilis*) might fit into one of three places on the model (and, conceivably, different populations referred to this species do in fact fit in different places). Possibly they are evolved Phase 1 hominids whose apparently unspecialised dental proportions might be attributed to an allometric effect of smaller size, as in *Theropithecus*. This interpretation, however, is unlikely, mainly because the size-difference between the robust and gracile groups seems insufficient to account for their divergences in shape by allomorphosis alone. Alternatively, they might be a truly primitive (Phase 1) stock from which both robust australopithecines and Phase 2 hominids evolved. This view has been widely espoused, and if dental proportions were all, it would be most plausible. However, the known *africanus* specimens are probably too late and too cerebrally advanced to be primitive. Most likely, they are at an early stage of Phase 2 evolution, with their osteodontokeratic culture, perhaps improved bipedalism, and some cerebral expansion beyond that seen in the *robustus* group (Robinson 1963). In this case their anterior dentition could be seen as secondarily somewhat enlarged from the primitive condition. This interpretation would favour sinking *Australopithecus* in *Homo*, while retaining *Paranthropus* for the evolved Phase 1 forms, as Robinson suggested.

* * *

The nature of an evolutionary model, concerned with unique events, is such that it cannot be tested experimentally. Its major test lies in its plausibility, especially in its ability to account for the data of comparative anatomy, behaviour, and the fossil record inclusively, comprehensively, and with a minimum of sub-hypotheses. It should also provide predictions which are in theory testable, as with a more complete fossil record, thus enabling discussion to move forward from mere assertion and counter-assertion. An evolutionary model which is designed to account for nothing beyond the data from which it is derived, may be entertaining, but has about as much scientific value as the *Just so stories*.

While none of the previous models of hominid differentiation is without plausibility, none is very convincing. Too few of the elements of the hominid complex are accounted for, and too often the end-products of hominid evolution have to be invoked in teleological "explanation." On the other hand, the nature of the causal factors invoked, especially behavioural ones, is often such as to make the hypothesis untestable.

The model presented here is based upon the nearest approach to an experimental situation that can be found in evolutionary studies, the parallel adaptation to a closely similar niche by a related organism. While based initially upon diet, and dental characters, it also accounts for hominid features as diverse as manual dexterity, shelfless mandible and epigamic hair, and for features of the fossil record such as the apparent paradox of *Paranthropus*, and the fact that hominid (or pseudo-hominid) dentitions apparently preceded tools by several million years. On the other hand, there seem to be no major departures from logic or from the data. It is therefore suggested that the two-phase model, with a seed-eating econiche for the first hominids, should at least be considered as an alternative working hypothesis against which to set new facts and fossils.

NOTE

This article is a revised and expanded version of a paper read in the Department of Vertebrate Palaeontology, Yale Peabody Museum, on February 14, 1969. The helpful comments of Drs. Colin Groves, David Pilbeam, Elwyn Simons, and Alan Walker on this and other occasions are gratefully acknowledged.

REFERENCES

Ansell, W. F. H. 1960. *Mammals of Northern Rhodesia*. Lusaka: Government Printer, Barbour, G. B. 1949. Ape or man? *Ohio Sci. J.* 49, 4.

Bartholomew, G. A. & J. B. Birdsell 1953. Ecology and the protohominids. *Am. Anthrop.* 55, 481–98.

Biegert, J. 1963. The evaluation of characteristics of the skull, hands and feet for primate taxonomy. In *Classification and human evolution* (ed.) S. L. Washburn (Viking Fd. Publ. Anthrop. 37). Chicago: Aldine.

Bishop, A. 1963. Use of the hand in lower primates. In *Evolutionary and genetic biology of the primates* (ed.) J. Buettner-Janusch. New York: Academic Press.

Brace, C. L. 1963. Structural reduction in evolution. *Am. Naturalist* 97, 39–49.

Chance, M. R. A. 1955. The sociability of monkeys. *Man* 55, 162–5.

———. 1967. Attention structure as the basis of primate rank orders. *Man* (N.S.) 2, 503–18.

Clark, W. E. Le Gros 1964. *The fossil evidence for human evolution* (2nd edn). Chicago: Univ. Press.

Crook, J. H. 1966. Gelada baboon herd structure and movement: a comparative report. *Symp. zool. Soc. Lond.* 18, 237–58.

———. 1967. Evolutionary change in primate societies. *Sci. J.* 3 (6), 66–72.

———. & P. Aldrich-Blake 1968. Ecological and behavioural contrasts between sympatric ground dwelling primates in Ethiopia. *Folia primat.* 8, 192–227.

———. & J. S. Gartlan 1966. Evolution of primate societies. *Nature, Lond.* 210, 1200–3.

Dart, R. A. 1949. The predatory implemental technique of *Australopithecus*. *Am. J. phys. Anthrop.* (N.S.) 7, 1–38.

Day, M. H. 1969. Femoral fragment of a robust Australopithecine from Olduvai Gorge, Tanzania. *Nature, Lond.* 221, 230–3.

———. & J. R. Napier 1964. Hominid fossils from Bed I Olduvai Gorge, Tanganyika: fossil foot bones. *Nature, Lond.* 201, 967–70.

DeVore, I. 1964. The evolution of social life. In *Horizons in anthropology* (ed.) S. Tax. Chicago: Univ. Press.

———. & S. L. Washburn 1963. Baboon ecology and human evolution. In *African ecology and human evolution* (eds) F. C. Howell & F. Bourlière (Viking Fd Publ. Anthrop. 36). Chicago: Aldine.

Goodall, J. 1964. Tool-using and aimed throwing in a community of freeliving chimpanzees. *Nature, Lond.* 201, 1264–6.

———. 1965. Chimpanzees of the Gombe Stream Reserve. In *Primate behavior: field studies of monkeys and apes* (ed.) I. DeVore. New York: Holt, Rinehart & Winston.

Hall, K. R. L. 1962. The sexual, agonistic and derived social behaviour patterns of the wild chacma baboon, *Papio ursinus*. *Proc. zool. Soc. Lond.* 139, 283–327.

———. R. C. Boelkins & M. J. Goswell 1965. Behaviour of patas monkeys (*Erythrocebus patas*) in captivity, with notes on the natural habitat. *Folia primat.* 3, 22–49.

Holloway, R. L. Jr. 1966. Structural reduction through the probable mutation effect: a critique with questions regarding human evolution. *Am. J. Phys. Anthrop.* 25, 7–11.

———. 1967. Tools and teeth: some speculations regarding canine reduction. *Am. Anthrop.* 69, 63–7.

Hopkins, B. 1965. *Forest and savanna*. Ibadan, London: Heinemann.

Howell, F. C. 1967. Recent advances in human

evolutionary studies. *Quart. Rev. Biol.* 42, 471–513.

Hürzeler, J. 1954. Zur systematischen Stellung von *Oreopithecus. Verh. naturf. Ges. Basel* 65, 88–95.

Jolly, C. J. 1963. A suggested case of evolution by sexual selection in primates. *Man* 63, 178–9.

——. 1965. The origins and specialisations of the long-faced Cercopithecoidea. Thesis, University of London.

——. 1969. The large African monkeys as an adaptive array. Paper presented at Wenner-Gren Symposium 43, *Systematics of the Old World Monkeys.*

——. in press. The classification and natural history of *Simopithecus* Andrews (= *Theropithecus* Geoffroy).

Kortlandt, A. 1967. Experimentation with chimpanzees in the wild. In *Progress in primatology* (eds) D. Starck et. al. Stuttgart: Gustav Fischer.

Krantz, G. S. 1963. The functional significance of the mastoid process in man. *Am. J. phys. Anthrop.* 21, 591–3.

Kummer, H. 1967. *Social organisation of hamadryas baboons.* (Bibliotheca primat 6). Basel: Karger.

Leakey, L. S. B. 1967. Notes on the mammalian faunas from the Miocene and Pleistocene of East Africa. In *Background to evolution in Africa* (eds) W. W. Bishop & J. D. Clark. Chicago: Univ. Press.

Leakey, L. S. B. & T. Whitworth 1958. *Notes on the genus* Simopithecus, *with description of a new species from Olduvai* (Coryndon Mem. Mus. occ. Pap. 6). Nairobi: Coryndon Memorial Museum.

——. P. V. Tobias & J. R. Napier 1964. A new species of the genus *Homo* from Olduvai Gorge. *Nature, Lond.* 202, 3–9.

Livingstone, F. B. 1962. Reconstructing man's Pliocene pongid ancestor. *Am. Anthrop.* 64, 301–5.

Matthews, L. H. 1956. The sexual skin of the gelada. *Trans. zool. Soc. Lond.* 28, 543–8.

Michelmore, A. P. G. 1939. Observations on tropical African grasslands. *J. Ecol.* 27, 283–312.

Mills, J. R. E. 1963. Occlusion and malocclusion in primates. In *Dental anthropology* (ed.) D. R. Brothwell. Oxford: Pergamon Press.

Moreau, R. E. 1951. Africa since the Mesozoic with particular reference to certain biological problems. *Proc. zool. Soc. Lond.* 121, 869–913.

Murdock, G. P. 1949. *Social structure.* New York: Macmillan.

Napier, J. R. 1960. Studies of the hands of living primates. *Proc. zool. Soc. Lond.* 134, 647–57.

——. 1962. Fossil hand bones from Olduvai Gorge. *Nature, Lond.* 196, 409–11.

——. 1964. The evolution of bipedal walking in the hominids. *Arch. Biol. (Liège)* 75 Suppt, 673–708.

——. 1967. The antiquity of human walking. *Sci. Am.* 216, 56–66.

——. 1968. Evolutionary aspects of primate locomotion. *Am. J. phys. Anthrop.* 27, 333–42.

——. & P. R. Davis 1959. The forelimb skeleton and associated remains of *Proconsul africanus. Brit. Mus. (nat. Hist.) Foss. Mam. Afr.* 16, 1–69.

——. & P. H. Napier 1967. *Handbook of living primates.* London: Methuen.

Oppenheimer, A. 1964. Tool use and crowded teeth in Australopithecinae. *Curr. Anthrop.* 5, 419–21.

Pilbeam, D. R. & E. L. Simons 1965. Some problems of Hominid classification. *Am. Sci.* 53, 237–59.

Pocock, R. I. 1925. External characters of the catarrhine monkeys and apes. *Proc. zool. Soc. Lond.* (2), 1479–579.

Rattray, J. M. 1960. *The grass cover of Africa.* New York: FAO.

Reynolds, V. 1966. Open groups in hominid evolution. *Man (N.S.)* 1, 441–52.

——. & F. Reynolds 1965. Chimpanzees in the Budongo forest. In *Primate behavior: field studies of monkeys and apes* (ed.) I. DeVore. New York: Holt, Rinehart & Winston.

Richards, P. W. 1952. *The tropical rain forest: an ecological study.* Chicago: Univ. Press.

Robinson, J. T. 1962. The origins and adaptive radiation of the Australopithecines. In *Evolution und Hominization* (ed.) G. Kurth. Stuttgart: Gustav Fischer.

——. 1963. Adaptive radiation in the Australopithecines and the origin of man. In *African ecology and human evolution* (eds) F. C. Howell & F. Bourlière (Viking Fd Publ. Anthrop. 36). Chicago: Aldine.

Sillans, R. 1958. *Les savanes de l' Afrique centrale.* Paris: Éditions P. Lechevalier.

Simons, E. L. 1965. The hunt for Darwin's third ape. *Med. Opinion Rev.* 1965 (Nov.) 74–81.

——. & D. Pilbeam 1965. Preliminary revision of the Dryopithecinae. *Folia primat.* 3, 81–152.

Swindler, D. R., H. A. McCoy & P. V. Hornbeck 1967. Dentition of the baboon *(Papio anubis).* In *The baboon in medical research,* vol. 2 (ed.) H. Vagtborg. Austin: Texas Univ. Press.

Tattersall, I. 1969. Ecology of the north Indian *Ramapithecus. Nature, Lond.* 221, 451–2.

Tobias, P. V. 1969. Cranial capacity in fossil Hominidae. Lecture, American Museum of Natural History, May 1969.

Walker, A. C. 1967. Locomotor adaptations in recent and fossil Madagascan lemurs. Thesis, University of London.

——. & M. Rose 1968. Fossil hominoid vertebra from the Miocene of Uganda. *Nature, Lond.* 217, 980–1.

Washburn, S. L. 1950. Analysis of primate locomotion. *Cold Spr. Harb. quart. Symp. Biol.* 15, 67–77.

———. 1963. Behavior and human evolution. In *Classification and human evolution* (ed.) S. L. Washburn (Viking Fd. Publ. Anthrop. 37). Chicago: Aldine.

———. 1968. On Holloway's "Tools and teeth." *Am. Anthrop.* 70, 97–101.

———. & C. S. Lancaster 1968. The evolution of hunting. In *Man the hunter* (eds) R. B. Lee & I. DeVore. Chicago: Aldine.

Wescott, R. W. 1967. Hominid uprightness and primate display. *Am. Anthrop.* 69, 78.

White, R. O., S. V. Venkatamanan & P. M. Dabadghao 1954. The grassland of India. *C. R. int. Congr. Bot.* 8, 46–53.

17

KNUCKLE-WALKING AND THE PROBLEM OF HUMAN ORIGINS
Russell H. Tuttle

When human anatomy is compared with the anatomy of the great apes, a number of questions arise concerning the evolution of each form and its relationship to the others. Did man descend from something like a modern great ape? How much and in what details has human form been altered from the prehuman ancestor? For that matter, how much has pongid form changed from the ape-human common ancestral condition? The fossil record is so sparse, particularly with regard to hand, foot, and limb bones, that most of the consideration of these questions has involved comparisons of living apes and men.

Man is obviously more closely related to the gorilla and especially to the chimpanzee than to any other primate. This relationship is attested to by numerous features—serological, anatomic, genetic, and behavioral—but as noted in the previous essay, there were dental, and evidently dietary, matters where fundamental differences have existed for a long time. What about other features, such as the locomotor aspects of the postcranial skeleton? Until recently many authorities took every aspect in which fossil hominid leg and foot bones differed from modern form as an indicator of less than fully upright posture. Now, however, there is general agreement that long ago the selective forces of the savanna-land life-way were sufficient to convert the hominid distal appendage from a grasping and climbing organ to a pendulum-like supportive organ. A recent biomechanical analysis has shown that despite the fact that the femoral neck length and head diameter in the earliest known hominids, the Australopithecines, differ from the comparable length and diameter of femora in modern man, the use of the lower limb was entirely comparable in both (Lovejoy, Heiple, and Burstein 1973). Evidently the hominid bipedal adaptation has been in effect for at least two million years.

But what about the hand and arm? Did the previous arboreal heritage produce an adaptation comparable to that of a gorilla or chimpanzee, or not? At one time it was felt, as Tuttle observes, that the suspensory role of the forelimb in a large-bodied arboreal brachiator led to the shortening of the flexor tendons of the forearm producing a condition in which the fingers could not be straightened out—that is, they constituted a permanent hook for ease of hanging. This, it was suggested, was a preadaptation that led to the adoption of a knuckle-walking posture when the creature descended to the ground. The feeling was that this would have constituted such a limiting specialization that it would have prevented the later development of the hand as a flexible manipulating organ. All this presumably demonstrated that man could not have descended from a heavy-bodied arboreal primate that used a form of suspensory locomotion.

Tuttle, however, presents a convincing demonstration that an arboreal suspensory form of locomotion need not produce such anatomical limitations. As Lancaster's discussion in the previous section has shown, chimpanzees are capable of fine manipulation and, besides, anatomical specializations are not quite so rigidly irreversible as they were once thought to be. Be that as it may, we concur with Tuttle's conclusion that the knuckle-walking adaptation of the African apes is a late adaptation to terrestrial quadrupedal locomotion and had not been a feature of the common pongid-hominid ancestor.

Lovejoy, C. O., K. G. Heiple, and A. H. Burstein. 1973. The gait of *Australopithecus. American Journal of Physical Anthropology,* in press.

While the taxonomic affinity of man and the African apes is generally undisputed, anthropologists have widely disparate opinions on the extent to which the common ancestors of man, chimpanzee, and gorilla resembled living pongids. Many authors proffer sketches of hominid evolution that include apelike stages (1), but few of these include details of the mechanisms whereby apelike forms evolved into more manlike apes which, in turn, culminated in man. Similarly, authors who suggest alternative theories that emphasize non-apelike precursors (2) have difficulty in delimiting the biomechanical and environmental changes involved in the transition from preman to man.

Several theories that have received special notice in discussions on human origins accentuate a "troglodytian" or great-ape stage immediately preceding the emergence of man, the plantigrade biped (1). In this article I assess the possibility of a troglodytian stage in human phylogeny in the light of recent behavioral and morphological studies on the hands of the great apes and man.

BRACHIATIONIST THEORY

In his initial formulation of an evolutionary pathway that possibly culminated in man, Sir Arthur Keith proposed three "stages": hylobatian, troglodytian, and plantigrade (3). Arboreal quadrupedal monkey-like primates evolved into "brachiating" gibbon-like apes that had a predilection for suspending themselves in orthograde postures beneath branches; these were Keith's hypothetical hylobatians.

Keith also emphasized brachiation in the second stage of his theory; the major difference between "hylobatians" and "troglodytians" was the greater size of the latter.

Man also is orthograde in posture, but instead of hanging ape-wise from a superstratum he stands bipedally on a substratum.

Keith and later brachiationists could point to many features, particularly in the forelimb (upper limb) and trunk, that are shared by men and apes. For example, the "brachiators," like man, have long arms relative to trunk length, and long forearms in particular; long second to fifth fingers; thumbs of

From *Science* 166 (21 November 1969): 953-961. Copyright 1969 by the American Association for the Advancement of Science. Reprinted by permission of the author and publisher.

notable absolute size (but short relative to total hand length in apes); broad, anteroposteriorly flattened chests; strongly angled ribs; protrusion of the vertebral column into the chest cavity; a broad sternum, with progressive fusion of the sternal elements in adults; long collarbones; shoulder blades located on the posterior aspects of the chest wall; large acromial processes on the shoulder blades; laterally directed shoulder joints; considerable mobility of the shoulder and elbow joints; a relatively short truncal segment of the vertebral column—in particular, a short lumbar region; no tail; and a smaller coccyx and more sacral vertebrae than other anthropoid primates have (4).

In addition to the general bodily proportions and skeletal features listed above, the "brachiators" have in common certain characteristics of soft parts that may be related to their semierect and orthograde posturing. These include large muscles that raise the arm and rotate the shoulder blade (5); a characteristic arrangement of muscle fibers in the diaphragm; characteristic positions of the heart, lungs, and other organs in the body cavity; the close attachment of some abdominal organs to the diaphragm and posterior abdominal wall; a muscular pelvic diaphragm in the pelvic outlet; and lumbar back muscles that are smaller and show less fasciculation than those of other anthropoid primates (3).

Of the three great apes (chimpanzee, gorilla, and orangutan), the chimpanzee is generally considered by brachiationists the form that most closely resembles the prototypic large-bodied ape near the base of hominid phylogeny. Gorillas generally are considered too large to serve as hypothetical ancestral apes. Orangutans are too highly specialized in a unique mode of arboreal habitation to represent a phase in the human lineage.

TERRESTRIALITY IN APES

The terrestrial habits of the African apes (chimpanzees and gorillas) have been noted by nearly all authors who have discussed their relevance to an understanding of human evolution, but the evolutionary significance of their terrestriality has been obscured by over-simplified concepts of the apes as "brachiators." Until recently this problem was further obfuscated by an insufficiency of naturalistic behavioral studies of the great apes. As recently as 1967, the locomotion of chimpanzees and gorillas was classified as "modified brachiation" in an authoritative handbook of living primates (6); accordingly, "modification" in the locomotor activities of great apes primarily referred to a "chimpanzee and orangutan type of brachiation" (6). This classification does not adequately consider the unique terrestrial locomotive patterns of the African apes, which distinguish them from all other living primates.

Success in elucidating the problem of a troglodytian phase in human evolution depends upon refinement of our understanding of the evolutionary biology of the African apes. Thus we may ask, what are the adaptive modes of chimpanzees and gorillas and what features of their locomotive behavior and morphology may be accentuated in discussions on the role of "troglodytians" in human phylogeny?

Chimpanzees and gorillas are basically forest dwellers, though chimpanzees have been observed to venture sporadically into sparsely wooded areas (7). Mountain gorillas in eastern Africa are predominantly terrestrial in foraging, feeding, nesting, and locomotive activities. (8). Little is known about the activity patterns of western and eastern lowland gorillas, but there is evidence that they are somewhat more arboreal, especially in feeding and nesting behavior, than mountain gorillas (8). Chimpanzees are usually arboreal in feeding and nesting, although they have been observed to eat grasses and other ground plants during the dry season in Tanzania (9).

The African apes normally move from one feeding or nesting site to another on terrestrial pathways. They are fundamentally semierect quadrupeds, assuming knuckle-walking postures both on the ground and on stout horizontal branches, even high in trees (8, 9). In the knuckle-walking posture the distal and middle segments of the fingers are flexed and the proximal segments are hyperextended. The palm is elevated and aligned with the wrist and forearm (Fig. 1). Thus, in knuckle-walkers only the backs of the middle segments of the fingers come in contact with the substratum (10, 11). These areas of the fingers are covered by "knuckle pads" that exhibit all features of typical frictional skin—namely, absence of pilosebaceous systems and the development of dermatoglyphic patterns, with eccrine sweat glands opening on the peaks of the epidermal ridges (12).

BIOMECHANICS OF KNUCKLE-WALKING

Many unique features of the bones, ligaments, and muscles in the hands of African apes are correlated with the biomechanical demands of knuckle-walking (11). In the knuckle-walking posture, the hand of a large-bodied ape is subjected to considerable compressive force, which tends to produce collapse downward at the wrist and metacarpophalangeal joints. The associated configurations of the articular surfaces in these joints increase their integrity in close-packed positions. Furthermore, the ligaments and tendons in the hand are so strengthened and so positioned that they absorb the tensile components of stresses incurred in knuckle-walking.

For instance, the carpal bones in the wrist articulate snugly with one another. Special bony ridges are present on the dorsal aspect of the distal articular surface of the radius and the scaphoid bone. In the close-packed position these ridges are apposed, thereby increasing the stability of the wrist when it is extended. The palmar portion of the wrist joint capsule is extremely thick, due to the development of oblique and horizontally directed ligaments that bind the carpal bones to the radius and ulna, to metacarpal bones II to V, and to each other (11, 13).

The hyperextended posture (Fig. 1) of the proximal segments of the fingers makes the metacarpophalangeal joints even more susceptible than the wrist to downward collapse. Considerable hyperextension at these joints occurs where the articular surfaces of the metacarpal head extend onto their dorsal aspects [(11) and Fig. 2]. A prominent transverse ridge is located at the base of the dorsal articular surface of each metacarpal head (Fig. 2). As in the wrist, these ridges are important for maintaining the integrity of the metacarpophalangeal joints in the close-packed position of hyperextension.

Although the bone-ligament mechanisms of the wrist are probably sufficient to maintain its integrity in static knuckle-walk-

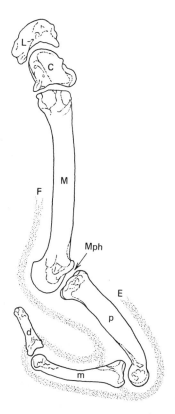

Figure 1. "Exploded" third digital ray and associated carpal bones and tendons in the hand of an adult female chimpanzee in the knuckle-walking posture. Note that considerable hyperextension is possible at the metacarpophalangeal joint *(Mph)* due to the backward extension of the articular surface of the metacarpal head *(M)*. *(L)* Lunate; *(C)* capitate; *(P)* proximal phalanx; *(M)* middle phalanx; *(D)* distal phalanx; *(E)* extensor tendon complex; *(F)* flexor tendon complex.

ing postures, the flexor muscles may provide important supplementary supporting forces during knuckle-walking progression. These muscles are prominently developed in chimpanzees and gorillas [(11) and Fig. 3a].

The metacarpophalangeal joints of the second to fifth fingers are supported by the powerful long digital flexor tendons that are closely apposed to their palmar surfaces. In chimpanzees and gorillas, these tendons are shortened; the distal segments of the fingers cannot be fully extended when the proximal segments of the fingers or the wrist are bent backward (11). The hyperextended position of the proximal segments of the fingers probably places the long flexor muscles in a state of passive stretch. This not only assists in supporting the metacarpophalangeal joints during the knuckle-walking stance but also provides some propulsive force at the

distal extemity of the forelimb as the hand clears the ground during knuckle-walking strides.

PATTERNS OF KNUCKLE-WALKING

In the foregoing discussion the common features related to knuckle-walking in the African apes are outlined. Now let us note some ways in which the knuckle-walking habitus of gorillas differs from that of chimpanzees—a situation not unexpected in view of the greater size and the advanced terrestriality of gorillas.

First, the bony and ligamentous structures that are prominently developed in knuckle-walkers have their most notable expression in gorillas *(11)*.

Second, while gorillas are indistinguishable from chimpanzees with respect to the relative development of major muscle groups in the forearm and hand, they are notably distinct from chimpanzees in possessing nearly equal development of total hand and total foot musculature. Chimpanzees, by contrast, possess a greater mass of total foot muscles than of total hand muscles [(11) and Fig. 4]. This may be related to the fact that chimpanzees climb trees more often than gorillas do.

Third, studies of captive chimpanzees and gorillas indicate that the gorillas consistently

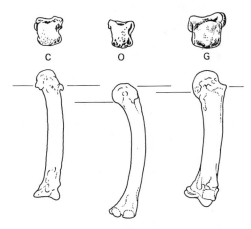

Figure 2. Medial aspect (bottom row) and distal end (upper row) of the third metacarpal bone of the chimpanzee *(C)* orangutan *(O)*, and gorilla *(G)*. The distal articular surfaces are indicated by shading. Horizontal lines indicate the extent of the anterior and posterior articular areas. Note the limited posterior extension of the distal articular surface and the greater curvature of the metacarpal in the orangutan.

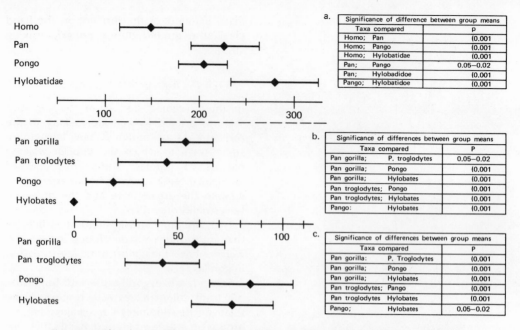

Figure 3. (a) The relative weights of total flexor muscles in the forearms of man (Homo), chimpanzees and gorillas (Pan), orangutans (Pongo), and gibbons and siamangs (Hylobatidae), expressed as percentages of the weights of total extensor muscles in the forearm: (total flexors × 100) / (total extensors). (b) Degrees of backward extension (dorsiflexion) of the metacarpophalangeal joints in digits II to V of gorillas (Pan gorilla), chimpanzees (Pan troglodytes), orangutans (Pongo), and gibbons (Hylobates). (c) Degree of backward extension (dorsiflexion) of the wrist in gorillas (Pan gorilla), chimpanzees (Pan troglodytes), orangutans (Pongo), and gibbons (Hylobates). Means and 90-percent fiducial limits are indicated by diamonds and horizontal bars, respectively. The significance of the differences between group means were determined by t-tests.

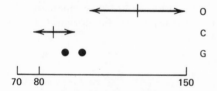

Figure 4. The relative weights of total forearm and hand muscles in orangutans (O), chimpanzees (C), and gorillas (G), expressed as percentages of total leg and foot musculature: (total forearm and hand muscles × 100) / (total leg and foot muscles). Means (vertical bars) and 90-percent fiducial limits (horizontal arrows) are indicated for samples of orangutan and chimpanzee. The dots represent individual specimens of gorilla. The weights for orangutans are significantly different from those for the African apes.

place all four fingers of a hand on the ground when knuckle-walking. In chimpanzees, the third and fourth fingers always make contact with the ground during each forelimb stride but the second and fifth digits are sometimes flexed and clear of the ground, with no apparent impairment of gait (11). I have not observed gorillas knuckle-walking with the second or fifth digit clear of the ground.

Finally, there are certain differences in the positioning of the hand. Individual chimpanzees assume a wide variety of knuckle-walking postures. They may fully pronate the hand, to a position approximately perpendicular to the line of travel; more frequently, however, they partially pronate it, to a position oblique or nearly parallel to the line of travel. By contrast, gorillas (even at an early age) are likely to fully pronate the hand during knuckle-walking. This gives gorillas a characteristic square-shouldered appearance, with shoulders jutting forward and elbows projecting laterally (11).

In the gorilla, pronation of the hand is effected by medial rotation of the shoulder and radioulnar joints. Differences in shoulder morphology between chimpanzees and gorillas (14) may partially explain the different knuckle-walking postures of the two forms. In addition, preliminary studies on the radioulnar joints of gorillas indicate that gorillas cannot supinate the hand to the extent that chimpanzees can (11). Thus care must be taken to avoid overgeneralization in considering hand posturing in the knuckle-walking apes *(15)*.

EVOLUTION OF KNUCKLE-WALKING

Numerous anatomical details in chimpanzees and gorillas attest to the fact that they evolved from ancestors that were adapted for arboreal climbing and probably also for suspensory posturing *(3-5)*. Furthermore, chimpanzees and, to a lesser extent, gorillas are active climbers today. Chimpanzees and young gorillas occasionally hang beneath, and arm-swing along, branches while foraging, playing, and engaging in agonistic displays *(8, 9)*.

The question thus arises, in what manner did the arboreal ancestry of the African apes predispose them to knuckle-walking? Keith and other brachiationists believed that the large size of the "troglodytians" may have inclined them toward terrestriality *(3)*.

The hands of great apes were commonly portrayed as inflexible anatomical hooks adapted for brachiation *(4, 10, 16)*. Hence it was supposed that, when on the ground, pongids would have little choice but to walk on the back surfaces of their hooked hands.

But orangutans, gibbons, spider monkeys, and other highly arboreal primates can flatten out their hands and assume palmigrade postures when forced to the ground [*(11)* and Fig. 5]. In natural habitats these primates engage in arm-swinging more frequently than African apes do. Furthermore, studies on anesthetized orangutans and gibbons reveal that, unlike African apes, they have flexible wrists (Fig. 3c) and that they lack the general permanent shortness of the long digital flexor tendons that is characteristic of chimpanzees and gorillas *(11)*. Thus, the hands of orangutans and gibbons are *not* inflexible anatomical hooks and are poorly designed for knuckle-walking.

During the adaptive shift to terrestriality, the long-fingered troglodytian ancestors of the African apes were probably faced with the following alternative: they could either adopt flexed-finger postures or undergo progressive shortening of the fingers. Long fingers are biomechanically inefficient and generally maladaptive in terrestrial primates. If the position of the fingers is such that they act effectively as propulsive levers—that is, if the extended fingers are parallel to the line

of travel when the hand is pronated and medially rotated—they will be subjected to considerable shear stress owing to their length. Thus, terrestrial monkeys, for instance, have fingers that are short by comparison with those of abroreal monkeys *(17)*.

When orangutans, gibbons, and spider monkeys assume full palmigrade postures during terrestrial locomotion, they rotate their hands laterally so that the extended fingers are markedly angled or perpendicular to the line of travel [*(11)* and Fig. 5]. This permits them to use the forelimbs as supporting props without the extended fingers' sustaining the injurious stresses that would otherwise be inevitable.

But in long-handed troglodytians, outwardly projecting fingers would be inefficient on the forest floor because they would snag on vegetation and other protrusions. Fully palmigrade locomotive postures may be observed in captive orangutans because cage floors offer little obstruction to their projecting hands. But orangutans generally flex their fingers during locomotion even in situations where they need not do so *(11)*.

In summary, on the basis of biomechanical considerations and the behavior of living long-handed primates, it may be inferred that the troglodytian ancestors of the African apes probably assumed flexed-finger postures during the initial shift to terrestriality.

The flexed-finger postures of early troglodytians may have been similar to the "fist-walking" or "modified palmigrade" postures of living orangutans. During fist-walking, orangutans flex their long fingers so that the backs of the *proximal* segments make contact with the ground *(11)*. In captive animals, fist-walking is observed much more frequently than palmigrade posturing. Free-ranging orangutans fist-walk along large horizontal branches *(18)* and use their fists to pack down nesting materials *(19)*.

In some phases of the fist-walking locomotive cycle, the palm and wrist are aligned with the forearm. But in young orangutans, the wrist bends backward to a notable extent when the load shifts onto the supporting hand [*(11)* and Fig. 6]. In some adult fist-walkers, the powerfully developed flexor muscles of the wrist may limit this backward extension.

If the early terrestrial troglodytians were

4

3

2

1

initially fist-walkers, one of the first changes that probably occurred as they advanced toward knuckle-walking was the development of intrinsic supporting mechanisms in the wrist. These features would permit alignment of the forearm, wrist, and palm with minimum exertion by the flexor muscles.

Biomechanically, the most challenging aspect of the adaptive shift by incipient knuckle-walkers probably involved elevation and hyperextension of the proximal digital segments, so that the load rested exclusively on the middle segments of the flexed fingers.

If early troglodytians had markedly curved fingers, resembling those of orangutans or gibbons, major modifications in the configuration of the bones and joints must have occurred before knuckle-walking could be implemented in their terrestrial descendants. Although Asian apes can fully extend their fingers, the fingers generally remain curved. In passive orangutans and gibbons, the proximal segments of the fingers cannot be bent backward very far beyond the normal extended position wherein the palm and fingers form a continuous cancave curve at the metacarpophalangeal joints (Fig. 3b). This curvature is determined not only by the shape of the bones themselves but also by the permanent flexion set of their articular surfaces in the joints *(11)*.

The assumption of modified palmigrade postures may have provided the selective complex whereby the bones and joints of the fingers in early terrestrial troglodytians became prospectively adapted for knuckle-walking. In the modified palmigrade posture the palm rests on the ground with the proximal segments of the fingers extended (or slightly hyperextended) and the middle and distal segments of the fingers flexed *(11)*. If the early troglodytians initially assumed modified palmigrade postures, changes in the wrist to restrict extension

Figure 5. Posterior view of orangutan engaged in rapid palmigrade locomotion. (1) Right forelimb and left hindlimb serve as supports while left hand is elevated and right foot is swung forward. (2) Right forelimb serves as chief supporting prop just prior to contact by right foot. Left forelimb is swung forward and left hindlimb is elevated. (3) Right hindlimb serves as major supporting prop as left forelimb and left hindlimb are swung forward. Right forelimb is elevated. (4) Left hand contacts the ground. Left forelimb and right hindlimb are principal supports. Right hand and left foot are clear of the ground.

Figure 6. Fist-walking locomotion in young orangutan compared with knuckle-walking locomotion in young chimpanzee. (1) Right hand just prior to elevation from the ground. (2) Right hand during swing phase of forelimb stride. (3) Right hand of orangutan in contact with the ground. Right hand of chimpanzee just prior to contact with the ground. (4) Support phase of right forelimb. Note the marked backward extension of the wrist in the orangutan. In the orangutan the proximal phalanges make contact with the ground, whereas in the chimpanzee the load rests on the middle phalanges of the right hand.

probably followed changes in the digits, because the wrist must be bent backward markedly in order for the animal to assume these postures.

In summary, two theoretical pathways are suggested for the evolution of knuckle-walking: (i) fist-walking → incipient knuckle-walking → consistent knuckle-walking, and

(ii) modified palmigrade locomotion → incipient knuckle-walking → consistent knuckle-walking. Perhaps future discoveries of fossil hands and biomechanical studies of the sort now in progress at the University of Chicago (20) will indicate which, if either, of these models approximates the actual evolutionary pathway.

THE PONGID RADIATION

The extent to which the common ancestors of the three great apes were adapted for suspensory posturing and locomotion cannot be determined with certainty. The fossil record contains little evidence that is of assistance in the reconstruction of postcranial anatomy in ancestral pongids. Available remains of pongids from Miocene and early Pliocene deposits generally do not exhibit advanced anatomical features related to suspensory posturing (11, 21). Postcranial remains of pongids from subsequent periods are completely lacking.

Many features that are commonly associated with brachiation have evolved in parallel at least three and possibly more than five times in the Primates. Gibbons and siamangs are uniquely adapted for ricochetal arm-swinging (11). Zoogeographical and anatomical evidence clearly documents independent evolution of adaptations for suspensory posturing in South American ateline monkeys (4). Substantial anatomical evidence also supports the inference that features related to suspensory posturing developed independently in Oreopithecus (22).

In contrast with these primate lineages, determining the expression of parallel evolution in the great apes is extremely problematical due to the paucity of paleontological and paleozoogeographical data. The most parsimonious hypothesis, based on comparative studies of living pongids, portrays the common ancestors of the great apes as possessing notable prospective adaptations for suspensory posturing and locomotion.

The divergence of orangutans and the African apes probably evinces a dichotomous pattern of evolution (23), wherein no living species closely resembles the common ancestral species. Whereas ancestral chimpanzees and gorillas experienced an adaptive shift to terrestriality, ancestral orangutans advanced, and specialized in, a unique mode of four-digit prehension and suspensory posturing (11).

Orangutans are easily the heaviest of strictly arboreal mammals. They prefer swamp-forest habitats in which the forest floor is seasonally or permanently flooded and thereby rendered unsuitable as a substratum for locomotion (18). The culmination of trends toward advanced ability to climb and cling in the forest canopy may have occurred during late Tertiary and Pleistocene times in response to periodic flooding of the Sunda Shelf region of Southeast Asia (11, 24).

The shortest, most parsimonious pathway for evolution of the African apes would be the derivation of gorillas, through increasingly advanced adaptation to terrestriality, from smaller apes not unlike living chimpanzees. Thus, the African apes evince an excurrent pattern of evolution (23) wherein the ancestral form of a species is represented among its closest living relatives.

The times of emergence of the three pongid lineages cannot be determined with certainty on the basis of available paleontological evidence. However, numerous teeth and associated cranial remains of Dryopithecus from Miocene and early Pliocene deposits in East Africa, South Asia, and Europe demonstrate remarkable similarities to corresponding parts of living apes, especially the African forms (25).

Simons and Pilbeam suggest that the ancestry of chimpanzees and gorillas may be discerned in different species of Dryopithecus (25). These workers believe that the separation of the two main lines of African apes occurred in middle or even early Miocene times, some 18 to 25 million years ago (25). Since available postcranial remains of Dryopithecus possess few features related to advanced suspensory posturing, it follows (i) that gorillas and chimpanzees evolved many features related to "brachiation" in parallel and (ii) that their adaptations to knuckle-walking are also parallelisms.

This interpretation of the fossil evidence is not consistent with the parsimonious evolutionary pathway that is inferred on the basis of comparative studies of living pongids. Final resolution of this problem depends upon further discoveries and studies on post-cranial remains of Dryopithecus, especially the large species, and of later fossil pongids. In addition, more detailed studies on variability in the dentitions and skulls of living and fossil pongids should be made, to provide broader bases for inference on possible evolutionary pathways.

Thus, until more convincing evidence is brought forward to support extreme parallelisms in the closely related species of African apes, it seems distinctly possible that only one species of *Dryopithecus* gave rise to the common ancestor of these forms. Despite the frequent occurrence of parallel evolution in the locomotive systems of primates, the similarities between chimpanzees and gorillas are so particular that I now favor the parsimonious view of evolution in the African apes.

WERE MAN'S ANCESTORS KNUCKLE-WALKERS?

If elucidating the evolution of extant apes presents many problems, elucidating the derivation of man from hypothetical apes presents far more. Several schools of thought have arisen in response to the fascinating challenge of man's theoretical origins. For convenience their adherents may be loosely grouped and termed brachiationists, antibrachiationists, and prebrachiationists.

The brachiationists (26) hold the view that man evolved from ancestral apes that were notably advanced with respect to suspensory posturing and arm-swinging. The antibrachiationists (27), on the other hand, suggest that the features of upper limb and trunk that man shares with the "brachiating apes" are parallelisms that evolved (through undetermined mechanisms) in direct response to orthograde bipedalism.

The prebrachiationists (28) occupy more or less conservative positions between these two poles. They suggest that, although the common ancestor of man and the troglodytian apes was not an advanced brachiator, it possessed notable evolutionary tendencies toward this pattern of movement and toward the associated morphology. Accordingly, the prebrachiationists also must grant a certain degree of parallel evolution in the upper limb and trunk of man and apes.

The diversity of locomotive patterning in living apes and the observation that arm-swinging is an infrequent component in the behavioral repertoires of African apes indi-

cate that reexamination of the chimpanzee model of human ancestry might be profitable. In particular, recognition of knuckle-walking as a unique terrestrial locomotive pattern in the African apes poses the following question for troglophilic brachiationists: Were man's ancestors knuckle-walkers before they were bipeds?

Washburn, an anthropologist who has persistently postulated a remarkably chimpanzee-like ancestor for man, recently responded to this question by interpolating a knuckle-walking stage between stages of brachiation and bipedalism (15, 29). He suggests that "the general ape anatomy" of the human hand and "the general reduction of hair on the dorsal surfaces of the fingers and toes" support the inference that man and chimpanzee evolved from a common knuckle-walking ancestor (15). This evolutionary model implies an excurrent pathway in human evolution.

Insofar as I can discern from dissections of numerous ape and human hands, there are no features in the bones, ligaments, or muscles of the latter that give evidence for a history of knuckle-walking (11). With the exception of "evidence" from the distribution of midphalangeal hair, all the features cited by Washburn may be considered parallelisms or common adaptations to a past history of suspensory posturing. Furthermore, there are notable differences between chimpanzee and man in "form of wrist," "development of flexion," and other features that Washburn lists as "general ape" characteristics in the hand. In fact there are considerable differences between the hands of African and of Asian apes, which should preclude overgeneralization on the manual anatomy of apes (11).

At first glance, the absence of mid-phalangeal hair on the fingers of African apes and man suggests a common knuckle-walking heritage. But more detailed genetic and histological studies are needed before this observation may be incorporated reliably into an evolutionary model. While depilation of the fingers in man may result from relatively simple genetic influence (30), the genetic mechanisms underlying the development of knuckle pads are probably different. Furthermore, in man, depilation of the toes is more usual than depilation of the fingers (30). Are we to conclude therefrom that man's feet once possessed knuckle-pads that were used for a unique pattern of "pedal knuckle-walking"?

Finally, in man, midphalangeal hair occurs with *greatest* frequency on the ring and middle fingers *(30)*. These are precisely the digits that the chimpanzee must use in knuckle-walking *(11)*.

Fossil evidence relevant to the possible use of hands for locomotion is more complete for man than for the African apes. Hand bones, belonging to more than one individual, have been recovered from Bed I of Olduvai Gorge, Tanzania. These bones are associated with cranial and other postcranial fragments that have been assigned to the taxon *Homo habilis*, a form evincing affinities with both the gracile form of *Australopithecus* and with later, more advanced hominids *(31)*. Preliminary studies on the original remains and published illustrations indicate that there are no features in the specimens that document unequivocally a knuckle-walking habitus or heritage *(11, 31)*. Unfortunately, there are no distal radii or metacarpal bones. From these bones the occurrence or nonoccurrence of knuckle-walking might be discerned more readily.

The proximal and middle phalanges are notably curved, indicating either that these animals used their hands for suspensory posturing or that their ancestors used their hands for this purpose.

This inference is supported also by evidence from fragmentary shoulder girdles of early Pleistocene hominids. Oxnard measured available fragments of a fossil shoulder blade and collarbone and compared these with an extensive series of measurements on comparable parts in living primates. The fossils compare most closely with the highly arboreal Asian apes *(32)*.

Furthermore, in a series of sophisticated biometrical and mathematical studies, Oxnard demonstrated that it is more likely that the human shoulder evolved from the shoulder of a large-bodied arboreal ape than from those of arboreal and terrestrial monkeys, ricochetal arm-swinging apes, or knuckle-walkers *(33)*. The minimum pathway for evolution of the human shoulder from a shoulder represented by living forms may have been a single step—"*loss* by the human shoulder of the single function of raising the arm above the head for purposes of suspen-sion . . . during foraging and locomotion" *(33)*. A selective complex for achieving integrity of the shoulder joint in positions of rest and manipulative activities may have acted to further modify the human shoulder in the direction of its modern configuration.

In summary, evidence from hominid upper limbs generally indicates that the ancestors of man probably engaged in some form of suspensory posturing, and that they assumed bipedal postures very soon after venturing to the ground. Accordingly, man probably did not pass through a knuckle-walking stage; the phylogeny of man and apes probably represents a dichotomous pattern of evolution.

If this pathway proves to be a correct assessment of human phylogeny, we must consider arboreal habitats as the environmental context in which the fundamental divergence of ancestral man and the troglodytians occurred. This divergence may have resulted from differential usage of the hindlimbs by populations of troglodytians such that the center of gravity shifted more toward the pelvis in man's ancestors. By contrast, ancestral chimpanzees probably made more use of the forelimbs in foraging and locomotion. Thus their centers of gravity remained in, or perhaps moved even higher into, the chest.

Subsequently, when arboreal populations shifted to terrestrial habitats, chimpanzees became semierect quadrupeds, while man was predisposed toward orthograde bipedality.

Adaptation to bipedal plantigrade locomotion has so altered the structure of the human lower limb, especially the foot, that it is difficult to discern precisely the arboreal usage of these organs in ancestral forms. Therefore, the mechanisms whereby ancestral hominids diverged from ancestral pongids are highly elusive. Studies on the use of the hindlimb as part of locomotor, foraging, and feeding behaviors in arboreal monkeys and apes, particularly in Asian langurs, orangutans, gibbons, siamangs, and advanced South American monkeys, may provide more basis for inferring possible evolutionary pathways of man and apes.

SUMMARY

In chimpanzees and gorillas many features

once thought to be characteristic of brachiating hands are in fact unique products of adaptation for terrestrial knuckle-walking.

The African apes can maintain static knuckle-walking postures with a minimum of muscular effort because of special bone-ligament-muscle mechanisms in their wrists and metacarpophalangeal joints. The powerfully developed wrist and digital flexor muscles are called into action during knuckle-walking strides. The knuckle-walking posture allows these muscles not only to serve supporting functions but also to provide propulsive forces at the distal extremity of the forelimb in various phases of the locomotive cycle.

Comparative anatomical and behavioral evidence indicates that, in early troglodytians, the shift from arboreal foraging and locomotion to terrestrial knuckle-walking entailed adaptations in hand posture and structure that were more complex than mere placement of an inflexible brachiating hook topsy-turvy on the ground. The terrestrial troglodytians probably evolved first through a fist-walking or modified palmigrade phase wherein the hand was used as a supporting prop but not as an effectual propulsive lever. This stage was probably followed by a phase of incipient knuckle-walking in which the wrist and finger bones and joints were further modified to effect a characteristic knuckle-walking habitus. In this posture, not only does the hand serve as a supporting prop but the fingers act as propulsive levers.

Gorillas probably evolved from chimpanzee-like knuckle-walking troglodytians through advanced adaptation for terrestrial foraging and feeding.

Divergence of the hominid lineage from the lineage of the African apes probably occurred before the evolution of knuckle-walking. Recent fossil discoveries and comparative anatomical studies support the hypothesis that man evolved from a large-bodied arboreal ape that was adapted for some degree of suspensory posturing and locomotion. It is suggested that the initial divergence between man and ape may have occurred in arboreal habitats through differential use of the forelimbs and the hindlimbs.

REFERENCES AND NOTES

[1] J. B. de Lamarck, *Philosophie Zoologique* (Paris, 1809), vol. 1; C. Darwin, *The Descent of Man and Selection in Relation to Sex* (Murray, London, 1871); E. Haeckel, *Anthropogenie oder Entwickelungsgeschichte des Menschen* (Engelmann, Leipzig, 1874); A. Keith, *Brit. Med. J.* 1, 451 (1923); W. K. Gregory, *Bull. Amer. Mus. Nat. Hist.* 35, 341 (1916); W. K. Gregory, *Man's Place Among the Anthropoids* (Clarendon, Oxford, 1934); D. J. Morton, *Amer. J. Phys. Anthropol.* 10, 173 (1927); H. Weinert, *Ursprung der Menschheit* (Enke, Stuttgart, 1932); S. L. Washburn, *Cold Spring Harbor Symp. Quant. Biol.* 15, 66 (1951).

[2] F. W. Jones, *The Problem of Man's Ancestry* (Society for Promoting Christian Knowledge, London, 1918); ———, *The Ancestry of Man* (Gillies, Brisbane, 1923); ———, *Man's Place Among the Mammals* (Longmans Green, New York, 1929); H. F. Osborn, *Science* 65, 481 (1927), *Hum. Biol.* 1, 4 (1929); W. L. Straus, *Quart. Rev. Biol.* 24, 200 (1949).

[3] A. Keith, *Brit. Med. J.* 1, 451 (1923).

[4] A. H. Schultz, *Quart. Rev. Biol.* 11, 259 (1936); ———, in *Primatologia*, H. Hofer, A. H. Schultz, D. Starck, Eds. (Karger, Basel, 1956), vol. 1, pp. 887-964; ———, in *Perspectives on Human Evolution*, S. L. Washburn and P. Jay, Eds. (Holt, Rinehart and Winston, New York, 1968), vol. 1, pp. 122-195; G. E. Erikson, *Symp. Zool. Soc. London* 10, 135 (1963).

[5] E. H. Ashton and C. E. Oxnard, *Trans. Zool. Soc. London* 29, 557 (1963).

[6] J. R. Napier and P. H. Napier, *A Handbook of Living Primates* (Academic Press, New York, 1967), p. 385.

[7] J. Itani and A. Suzuki, *Primates* 8, 335 (1967).

[8] G. B. Schaller, *The Mountain Gorilla: Ecology and Behavior* (Univ. of Chicago Press, Chicago, 1963).

[9] J. M. Goodall, *Ann. N.Y. Acad. Sci.* 102, 455 (1962); ———. *Symp. Zool. Soc. London* 10, 39 (1963); ———. in *Primate Behavior*, I. De Vore, Ed. (Holt, Rinehart and Winston, New York, 1965), pp. 425-473; ———. personal communication; V. Reynolds and F. Reynolds, in *Primate Behavior*, I. DeVore, Ed. (Holt, Rinehart and Winston, New York, 1965), pp. 368-424; H. W. Nissen, *Comp. Psychol. Monogr.* 8 (1931).

[10] W. L. Straus, *Amer. J. Phys. Anthropol.* 27, 199 (1940).

[11] R. H. Tuttle, *ibid.* 26, 171 (1967); ———, *J. Morphol.* 128, 309 (1969); ———, in *The Chimpanzee*, G. H. Bourne, Ed. (Krager, Basel, 1969), vol. 2.

[12] R. A. Ellis and W. Montagna, *Amer. J. Phys. Anthropol.* 20, 79 (1962); W. Montagna and J. S. Yun, *ibid.* 21, 189 (1963).

[13] J. Schreiber, *Gegenbaurs Morphol. Jahrb.* 77, 22 (1936).

[14] C. E. Oxnard, *Amer. J. Phys. Anthropol.* 26, 219 (1967); ———. *J. Morphol.* 126, 249 (1968); ———. *J. Biomech.* 2 (1969); C. E. Oxnard and P. M. Neely, *J. Morphol.*, in press.

[15]S. L. Washburn [*Condon Lectures* (Oregon State System of Higher Education, Eugene, 1968), p. 24] is overgeneralizing when he states that a "position of partial supination is . . . taken by the great apes in quadrupedal locomotion."

[16]F. K. Jouffroy and J. Lessertisseur, *Mammalia* 24, 93 (1960).

[17]C. Midlo, *Amer. J. Phys. Anthropol.* 19, 337 (1934).

[18]A. R. Wallace, *The Malay Archipelago, The Land of the Orang-Utan and the Bird of Paradise* (1890; Dover, New York, rev. ed. 10, 1964). The animal that Wallace observed walking "on his knuckles" probably was walking on its *proximal* phalanges; many early observers did not distinguish the unique flexed-finger posture of the African apes (knuckle-walkers) from the flexed-finger postures of orangutans.

[19]B. Harrisson, *Orang-utan* (Collins, London, 1962), pp. 71 and 78.

[20]C. E. Oxnard, *Anat. Rec.* 163, 239 (1969); ———, and R. H. Tuttle, *Amer. J. Phys. Anthropol.*, in press. In these studies, aspects of the mechanical efficiency of the hands of apes and man are determined in two-dimensional photoelastic models.

[21]J. R. Napier and P. R. Davis, *Fossil Mammals Africa* 16 (1959).

[22]W. L. Straus, in *Classification and Human Evolution*, S. L. Washburn, Ed. (Aldine, Chicago, 1963), pp. 146-177.

[23]V. Grant. *The Origin of Adaptations* (Columbia Univ. Press, New York, 1963), pp. 452-453.

[24]R. H. Tuttle, *Bull. Amer. Anthropol. Ass.* 1, 141 (1968).

[25]E. L. Simons and D. R. Pilbeam, *Folia Primatol.* 3, 81 (1965); D. R. Pilbeam, *Nature* 219, 1335 (1968).

[26]W. K. Gregory, D. J. Morton, and S. L. Washburn, in addition to Keith, may be considered "brachiationists." Keith, Gregory, and Washburn proposed a large-bodied ape as progenitor of man, while Morton favored a small-bodied ape.

[27]Among the "antibrachiationists" are F. W. Jones, H. F. Osborn, and W. L. Straus. Jones favored a tarsioid form as ancestral to man, Osborn proposed a large-brained "pro-dawn" man, and Straus favors a pronograde quadrupedal form.

[28]Prominent among the "prebrachiationists" are W. E. LeGros Clark, L. S. B. Leakey, J. R. Napier, and A. H. Schultz. The first three authors were impressed by the generalized anatomy of *Dryopithecus (Proconsul) africanus* and believe that it provides a reasonable model of both great-ape and human ancestral morphology.

[29]S. L. Washburn, "The Huxley Memorial Lecture 1967," in *Proc. Roy. Anthropol. Inst. Gt. Brit. Ireland* (Aldine, Chicago, 1967), pp. 21-27.

[30]C. H. Danforth, *Amer. J. Phys. Anthropol.* 4, 189 (1921); M. M. Bernstein and B. S. Burks, *J. Hered.* 33, 45 (1942); M. M. Bernstein, *ibid.* 40, 127 (1949).

[31]J. R. Napier, *Nature* 196, 409 (1962).

[32]C. E. Oxnard, *Amer. J. Phys. Anthropol.* 28, 213 (1968); *ibid.* 29, 429 (1968).

[33]———.

[33]———. *ibid.*, in press.

[34]I thank Drs. F. C. Howell, C. E. Oxnard, R. Singer, and L. VanValen, of the University of Chicago, for their helpful suggestions and improvements of the text. The drawings were made by Mr. P. Murray, University of Chicago. This research was supported by National Science Foundation grants GS-834 and GS-1888 and by Public Health Service research career development award No. 1-K04-GM16347-01 from the National Institutes of Health. Supplementary support was provided by U.S. Public Health Service general research support grant No. FR-5367 to the University of Chicago; by NIH grant No. FR-00165 to the Yerkes Regional Primate Research Center, Atlanta, Georgia; and by the Wenner-Gren Foundation for Anthropological Research.

18

BRACHIATION AND BRACHIATORS
John Napier

After reading Napier's discussion of brachiation, you may wonder why the subject has generated such extended discussion. From the time of Thomas Henry Huxley more than a century ago, it has been realized that the detailed similarity of shoulder, arm, and elbow of men and apes not only indicated close evolutionary kinship but also reflected the consequences of selection for the performance of similar activities. Since men could operate just as effectively with the arms and shoulders of monkeys or lemurs, it is clear that the selective forces that shaped the human upper limb are not related to the human life-way. Hence the interest in the mode of life of man's close relatives where anatomy is related to the activities performed. It is quite clear that some form of suspensory locomotion, whether full or partial brachiation, represents the past conditions that shaped the pongid—and human—arm, shoulder, and chest.

Chimpanzees and orangs still make extensive use of suspensory locomotion. Although gorillas and men do so rarely, if at all, their anatomy reflects the fact that this was a shaping force in the evolutionary past of both species. Whether the human ancestor ever was adapted to brachiating to the extent visible in modern chimpanzees is debatable. Most authrorities do not feel that it was, although most accept the view that man's ancestry involved at least a partial brachiating phase.

Interestingly enough, one of the anatomists who has recently had second thoughts about these matters is none other than Napier himself (Napier and Walker 1967). Instead of relying on the more accepted view that the upright posture of the human head, neck, and trunk was a consequence of suspensory locomotion, he has returned to a version of the "tarsioid hypothises" of the late British anatomist, F. Wood Jones, and suggested that some kind of "vertical clinging and leaping" in the remote pre-pongid ancestor may have been responsible. From our point of view, however, the evidence for this is nonexistent and the logic less than compelling, so we are content to stick with the more conventional brachiating point of view.

> Napier, J. R. and A. C. Walker. 1967. Vertical clinging and leaping: a newly recognized category of locomotor behaviour of primates. *Folia Primatologica* 6:204-219.

INTRODUCTION

Sooner or later discussions relating to the subject of human ancestry inevitably touch on brachiation, and within a short space of time the participants are involved in useless terminological controversy. The purpose of this paper is to discuss the significance of the term and its cognates and to propose a new classification which, it is hoped, will be generally acceptable.

The author is fully aware that no single classification is likely to please everyone particularly when it concerns a subject which

is in a state of flux. A considerable amount of work is being done at the present time, on primate locomotion that will undoubtedly lead, in a few years time, to a much better understanding of mechanisms and relationships. In the meantime there is a need for unhampered communication between workers in this research field and the present classification is therefore offered as a temporary expedient.

The philology of the terms brachiation which has been dealt with elsewhere in this volume by Trevor, indicates that, for Owen, "brachiator" had a strictly limited significance; it simply implied the gibbon and its mode of locomotion. Keith, to whom the term is commonly credited, also employed "brachiator" in Owen's sense, but later extended it to include the orang. Since then our knowledge in the fields of primate behaviour and human evolution has made it clear that the use of the forelimbs in arboreal suspension is more widespread an activity than was originally supposed. We know for instance that the gorilla and chimpanzee although largely "knuckle-walkers" in Owen's sense, possess the morphology and occasionally show the behavioural character of a gibbon-like brachiator. We now have information from field studies in the New York as well as the Old World that the selective use of the forelimbs both as suspensory agents in movement along a bough, and as reaching and grasping agents in jumping from one level of the trees to another, is widespread among simian Primates. We are also aware that during the evolution of the higher Primates there were certain forms such as *Proconsul*, *Limnopithecus* and *Pliopithecus* showing incipient morphological specializations in the direction of a true brachiator, although none of these fossil forms had achieved a morphological status comparable with modern apes.

The tendency today is to extend the use of the terms to include all four anthropoid apes. There is also a tendency to modify the terms by the use of qualifying adjectives e.g. habitual brachiation or by addition of a prefix such as "semi" as in semibrachiator. These trends would seem to argue a certain inadequacy of present terminology in the light of modern knowledge. There is no great harm in qualification of the terms providing the terms themselves are fully defined and understood. The alternative to such a procedure is to leave the terms as they are and limit their usage to the sense in which they were used by Owen and Keith. To do this, however, is to run the risk of perpetuating the sort of typological thinking that Patterson (1954) envisaged so expressively ". . . living gibbons are brachiators *par excellence*. Propliopithecus* was a gibbon *ergo;* it was an excellent brachiator; the ancestral pongines must have been too; man does not brachiate, *ergo* his ancestors must have branched off before this adaptation became established; *Proplipithecus* is early Oligocene in age, *ergo* the Hominidae arose in the Eocene. Q.E.D." While Patterson's logic is intentionally extravagant there is no doubt that much confusion has arisen through misinterpretation of what is meant by a "brachiator," as Le Gros Clark (1959) indicates (p. 345) ". . . the other objection (to deriving the Hominidae from a known Miocene genus of anthropoid apes) seems to have been based on the tacit assumption that because the dentition of the fossil apes is typically pongid therefore the creatures were like modern anthropoid apes in other respects—including the extreme modifications of the limbs for specialized habits of brachiation." This tendency to regard brachiation as an "all-or-none" phenomenon, immune as it were from the slow process of improvement that characterises the evolution of any locomotor specialization (c.f. bipedal walking in hominids), is a serious reflexion of the inflexibility of the terms.

As our knowledge of the fossil record of Primates increases we can expect to find forms representing many of the intermediate morphological stages in the transition from quadruped to brachiator. It is clear that if the term "brachiator" is used to describe the morphology of a Miocene ape such as *Proconsul*, which was neither structurally nor functionally as advanced as modern apes, the word has already been stretched far beyond its original meaning and the door has been oped wide to the sort of circular arguments that Patterson (*loc. cit.*) envisages. It was for this reason that the term "generalized brachiator" (now recognized as unsatisfactory) was proposed by Napier & Davis (1959) in order to mitigate the confusion that might have arisen were the morphology of *Proconsul's* limb skeleton described as being that of a "brachiator."

BRACHIATION IN LIVING ANTHROPOID APES

Among living anthropoid apes only the gibbons and the siamangs can be regarded as "full-time" brachiators.[1] Orang-utans, while entirely arboreal in habitat do not, when adult, habitually progress by means of the suspensory activities of the forelimbs alone. They climb and move cautiously, aided by

[1]Even among gibbons, as Washburn has pointed out (personal communication), progression may be bipedal or quadrupedal when in trees depending on the particular situation in which they find themselves.

the hind limbs and never, as far as is known, project themselves into space by means of the angular momentum of the forelimbs as do the gibbons.

Gorillas are forest-floor animals; the females and immature males are said to spend an appreciable time in trees where they have been seen to brachiate (Bingham, 1932). According to more recent studies (Donisthorpe, 1958; gorillas spend less than 10 per cent of their time in trees, and have not been seen to brachiate in the sense of hand-over-hand suspended locomotion, but rather in the manner of orangs, with the aid of the hindlimbs.

Chimpanzees appear to occupy an intermediate position between gibbons and orangs as brachiating forms. They are probably less arboreal in terms of habitat than orangs but when in trees they brachiate more fully than orangs, depending less on the lower limbs for support. In the wild, chimpanzees occupy a wide range of habitats from tropical rain forest to open woodlands and generalizations about their locomotor habits are dangerous. It is quite clear, however, that among the anthropoid apes there is a *spectrum* of brachiation, both in the sense of time spent and in manner of performance, ranging perhaps from 100 per cent brachiation for 95 per cent of the time in gibbons, to 50 per cent brachiation for 10 per cent of the time in gorillas.

All four apes however *can* brachiate; that is to say they have in common certain distinctive morphological adaptations to hand-over-hand suspended progress through the trees with the trunk held vertically. Morphologically they are brachiators in spite of certain secondary modifications in living forms. The fact that anthropoid apes do not brachiate to the same extent or degree is due to a variety of factors, such as an increase in body weight (gorillas and orangs), secondary structural specializations (gorillas) and for reasons of altered habitat (mountain gorillas and some chimpanzees). Correlated with this variation there are certain quantitative differences in the morphology of the four living Pongidae. Schultz (1930) has shown that while it is true to say, on the grounds of skeletal structure that the higher Primates as a group are clearly separated from all the rest of the Primates, each higher primate has a number of skeletal features which are more

specialized than in any other higher primate. For instance, the hand of the orang is relatively longer and the thumb relatively shorter, than in the remaining apes; the thumb of the gibbon has a mechanism unique among the higher Primates; the hand and foot of the gorilla have a certain specialization related to a secondary terrestrial way of life not seen in the other apes. Thus, while higher Primates share a common overall pattern related to broadly similar ecological influences, there is no reason to doubt that these influences were neither precisely the same nor that they were of the same duration in all. It is clear, for instance, from the evidence of morphology that the structural characteristics of a brachiator were aquired quite independently in the gibbons and the African anthropoids; indeed as Avis (1962) points out, a gibbon's brachiating technique is distinct from that of the other apes. It is also clear that active brachiation persisted in the ancestral Pongidae long after it had been discontinued in early Hominidae.

ARM-SWINGING IN MONKEYS

Arm-swinging as a mode of locomotion in which the arms are selectively used to a greater or less extent, also figures in the behaviour of non-hominoid Primates. In a recent review (in litt.) Ashton & Oxnard have collected and classified field observations reported in the literature relating to the locomotion of the whole primate order. This review forms part of a long-term research project which sets out to correlate primate locomotor patterns with the form, function and disposition of muscles and bones by quantitative methods. Their work focuses attention on the existence of an intermediate locomotor group, intermediate in both a behavioural and structural sense (Ashton & Oxnard 1963). This group, termed semibrachiators (Napier, 1961), include, according to Ashton and Oxnard, the following genera.
CEBOIDEA.   *Ateles, Brachyteles, Lagothrix, Alouatta.*
CERCOPITHECOIDEA.   *Rhinopithecus, Presbytis, Colobus.*

The mode of locomotion of semibrachiators is basically that of an arboreal quadruped but, in addition, a variable amount of time is spent in swinging by the arms and leaping with the forelimbs outstretched to grasp a hand-hold. Perhaps the most illuminating account of the particular mode of locomotion of semibrachiators is given by Tennent (1861) whose description of *Presbytis cephalopterus* is as follows: ". . . their progress is made not so much by leaping as by swinging from branch to branch, using their powerful arms alternately; and when baffled by distance flinging themselves obliquely so as to catch the lower boughs of an opposite tree, the momentum acquired by their descent being sufficient to cause a rebound of the branch that carries them upward again. . . ."

A jumping sequence similar to that described by Tennent is illustrated in Fig. 1. These action strips were made by tracing individual 16 mm ciné-film frames and then combining them in a single diagram. Figure 1 is an adult male *Nasalis larvatus* leaping from a higher to a lower level of a riverine forest in Borneo. The hindlimbs are fully extended at the hips and knees at the take-off, the forelimbs are extended above the head, reaching forward to grasp at the plexus of small branches of the landing site. In Fig. 2,

also of *Nasalis*, the jump is in a slightly upward direction and illustrates even more clearly the attitude of the forelimbs.[2] Figure 3 illustrates a jumping sequence in *Cercopithecus nictitans*, similar in length and duration to that shown in Fig. 1, taken from a 16 mm film made in the Ituri Forest of the Congo. The jumping posture of the quadrupedal *C. nictitans* is in strong contrast to that of *Nasalis* being altogether more foursquare and dog-like, lacking particularly the overhead extension of the forelimbs.

Field observations of arm-swinging by *Colobus* are numerous. Recent reports include Booth (1956), Haddow (1952, 1956 and personal communication) and Goodall 1962 (personal communication).

[2]In a recent article (1962) in the Straits Times Press (Malaya) Ltd. Tom Harrisson describes the leaping activities of the Banded Leaf Monkey, *P. melalophos* in the following terms: "The monkey . . . then literally hurls itself forward and out with an immensely powerful thrust from the hind legs; the arms grope wildly out ahead, the body arcs in tension, the back legs unwind and the tail flies high."

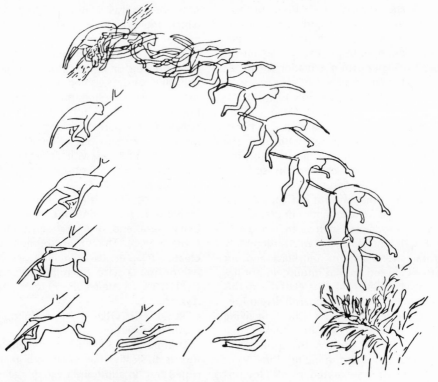

Figure 1. Action strip of *Nasalis larvatus* leaping from a high to a lower level in riverine forest in Borneo. Prepared from individual frames of 16 mm cine film from "Zoo quest for a dragon" (B.B.C.).

Figure 2. *Nasalis larvatus* leaping slightly upwards.

Figure 3. Action strip of *Cercopithecus nictitans* jumping from a high to a lower level in Ituri Forest, Congo. Prepared from individual frames of 16 mm cine film "No room for wild animals."

Arm-swinging in the New World monkeys has been described by Erikson (1952, 1954, 1957) who has described New World forms as "prehensile-tailed brachiators." In the captive state, woolly and spider monkeys "brachiate" freely in the manner of the gibbon although in addition to the forelimbs, the prehensile tail is used. In leaping however the hind limbs of the woolly monkey are tucked in under the body (Hill, 1962). This is in contrast to the leaping posture of Old World semibrachiators.

There is, thus, a considerable body of field evidence for the free use of the forelimbs in suspending the body, projecting it through space and reaching ahead with the arms during leaping, among certain non-anthropoid simian Primates. There is also structural evidence based on studies of the shoulder region that some of these forms show adaptations that are intermediate between those of a true brachiator and a quadruped (Ashton & Oxnard, 1963; Oxnard, this volume). There seems therefore adequate justification for describing those non-anthropoid forms as semibrachiators and their mode of locomotion as semibrachiation. The African semibrachiating *Colobus* shows a decided preference for the higher strata of the forest canopy (Booth, 1957). This preference is presumably largely dietetic in origin, the leaves of *Triplochiton* a high emergent in the semi-deciduous closed forest are relished by *Colobus*. One of the physical characteristics of the upper storey of closed canopy forest is a *discontinuity* of the crowns of the emergent trees (Richards, 1952). Animals living and feeding at these levels of the forest must, in moving through the forest, either descend to lower levels where the canopy is *continuous* or pass from crown to crown in the *discontinuous* stratum by leaping or brachiating.

In contrast, many generalized arboreal quadrupedal monkeys (some of the guenons provide the best example in Africa), live mainly in the middle or lower storeys. At this level the canopy is closed, the interwoven foliage forming an almost continuous vegetational mat. Animals living at this level can move through the forest by direct pathways, using a combination of running, climbing and jumping; unlike some of the Colobidae, *Cercopithecus* crosses gaps too great to span by jumping, at forest-floor level.

Much more work, both experimental and in the field, is needed to determine the relationship between arboreal stratification and primate locomotor patterns (Napier, 1962) but it seems reasonable to suppose that the morphology of forests and, in particular, the *level* which different species habitually occupy, has played a large part in the phylogeny of primate locomotion including brachiation and semibrachiation.

It has been argued that by extending the concept of brachiation to include non-anthropoid forms, it becomes impossible to exclude any catarrhine or platyrrhine monkey from this category. This is a valid criticism, for almost all monkeys—even baboons (Wells, 1931)—at some time or other during arboreal locomotion, use their arms in suspending themselves below a branch if only in the process of dropping to the ground (Avis, 1962). It is not surprising in view of the generalized form of the primate shoulder girdle, arm, forearm and hand, that arm-swinging locomotion is so widespread among Primates. The generalized primate forelimb is pre-adaptive for the whole spectrum of arm-swinging, from the very occasional arm-swinging by, for instannce, the guenons to the full-scale brachiation of the gibbons. The secondary modifications found in the shoulder girdle and forelimb of savanna-living baboons prohibit more than token arm-swinging. It is possible that similar considerations may apply to other genera of the Cercopithecinae.

PHYLOGENY OF BRACHIATION

Body-size may well have been an important factor in the evolution of arm-swinging locomotion. This has been suggested elsewhere (Napier, 1961) as comprising at least one factor in the evolution of prehensility of the primate hand. Living semibrachiators are all relatively large Primates, as indeed was the fossil form *Proconsul africanus* whose locomotor functions, it is inferred, has much in common with living semibrachiators. There must be a critical relationship between the weight and size of an arboreal animal and the diameter of the branch on which it is moving. Beyond this critical size in order to reach the more slender and flexible branches at the periphery of the crown, an animal is driven to *suspending* itself from the branch by means of fore- and hindlimbs, in order to maintain stability. If this particular pattern of behaviour proved advantageous, in terms of feeding, for example, a selective evolutionary pressure would be set up in the direction of long-limbed forms with mobile shoulder joints and prehensile hands and feet.

In a recent experimental study on brachiation, Avis (1962) points out that in a "small-branch setting" in which the arboreal supports are both slender and flexible, it is almost obligatory for an animal to suspend itself below the branch. She found that monkeys preferred the more solid branches while apes showed a preference for the more flexible branches. The ability of apes to grasp slender twigs is no doubt facilitated by the unique mechanism of their fingers known as "double-locking" (Napier, 1960) which permits a chimpanzee or orang to obtain a firm grip on, for instance, a slender piece of string without the help of the thumb.

Taking the known facts and matters of observation into account, there seems little reason why the concept of brachiation should not be extended beyond the limits of its historical connotation, if confusion is thereby avoided. There is, however, a serious disadvantage in so doing. If the use of the abstract noun "brachiation" is extended then its cognate, "brachiator" must be extended also. The term brachiator, however, has a structural connotation as well as a behavioural one (Hooton, 1946); a brachiator is one which brachiates, but it is also a primate with a well-recognized morphology that is peculiarly adapted in a particular way for arm-swinging. Monkeys are *not* brachiators in this sense, however much they may appear to be in certain aspects of their locomotor behaviour.

It has been suggested that in order to obviate this difficulty, the term brachiator should never be used in a structural and functional sense, but only a behavioural one—to describe an exponent of an observed locomotor pattern. To agree to this, would be to render brachiator invalid as a phylogenetic concept, for only *living* animals could then be classified as brachiators; and it is perhaps in phylogeny, above all, that the terms are of the greatest value.

Avis concluded from the evidence of her experimental study (1962 *loc. cit.*) that arm-swinging in monkeys was clearly distinguishable from the brachiation of the apes. On doubts if such a clear-cut conclusion woul have been possible if New World forms suc as *Ateles* or *Lagothrix* had been included in her series. These forms in many ways provide the essential link in the spectrum of arm swinging among the Primates. As Washburn (1950) pointed out "Spider monkeys brachiate *(sic)* . . . they also move in a quadrupedal fashion . . . the combination of brachiation and quadrupedal locomotion . . . shows how the ape-type of locomotion may have arisen." In the hierarchy of primate arm-swinging, the spider monkey and forms closely related to it are intermediate between the anthropoid brachiators and the Old World semibrachiators as Ashton and Oxnard *(in litt)* indicate in their recent review. If only the catarrhine monkeys are taken into account then arm-swinging locomotion might well appear to be a discontinuous phenomenon with brachiators on one hand and quadrupeds on the other. By introducing the New World monkeys, the gap is largely bridged and it becomes easier to view arm-swinging among Primates as a spectrum of activity ranging from the occasional to the habitual. In phylogenetic terms it is not difficult to see how the arm-swinging of the modern gibbon could have evolved from the occasional arm-swinging of a *hypothetical* early catarrhine having a locomotor pattern similar to that shown by certain living Old World—or for that matter —New World monkeys; this is of particular moment when one recalls the similarity of the upper limb structure of *Limnopithecus* to that of modern *Ateles* (Le Gros Clark & Thomas, 1951).

The present communication however concerns not so much the activity of arm-swinging itself, but the deployment and interpretation of the existing terminology used to describe it.

SUGGESTED TERMINOLOGY

The simplest solution and one at the same time that does not conflict with customary usage seems to be: (1) To limit the use of brachiation and brachiator to a strictly traditional sense (though even this is to expand the terms beyond Owen's original usage); (2) To retain the neologism "semibrachiator," limiting its use to those monkeys that show

BRACHIATION (Brachiators)	(1) True brachiation	Hylobates, Symphalangus.
	(2) Modified brachiation	Gorilla, Pan, Pongo.
	(3) Pro-brachiation	Proconsul africanus, Limno-pithecus etc.
SEMI-BRACHIATION (Semibrachiators)	(1) New World monkey semibrachiation	Ateles, Brachyteles, Lagothrix, Alouatta.
	(2) Old World monkey semibrachiation	Nasalis, Rhinopithecus, Presby-tis, Colobus.

both structural and behavioural adaptations towards brachiators and brachiation. Until the locomotor patterns of monkeys are better understood it is probably better to sub-classify New World and Old World semibrachiators into separate groups. (3) To distinguish between the habitual, full-scale brachiation of the gibbons and the modified brachiation of the other anthropid apes and (4) To distinguish the incipient specializations of brachiating fossil forms, such as *Proconsul africanus* and *Limnopithecus*, from the fully evolved facility of modern apes, by employing the designation "pro-brachiator."[3]

Once more it must be emphasized that the following classification is only a temporary expedient. Considerable work on primate locomotion is now going forward in Great Britain and America which will undoubtedly lead to a better understanding of primate locomotor patterns in the future, and particularly, of their significance for the origins of man. It is clearly very important that some sort of interim agreement should be reached on the use of the terms.

This classification does not include the large group of monkeys in which the arms are occasionally, incidentally and briefly used to suspend the body or to reach ahead to grasp at the end of a leap. These monkeys are *essentially* quadrupedal Primates and do not show any special morphological adaptations for vertical suspension. Such mobility of the forelimbs as these animals show, and which permit the occasional use of the limbs as

[3]The terms semibrachiation and semibrachiator have been used by the author to describe both the locomotor pattern and structure of certain *fossil hominoids* (e.g. *Proconsul africanus*) as well as that of *modern monkeys*. While there is a possibility that future study will reveal that the locomotor adaptations of the two groups are in fact quite similar, it is clearly necessary to distinguish for the time being the incipient hominoid brachiators ancestral to modern apes from the living cercopithecoid and ceboid semibrachiators.

suspensory agents, is a result of the generalized form of the primate skeleton in which the primitive mobility of the shoulder girdle and forelimb has been retained.

The three groups of arm-swinging Primates are defined in terms of behaviour, structure and function as follows:

TRUE BRACHIATION AND TRUE BRACHIATORS

True brachiation is a form of arboreal locomotion in which the forelimbs alone fully extended above the head, are used to suspend the body and to propel it through space.

Primates that habitually employ this form of arboreal locomotion to the exclusion of movements of running and leaping are termed true brachiators.

True brachiators possess distinctive structural adaptations to vertical suspension and arm-swinging locomotion, particularly in the forelimb and trunk.

MODIFIED BRACHIATION AND MODIFIED BRACHIATORS

Modified brachiation is a form of arboreal locomotion in which the forelimbs fully extended above the head play a major role in suspending the body or propelling it through space. The hindlimbs contribute to locomotion to a greater or lesser extent (depending largely on the size of the animal) by providing partial support for the weight of the body from below.

Primates that habitually employ this form of locomotion, when moving in trees, to the exclusion of movements of running and leaping are termed modified brachiators.

Modified brachiators possess distinctive structural adaptations to vertical suspension and arm-swinging locomotion particularly in the forelimb and trunk. There may, however, be evidence of adaptations that are secondary in nature and which modify the primary adaptations for vertical suspension.

PRO-BRACHIATION AND PRO-BRACHIA-TORS

Pro-brachiation is a term used to define the hypothetical behaviour of fossil Primates whose structural and functional morphology shows the incipient or early stages of adaptation in the direction of brachiators.

SEMIBRACHIATION AND SEMIBRACHIA-TORS.

Semibrachiation is a form of arboreal loco-motion in which the forelimbs are used extended above the head to suspend the body, propel it through space or to reach forward in order to check its momentum at the end of a leap. The forelimbs may be used in association with the hindlimbs (Old World Monkey semibrachiation) and/or the tail, (New World Monkey semibrachiation).

Primates that are *essentially quadrupedal* in habit but in which this form of locomotion is used intermittently are termed semibrachiators.

Semibrachiators possess structural adaptations particularly of the forelimb and shoulder girdle quantitatively intermediate between those of brachiators and arboreal quadrupeds.

SUMMARY

The present and historical usage of the terms "brachiation" and "brachiator" is reviewed in the light of what is known of the locomotor habits of anthropoid apes and monkeys. It is pointed out that any locomotor classification of Primates at this stage of knowledge can only be a temporary expedient; however it is clearly important that some sort of interim agreement should be reached on the use of these descriptive terms. A classification of arm-swinging locomotion is presented and the terms used are clearly defined.

ACKNOWLEDGMENTS

I wish to acknowledge my indebtedness to a number of my colleagues with whom I have discussed—and argued—this subject interminably. Many of their ideas and suggestions have been incorporated in this paper. They are: Professor Sir Wilfrid E. Le Gros Clark, Professor Adolph Schultz, Drs. Eric Ashton, Peter Davis, Michael Day, G. E. Erikson, W. C. Osman Hill, Charles Oxnard, W. L. Straus, Jnr. and Sherwood L. Washburn.

I would also like to thank Mrs. E. Broome who prepared the action strips. My thanks are due to David Attenborough and the B.B.C. from whose film "Zoo Quest for a Dragon" the proboscis monkey material was obtained.[4]

I am grateful to the Wenner-Gren Foundation for Anthropological Research whose generosity has made possible certain observations reported in this paper.

REFERENCES

Ashton, E. H. & Oxnard, C. E. (1963). Locomotor pattern in primates. *Proc. zool. Soc. Lond.* 141. In the press.

Ashton, E. H. & Oxnard, C. E. (1963). The musculature of the primate shoulder, *Trans. zool. Soc. Lond.* 29: 553.

Avis, V. (1962). Brachiation: the crucial issue for man's ancestry. *Southwestern J. Anthrop.* 18: 119.

Bingham, H. C. (1932). Gorillas in a native habitat. *Publ. Carneg. Instn.* No. 426: 1.

Booth, A. H. (1956). Distribution of primates in the Gold Coast. *J. W. Afr. Sci. Ass.* 2: 122.

Booth, A. H. (1957). Observations on the natural history of the olive colobus monkey, *Procolobus verus* (van Beneden). *Proc. zool. Soc. Lond.* 129: 421-430.

Clark, W. E. Le Gros (1959). *The antecedents of man.* Edinburgh: University Press.

Clark, W. E. Le Gros & Thomas, D. P. (1951). Associated jaws and limb bones of *Limnopithecus macinnesi. Fossil mammals of Africa.* No. 3 London: Brit. Mus. (N.H.).

Donisthorpe, J. (1958). Pilot study of the mountain gorilla in S.W. Uganda. *S.Afr. J.* 54: 195.

Erikson G. E. (1952). Locomotor types and body proportions in the New World primates. *Anat. Rec.* 112: 326.

Erikson, G. E. (1954). Comparative anatomy of New World primates and its bearing on the phylogeny of anthropoid apes and men. *Hum. Biol.* 26: 210.

Erikson, G. E. (1957). The hands of the New World primates with comparative functional observations on the hands of other primates. *Amer. J. phys. Anthrop.* (n.s.) 15: 446.

Goodall, J. (1962). Personal communication.

Haddow, A. J. (1956). The blue monkey group in Uganda. *Uganda Wild Life Sport* 1: 22.

Hooton, E. A. (1946). *Up from the ape.* New York: Macmillan.

[4]My thanks is also due to Dr. Grzimek for the *Cercopithecus* jumping sequence from his film "No Room for Wild Animals".

Napier, J. R. (1960). Studies of the hand in living primates. *Proc. zool. Soc. Lond. 134:* 647.

Napier, J. R. (1961). Prehensility and opposability in the hands of primates. *Symp. zool. Soc. Lond.* No. *5:* 115.

Napier, J. R. (1962). Monkeys and their habitats. *New Scientist 15:* 88.

Napier, J. R. & Davis, P. R. (1959). The forelimbs skeleton and associated remains of *Proconsul africanus. Fossil mammals of Africa.* No. 16. London: Brit. Mus. (N.H.).

Patterson, B. (1954). Non-hominoid primates in the Old World. *Hum. Biol. 26:* 191-208.

Richards, P. W. (1952). *The tropical rain forest.* Cambridge: University Press.

Schultz, A. H. (1930). Skeleton of the trunk and limbs of higher primates. *Hum. Biol. 2:*303.

Tennent, J. E. (1861). *Sketches of the natural history of Ceylon.* 4th Ed. 1. London: Longmans Green.

Washburn, S. L. (1950). The analysis of primate evolution with particular reference to the origin of man. *Cold Spring Harbor Symp. Quart. Biol. 15:* 67.

Washburn, S. L. (1962). Personal communication.

Wells, L. H. (1931). Foot of South African native. *Amer. J. phys. Anthrop. 15:* 185.

19

EARLY MAN IN EAST AFRICA
Phillip V. Tobias

Reader beware! This article is a classic example of what Simons warned against in selection 15. In spite of Tobias' enthusiastic confidence, the taxon "Homo habilis" was inadequately proposed in the first place, and, in fact, there never was any reason for it. The type specimen, Olduvai Hominid 7, not only fails to fall outside the Australopithecine range of variation, it can almost be taken for a classic textbook example of a typical Australopithecine. Measurement by measurement it duplicates the Australopithecine mean (Brace, Mahler, and Rosen 1973). The one aspect in which it is not typical is almost certainly due to its relative youth; this is in the length-breadth proportions of the teeth—especially the premolars. The individual was the equivalent of a modern twelve year old, and the premolars had hardly finished erupting and are completely unworn. In a normal adult, not only is there wear on the chewing surface of the teeth, but also where adjacent teeth come in contact with each other—interproximal attrition. This shortens the length (mesial-distal) of the tooth crown (Wolpoff 1971). It is the complete absence of such wear that is responsible for the difference in length-breadth proportions between the youthful Olduvai Hominid 7 and the average adult Australopithecine.

If the taxon "Homo habilis" cannot be justified on the basis of the type specimen, how about the most complete paratype, Olduvai Hominid 13 from Bed II, perhaps a million years later? This specimen is metrically indistinguishable from Homo erectus. If the most complete specimens attributed to "Homo habilis" are both contained comfortably within other established taxa, then the very reason for suggesting the group ceases to exist. Certainly it cannot be sustained from the other incomplete and poorly described fragments. Conclusion number 6 by Brace, Mahler, and Rosen (1973) is that "Since the taxon Homo habilis is without a type specimen, a usable paratype or any unequivocal referred material, it is an empty taxon inadequately proposed and should be formally sunk."

At this point, the reader may wonder why "Homo habilis" was proposed in the first place. The reason is to be found, if reason it be, in the interpretive traditions of paleoanthropology. As the field developed in France in the late nineteenth and early twentieth centuries, there was a strong bias against Darwinian evolution. Applied to the hominid fossil record, this resulted in a reluctance to accept any non-modern fossil as ancestral to modern man. The form of the true ancestor, it was felt, was in fact already much more modern than, say, Neanderthals or Pithecanthropines (Homo erectus), and much effort was expended in proving that modern forms were contemporaries of these nonmodern fossils.

When the British to their surprise became allies of the French at the outbreak of World War I, they adopted a number of French attitudes toward human populations, past as well as present. Starting at that time and continuing into the present, paleoanthropologists trained in the British sphere—for example, Leakey and Tobias—have exhibited a reluctance to accept nonmodern fossils as human ancestors and an enthusiasm for identifying various early fragments as modern until proven otherwise. For years they were even willing to accept what was later shown to be a deliberate fraud—Piltdown—as the ancient modern they simply "knew" must exist. From time to time over the last half century, a questionable scrap was advanced to candidacy and "Homo habilis" is only the latest of a long list.

All of the points that Tobias raises in favor of "Homo habilis" have been shown to be inadequate or erroneous, but such is the strength of scholarly tradition that the idea lives on in the absence of evidence. And if the original specimens fail for one reason or another, more are brought forth and offered as proof in spite of the fact that only the briefest of preliminary reports have been published (Leakey, Clarke, and Leakey 1971; Leakey 1971, 1972). And if these fail too, others will surely be found.

Brace, C. L., P. E. Mahler, and R. E. Rosen. 1973. Tooth measurements and the rejection of the taxon "Homo habilis." *Yearbook of Physical Anthropology*, in press.

Leakey, M. D., R. J. Clarke, and L. S. B. Leakey. 1971. A new hominid skull from Bed 1, Olduvai Gorge, Tanzania. *Nature 232:308-312.*

Leakey, R. E. F. 1971. Further evidence of lower Pleistocene hominids from East Rudolf, North Kenya. *Nature 231:241-245.*

————. 1972. Further evidence of lower Pleistocene hominids from East Rudolf, North Kenya. *Nature 237:264-269.*

Wolpoff, Milford H. 1972. Interstitial wear. *American Journal of Physical Anthropology 34:205-228.*

Olduvai Gorge in Northern Tanganyika (Republic of Tanzania) has in recent years thrown a flood of light on an early chapter in the evolution of man. Between 1955 and 1963, L. S. B. Leakey, M. D. Leakey, and their sons and helpers uncovered fossil bones representing no fewer than 14 individuals from various levels in the Olduvai strata (1). Although detailed descriptions are yet to be published (2), it is clear that earlier and lower mid-Pleistocene deposits of East Africa contain the remains of at least two different kinds of fossil hominids (that is, members of the Hominidae, the family of man). The first group of fossils fits comfortably into a well-defined category, the australopithecines, which have long been recognized as a partially hominized group, that is, a group possessing some characteristics like those of *Homo*. The second assemblage has proved most difficult to place in any existing category. After exploring every other possibility, we have been forced to attribute this second group of fossils to a new and lowly species of *Homo*, namely *Homo habilis*: this species represents a more markedly hominized lineage than the australopithecines and comprises a hitherto-unrecognized and even unsuspected transitional or intermediate form of early man (3).

In this article I consider the history and some of the characteristics of the new fossils, as well as their cultural and evolutionary position, and propose modifications to some existing schemes of hominid phylogeny in the light of these new discoveries.

From *Science 149* (1965):22-33. Copyright 1965 by the American Association for the Advancement of Science. Reprinted by permission of the author and publisher.

THE OLDUVAI SEQUENCE

Before I review the new discoveries in detail, it may be useful to describe briefly the Olduvai stratigraphic succession (Fig. 1).

Olduvai Gorge has been cut by river action through a deep succession of old sediments, tuffs, and lavas. From the exposed strata, a remarkable series of fossils and implements has been recovered, ranging in age from Lower to Upper Pleistocene.

The strata exposed in the walls of Olduvai Gorge were divided by Hans Reck into five beds numbered I to V, from the lowest upwards. This classification was adopted and the limits of the beds were more precisely defined by Leakey and, more recently, by Hay (4). It should be stressed, however, that these beds are not absolute stratigraphic units corresponding to sharp divisions in the Pleistocene sequence of events. Rather they are conveniently mappable units. Thus, as Hay has pointed out, two different marker beds have in various parts of the Gorge been regarded as the top of Bed I. Again, while Reck defined the base of Bed I as the basalt flows, Hay has preferred to include within Bed I the tuffs beneath the basalt. Hay thus regards the basalt flows as a constituent of Bed I in the eastern part of the Gorge.

Further, the newer analyses of fauna made by Leakey and his collaborators (5) tend to relate the fauna of the lower part of Bed II to that of Bed I and to interpret both as belonging to a final Villafranchian faunal stage. On the other hand, the fauna of the middle and upper part of Bed II is considered post-Villafranchian and so to be associated with that of Beds III and IV. The complex of

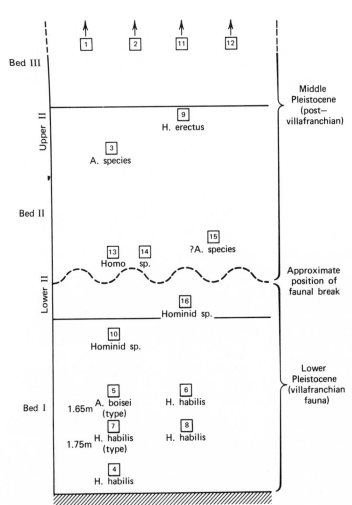

Bed III

Upper II

Bed II

Lower II

Bed I

1.65m

1.75m

| 1 | 2 | 11 | 12 |

Middle
Pleistocene
(post—
villafranchian)

9
H. erectus

3
A. species

15
?A. species

13   14
Homo   sp.

Approximate
position of
faunal break

16
Hominid sp.

10
Hominid sp.

Lower
Pleistocene
(villafranchian
fauna)

5
A. boisei
(type)

6
H. habilis

7
H. habilis
(type)

8
H. habilis

4
H. habilis

Figure 1. Schematic representation of the lower half of the Olduvai sequence, showing the approximate vertical positions of hominid fossils (numerals enclosed in squares). The potassium argon dates are indicated near the left margin (m = million years).

Middle and Upper II, III and IV comprises a mid-Pleistocene stratigraphic sequence.

In this presentation, the subdivision into five beds will be used to provide a background against which to consider the hominid remains.

Potassium-argon dates are available for several levels within Bed I. The span of time represented by these Beds is suggested by ages 1.75 and 1.65 million years for two levels in the lower half of Bed I. In a word, the chapters of human evolution which are dealt with here cover the period from about 2 million to about half a million years ago.

THE AUSTRALOPITHECINE CHAPTER

Exactly 40 years have elapsed since R. A. Dart published a description of a new kind of higher primate which had been recovered from a limestone figure at Taung in South Africa (6). This discovery was one of the most remarkable, perhaps the most important, in the history of paleoanthropology. Earlier discoveries of fossilized human ancestors had shown unequivocally human affinities: this is true of the Neanderthal group and even of the earlier and morphologically more primitive Java ape-man, *Homo erectus* (or *Pithecanthropus*, as he has been called until fairly recently). But the Taung specimen differed from the others in being so much smaller-brained, bigger-toothed, and in other respects morphologically more archaic, that its precise affinities remained a cause of dispute for decades. Initially, Dart claimed no more than that it was an ape with a number of features suggesting hominization, that is, an advance in a general human direction. He therefore called it *Australopi-*

thecus africanus—simply the "southern ape of Africa."

With the wisdom of hindsight, we are today able to recognize in Dart's fossil the first real proof of the animal origins of man, the first concrete fossil evidence that Darwin's theory of the origin of species by small modifying steps and gradation from other pre-existing species is applicable to man. For here was an apelike creature which showed in its anatomical make-up a greater number of resemblances to hominids than are shown by any of the existing manlike apes of Africa or Asia.

It took time, as well as the discovery of many new specimens of *Australopithecus* (Table 1), the patient study of their anatomical features, and a closer look at the living great apes, to reach the now widely accepted conclusion that the australopithecines were an early branch of the Hominidae, the family of man, rather than of the Pongidae, the family of the apes. No fewer than eight sites in Africa have yielded australopithecine fossils (Fig. 2).

Most of the African australopithecines belong to deposits which have been classified, on comparative faunal evidence, as Lower Pleistocene. At least three sites have provided evidence that the australopithecines survived in Africa into the Middle Pleistocene—namely Swartkrans and Kromdraai in the Transvaal and Peninj (Natron) in Tanganyika.

Of all early hominid groups, the Australopithecinae are the best represented in our fossil storehouses. From the South African sites alone, no fewer than 315 australopithecine entries have been prepared for the forthcoming new edition of the

Table 1
DATES OF DISCOVERY OF AUSTRALOPITHECINE FOSSILS

1924	Taung (S. Afr.)
1936-1949	Sterkfontein Type Site (S. Afr.)
1938-1954	Kromdraai (S. Afr.)
1939	Garusi (E. Afr.)
1947-1961	Makapansgat (S. Afr.)
1948-1952	Swartkrans (S. Afr.)
1955-1959	Olduvai (E. Afr.)
1957-1958	Sterkfontein Extension Site (S. Afr.)
1964	Peninj, Lake Natron (E. Afr.)

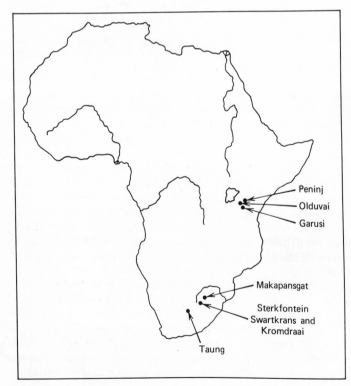

Figure 2. The African sites which have yielded fossilized remains of *Australopithecus*, popularly known as apemen, near-men, or half-men. The three northern sites are in the Republic of Tanzania; the five southern sites are in the Republic of South Africa.

International Catalogue of Fossil Man: some comprise a single isolated tooth, some an almost complete cranium. If we accept that all the isolated teeth from Swartkrans and Sterkfontein do indeed belong to australopithecines, the total number of australopithecine teeth now available is over 600 (Table 2). The figure for Olduvai includes only the 16 maxillary teeth of the type specimen of A. boisei (7), although others may need to be added to this total on further study. Juvenile and adult specimens are known, as well as male and female. Apart from age and sex variations, more than one kind of australopithecine is represented; the diversity is such that some would classify them as different genera, while others have lumped them into one genus (Australopithecus) with several subgenera; yet others would see them as simply different species of a single genus.

Whatever the proper classification, there is an abundance of evidence bearing on the anatomical structure and variation, the behavioral (or cultural) characteristics, and the ecological, geographical, and temporal background of the australopithecines. These lines of evidence concur in demonstrating that at least some of the known australopithecines, or of slightly earlier creatures of very similar aspect, fulfill the morphological requirements for a hypothetical human ancestor.

EAST AFRICAN AUSTRALOPITHECINES

Australopithecines have been found at three East African sites, Garusi (1939), Olduvai (1955, 1959, and 1963), and Peninj (1964), all situated in northern Tanganyika.

The first specimen was found by Kohl-Larsen at Garusi in 1939. It comprises a fragment of upper jawbone containing both premolars. In 1943 Kohl-Larsen stated that his specimen resembled Australopithecus (8), but Weinert later reclassified it as an African species of Meganthropus (9). However, Robinson (10) has shown convincingly that the premolars fall within the range for the South African Australopithecus from Sterkfontein. This is the smaller-toothed Australopithecus which is usually classified today as A. africanus. As yet, the Garusi specimen is the only evidence we have suggesting the presence in East Africa of the gracile africanus species of australopithecine. The other East

Table 2

NUMBER OF AUSTRALOPITHECINE TEETH FROM VARIOUS SITES AVAILABLE FOR STUDY

Taung	24
Sterkfontein	162
Kromdraai	39
Swartkrans (35)	311
Makapansgat	55
Garusi	2
Peninj (Natron)	16
Olduvai (7)	16
Total	621

African australopithecines are of the larger-toothed boisei or robustus species.

The most important East African australopithecine is the specimen originally called by Leakey Zinjanthropus boisei (11) and now reclassified by Leakey, Tobias, and Napier as a species of the genus Australopithecus, namely A. boisei (3). For the time being the name Zinjanthropus is being retained to designate a subgenus within the genus Australopithecus. The specimen comprises a very complete cranium, including all 16 upper teeth; the wisdom teeth or third molars were still in process of erupting, suggesting that the individual was in his late teens at the time of death. A brief preliminary description has been given by Leaky (1, 11). Tobias (12) has placed on record the cranial capacity as 530 cubic centimeters; that is, the specimen's brain was no larger than that of the small-toothed A. africanus child from Taung. A detailed monograph on A. boisei will appear as part of a series of volumes on Olduvai Gorge by Leakey and his collaborators (2). It may be mentioned here that A. boisei is the biggest-toothed and most robust of all the australopithecines, exceeding in most dental dimensions even the largest-toothed of the crassident A. robustus group from Swartkrans in the Transvaal.

It is probable that more large-toothed australopithecines are present in the Olduvai deposits. Three adult teeth, found at the site MNK II, in the lower middle part of Bed II, are for the most part of australopithecine form, shape, and dimensions (Fig. 1, hominid 15). According to Leakey (5), this part of Bed II is characterized by a post-Villafranchian fauna; it is early mid-Pleistocene. These teeth were referred to by Leakey and Leakey (1), but no attempt has yet been made to identify them specifically. Other australopithecine remains may well be present in Bed II, including the very large molar discovered in 1955, high in Bed II (13). Detailed studies of all these specimens are under way, and it will be some years before the complete series of full reports is published.

The third site in East Africa to yield an australopithecine is Peninj, on the west side of Lake Natron, about 80 kilometers northeast of Olduvai Gorge. Here, in January 1964, one of Leakey's assistants, Kamoya Kimeu, a member of the expedition led by Richard Leakey and Glynn Isaac, discovered a nearly complete and superbly preserved mandible of a large-toothed australopithecine (1). According to Leakey's provisional identification of the fauna from this new site, it is of early mid-Pleistocene age and thus much later than the original A. boisei from Olduvai. It would seem to be equivalent in age to the upper part of Bed II, or even to the overlying Beds III and IV, in the Olduvai sequence. Despite this age difference, it is of interest to note that the mandibular dental arcade fits that of the maxilla of the Olduvai A. boisei almost perfectly and may be provisionally identified as a mandible of A. boisei. Although age comparisons between East and South Africa are fraught with difficulties, it would seem likely that the Peninj australopithecine is comparable in age with those of Swartkrans and Kromdraai. The three sites give evidence that the large-toothed australopithecines survived in Africa well into the Mid-Pleistocene (Table 3).

UNLIKELY CLAIMANTS FOR AUSTRALOPITHECINE STATUS

At least one other fossil from Africa has been claimed to be australopithecine, namely an incomplete cranium discovered in northern Chad and described by Coppens as an australopithecine (14). In 1963, we invited Coppens to visit South Africa and study the original australopithecine material. As a result of his study, Coppens has reached the same conclusion as Leakey and I reached independently, namely that the Chad fragment represented a more advanced hominid than Australopithecus. It may belong to the new species, Homo habilis, or even to the more advanced Homo erectus. The original

Table 3

Chronological and geographical distribution of australopithecines. The relative chronological positions of the East and South African sites are uncertain, as indicated by the question marks. Whereas potassium-argon dates are available for Olduvai, none is available for South African sites. Comparisons of fauna are valuable among the sites within each major geographical zone, as exemplified by forthcoming new analyses of fauna from South African sites by H. B. S. Cooke and from East African sites by L. S. B. Leakey. Since comparisons between fauna from the East and South African sites are somewhat vitiated by the large distance and ecological differences between the areas, this scheme must be regarded as highly provisional.

	South Africa	East Africa
	Kromdraai	?Olduvai II (Upper)
Middle		?Peninj (Natron)
Pleistocene	Swartkrans	?Olduvai II (Middle)
	?Sterkfontein	
	Extension Site	?Olduvai II (Lower)
		?Garusi
Lower	Makapansgat	
Pleistocene	Sterkfontein Type Site	
	Taung	
		Olduvai I

diagnosis of the Chad fauna as very early Villafranchian is likewise being revised by Coppens; the site is apparently late Villafranchian. Unfortunately, the extremely weathered and distorted state of the Chad specimen may preclude exact comparison with other hominine remains, but it is possible that further hominid material and stone tools may yet be discovered in the area.

The possibility has been raised that the teeth and cranial fragments found outside Africa, at Ubeidiya on the Jordan River in Israel, may have belonged to an australopithecine (15). From a preliminary study of the scanty human remnants, generously placed at my disposal by M. Stekelis, these remains are highly likely to have belonged to Homo rather than to Australopithecus, although it may be impossible, without the discovery of further material, to attribute them to a particular species of Homo.

From Java has come another form of early

hominid known as *Meganthropus pa-laeojavanicus*, of which three or possibly four mandibular fragments were found in the Djetis Beds dated to the beginning of the Middle Pleistocene *(16)*. Robinson has suggested that this Javanese *Meganthropus* is simply an australopithecine *(10)*. However, from a recent reexamination of the originals of *Meganthropus* I and II in comparison with original material from Africa, von Koenigswald and I concluded that, while *Meganthropus palaeojavanicus* has some strong resemblances to australopithecines, it shows several features in which it is somewhat advanced beyond the australopithecine grade *(17)*. In this sense, it stands in the same relation to *Australopithecus* as does *Homo habilis* in Africa, except that *Homo habilis* has departed further from *Australopithecus* in some respects.

Another group of Asian fossils has been thought to possess australopithecine status, namely a group of isolated teeth from China attributed by von Koenigswald to *Heman-thropus peii (18)*. Simons has suggested that these teeth are australopithecine *(19)*. It is not impossible, however, that they may represent a more advanced hominid, such as *Homo habilis*; but it may be impossible to resolve the problem of their status until more

specimen are recovered, including teeth in a mandible or cranium *(17)*. The position of some claimants to australopithecine status is summarized in Table 4.

In sum, the case for the existence of an australopithecine stage in Asia remains unproven; the only convincing australopithecine sites remain the eight East and South African sites listed in Table 1.

THE GAP BETWEEN AUSTRALOPITHECUS AND HOMO

Although *Australopithecus* fulfills the morphological requirements for an ancestor of man, there remains a substantial gap between the australopithecines and the most lowly representative of the hominines hitherto recognized (that is, *Homo erectus*, formerly called *Pithecanthropus, Sinanthropus, Atlanthropus*, and so on). The size of this morphological gap may best be illustrated by reference to three parameters which have shown most marked change during the process of hominization in the Pleistocene: brain size, tooth size, and tooth shape. Unfortunately, we cannot use the evidence of hand and foot bones, since we have insufficient evidence bearing on these features in *Australopithecus* and in *Homo*

Table 4
SOME FOSSIL HOMINIDS WHICH HAVE BEEN CLAIMED TO BE AUSTRALOPITHECINES

Nature of specimen	Original designation	Revised attribution	Latest interpretation
	Swartkrans		
1 mandible, 1 mandibular fragment, and 1 radial fragment	*Telanthropus capensis*	Australopithecine (Dart, Le Gros Clark)	*Pithecanthropus* (Simonetta), *Homo erectus* (Robinson)
	Chad		
Craniofacial fragment	Australopithecine	*Homo* sp.	*Homo* sp. (unpublished)
	Ubeidiya		
2 teeth and 4 cranial fragments	Hominid	?Australopithecine	*Homo* sp. (unpublished)
	Sangiran (Djetis Beds)		
3 mandibular fragments	*Meganthropus palaeojavanicus*	Australopithecine (Robinson)	More advanced than African Australopithecine (?*Homo* sp.) (Tobias and von Koenigswald)
	China		
Isolated teeth	*Hemanthropus peii* (originally *Hemianthropus peii*)	Australopithecine (Simons)	Status not clear (?*Homo habilis*)

erectus. On the other hand, good samples of teeth and fair samples of braincases and endocranial casts exist for both of these groups.

From seven australopithecine crania it has been possible to make fair estimates of cranial capacity. One of these crania is the Olduvai type specimen of *A. boisei* and six are of small-toothed South African specimens. They include the child from Taung, whose estimated capacity is 500 to 520 cm³; when allowance was made for probable changes with growth, his adult capacity was estimated by various workers *(12)* as 570, 600, and 624 cm³, bigger, in fact, than any australopithecine capacity actually measured. Selecting the median value (600 cm³), we obtain an australopithecine range of 435 to 600 cm³ and a mean of 508 cm³. The range for nine *Homo erectus* crania, including 1000 cm³ for Olduvai hominid 9 *(20)*, is 775 to 1225 cm³ with a mean of 978 cm³. The cranial capacity of the smallest-brained *H. erectus* was originally estimated by von Koenigswald as 750 cm³; an earlier estimate by Weidenreich *(21)*, subsequently disavowed by him, was 850 cm³, while Boule and Vallois give 815 cm³ *(22)*. Most workers have accepted Weidenreich's final estimate of 775 cm³. These variations, however, reinforce an impression I gained recently when, through the courtesy of D. Hooijer and G. H. R. von Koenigswald, I examined the original Javanese crania: there is a need for reassessment of the capacities of the several Javanese crania of *Homo erectus (23)*.

Figure 3 represents the ranges and the gap between the presently accepted estimates of cranial capacity for *Australopithecus* and *H. erectus*. There is an interval of 175 cm³ between the capacities of the largest-brained australopithecine and the smallest-brained *H. erectus*. However, this difference is rather meaningless unless we consider the estimated body size of the two forms. Jerison has

analyzed brain size (to which cranial capacity is an approximation) into two independent components, one of which is determined by body size and the other of which is associated with improved adaptive capacities *(24)*. Given certain assumptions, it has further been possible to estimate the number of cortical nerve cells in the brain as a whole, as well as in each of the two components. The number of "excess" nerve cells—that is, of cells over and above those which can be accounted for by body size—may then be taken as a measure of the real advancement in brain volume, irrespective of body size.

The following are estimates of the numbers of excess nerve cells based partly on Jerison's estimates and partly on my own *(25)*:

African great apes	3.4 to 3.6 billion
Australopithecines	4.0 to 5.0 billion
Homo erectus	5.8 to 8.4 billion
Homo sapiens	8.4 to 8.9 billion

If our estimates are correct, there is a bigger gap between *Australopithecus* and *H. erectus* than between the apes and the australopithecines or between *H. erectus* and *H. sapiens*. If, instead of comparing ranges, we compare the mid-values for the groups, we obtain values of 3.5, 4.5, 7.1, and 8.65 billion for the four groups, respectively. Clearly, there is a greater distance between *Australopithecus* and *H. erectus* than between any other two consecutive groups.

To compare dental features of the two groups, it is necessary to point out that on the basis of tooth size, the australopithecines fall into two more or less well-defined subgroups. The first—represented by the fossils from Taung, Sterkfontein, Makapansgat, and Garusi—has somewhat smaller cheek teeth (premolars and molars), but somewhat larger anterior teeth (incisors and canines); this group is called *Australopi-*

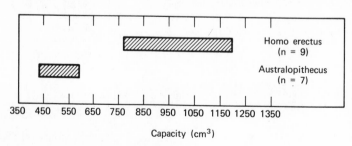

Homo erectus (n = 9)

Australopithecus (n = 7)

Capacity (cm³)

350 450 550 650 750 850 950 1050 1150 1250 1350

Figure 3. The ranges and means of cranial capacity in two early hominids, *Australopithecus* (including both small- and large-toothed forms) and *Homo erectus* (formerly known as *Pithecanthropus*). The largest estimated australopithecine capacity is 600 cm³ and the smallest of *Homo erectus* 775 cm³.

thecus africanus. The second—represented by the australopithecine fossils from Swartkrans, Kromdraai, Olduvai, and Peninj (Natron)—has larger cheek teeth and smaller front teeth; this group comprises A. robustus and A. boisei in the most recent classifications.

Figure 4 demonstrates the ranges of tooth sizes for A. africanus and H. erectus. Once more the extent of the morphological distance between the Australopithecinae and H. erectus is apparent. The differences are more striking when A. robustus and A. boisei are compared with H. erectus.

Similarly, Fig. 5 reflects variations in the shape and size of the teeth of A. africanus and Homo erectus. In a word, australopithecine cheek teeth are broader buccolingually, while hominine cheek teeth are narrower (but more elongate) from front to back.

On the basis of these three parameters, there is a clear and sizable gap between known australopithecines and Homo erectus. Until recently, it has apparently been tacitly assumed that Australopithecus graded more or less insensibly into Homo erectus in the manner postulated in general terms by Charles Darwin. It is therefore of no small

interest to note that so large a gap exists, not only with respect to one paramenter, brain size, but, in the same creatures, with respect to dental traits.

It is this gap that has been filled by Homo habilis, the newly discovered hominid which, with respect to the three parameters used to characterize the gap, as well as with respect to other morphological markers, lies in a largely intermediate position.

HOMO HABILIS: THE EARLY PLEISTOCENE HOMININE

The family Hominidae may be divided into two subfamilies, the Australopithecinae and the Homininae. The term "hominine" is the common or colloquial name connoting a member of the subfamily Homininae.

From at least four levels in Bed I and the lower (Villafranchian) and middle parts of Bed II in the Olduvai succession have come skeletal remains of another type of hominid (Fig. 1). This hominid differs widely from A. boisei, the large-toothed australopithecine found in the same beds. For instance, the teeth are appreciably smaller than those of A. boisei. While the sizes of the teeth of A.

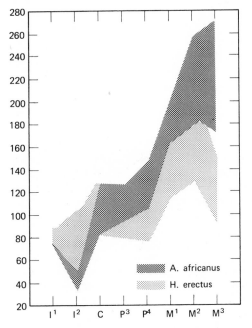 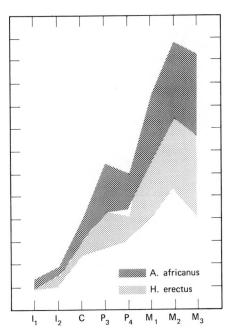

Figure 4. Crown areas of the maxillary (left) and mandibular (right) teeth of A. africanus (the australopithecine from Taung, Sterkfontein, Makapansgat, and Garusi) compared with those of Hearecius from Africa, Asia, and Europe. Crown area is the product of the length and breadth of the crown of a tooth; values are in square millimeters.

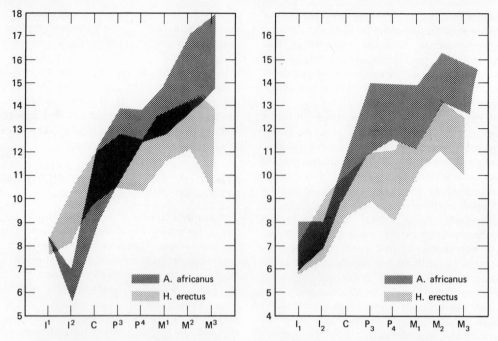

Figure 5. Buccolingual breadths (in millimeters) of the maxiliary (left) and mandibular (right) teeth of *A. africanus* and *H. erectus*. The cheek teeth (from P3 to M3) of the australopithecines are characteristically broadened, as contrasted with those of the hominines, represented here by *Homo erectus*.

boisei in general fall above the top of the range for the South African australopithecines, the teeth of this second hominid, especially the premolars, fall at or below the lower end of the australopithecine range *(23)*. Such wide divergence between the two hominids from the same site is far in exess of what can be attributed to sexual dimorphism: in any event, it is accompanied by divergences in shape, proportions, and detailed morphology of the teeth, in cranial shape and curvature, and in cranial capacity. Clearly the second batch of fossils represents another type of hominid. In almost all the departures of the second hominid from the australopithecine morphological pattern, it approaches more closely to the hominine pattern. In other words, the total pattern is more markedly hominized than that of *Australopithecus*. To the Bed I form characterized by these more hominized features we have given the name *Homo habilis*.

The formal naming of the species was announced by Leakey, Tobias, and Napier on 4 April 1964 *(3)*. The generic name implies that this primitive hominid belonged to the genus *Homo*, while the specific name *habilis*, which was suggested by R. A. Dart, means

"able, handy, mentally skillful, vigorous," from the inferred ability of the man to make stone tools.

In accordance with international convention in the naming of new species, one set of remains was selected as the "type specimen" of *Homo habilis*. These were the remains of a juvenile (No. 7 in Fig. 1) whose bones—comprising a lower jaw with teeth, an upper molar tooth, the incomplete parietal bones of the cranial vault, and a set of hand bones—were found scattered on a single floor at the site FLK NNI in the Olduvai Gorge. In the 3 years that elapsed between his discovery and his naming, he was known as "pre-Zinjanthropus" because the living floor on which his bones were found lies some 35 cm *below* the living floor on which "Zinjanthropus" (or *A. boisei*) had been found. The youth of the individual represented was attested by the state of eruption of the teeth and by the signs of incomplete growth and ossification of the other bones, thus permitting the confident association of this group of bones as those of a single individual.

Apart from the type specimen, remains of four other individuals—three from Bed I (hominids 4, 6, and 8 in Fig. 1) and one from the middle part of Bed II (hominid 13)—were listed as "paratypes" of *Homo habilis*. Bones from two further individuals in the lower and middle parts of Bed II (hominids 14 and 16 in Fig. 1) were referred to the same species, but one of these only provisionally. All told, this batch of remains comprises some 40 teeth, two tolerably complete lower jawbones and a fragment of a third, parts of a pair of upper jawbones, varying portions of the braincases of four skulls, the hand bones of at least two individuals, foot bones and a collarbone. In addition, two leg bones (tibia and fibula) *may* belong to *H. habilis*, but we cannot rule out the possibility that they belonged to an australopithecine.

The features which distinguish *H. habilis* remains from those of australopithecines and relate them rather to the more advanced Homininae include the capacity of the braincase, both absolutely and in relation to estimated body size, the size, proportions and shape of the teeth, the shape and size of the jaws, and the curvature of the cranial bones. In addition, the post-cranial bones help us to obtain a picture of the very hominine morphological pattern of *Homo habilis*, but they do not assist in the taxonomic problem of deciding whether, for instance, the hand of *H. habilis* was closer to that of *Australopithecus* or to that of the Homininae. This is because we do not know enough about the structure of the hand in either the australopithecines or *H. erectus*.

In all those parts for which we do possess adequate comparative material for both australopithecines and early hominines, most of the bones of *H. habilis* fall at the extreme or beyond the range of variation for the australopithecines.

One important example of the greater degree of hominization shown by *H. habilis* is provided by his cranial capacity. Although the cranial vault of the type specimen is incomplete, it has been possible to estimate the capacity of the intact vault (26). The estimates range from 643 to 724 cm^3, with central values 674 and 681 cm^3. This is some 80 cm^3 more than the largest known capacity of *Australopithecus* and 95 cm^3 smaller than the smallest known capacity of *H. erectus*.

When Jerison's formulae (24) are applied to the estimate of 680 cm^3, the body size being estimated from the size of the foot bones, a value of 5.3 to 5.4 billion "excess nerve cells" is obtained. That is, the "intelligence" component of the brain of *H. habilis* has about 0.8 to 1.0 billion more neurons than that of the australopithecines, but about 1.7 to 1.8 billion fewer than that of *H. erectus* (25). Jerison's formulae thus provide striking confirmation of the evidence provided by absolute cranial capacity that *H. habilis* is a more advanced hominid than *Australopithecus* but not so advanced as *H. erectus*.

The parameter of tooth size has the same story to tell. Most of the teeth of *H. habilis* are smaller than those of most australopithecines. Thus, in 30 out of 38 comparisons, the absolute sizes of the *H. habilis* teeth lie at the extreme of the range for *Australopithecus* or outside the range.

Not only the size, but the shape of the teeth is distinctly different from that of *Australopithecus* (Fig. 6). Instead of possessing the great breadth characteristic of the teeth of the latter, the teeth of *H. habilis* are narrow and relatively elongated, this departure being found in 20 out of 30 comparisons with the australopithecine teeth. In this respect, the teeth of *H. habilis* resemble those of *H. erectus*.

In sum, *H. habilis* was a pygmy-sized hominid with a relatively large cranial capacity, reduced and narrow teeth, and a number of markedly hominine features in his limb bones. His total structural pattern was that of a creature appreciably more hominized than any of the large group of australopithecines of South and East Africa. The advanced features, moreover, were not those of an individual extreme variant, but characterized all the individuals represented over some considerable time. Clearly, this strain represents a distinct taxon intermediate between the most advanced *Australopithecus* and the most primitive *Homo*.

Since the original description was published in April 1964, a detailed comparison has been made between the original specimens from Tanganyika and those from Java. As a result, G. H. R. von Koenigswald and I have concluded that in the Bed II paratype of *H. habilis* (which lived some 3/4 million years later than the type specimen), the hominizing trends have been carried still further; as a result, the jaws and teeth of the later specimen closely resemble those of *H. erectus* attributed to the early Middle Pleis-

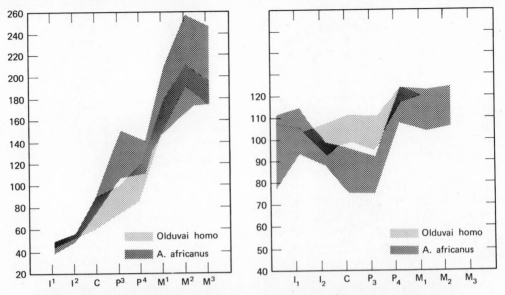

Figure 6. Ranges of size and shape of mandibular teeth in the *H. habilis* from Bed I and the hominine from lower Bed II compared with those of *Australopithecus africanus*. *Left*, crown areas (mm²). *Right*, the length of the tooth expressed as a percentage of the breadth. The cheek teeth (premolars and molars) of the hominines have higher indices because they are elongated and lack the characteristic australopithecine broadening of these teeth.

tocene Djetis Beds of Java *(17)*. If these features represent sequential changes, we are virtually seeing here evolution in action, with subtle intergrades from one level of hominization to the next.

CULTURAL STATUS OF HOMO HABILIS

It is accepted that cultural or ethological evidence may be added to morphological evidence in assessing the taxonomic status of a group. We may ask the question: Did *H. habilis* behave like an *Australopithecus* or like a *Homo?*

At each of the levels in Bed I where remains of *Homo habilis* have been found, primitive stone implements have been recovered. These artifacts are commonly made from pebbles or irregular fragments, and the cultural phase represented by the succession of stone industries constitutes the Oldowan Culture, formerly known as the Oldowan phase of the pre-Chelles-Acheul Culture. For long, the identity of the makers of the Oldowan Culture tools has been uncertain: some have maintained that the australopithecines were responsible, others have attributed the tools to early members of *Homo erectus*—but always on the basis of very indirect arguments. When in 1959 the cranium of the Olduvai australopithecine (*A.*

boisei) was found on a living floor alongside Oldowan tools, at a time when no other adequate hominid remains were known to be associated with these tools, Leakey claimed that this australopithecine must have been the Oldowan toolmaker *(1)*. This left a difficult problem: Why was the East African australopithecine associated with stone tools, whereas the Makapansgat australopithecine was associated with the bone, tooth, and horn tools described by Dart? Subsequently, however, remains of *H. habilis* were found on the same living floor as *A. boisei* and the tools. Furthermore, remains of *H. habilis* were found on the lower (earlier) living floors in Bed I, in each instance associated with Oldowan artifacts. While it is possible that both *A. boisei* and *H. habilis* made tools, it is is probable that *H. habilis* was at least the more advanced toolmaker.

Furthermore, if we make a survey of all the evidence from South and East Africa, we see that *Australopithecus* alone has not yet been found with stone objects which are undoubtedly tools, except where advanced hominid remains were present as well *(20, 25)*. Six out of 12 deposits have yielded australopithecine remains with no stone tools *(27)*; four sites which have australopithecines and stone tools contain, in addition, indications of a more advanced hominid. The remaining two deposits contain only the more advanced hominid and stone tools. At no site where australopithecine remains are the only hominid remains present are there any stone implements; conversely, at every site which has yielded stone implements and associated hominid remains, these hominid remains include those of a more advanced hominid, whether or not australopithecine remains are present in addition. Furthermore, at every site which has yielded the more advanced hominid, stone tools are present.

It has tentatively been concluded from these associations that no unequivocal evidence exists that *Australopithecus* made Oldowan stone tools to a set and regular pattern and according to a developing cultural trend. On the other hand, it seems very probable that *H. habilis* was the maker of the Oldowan stone tools, while *H. erectus* made the later (Chelles-Acheul) implements.

Dart (28) has demonstrated that the australopithecines were capable of a wide range of cultural activities. It may, however, be argued that all of these activities fall into the categories which Napier (29) has classified as *ad hoc* tool-using, purposeful tool-using, tool-modifying for an immediate or even for a future purpose, and possibly even *ad hoc* tool-making. But it may be questioned whether these australopithecine activities constitute cultural tool-making—that is, whether they exhibit a set and regular complex of patterns which, moreover, show developmental trends with the passage of time.

If this interpretation is correct, ethological or cultural evidence could be added to the anatomical evidence which tends to ally *H. habilis* with the hominines rather than with the australopithecines.

One further probable manifestation of the culture of the early Olduvai hominids is a rough circle of loosely piled stones discovered on a living floor at DK I in the lower part of Bed I (3). It suggests a crude shelter or windbreak and is on the same level as that on which the earliest remains of *H. habilis* were found (MK I). *H. habilis* may have been responsible for this rude structure.

SIGNIFICANCE OF HOMO HABILIS

Both its structure and its place in time impart a unique significance to *Homo habilis* while,

culturally, it seems to provide us for the first time with a knowledge of the makers of the Oldowan Culture.

Structurally, *H. habilis* may be regarded as a most effective link between the Australopithecinae and the Homininae, between which, as has been mentioned, there is a larger gap than has hitherto been recognized. Its very intermediacy is underlined by the fact that some workers would regard the newly discovered form as the most advanced australopithecine and others as the most primitive hominine. Thus, even in the short time since the new fossils were discovered, various workers have believed that the habilines were simply another australopithecine (30), a new genus between *Australopithecus* and *Homo* (31), a new lowliest species of *Homo*, namely *H. habilis* (3), and even a new subspecies of *H. erectus*, namely *H. erectus habilis* (32). The position adopted by my colleagues and myself would seem to be a compromise between the extreme views on either side. Although argument on the exact taxonomic position may continue for some time, it seems that there is already fairly general agreement on this virtually uniquely linking position of *H. habilis*. Perhaps only *Meganthropus palaeojavanicus* of Sangiran, Java lies in a similarly intermediate position between the Australopithecinae and the Homininae, albeit a little nearer to the australopithecines than is *H. habilis* (17).

Chronologically, the recognition of *H. habilis* means that a more hominized line of creatures was evolving alongside the somewhat less hominized australopithecines even in the Lower Pleistocene. Previously, the *H. erectus* remains of the Djetis Beds, agreed by most as belonging to the beginning of the Mid-Pleistocene, represented the earliest recognized hominine. It was still possible then to claim that, if indeed the Homininae stemmed off from an australopithecine ancestral group, this lineage of *Homo* need not have arisen any earlier than the end of the Lower Pleistocene. It now seems clear that, if the habilines are in fact members of the Homininae, then hominines were already present in Africa, and perhaps in Asia, during at least the second half of the Lower Pleistocene. The departure of the hominine line from its presumed australopithecine ancestor must then have occurred as early as at least the Upper Pliocene or the first part of the Lower Pleistocene.

The early hominines must have been contemporaries of several diversified australopithecines—a megadont line *(A. boisei)*, a macrodont line *(A. robustus)*, and a mesodont line *(A. africanus)*. In fact, at least in East Africa, and probably, too, in South Africa, *H. habilis* and *Australopithecus* spp. were sympatric and synchronic. More precisely, Olduvai I provides us with early evidence of the sympatric co-existence of the largest-toothed australopithecine *(A. boisei)* and *H. habilis*, while Swartkrans gives us later evidence for the sympatric compresence of the large-toothed *A. robustus* and a more advanced hominine, *H. erectus ("Telanthropus")*. Doubtless, ecological differences permitted this situation to persist right through until the middle part of the mid-Pleistocene (Fig. 7).

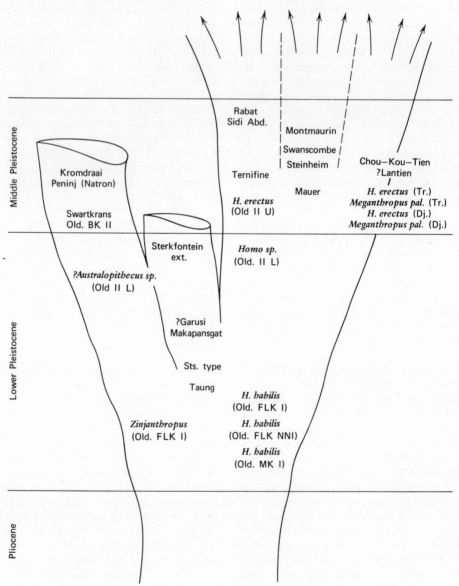

Figure 7. Schema of Lower and Middle Pleistocene hominids, showing the position in time and space of the most important specimens discovered to date. The left trunk of the tree represents the large-toothed australopithecine line; the middle trunk the small-toothed australopithecine line; and the right trunk the hominine line leading to modern man. *Sts.*, Sterkfontein; *Sidi Abd.*, Sidi Abderrahman; *Old.II*, Olduvai Bed II; *U*, upper; *L*, lower; *Tr.*, Trinil beds; *Dj.*, Djetis beds.

BEARINGS ON HOMINID EVOLUTION

As a total morphological complex, *H. habilis* represents a more advanced grade of hominid organization than *Australopithecus*. Have the habilines arisen from the australopithecines? Since they are contemporary with *H. habilis*, the australopithecine populations represented by the actual fossils recovered to date are clearly too late—and possibly slightly too specialized—to have been on the actual human line, unless we are to postulate a polyphyletic origin of the Homininae at varying times from australopithecine stock. Morphologically, the gracile *A. africanus* is closest to *H. habilis* and seemingly least specialized. It would not be rash therefore to suggest that of the various australopithecines *A. africanus* has departed least from the common ancestor of *A. africanus* and *H. habilis*. On the other hand, the large-toothed, specialized *A. robustus* and *A. boisei* would seem to be far off the common *africanus-habilis* line. Two possible interpretations spring to mind.

(1) The Pliocene ancestral australopithecine was large-toothed and perhaps adapted to a vegetarian diet *(33)*; *A. boisei* and *A. robustus* would then represent a conservative line which maintained these qualities right through into the Middle Pleistocene, while *A. africanus* developed different ecological requirements which, perhaps through a more carnivorous or, at least, omnivorous diet, led to a relaxation of selective pressures maintaining large teeth. The gracile *H. habilis* stemmed off from this smaller-toothed line of australopithecines and became selected for increasingly hominine features.

(2) The ancestral australopithecine was unspecialized, small-toothed, omnivorous. At some time in the Upper Pliocene, it diversified into macrodontic and megadontic lines (*A. robustus* and *A. boisei*), with specialized dentition, perhaps accompanying a specialized, essentially herbivorous diet. Another line remained little changed and unspecialized, eventually to dichotomize into a progressively more hominized line represented by *H. habilis* in Africa and perhaps *Meganthropus* in Asia and a more conservative residual line (*A. africanus*) which, be-

cause of ecological similarities to *H. habilis*, did not long outlast the emergence of this hominine.

Which of the two interpretations is correct, or whether other alternatives should be considered, only the direct evidence of Pliocene fossils will determine. Pending their discovery, I incline to favor the second view, on indirect lines of evidence to be presented elsewhere. That is, I tend to regard the large teeth and supporting structures of *A. robustus* and *A. boisei* as secondary specializations, rather than as primitive or ancestral features which J. T. Robinson seems to believe *(33)*.

Irrespective of which interpretation we adopt, it seems reasonable to infer that late in the Pliocene, or thereabouts, some populations of ancestral *Australopithecus*-like hominids moved forward to a further grade of hominization, thus generating the Homininae. We may tentatively conclude that *H. habilis* is on this direct hominine line. Such is the message of his morphology and his culture, while his position in space and time is compatible with this conclusion *(34)*. As a Lower Pleistocene hominine, he bids fair to provide us with a population, one or more sections of which were ancestral to the mid-Pleistocene hominines (Fig. 8). Nothing in the structure or dating of the relevant fossils rules out the possibility that some populations of *H. habilis* underwent further hominizing changes by plyletic evolution late in the Lower Pleistocene, to attain the *H. erectus* grade of hominization.

Such a reconstruction permits us to recognize a series of grades of hominization, within which we may classify the available fossils. Despite wide variation within each grade—only a fraction of which is as yet known for most grades—we may recognize: (i) an australopithecine grade, represented convincingly only in South and East Africa; (ii) a habiline grade from Africa, perhaps corresponding to a meganthropine grade in Asia; (iii) an earlier *H. erectus* grade, represented in Africa possibly by remains from middle Bed II, Olduvai, and by "*Telanthropus*" from Swartkrans, and in Asia by the Djetis Beds hominines from Sangiran, Java; (iv) a later *H. erectus* grade, represented in Africa by "Chellean Man" from upper Bed II, Olduvai and by "*Atlanthropus*" of Northwest

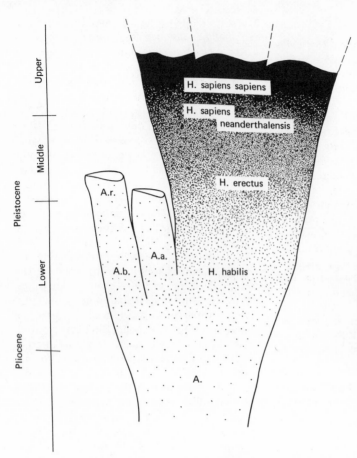

Figure 8. A provisional schema of hominid phylogeny from Upper Pliocene times to the Upper Pleistocene. Increasing intensity of shading represents increasing degrees of approach toward the structure and behavior of modern man. A, the hypothetical ancestral australopithecine; *A.b.*, *Australopithecus (Zinjanthropus) boisei*; *A.r.*, *Australopithecus robustus*; *A.a.*, *Australopithecus africanus*. The schema indicates the synchronic coexistence of several different hominids in the Lower and Middle Pleistocene, the australopithecines surviving into the Middle Pleistocene alongside more advanced hominids of the genus *Homo*. This figure should be considered in conjunction with Fig. 7.

Africa by "Chellean Man" from upper Bed II, Olduvai and by *"Atlanthropus"* of Northwest Africa; in Asia by the Trinil Beds and Chou-Kou-Tien hominines; and in Europe possibly by the remains of Mauer; (v) an earlier *H. sapiens* grade (Neanderthal) widely distributed in the Old World; and (vi) a later *H. sapiens* grade, ultimately worldwide in distribution. This sequence shows remarkable parallels between Africa and Asia from grade 2 onwards *(17)*.

We see in conclusion that *H. habilis* has bridged the last remaining major gap in the Pleistocene part of the story of human evolution.

SUMMARY

Recent discoveries of early Pleistocene hominids in East Africa have revealed a new stage in human evolution. The remains of *Homo habilis*, discovered by L. S. B. Leakey and his family, bridge the hiatus between the most advanced australopithecines and the most primitive hominines. The new species was bigger-brained and smaller-toothed than *Australopithecus*, the fossil apeman from South and East Africa. It is very probable that *Homo habilis* was, as his name implies, a "handyman," maker of the earliest stone culture, the Oldowan.

These primitive hominines were already in existence in the Lower Pleistocene, living alongside a variety of more conservative hominids, the australopithecines. The closeness of morphology between *H. habilis* and *Australopithecus africanus* points strongly to a common ancestry in the Upper Pliocene or the very beginning of the Pleistocene. The large-toothed *A. robustus* and *A. boisei* were already diverging by specialization from the postulated unspecialized ancestral australopithecine. The first hominines must thus have come into being by the beginning of the Pleistocene. Later, some populations of *H. habilis* seemingly underwent further hominizing changes to generate a new species, *Homo erectus*, bigger men with larger and more effective brains, smaller and more modern human teeth, probably more complete adjustment to upright stance and bipedal gait, a more precise manual grip, and an appreciably advanced material culture.

Homo habilis thus fills in the last remaining major gap in the Pleistocene story of human evolution.

REFERENCES AND NOTES

[1]L. S. B. Leakey, *Nature* 184, 491 (1959); 189, 649 (1961); ———, and M. D. Leakey, *ibid.* 202, 5 (1964).

[2]The skulls and teeth have been entrusted to me by Dr. Leakey for detailed study, while Drs. J. Napier, P. Davis, and M. Day of London are studying the other (postcranial) parts of the skeleton. Our detailed reports will appear in a new series of volumes on the Olduvai Gorge to be published by Cambridge University Press.

[3]L. S. B. Leakey, P. V. Tobias, J. R. Napier, *Nature* 202, 7 (1964).

[4]R. Hay, *Science* 139, 829 (1963).

[5]L. S. B. Leakey, *Olduvai Gorge 1951–1961*, vol. 1, *A Preliminary Report on the Geology and Fauna* (Cambridge Univ. Press, Cambridge, 1965).

[6]R. A. Dart, *Nature* 115, 195 (1925).

[7]There are some 54 additional teeth from Olduvai. Some of them belong to *H. habilis;* some may be australopithecine; while others are as yet of unknown affinities.

[8]L. Kohl-Larsen, *Auf den Spuren des Vormenschen* (Strecker and Schröder, Stuttgart, 1943).

[9]H. Weinert, *Z. Morphol. Anthropol.* 42, 113 (1950); 43, 73 (1951).

[10]J. T. Robinson, *Am. J. Phys. Anthropol.* 11, 1 (1953); 13, 429 (1955).

[11]L. S. B. Leakey, *Nature* 186, 456 (1960).

[12]P. V. Tobias, *ibid.* 197, 743 (1963).

[13]L. S. B. Leakey, *ibid.* 181, 1099 (1958); J. T. Robinson, *ibid.* 185, 407 (1960); G. H. R. von Koenigswald, *Koninkl. Ned. Akad. Wetenschap. Proc. Ser. B* 63, 20, (1960); A. A. Dahlberg, *Nature* 188, 962 (1960).

[14]Y. Coppens, *Compt. Rend.* 252, 3851 (1961); *Bull. Soc. Préhistorique Franc.* 58, 756 (1961); in *Problèmes Actuels de Paléontologie (Évolution des Vertébrés)* (Centre National de Recherche Scientifique, Paris, 1962), p. 455.

[15]M. Stekelis, L. Picard, N. Schulman, G. Haas, *Bull. Res. Council Israel* 9G, 175 (1960).

[16]F. Weidenreich, *Amer. Mus. Nat. Hist. Anthropol. Papers* 40, 1 (1945).

[17]P. V. Tobias and G. H. R. von Koenigswald, *Nature* 204, 515 (1964).

[18]G. H. R. von Koenigswald, *Koninkl. Ned. Akad. Wetenschappen Proc. Ser. B* 60, 153 (1957).

[19]E. L. Simons, *Science* 141, 879 (1963).

[20]P. V. Tobias, *Current Anthropol.* in press.

[21]F. Weidenreich, *Palaeontol. Sinica* n.s. D10, 1 (1943).

[22]M. Boule and H. V. Vallois, *Fossil Men* (Thames and Hudson, London, 1957).

[23]P. V. Tobias, "Festschrift on the 65th birthday of Juan Comas," in press.

[24]H. J. Jerison, *Human Biol.* 35, 263 (1963).

[25]P. V. Tobias, in *Proc. 8th Intern. Congr. Anthropol. Ethnol. Sci.*, Moscow, August 1964, (1965).

[26]P. V. Tobias, *Nature* 202, 3 (1964).

[27]Although cultural material and an australopithecine mandible are known from Peninj (Lake Natron), the implements are not associated with the mandible. I am indebted to Glynn Isaac for the information that excavation of the jaw site itself has yielded no cultural material. Scattered stone artifacts and two early Acheulian sites occur some distance from the mandible site. G. Isaac. *Quaternaria*, 7, 101 (1965).

[28]R. A. Dart, "The Osteodontokeratic Culture of *Australopithecus prometheus*," *Transvaal Museum Mem. 10* (1957).

[29]J. R. Napier, in *Classification and Human Evolution*, S. L. Washburn, Ed. (Viking Fund, Chicago, 1963), p. 178.

[30]W. E. le Gros Clark, *Discovery* 25, 49 (1964).

[31]G. H. R. von Koenigswald, personal communication.

[32]D. R. Hughes, *The Times*, London, 10 June 1964.

[33]J. T. Robinson, in *Evolution und Hominisation*, G. Kurth, Ed. (G. Fischer, Stuttgart, 1962), p. 210; J. T. Robinson, *S. African Archaeol. Bull.* 19, 3 (1964).

[34]P. V. Tobias, in *Britannica Book of the Year, 1964* (Encyclopaedia Britannica, Chicago, 1964).

[35]As a second type of hominid (*Homo erectus* or *Telanthropus*) is known to be present in the Swartkrans deposit, the possibility cannot be excluded that some of the large numbers of isolated teeth from this deposit may *not* belong to the australopithecine.

[36]I thank Dr. L. S. B. Leakey for entrusting the fossils to me for study; Prof. G. H. R. von Koenigswald and Dr. D. Hooijer for helpful cooperation: L. P. Morley, A. R. Hughes, Miss J. Soussi, and Mrs. R. W. Levine for technical assistance: the South African Council for Scientific and Industrial Research, the Boise Fund, the Wenner-Gren Foundation for Anthropological Research, Cambridge University, the University of the Witwatersrand, and the National Geographic Society for financial assistance.

20

SEXUAL DIMORPHISM IN HUMAN EVOLUTION
C. Loring Brace[1]

Until the growth of the synthetic theory of evolution during the last generation, it was not recognized that the significant evolutionary unit was the population rather than the individual. Consequently, earlier paleontologists tended to look at their discoveries without the perspective of the probable range of variation of the population from which these discoveries were drawn. Each new specimen tended to receive a new, specific designation, a tradition with lingering adherents despite advances in population genetics and evolutionary theory.

Where considerations of the hominid fossil record are the concern, when population-thinking finally began to influence workers in the field, the population that was used as a referent was modern Homo sapiens. It seemed reasonable to assume that individuals of early human populations would differ from the group average to about the same extent that modern individuals do, even if the group average itself might be removed from the modern average to a considerable degree. As it turns out, this may very well be a mistaken assumption. Since all other terrestrial primates except man display a pronounced degree of sexual dimorphism—males being roughly twice the bulk of females—might we not expect man's condition to have evolved from the more common terrestrial primate situation? If this were the case, we would expect sexual dimorphism to become more pronounced as we go back in the fossil record until, at the earliest hominid levels, the degree of male-female difference is as great as that visible in modern baboons or gorillas. The following article makes the most recent suggestion to that effect, and since it has just been published, we do not feel it necessary to add further references to this introduction.

The comparison of Sterkfontein with Swartkrans:

" . . . is one of the reasons for excluding the hypothesis that the difference between the heavily built and the lighter forms of hominid creatures from two million years ago is an example of sexual dimorphism—why should one site yield females only and the other predominantly males?"

Editorial in Nature 228: 315
October 24, 1971

Earlier in this current century it was a commonplace observation, in general works dealing with human evolution, that the acknowledged immediate ancestors of modern Europeans—the Upper Paleolithic inhabitants of western Europe—displayed a more pronounced degree of sexual dimorphism than is generally visible among their descendants today (Osborn 1916:296; Hooton 1931:365). The gradual abandonment of this observation is well demonstrated when one

compares Coon's earlier assertion that "there is a greater difference between the sexes than is usual among more recent groups of man" (Coon 1939:31) with his more recent caution that "in fossil man there is evidence of sexual dimorphism, but it is clouded by the paucity of material available for study" (Coon 1962:26). Still more recent works have dropped all reference to a previously greater degree of sexual dimorphism (Hulse 1963, 1971; Brace and Montagu 1965; Campbell 1966; Howells 1967; Kelso 1970; and Pilbeam 1970).

A graphic review of the skeletal evidence for human evolution, however, reaffirms the assessment of those scholars of a generation gone by that sexual dimorphism in prehistoric hominids was indeed more marked than is now the case (for example, see the simplistic impression one gets from Brace, Nelson and Korn 1971). That the difference was yet more evident in populations previous to the appearance of undoubted *Homo sapiens* has recently been suggested by the de Lumleys

Reprinted with the permission of the author and the 1973 Yearbook of Physical Anthropology.

in their comparison of the mandibles Arago II and XIII from the French Pyrenees (de Lumley and de Lumley 1971; Veber and Rossion 1971:60).

It would seem, then, that the time has come to review Bonnet's largely forgotten assertion that sexual dimorphism in the hominid fossil record becomes "ever more pronounced the more primitive the form" (1919:23). Bonnet made this observation without discussing the reasons why one might expect such a state of affairs, and he leaves his readers with the suspicion that his explanation would have been characterized by a non-Darwinian form of orthogenesis of the kind which enjoyed some popularity at that time. Today we have a great deal more early hominid skeletal material with which to test his observation, including most of the Pithecanthropine and virtually all of the Australopithecine discoveries. Furthermore we have the benefit of a full generation of combined genetic and Darwinian evolutionary theory as well as an impressive roster of field studies of non-human Primates. To anticipate the conclusion of this paper, a review of the evidence shows that Bonnet's prediction is amply confirmed. And a review of theoretical considerations suggests that we have been somewhat remiss in not looking for and expecting to find an increasing degree of sexual dimorphism in progressively earlier hominids.

THEORETICAL CONSIDERATIONS

From the relatively few primate field studies done prior to 1940, it was evident that there were sharp differences between groups where aggressive male dominance behavior was concerned. At one time, the suggestion was offered that the differences represented an Old World/New World dichotomy, with New World monkeys displaying relatively little within-group status differential and little male aggressive behavior, while Old World monkeys emphasized both hierarchy and male aggressiveness (Hooton 1942: 324–326). The subsequent proliferation of field studies has cast a new light on the earlier observations, and it now seems relatively certain that the behavior differences observed were not manifestations of differing hemispheric heritages but rather of different ecological adaptations. Specifically,

the split represents the different adaptations which selection has produced to face the differing survival problems presented by arboreal versus terrestrial ecological niches (DeVore 1963).

If the basic primate adaptation is regarded as arboreal, the present partially or fully terrestrial forms must be considered as secondary and more recent developments in the primate adaptive radiation (Washburn 1951). The traits in which they differ from arboreal primates then can be viewed as having arisen as a consequence of the selective pressures exerted by the terrestrial way of life. One of the most striking differences between arboreal and terrestrial primates is the marked sexual dimorphism of the latter. In general, the more thoroughly terrestrial the primate the more marked the degree of sexual dimorphism, with the most terrestrial forms such as baboon and gorilla groups being characterized by males which are fully double the bulk of females. Only the orang among the arboreal groups displays a comparable degree of dimorphism, an enigma which so far has resisted interpretation. Of the thoroughly terrestrial primates, only *Homo sapiens* fails to conform to the expected degree of dimorphism. This, however, should be relatively easy to account for as will be shown in the subsequent discussion.

The significance of the behavioral and morphological attributes of male terrestrial primates has been convincingly demonstrated in a number of studies (Washburn and DeVore 1961; DeVore and Washburn 1963; Hall 1967; Kummer 1968; and see in DeVore ed. 1965). Evidently size, strength and aggressiveness are important both as a defense against predation and as a mechanism for maintaining group separation for maximum efficiency of resource utilization. If pronounced sexual dimorphism arose as a response to these selective pressures in the non-human primates, should we not expect a similar phenomenon among the earliest hominids? The contrast between the arboreal and terrestrial primates where areal restriction and speciation are concerned has already been used to suggest that early hominids, following the terrestrial primate model, occupied extensive areas with little if any specific differentiation (Washburn 1951: Washburn and DeVore 1961).

It would seem that the same model could be extended to argue for the probable development of a marked sexual dimorphism amongst the earliest hominids. While it has been noted that the development of culture has drastically altered the nature of the selective forces that have acted to shape the human physique (Washburn 1959; Brace 1967b), it should also follow that the earlier the hominid the less effective was the cultural solution to environmentally imposed obstacles to survival. This line of thinking provides a mechanism which can account for Bonnet's observations of more than half a century ago, and further leads to the suspicion that sexual dimorphism among the earliest hominids may have been fully as pronounced as it is today among the terrestrial non-human primates (Brace 1970).

Oddly enough, until very recently (Leakey 1971a,b; Leakey, Clarke and Leakey 1971; de Lumley and de Lumley 1971), there seems to have been a tendency to minimize the importance of sexual dimorphism in assessing the remains of the earliest known hominids (Robinson 1955:439, 1956:153; Pilbeam 1971[2]). The persistence of this approach, where the Australopithecines are concerned, is clearly shown in the reaction to the suggestion that insufficient attention has previously been allotted to this matter:

"Brace has suggested that robust and gracile forms are but male and female specimens, that is, that the difference is nothing more than sexual dimorphism. On the basis of the above results (reconstructions of cranial capacity), a sexual dimorphism of 16.6 percent would result, given this assumption. This is a most unlikely explanation when it is remembered that the gorilla, a species with extraordinary sexual dimorphism among primates, shows only 16.3 percent dimorphism."

Holloway 1970:968

On the contrary, however, if in fact one follows the argument being developed here, this is just the kind of contrast that should have been expected. Even though the old rigid typological view, wherein each different specimen is assigned to a separate taxon, is slowly giving way to interpretations where fossils are considered in terms of possible population ranges of variation, it still seems to be true that the reference population that sticks in the mind of most scholars has a range of variation similar to that of modern *Homo sapiens*. This, however, as Simons has noted (1968), is not necessarily the most productive approach, and it might in fact be fruitful to review the available fossil evidence with a somewhat less restrictive set of assumptions.

THE AUSTRALOPITHECINES

Contrary to what is assumed in the opening quote from the editorial in *Nature* (October 24, 1971) and elsewhere, I do not now and never did assume that the contrast between the Swartkrans and Sterkfontein *populations* was a male/female contrast. As the previous section indicates, I suspect that sexual dimorphism within a given Australopithecine population was considerably greater than that within a given population of modern man. Where only one individual is taken to represent a whole population—as is the case with OH 5 (Zinj) at Olduvai and Sts. 5 (Mrs. Ples) at Sterkfontein—the specimen will fall either well above (if male) or well below (if female) the population (male + female) mean.

A male from one site compared with a female from another may be taken as representing a generic or a specific distinction if the *Homo sapiens* range of variation is used as the standard of reference, whereas, in reality, the difference in the means of all the individuals from the two sites may be slight or non-existent. My suspicion is that this is the case where Swartkrans and Sterkfontein are concerned. The popular image of robust Swartkrans versus gracile Sterkfontein may very well be due to male/female contrasts. The problem, however, is not located in the view erroneously attributed to me that all the males lived at one site and all the females lived at the other, but rather in the fact that male specimens have been chiefly used to characterize one site and female ones chiefly used to characterize the other—a very easy trap to fall into where the sample size of relatively complete specimens is as small as it is. I further suspect that if a male-female range could be constructed for each site, the average difference between the sites would in fact be far less than that held in the popular stereotype.

Nearly all students now assume that there are no less than two kinds (whether species or genera) of Australopithecines; and at least one modern representative of the persistent "splitters" school claims that there are four and perhaps five (Pilbeam 1972). The assumption of at least two different forms was originally based on the interpretation of material found in the Transvaal region of South Africa (Broom 1938). This assessment was not made with any concern for the possible ranges of variation of either hominids or non-hominids, and, although attempts were made to consider subsequent discoveries and a still further proliferation of names (Broom and Schepers 1946; Dart 1948; Broom and Robinson 1952) to be members of a single taxon, whether *Australopithecus* (Washburn and Patterson 1951) or *Homo* (Mayr 1951), the interpretation that has continued to have the most influence (Robinson 1954a) was based on the recognition of two taxonomically distinct groups of fossil hominids in the Transvaal. The frame of reference in fact differed little from that originally used by Broom.

Robinson has attempted to account for the persistence of two Australopithecine[3] groups by suggesting that they represented ecologically distinct adaptations. This is what has been called "the dietary hypothesis" where the robust form is considered to have been a specialized vegetarian and the gracile form a "meat-eater" (Robinson 1954b:328, 333; 1956:150; 1962:126, 134; 1963a:411; 1963b:598). Whether this explanation has been generally accepted (Howell 1965) or rejected (Brace 1965; Tobias 1967:225–228), there has been a tendency to describe the features of robust specimens as being "specialized," "primitive," or "aberrant." Their possessors are then regarded as an evolutionary dead end, doomed to extinction without having contributed further to the course of ongoing hominid evolution. The similarity which such attitudes bears to those so frequently evident where the classic Neanderthals are concerned has been remarked upon (Brace 1965[4]), although few contemporary writers have gone so far as the late Sir Arthur Keith whose own version of the dietary hypothesis spoke of the Neanderthal dentition as a "specialization" fitting the possessors "to live on a rough vegetable diet" (Keith 1915:151).

The main evidence for the presumed adaptive difference between the presumed two forms of Transvaal Australopithecines is confined to the assessment of cranio-facial form and was based largely upon one skull from each group, Sts. 5 from Sterkfontein and Sk. 48 from Swartkrans. Supposedly the robust form is characterized by a relatively low elevation of the portion of the brain case that rises above the orbits, while the relatively greater elevation of the cranial vault of the gracile form has been attributed to a "reorganization of the . . . brain" (Rosen and McKern 1971:72). In an almost phrenological manner, suggestions of greater intelligence also accompany claims for the latter condition (Robinson 1963a:410; 1963b:597).

Unfortunately no attempt was made to compensate for the factors which altered the shape of the two specimens utilized (Robinson, personal communication). One can suspect that the elevation of the vault of Sts. 5 was somewhat enhanced when the cap was set back upon a layer of plaster to unite it with the base after it had been dropped in the laboratory. Conversely the elevation of vertex in Sk. 48 was clearly reduced as a result of post-mortem crushing (Broom and Robinson 1952:10). Some of this problem in comparison should be evident from a perusal of Figures 1 and 2. There may indeed be a difference in the face/braincase relationship between various Australopithecine specimens, but, because of the nature of the specimens used in previous studies, this should not yet be taken as established. Where the issue of the existence of different taxa is concerned, a recent review, dealing not just with a few specimens but with all the evidence available, has shown that the data repeatedly offered in defense of the assumption of multiple taxa are simply inadequate (Wolpoff 1970).

Differences in face/braincase proportions would in fact be suspected if there were marked differences in body size of the individuals being compared. Within a given lineage the proportion of brain size to body size drops as bulk increases (Schultz 1941). Brain size does increase, but body size increases in an exponential rather than a linear proportion. The change in relationships between the face and the brain-case going from infant through adolescent to mature female and finally mature male is

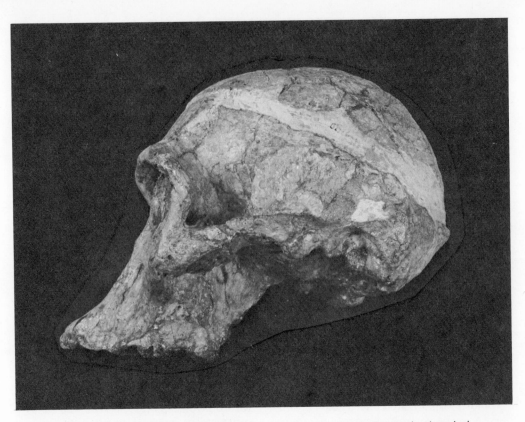

Figure 1. Sts. 5—Mrs. Ples—the most complete specimen from Sterkfontein, showing the plaster bed on which the skull-cap rests.

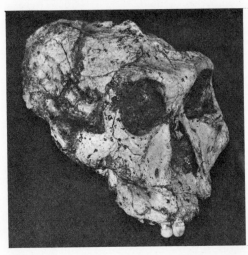

Figure 2. Sk. 48, the most complete specimen from Swart-krans, giving an impression of the extent to which post-mortem crushing distorted the form of the skull.

particularly dramatic where the gorilla is concerned. The change in proportions is essentially an allometric change (Giles 1956), and if the theoretical considerations offered earlier in this paper have merit, one should suspect that a substantial allometric transformation could account for many if not all of the differences in proportion between the small and the large Australopithecines, with the bulkier individuals showing only slightly larger cranial capacities but vastly enlarged facial skeletons and muscle attachments.

If, as I have suggested, the Australopithecines had a male/female dimorphism of a baboon-like or gorilloid degree, we should expect that male/female cranial form differed in like proportion. It may very well be that the individual specimens taken to represent the populations from which they are drawn belonged to the opposite sexes. Here, however, one would have to agree with Coon that the "paucity of material available for study" should inject a note of caution to either the attempt to identify the sex of individual specimens or the attempt to use only one or two individuals to characterize whole populations where the range of variation remains unknown.

The only aspects of Australopithecine

populations where we have anything like a significant sample are connected with the dentition. Fortunately teeth are not only easily preserved but they are also closer reflections of the underlying genotypes than most other parts of the skeleton, and, further, they can be directly related to the forces of selection. A rough, abrasive diet will produce heavy wear, and the adaptive compensation is the development and maintenance at least of robust molars.

Figure 3 shows the profile of mean mandibular cross-section areas (see description in Brace 1967a and Brace and Mahler 1971), tooth by tooth for the claimed robust and gracile Australopithecine populations from the Transvaal.[5] The average differences are no more dramatic than those that have arisen within a single recognized lineage of *Homo sapiens* during the last 30,000 years (see Figure 4), and, in fact, less than those that distinguish some modern populations from each other (see Figure 5). Not only is there no reason to make formal taxonomic

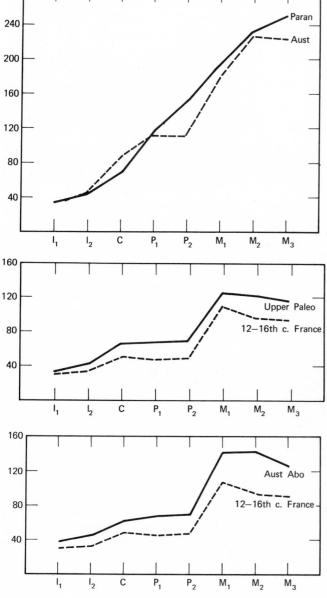

Figure 3. Profile of mean mandibular tooth cross-section areas in sq. mm. for robust and gracile Transvaal Australopithecines. Robust specimens are from Swartkrans and gracile ones are from Sterkfontein. Based on the data in Table 1.

Figure 4. Profile of mean mandibular tooth cross-section areas in sq. mm. for Upper Paleolithic Europeans compared with modern Europeans as retresented in a medieval (12th–16th centuries) cemetery on the border of France and Belgium. Based on data in Table 1.

Figure 5. Profile of mean mandibular tooth cross-section areas in sq. mm. for Australian aborigines compared with modern Europeans as represented in a medieval (12th–16th centuries) cemetery on the border of France and Belgium. Based on data in Table 1.

distinctions from the available data, there is no reason to suggest any marked ecological differences in adaptation between the Australopithecine groups. Figure 6 demonstrates the extent of the overlap in the ranges encompassed by the largest and smallest teeth from each population. The principal visible distinction is the size of the second premolar, but the mean figure for the supposed gracile population (Figure 3, Table 1) and the range shown in Figure 6 (Table 2) are based on only six teeth, and one can suspect the possibility of the bias imposed by such a small sample.

In Figure 7, the difference between male and female Liberian chimpanzees is plotted. Except for the canine and the sectorial premolar, there is only a small difference, as one would expect from a primate which is more arboreal than not. In baboons (Figure 8), again ignoring the canine and sectorial premolar, the difference is more pronounced, as it also is in the case of the gorillas (Figure 9).[6]

Reinforcing our assumption of a robust/gracile population difference that is principally due to the chance of individual specimen preservation, Figure 10 shows that the three complete and one nearly complete Transvaal mandibular dentitions differ far more than the differences between the means of the populations to which they belong. As it happens, the three Swartkrans mandibles are larger on the average than the rest of the Swartkrans material while the one complete Sterkfontein mandible is decidedly smaller than the average for that site. Demonstrating the range of variation present

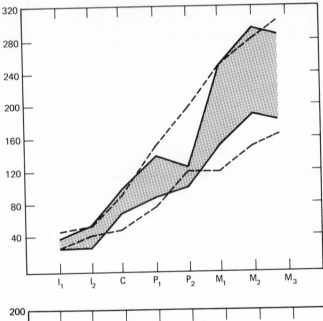

Figure 6. The range of variation of cross-section areas in sq. mm. for the mandibular dentitions of the Transvaal Australopithecines showing the nearly complete overlap of gracile and robust forms. The gracile (= Sterkfontein and Makapan) range is indicated by cross-hatching, and the robust (= Swartkrans and Kromdraai) is indicated by horizontal shading.

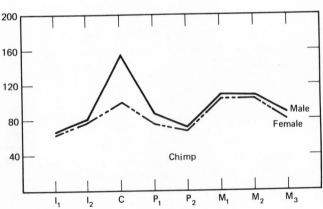

Figure 7. Profile of mean mandibular tooth cross-section areas in sq. mm. for the male compared with the female Liberian chimpanzees from the collection at the Peabody Museum of Archaeology and Ethnology, Harvard University. Based on data in Table 1.

Table 1

Mandibular tooth cross section areas in square millimeters. The number of specimens from which the means were calculated is indicated in parentheses beside each mean. The Sterkfontein, Swartkrans, chimpanzee and Olduvai Hominid 13 measurements were taken by the author. The baboon and gorilla measurements were taken by Paul E. Mahler; the 12–16th century French figures are from Twiesselmann and Brabant 1960; the Australian aboriginal measurements are from Campbell 1925; and the Upper Paleolithic and *Homo erectus* measurements are from Brace and Mahler 1971. Standard deviations are reported for the chimpanzees, baboons and gorillas and are included since these measurements have not been published before.

	I_1	I_2	C	P_1	P_2	M_1	M_2	M_3
Sterkfontein	33.8(7)	45.6(18)	90.58(9)	113.7(8)	113.3(6)	181.2(13)	227.6(14)	225.7(13)
Swartkrans	34.6(7)	44.6(4)	67.9(13)	115.5(20)	150.9(18)	196.1(24)	231.8(21)	247.9(21)
Upper Paleolithic	34.69(31)	41.49(31)	45.48(32)	57.48(35)	61.11(41)	125.48(58)	121.69(52)	117.53(34)
Australian aborigines	37.80(43)	44.22(51)	63.08(88)	66.88(93)	68.53(79)	146.37(139)	146.25(152)	132.09(136)
12th—16th century French	30.60(102)	35.91(107)	51.48(109)	46.72(108)	52.14(109)	110.20(107)	97.00(109)	95.00(99)
Chimpanzees, male	68.09(26) ±9.09	83.34(26) ±10.85	158.50(26) ±25.68	90.04(26) ±14.26	75.55(26) ±8.01	114.36(26) ±11.33	113.26(26) ±14.76	96.95(26) ±15.50
Chimpanzees, female	65.15(32) ±7.90	79.70(32) ±8.49	103.64(32) ±12.78	79.55(32) ±8.14	71.13(32) ±6.39	108.25(32) ±11.03	109.80(32) ±13.59	86.09(32) ±16.66
Baboons, male	50.73(8) ±8.95	42.27(8) ±6.55	107.74(8) ±14.34	97.37(8) ±21.85	57.95(8) ±4.64	80.73(8) ±4.93	131.74(8) ±9.11	162.49(8) ±19.32
Baboons, female	42.68(4) ±9.02	36.61(4) ±7.16	36.34(4) ±6.43	37.64(4) ±4.41	46.19(4) ±2.35	66.91(4) ±3.36	103.00(4) ±5.56	129.35(4) ±9.90
Gorillas, male	70.36(89) ±11.24	97.64(89) ±15.14	275.22(89) ±43.34	211.65(89) ±27.91	154.12(89) ±20.25	216.62(89) ±20.86	272.74(89) ±31.04	265.76(89) ±33.61
Gorillas, female	61.27(62) ±9.89	81.85(62) ±13.76	141.28(62) ±20.79	157.59(62) ±18.49	135.53(62) ±15.36	193.50(62) ±18.29	239.57(62) ±22.30	223.24(62) ±24.67
Olduvai Hominid 13 186.00 140.39(21)		—	28.09	63.20	78.32	88.61	142.49	160.29
Homo erectus	40.28(13)	49.55(19)	75.14(15)	87.53(22)	86.65(17)	150.15(25)	159.89(23)	

Table 2

Maximum and minimum cross section areas tooth for tooth for the Transvaal Australopithecines (gracile = Sterkfontein and Makapan; robust = Swartkrans and Kromdraai). The catalogue number of the specimen giving the measurement is indicated underneath each figure.

	I_1	I_2	C	P_1	P_2	M_1	M_2	M_3	
Maximum	42.00 Sts.52b	58.32 Sts.52b	103.55 Sts.36	140.17 MLD 2	128.40 Sts.7	247.50 Sts.28	298.48 Sts.36	288.75 Sts.36	Gracile Australopithecines
Minimum	27.90 MLD 18	30.81 Sts.62	71.89 MLD 40	88.92 MLD 18	102.85 MLD 18	155.00 MLD 18	192.85 Sts.4	180.60 Sts.52b	
Maximum	40.90 Sk.858	52.40 Sk.858	94.00 Sk.876	156.00 Sk.858	188.20 Sk.34	252.70 Sk.6	286.70 Sk.6	314.28 Sk.851	Robust Australopithecines
Minimum	29.15 Sk.62	42.70 Sk.34	51.83 Sk.820	79.12 Sk.96	124.26 TM 1600	123.20 Sk.45	153.76 Sk.45	173.80 Sk.15	

among the specimens from a single site, the contrast between Sk. 12 and Sk. 74 (Figure 11) finds no parallels in more recent hominids. The persistence of both large and small individuals at Omo and in the East Rudolf area adds to the suspicion that sexual dimorphism characterized Australopithecine populations for a long period of time.

Recalling the dietary hypothesis, it is interesting to see that, while the one complete mandible from Sterkfontein represents a minimum, the contrast between the complete hominid specimens from the Transvaal Australopithecine sites is scarcely more pronounced than the average male-female differences among gorillas, and, furthermore, the molar teeth are in the gorilloid size range (see Figure 12). Since the

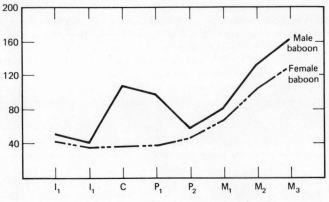

Figure 8. Profile of mean mandibular tooth cross-section areas in sq. mm. for the male compared with the female baboons (*Papio papio*) from the Hamann collection at the Cleveland Museum of Natural History. Based on data in Table 1.

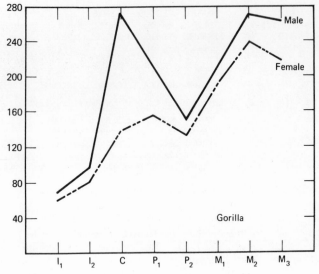

Figure 9. Profile of mean mandibular tooth cross-section areas in sq. mm. for the male compared with the female gorillas in the Hamann collection at the Cleveland Museum of Natural History. Based on data in Table. 1.

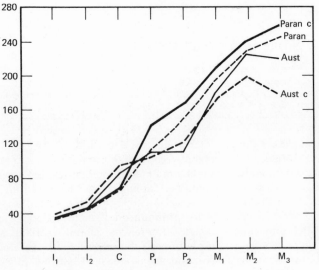

Figure 10. Mandibular tooth cross-section areas in sq. mm. of the three most complete Swartkrans mandibular dentitions (Paran c = S. 23, Sk. 34 and Sk. 858) compared with the Swartkrans mean (Paran), the Sterkfontein mean (Aust) and the one complete maneibular dentition from Sterkfontein (Aust c = Sts. 52b). Based on data in Tables 1 and 3.

Table 3
Tooth cross-section areas in sq. mm. for the two complete (Sk. 23 and Sk. 34) and one nearly complete (Sk. 858) mandibular dentitions from Swartkrans; the means calculated from them, and the areas for the one complete mandibular dentition (Sts. 52b) from Sterkfontein.

	Sk.23	Sk.34	Sk.858	Mean Sk.	Sts.52b
I_1	35.09	36.72	37.18	36.32	40.00
I_2	45.88	42.70	52.36	46.98	54.10
C	66.36	72.98	73.60	70.98	96.82
P_1	112.58	129.00	156.00	132.53	107.69
P_2	151.02	177.74	178.55	169.10	123.75
M_1	212.42	200.11	216.68	209.74	172.90
M_2	223.50	261.54	241.60	242.21	202.04
M_3	230.23	291.75		261.00	180.69

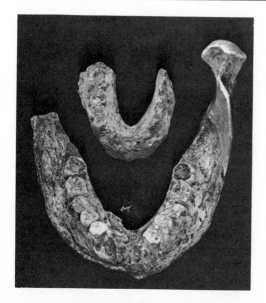

Figure 11. Sk. 74 (above) and Sk. 12 (below) illustrating the range in size and robustness of Swartkrans mandibles.

best recent estimates of Australopithecine body size indicate that they were certainly not of gorilloid bulk (Lovejoy and Heiple 1970; Burns 1971), it would seem that the molars of both forms (if indeed such a distinction can still be made) were being used for the processing of highly abrasive ingested material (Wolpoff 1971). Certainly the evidence shows that the dietary hypothesis as originally supported can hardly be sustained (Wolpoff in press).

Recently there has been an increased willingness to recognize the role of sexual dimorphism among the Australopithecines (R. E. F. Leakey 1971a, 1971b). For instance, it has been suggested that the Australopithecine crania found in 1969 and 1970 at Ileret in the East Rudolf area of northern Kenya—ER 406 and ER 732—represent male and female specimens of the same population. While this represents quite a break with the traditional way of looking at early hominid variation, it has not gone so far as to suggest that all the Australopithecine extremes can be subsumed under the rubric of sexual dimorphism. This vestige of reluctance seems a little puzzling since the contrast in form between ER 406 and ER 732, considered male and female of the same species, is clearly greater than that between ER 732 and Olduvai Hominid 24. The latter contrast, however, is considered sufficient to warrant generic distinction although this assertion has not gone unchallenged (Brace, Mahler and Rosen in press). (And compare Figures 13 and 14).

THE PITHECANTHROPINES

By the Middle Pleistocene, the refinement of the hominids' cultural adaptation should have reduced some of the selective pressure previously exerted to maintain the earlier extreme of sexual dimorphism. It has been suggested that problems related to the birth of bigger-brained infants led to pelvic changes and increases in body size among females in the erectus populations (Lovejoy, Heiple and Burstein in press). Even so, it might be legitimate to suspect that a greater degree of sexual dimorphism was preserved than that visible in modern human populations. Cultural adaptation, while improved, was still far from suspending all pressures on the male physique. And the hunting of large-sized game animals where contact at close quarters regularly occurred must have

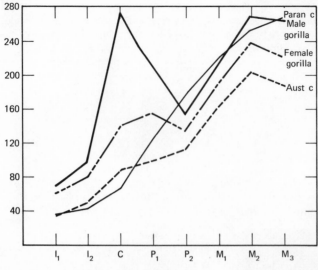

Figure 12. Tooth cross-section areas for the mandibular dentitions of male and female gorillas, the one complete mandible from Sterkfontein (Aust c = Sts. 52b) and the mean of the three most complete mandibular dentitions from Swartkrans (Paran c = Sk. 23, 34, and 858). Based on data in Tables 1 and 3.

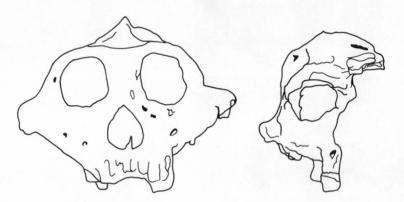

Figure 13. Male and female Australopithecines from Ileret in the East Rudolf area (ER 406 on the left and ER 732 on the right) showing what is now being suggested as an example of Australopithecine sexual dimorphism. Drawn with the aid of a camera lucida from photographs of the casts in the Peabody Museum of Archaeology and Ethnology, Harvard Unversity.

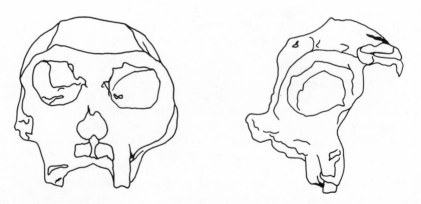

Figure 14. A claimed *Homo habilis* skull from Olduvai Gorge (Olduvai Hominid 24 on the left) compared with a female Australopithecine from Ileret in the East Rudolf (ER 732 on the right).[8]

maintained the probability of traumatic injury at a relatively high level, at least for males. It is not surprising, then, that Weidenreich (1943:178–184) observed a substantial difference between individual specimens. Weidenreich, however, could not quite bring himself to believe that sexual dimorphism accounted for all of the size variation in the Choukoutien skeletal remains, and spoke of the possibility of finding evidence for a population of *erectus*-type dwarfs (1943:178). One suspects, however, that he too was governed by the expectation that sexual dimorphism in *Homo erectus* populations was on the order of that found in *Homo sapiens*.

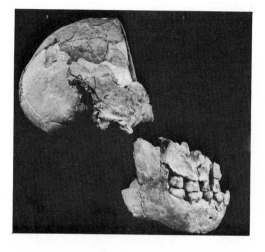

Figure 15. Olduvai Hominid 13, a small *erectus* specimen from above the faunal break in Bed II of Olduvai Gorge.

Figure 15 shows the fragments of Olduvai Hominid 13 ("Cinderella") from above the faunal break in Bed II.[7] Although this has been called a paratype of "*Homo habilis*" (Leakey, Tobias and Napier 1964), it is obvious that the dentition (Figure 16) is of practically the identical size as the mean for *Homo erectus*. Multivariate analysis confirms the simple picture presented in Figure 16 (Brace, Mahler and Rosen *in press*).

Evidently the picture derived from the dentition allows us to rank OH 13 comfortably with the known specimens of *H. erectus*, even though it is clear from an examination of the skull that it was an individual of small size. It would be instructive then to compare it with Weidenreich's reconstruction of a small female specimen of *H. erectus* (Figure 17). When the outline of this specimen is superimposed (to the same scale) on that of OH 13 (Figure 18) it shows that the latter must have been an individual of remarkably similar size. The landmarks of the mandible are practically identical, the back of the skull must have been of nearly the same size, and the only clear difference appears in the lower elevation of vertex on OH 13 (Brace, Mahler and Rosen *in press*).

If this picture adds further to the suspicion that OH 13 was an *erectus* specimen, then Figure 19 which shows it next to OH 9 (on the right)—"Chellean Man" from LLK II, and an accepted *erectus*—demonstrates the relative difference in size and robustness between two *erectus* specimens from Bed II of Olduvai Gorge. It is most tempting to regard

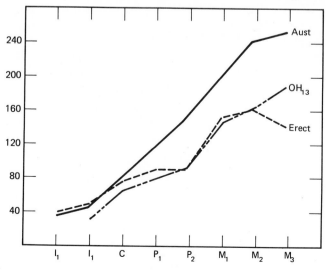

Figure 16. Profile of tooth cross-section areas in sq. mm. for the mandibular dentition of Olduvai Hominid 13 compared with the means for Australopithecine and Pithecanthropine mandibular teeth. From data in Table 1 and from Brace, Mahler and Rosen (*in press*.)

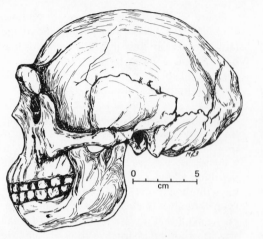

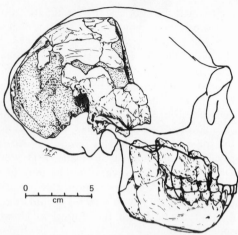

Figure 17. Weidenreich's reconstruction of a female *Homo erectus* from Choukoutien. From Brace, Nelson and Korn 1971.

Figure 18. The outline of Weidenreich's reconstruction of a female *Homo erectus* superimposed (and drawn to the same scale) on Olduvai Hominid 13. Drawn by M. L. Brace.

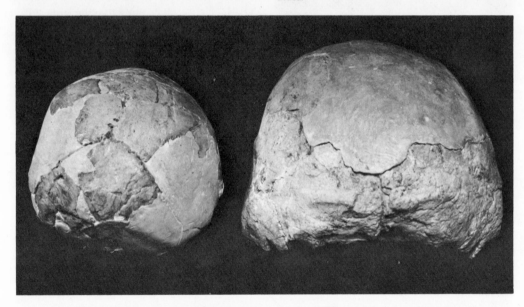

Figure 19. Two *Homo erectus* specimens from above the faunal break in Bed II of Olduvai Gorge, seen in *norma occipitalis*. Olduvai Hominid 13, a presumed female, is on the left and Olduvai Hominid 9, a presumed male, is on the right.[7]

this as a manifestation of sexual dimorphism at the *erectus* level—less than in the Australopithecines, but greater than in modern man.

NEANDERTHALS AND MODERNS

If sexual dimorphism has been reducing during the last several hundred thousand years, as our model predicts it should have been, then it should be still less pronounced in the Neanderthals although more marked than in recent *Homo sapiens*. La Ferrassie II has long been recognized as a much smaller and more lightly built skull than La Ferrassie I, Gibraltar likewise is much less robust than La Chapelle-aux-Saints, and Tabūn I contrasts in similar fashion with Shanidar I, the latter two being respectively female and male classic Neanderthals from the Near East (see pictures in Brace, Nelson and Korn 1971).

In the Upper Paleolithic, the Obercassel male is far more rugged than the female from the same site as Bonnet realized more than half a century ago. Although the contrast is less striking than that between male and female Neanderthals, it is still more pronounced than that visible in modern males and females of European extraction (again, see the illustrations in Brace, Nelson and Korn 1971, pp. 139–143).

CONCLUSIONS

The brief review presented above can hardly be regarded as proof for the ideas proposed, but at least it can serve to give them something of an airing and indicate the direction of the research that will be needed to put them to an adequate test. It is the thesis of this paper that, because we have judged variation in the hominid fossil record from the standards derived from the spectrum of known male/female differences in modern *Homo sapiens*, we may very well have seriously underestimated its importance in earlier hominid populations. Doubtless some will continue to regard this suggestion as having little merit,[2] but it is offered in the hopes that it might contribute to our ability to understand the earlier steps in the process of human evolution.

I suggest that as we examine material at earlier levels, we should be alert to the possibility of greater male/female contrasts than those that characterize more recent human populations. The earliest terrestrial hominid populations could be expected to have had the least effective cultural means for promoting group defense. Consequently we might expect that they would have displayed a degree of sexual dimorphism approaching and perhaps equalling that visible in those terrestrial primates which do not depend on culture for their survival.

Granted that the very skimpy fossil record can give us little more than general impressions at best and suspicions at worst, these should not be without value as a framework of possible expectations against which to test the actual pieces of data as they become available. To record some such general impressions, there would appear to have been a more pronounced degree of sexual dimorphism in the Upper Paleolithic than is the general case today. Looking at the very

few Neanderthal skeletons that can be confidently assessed for sexual identity, the contrast between male and female form appears to be even more striking than it is for the Upper Paleolithic. While no conclusive attribution of sex can be given for any specimens of *Homo erectus*, the contrast in robustness between individuals of the same population appears to be greater still and certainly far greater than one would expect to find given the random discovery of the same number of skeletal fragments from recent human populations. It is hardly out of line to entertain the suspicion that a greater degree of sexual dimorphism existed among the Pithecanthropines than in more recent human groups.

Our ability to appraise the nature of within population variation at the Australopithecine level is even less certain, but if the contrast in robustness between the fragments at the single site of Swartkrans can tell us anything, then it would appear that variation in robustness was still more extreme than in the more recent *erectus* stage. Whether sexual dimorphism can account for all the variation observed between Australopithecines from different sites or not is still a matter for debate. In many instances we have no idea whether the sites from which Australopithecine specimens have come are contemporary or hundreds of thousands of years apart in age. When we recall that changes in human ecological adaptations in the last few thousand or tens of thousands of years have been accompanied by skeletal and dental changes of the same order of magnitude as that given formal generic recognition when encountered at the Australopithecine level, it should give us pause. There may well have been ecological differences between Australopithecine populations and consequent differences in adaptive traits, but this remains sheer speculation. For the moment we do not even know whether such differences existed, let alone whether they represented contemporary diversity or changes in adaptation over considerable periods of time. In fact, such has been the hold of the type concept on interpretations made so far that we really have only the haziest ideas concerning the nature of variation *within* any given Australopithecine population.

If we can generalize from the richest Australopithecine site of them all, Swartkrans, the range of variation is considerably greater than the average difference between Swartkrans and Sterkfontein or any other site with enough specimens to give some idea of the actual population range represented. In fact, it would appear that within population variation at Swartkrans was greater than at any subsequent stage in hominid evolution. It seems reasonable to suspect that this reflects an adaptive sexual dimorphism comparable to that of the non-hominid terrestrial primates. Perhaps all the extremes of variation between as well as within the populations of early hominids can be accounted for by sexual dimorphism. Perhaps not. But until we put this hypothesis to a serious and systematic test, we shall not know; and all our claims and counter claims will be no more than so much empty verbiage.

Surely this is a subject that deserves more attention than it has received in the recent past. If an exhortation is needed to stimulate further thought and research, I invoke the Gallic enthusiasm which produced what could serve as our rallying cry, echoing the French statesman who arose to declare *"Vive la difference!"*

FOOTNOTES

[1]Previous versions of this paper were read at the annual meetings of the American Association of Physical Anthropologists in 1969 (Mexico City) and 1971 (Boston), and of the American Anthropological Association in 1969 (New Orleans) and 1971 (New York).

[2]Anticipating the approach that might be taken in this paper, Pilbeam has offered a rebuttal in advance. The situation, he suggests, fits into the category of a "tragedy" as defined by T. H. Huxley, that is, "a beautiful hypothesis slain by an ugly fact." In reply, I suggest that before the hypothesis is judged either beautiful or duly slain, it deserves at least the opportunity for a decent exposition.

[3]His most recently published assessment considers the term "Australopithecines" to be useless (1967:98–99).

[4]This paper was included in the folio volume distributed to the participants of the First International Symposium on Dental Morphology and Anthropology, Fredensborg, Denmark, Sept. 27–29, 1965. It was requested by the editors to appear in the published proceedings of the symposium, but when these appeared (*Journal of Dental Research*, supplement to Volume 46, 1967), the paper inexplicably had not been included.

[5]The measurements were made on the material in the Transvaal Museum in Pretoria and the Department of Anatomy of the University of the Witwatersrand's Medical College in Johannesburg. I am deeply indebted to Dr. C. K. Brain, Director of the Transvaal Museum, and to Prof. P. V. Tobias for access to the specimens under their jurisdiction.

[6]The measurements of the baboon and gorilla teeth were taken by Mr. Paul E. Mahler on the specimens in the Hamann collection in the Cleveland Museum of Natural History. The sample size for the baboons is admittedly small, but it is all that were available.

[7]I am deeply grateful to Dr. and Mrs. L. S. B. Leakey for the opportunity to study the original fragments of Olduvai Hominid 13 in the Centre for Prehistory and Palaeontology at the Keny National Museum in Nairobi.

[8]Since the University of Michigan Department of Anthropology previously did not own the cast of Olduvai Hominid 24, I am grateful to Prof. W. W. Howells for access to the cast purchased by Harvard University.

LITERATURE CITED

Bonnet, R. 1919 Die Skelete *in* M. Verworn, R. Bonnet and G. Steinmann (eds.), *Der Diluviale Menschenfund von Obercassel bei Bonn*, J. F. Bergmann Verlag, Wiesbaden. pp. 11–185.

Brace, C. L. 1965 The dietary hypothesis and early hominid interpretations. *Folio Volume of the First International Symposium on Dental Morphology and Anthropology*, Fredensborg, Denmark. 33 pp.

———. 1967a Environment, tooth form and size in the Pleistocene. *Journal of Dental Research 46* (Supplement):809–816.

———. 1967b *The Stages of Human Evolution: Human and Cultural Origins*. Prentice-Hall, Englewood Cliffs, N.J.

———. 1970 The origin of man. *Natural History 79*:46–49.

Brace, C. L., and Paul E. Mahler 1971 Post-Pleistocene changes in the human dentition. *American Journal of Physical Anthropology 34*:191–204.

Brace, C. L., P. E. Mahler and R. B. Rosen *in press* Tooth measurements and the rejection of the taxon *Homo habilis*. *Yearbook of Physical Anthropology*.

Brace, C. L., and M. F. A. Montagu 1965 *Man's Evolution: An Introduction to Physical Anthropology*. Macmillan, New York.

Brace, C. L., H. Nelson and N. Korn 1971 *Atlas of Fossil Man*. Holt, Rinehart and Winston, New York.

Broom, R. 1938 The Pleistocene anthropoid apes of South Africa. *Nature 142*:377–379.

Broom, R., and J. T. Robinson 1952 Swartkrans ape-man *Paranthropus crassidenss, Transvaal*

Museum Memoir No. 6, Transvaal Museum, Pretoria.

Broom, R., and C. W. H. Schepers 1946 The South African fossil ape-men: the Australopithecinae. *Transvaal Museum Memoir No. 2*, Transvaal Museum, Pretoria.

Burns, P. 1971 New determination of australopithecine height. *Nature* 232:350.

Campbell, Bernard G. 1966 *Human Evolution: An Introduction to Man's Adaptations*. Aldine, Chicago.

Campbell, T. D. 1925 *Dentition and Palate of the Australian Aboriginal*. The Hassell Press, Adelaide.

Coon, C. S. 1939 *The Races of Europe*. Macmillan, New York.

———. 1962 *The Origin of Races*. Knopf, New York.

Dart, R. A. 1948 The Makapansgat proto-human *Australopithecus prometheus*. *American Journal of Physical Anthropology* 6:259–281.

DeVore, I. 1963 A comparison of the ecology and behavior of monkeys and apes. *in* S. L. Washburn (ed.) *Classification and Human Evolution*, Viking Fund Publications in Anthropology, No. 37. Wenner-Gren Foundation for Anthropological Research, New York. pp. 301–319.

———. (ed.) 1965 *Primate Behavior: Field Studies of Monkeys and Apes*. Holt, Rinehart and Winston, New York.

DeVore, I., and S. L. Washburn 1963 Baboon ecology and human evolution. *in* F. C. Howell and F. Bourlière (eds.) *African Ecology and Human Evolution*, Viking Fund Publications in Anthropology, No. 36. Wenner-Gren Foundation for Anthropological Research, New York. pp. 335–367.

Giles, E. 1956 Cranial allometry in the great apes. *Human Biology* 28:43–58.

Hall, K. B. L. 1967 Social interactions of the adult male and adult females of a Patas monkey group. *in* S. A. Altmann (ed.) *Social Communication Among Primates*.

Holloway, R. L. 1970 Australopithecine endocast (Taung specimen, 1924): A new volume determination. *Science* 168:966–968.

Hooton, E. A. 1931 *Up From the Ape*. Macmillan, New York.

———. 1942 *Man's Poor Relations*. Doubleday, Doran, Garden City, N.Y.

Howell, F. Clark 1965 *Early Man*. Life Nature Library, Time Inc., New York.

Howells, W. W. 1967 *Mankind in the Making: The Story of Human Evolution*. Revised edition. Doubleday, Garden City, N.Y.

Hulse, F. S. 1963 *The Human Species: An Introduction to Physical Anthropology*. Random House, New York.

———. 1971 *The Human Species: An Introduction to Physical Anthropology*, 2nd ed. Random House, N.Y.

Keith, Arthur 1915 *The Antiquity of Man*. Williams and Norgate, London.

Kelso, A. J. 1970 *Physical Anthropology: An Introduction*. Lippincott, Philadelphia.

Kummer, H. 1968 *Social Organization of Hamadryas Baboons: A Field Study*. University of Chicago Press, Chicago.

Leakey, L. S. B., P. V. Tobias and J. R. Napier 1964 A new species of the genus *Homo* from Olduvai Gorge. *Nature* 202:7–9.

Leakey, M.D., R. J. Clarke and L. S. B. Leakey 1971 A new hominid skull from Bed I, Olduvai Gorge, Tanzania. *Nature* 232:308–312.

Leakey, R. E. F. 1971a Further evidence of lower Pleistocene hominids from East Rudolf, North Kenya. *Nature* 231:241–245.

———. 1971b New fossil evidence for the evolution of man. Presentation before the annual meetings of the American Eugenics Society, American Museum of Natural History, New York.

Lovejoy, C. O., and K. G. Heiple 1970 A reconstruction of the femur of *Australopithecus africanus*. *American Journal of Physical Anthropology* 32:33–40.

Lovejoy, C. O., K. G. Heiple and A. H. Burstein *in press* The gait of *Australopithecus*. *American Journal of Physical Anthropology*.

de Lumley, H., and M-A. de Lumley 1971 Découverte de restes humains anténéandertaliens datés du début du Riss à la Caune de l'Arago (Tautavel, Pyrénées-Orientales). *Comptes Rendus de l'Académie des Sciences, Paris* 272:1739–1742.

Mayr, E. 1951 Taxonomic categories in fossil hominids. *Cold Spring Harbor Symposia on Quantitative Biology* 15:109–118.

Osborn, H. F. 1916 *Men of the Old Stone Age: Their Environment, Life and Art*. Charles Scribner's Sons, New York.

Pilbeam, D. 1970 *The Evolution of Man*. Thames and Hudson, London.

———. 1971 Adaptive response of hominids to their environments as ascertained by fossil evidence. Presentation before the annual meetings of the American Eugenics Society, American Museum of Natural History, New York.

———. 1972 *The Ascent of Man*. Macmillan, New York.

Robinson, J. T. 1954a The genera and species of the Australopithecinae. *American Journal of Physical Anthropology* 12:181–200.

———. 1954b Prehominid dentition and hominid evolution. *Evolution* 8:324–334.

———. 1955 Further remarks on the relationship between 'Meganthropus' and Australopithecines. *American Journal of Physical Anthropology* 13:429–446.

———. 1956 The dentition of the Australopithecinae. *Transvaal Museum Memoir No. 9*, Transvaal Museum, Pretoria.

————. 1962 The origin and adaptive radiation of the Australopithecines. *in* G. Kurth (ed.) *Evolution und Hominisation.* Gustav Fischer, Stuttgart. pp. 120–140.

————. 1963a Adaptive radiation in the Australopithecines and the origin of man. *in* F. C. Howell and F. Bourlière (eds.) *African Ecology and Human Evolution.* Viking Fund Publications on Anthropology, No. 36. Wenner-Gren Foundation for Anthropological Research, N.Y. pp. 385–416.

————. 1963b Australopithecines, culture and phylogeny. *American Journal of Physical Anthropology* 21:595–605.

————. 1967 Variation and the taxonomy of the early hominids. *in* T. Dobzhansky, M. K. Hecht and W. C. Steere (eds.) *Evolutionary Biology.* Vol. I. Appleton-Century Crofts, New York. pp. 69–100.

Rosen, S. I., and T. W. McKern 1971 Several cranial indices and their relevance to fossil man. *American Journal of Physical Anthropology* 35:69–74.

Schultz, A. H. 1941 The relative size of the cranial capacity in primates. *American Journal of Physical Anthropology* 28:273–287.

Simons, E. L. Review of *The Cranium and Maxillary Dentition of Australopithecus (Zinjanthropus) boisei* by P. V. Tobias, in *Science* 160:672–675.

Tobias, P. V. 1967 *The Cranium and Maxillary Dentition of Australopithecus (Zinjanthropus) boisei.* Vol. 2 of *Olduvai Gorge,* L. S. B. Leakey (ed.) Cambridge University Press, Cambridge.

Twiesselmann, F., and H. Brabant 1960 Recherches sur les dents et les maxillaires d'une population d'age Franc de Coxyde. *Bulletin du Groupement International pour la Recherche Scientifique en Stomatologie* 3:99–171;355–400.

Veber, M., and P. Rossion 1971 L'homme de Tautavel, plus vieux citoyen d'Europe. *Science et Vie* 120:56–63.

Washburn, S. L. 1951 The analysis of primate evolution with particular reference to the origin of man. *Cold Spring Harbor Symposia on Quantitative Biology* 15:67–78.

————. 1959 Speculations on the interrelations of the history of tools and biological evolution. *Human Biology* 31:21–31.

Washburn, S. L., and I. DeVore 1961 Social Behavior of baboons and early man. *in* S. L. Washburn (ed.) *The Social Life of Early Man.* Viking Fund Publications in Anthropology, No. 31. Wenner-Gren Foundation for Anthropological Research, New York. pp. 91–105.

Washburn, S. L., and B. Patterson 1951 Evolutionary importance of the South African 'man-apes.' *Nature* 167:650–651.

Weidenreich, F. 1943 The skull of *Sinanthropus pekinensis. Palaeontologia Sinica* n.s. *10,* Whole Series No. 127. 485 pp.

Wolpoff, M. H. 1970 The evidence for multiple hominid taxa at Swartkrans. *American Anthropologist* 72:576–607.

————. 1971 Interstitial wear. *American Journal of Physical Anthropology* 34:205–228.

————. *in press* Tooth size, body size and diet in gracile australopithecines. *American Journal of Physical Anthropology.*

21

"TELANTHROPUS" AND THE SINGLE SPECIES HYPOTHESIS[1]
Milford H. Wolpoff

In the interpretive tradition seeking to deny the possibility that various non-modern fossil hominids could be the ancestors of modern man, there have been two arguments that have recurred since early in this century. One emphasized the relatively recent date of the fossil form being considered, from which it could be concluded that there simply had not been sufficient time for it to have evolved into modern man. Forty years ago when the Pleistocene was thought to have lasted only about two hundred thousand years, this argument had some force. However, recent radiometric dating techniques have given us a picture of a Pleistocene of about three million years long, and the insufficient-time arguments have tended to lapse.

This development has intensified stress on the argument that modern forms of men have existed all along and were contemporaries of the various non-moderns. If this were true, it is obvious that the non-moderns could hardly be ancestral to their own contemporaries. We have already seen how the urge to identify this ancient modern led to the creation of "Homo habilis" with no justification other than the faith that such a form must have existed. With one or two possible exceptions, all such candidates for ancient modern status have either proven to be non-ancient (Piltdown, Galley Hill) or non-modern (Swanscombe, "Homo habilis"). One of the possible exceptions is the collection of fragments from the South African Australopithecine site of Swartkrans. Originally called "Telanthropus," these fragments have been regarded by many authorities as belonging to a Homo erectus individual.

Wolpoff examines the questions surrounding both the morphology and the date of "Telanthropus." If it were an erectus specimen and a contemporary of the Australopithecines at Swartkrans, then the claims of the ancient modern supporters would have partial vindication. It is only one specimen, however, and with the doubts surrounding it, no final conclusions can be drawn.

Actually Wolpoff's article is more interesting for the debate that it stirred up than for the substance of its claims. Defending the ancient modernist view, V. J. Gutgesell (1970) produced a critique that repeated the list of anatomical nuances traditionally used to emphasize the supposed distinctions between the various claimed ancient hominids at Swartkrans. This was met by a detailed rebuttal (Wolpoff 1970) in which the observed range of variation of the traits was discussed for both modern Homo sapiens and modern non-human primates, using extensive museum collections. As a result, it is evident that the claims for distinctive status had been made without regard for the expectable range of variation in a normal population. We considered reprinting the entire debate here, but it is very long, detailed and technical. The interested student can find it in the American Anthropologist (June 1970). Suffice it to say here that Dr. Wolpoff sustained his views in convincing and overwhelming fashion.

Gutgesell, V. J. 1970. "Telanthropus" and the single species hypothesis: a reexamination. *American Anthropologist* 72:565–576.

Wolpoff, M. H. 1970. The evidence for multiple hominid taxa at Swartkrans. *American Anthropologist* 72:576–607.

Although there are a great number of individual specimens of Lower Pleistocene

From *American Anthropologist* 70 (1968):477–493. Reprinted with the permission of the author and publisher.

hominids, or "australopithecines," speculation about the relation of the specimens to each other, and about the relation of the specimens to Middle and Upper Pleistocene hominids could conceivably vary no more greatly. Thus, while Le Gros Clark (1967), Bielicki (1966), and Dart (1955) find only one genus and perhaps even only one species present, Tobias (1965a, 1965b, 1966), and L. S. B. Leakey (1963a, 1963b) find at least three genera. While Buettner-Janusch (1966) and Brace (Brace and Montagu 1965) hold that all specimens fall on the direct line of human descent, von Koenigswald (1962) and L. S. B. Leakey (1963a, 1963b) feel that almost none do so. There are almost as many intermediate views as there are specimens.

The interpretative problem is inevitable in the study of fossil man, and the question of which specimens do or do not constitute a species will always remain open. In discriminating fossil species in closely related animals, we are forced to give a morphological answer to a behavioral question (Mayr 1963; Simpson 1953, 1961, 1963), and this answer can never be completely satisfactory.

For hominids, other data can be brought to bear upon this behavioral question. Archeological information is quite important in this respect, as artifacts are the result of structured behavior. Ecological ranges can often be inferred from associated fauna. The stratigraphy of a site, and the temporal relations between sites, can be of crucial importance. However, our final interpretation must ultimately rest upon the framework that we accept, generated by our hypotheses about the selective pressures that oriented human evolution. And these hypotheses can never be completely tested, because they refer to an animal with no living analog.

There is really no good solution to this problem—other than to accept the framework with the best verified hypotheses, most closely fitting the "facts." These "facts" don't speak for themselves, but we can always manage to do a good deal of talking for them.

Such a framework was suggested by Washburn (1951, 1960, 1963) and amplified by Bartholomew and Birdsell (1953), Dart (1957), Oakley (1959), Brace (1964), Bielicki (1966), at one time Mayr (1950), and others. This framework is based on the hypothesis that, for ecological reasons stemming from man's primary cultural adaptation, no more than one culture-bearing hominid species could have arisen or have been maintained.

Critics have suggested a number of early hominid finds as refutations of the single species hypothesis. For instance, Robinson (1965b) divides the australopithecines into two contemporaneous genera: Homo and Paranthropus. Leakey, Tobias, and Napier (1964) distinguish the "pre-Zinj" Olduvai juvenile with a separate generic status. The Lake Natron mandible (Isaac 1965) is suggested as an autralopithecine contemporary with Homo erectus (Leakey and Leakey 1964) in East Africa, and similarly "Meganthropus" is claimed as an example of an australopithecine contemporary with Homo erectus in Java (Robinson 1955). The Chad australopithecine has been given a separate generic name (Coppens 1966), and the Lake Eyassi find has been given both a distinct generic name (Praänthropus) by Hennig (1948), and sunk into the genus "Meganthropus" by Weinert (1950, 1951). Lastly, a distinct generic status was claimed for the "Telanthropus" material by Robinson (1953), although he later included this genus in Homo erectus (1961a, 1961b), claiming contemporaneity between Homo erectus and the australopithecines in South Africa.

On the other hand, a number of authors question a generic, if not a specific, distinction among the australopithecines (Le Gros Clark 1967; Buettner-Janusch 1966; Brace and Montagu 1965; Lasker 1961; Dart 1964; Bielicki 1966). Several of these authors have personally examined the material and have published a number of detailed morphological studies. The claim of a specific distinction for "Homo habilis," separate from the smaller australopithecines, has been effectively demolished (Robinson 1965b). The "Meganthropus" material (Weidenreich 1945; Marks 1953) is, on the one hand, not distinguishable on the specific level from the larger australopithecines (Robinson 1955), while on the other hand, it is also not distinguishable on the specific level from the Javanese Homo erectus specimens (von Koenigswald 1957; Le Gros Clark 1967). This creates a rather curious situation for those authors who view the larger australopithecines as a distinct genus, extinct without issue. In any event, the stratigraphic position of "Meganthropus" with respect to Homo erectus is far from clear (Butzer 1964; von Koenigswald 1957; Movius 1955).

Both the Chad and the Lake Eyassi specimens are generally regarded as indistinguishable from the other australopithecine specimens (Le Gros Clark 1967; Tobias 1965a, 1965b; Robinson 1961b). Lastly, the first potassium-argon dates for the Natron mandible are 1.6 million years (Isaac 1967), greatly changing the temporal position of the mandible from that based on the previous paleomagnetic reversal estimate of 0.9 million years. The Natron mandible is now dated with the Olduvai australopithecine material.

Therefore, the material presented in refutation of the single species hypothesis is far from unquestionable, and the interpretation of these specimens as representatives of hominid species, or genera, sympatric with the australopithecines, is open to serious doubt.

The purpose of this study is to examine the "Telanthropus" material from Swartkrans in order to determine whether it can validly serve as a refutation of the single species hypothesis. The study is not meant to stand as a final proof of the hypothesis, but is rather a critical examination of *one* of the proposed refutations. Both the hypothesis and the relation of the "Telanthropus" stratigraphy and morphology to the hypothesis must be considered in detail.

CULTURE AS A NICHE AND AS AN ADAPTIVE MECHANISM

The single species hypothesis rests on the nature of the primary hominid adaptation. As Washburn has often stressed (1951, 1960), the primary hominid morphological adaptation centers about bipedal locomotion. Other distinctive hominid characteristics either arise from this adaptation, or form secondary adaptations.

We must, therefore, consider what selective pressures lead to bipedalism, and what selective advantages did bipedalism confer on these very early hominids. Many answers to these questions have been proposed in the literature. For instance, Hewes suggests food transport across the savanna as the primary adaptive advantage of bipedal locomotion (1961), while Leakey suggests the ability to see over tall grass (personal communication). While these suggestions obviously form part of the adaptive explanation, by themselves they fall far short of providing an early hominid with a selective advantage strong enough to compensate for

the loss of quadrupedal mobility (Washburn 1951:69; Oakley 1959:443) and for the predatory dangers of a savanna existence.

"It would seem that a weaponless biped trudging over the savannah with a load of ripe meat would be an exceedingly poor bet for survival" (Brace 1962:607).

Weapons provide the crucial factor. A dependence upon tools both in offensive and defensive behavior explains the selective advantage of bipedal locomotion, freeing the hands during locomotion and allowing a tool or weapon to be available at all times. The question of availability at all times is crucial, for the great apes can both produce and carry tools (Goodall 1964). However, tool use in chimpanzees differs from tool use in man in that the chimps do not regularly use their tools as weapons, nor do they depend upon tools as a means of defense (Van Lawick-Goodall and Van Lawick 1965). Thus, because the ability to make and use tools as a learned and ecologically important behavior is not restricted to hominids, the unique hominid dependence upon tools and weapons is all the more revealing. The reduced canines found in even the earliest hominids similarly indicate an early replacement of the canine defensive function by the regular employment of weapons.

Thus, the early employment of tools as a means of defense led to the differentiation of the hominid stock, necessitating bipedal locomotion as well as providing its selective advantage. Culture, in this context, can be viewed as an adaptation to insure the effective transmission of tool use from generation to generation. Selection acted to modify the hominid morphology in the direction of producing a more efficient culture-bearing animal, allowing both the structuring and the transmission of survival-oriented behaviors.

The process of morphological hominization was selectively linked to an increasing dependence upon culture for the survival of the population. As one major implication, any bipedal hominid population must not only have been culture-bearing, but indeed must have been dependent upon culture for its survival. African archeology offers support for this contention, as tools have been associated with the earliest known bipedal hominids at Sterkfontein (Robinson 1957), at Olduvai (Leakey, Tobias, and Napier 1964), at

Makapansgat (Dart 1957), and at Swartkrans (Robinson 1961a). Unless one wishes to claim that an "advanced hominid" is responsible for all of these archeological deposits (see Robinson 1965a and Bielicki 1966 for rejoinders to this claim), the evidence associates both large and small australopithecine forms with the use and manufacture of tools.

The argument that small-brained hominids could not be capable of cultural behavior may be rejected on the basis of Goodall's (1964) observation of such behavior among chimpanzees. The association of the earliest known hominids with tools, predicted by the single species hypothesis, is apparently substantiated by the archeological record.

Just as the morphological evidence of fossil horse teeth and limbs demonstrates the adaptation of the horse to a grass-eating and defensive running environmental niche, I suggest the morphological evidence offered by early hominid bipedalism similarly demonstrates the adaptation of hominids to a culture-dependent environmental niche. There is, however, an important difference between the adaptation of the horse and the adaptation of man. The horse adapted to a restricted grasslands environment by means of progressive specializations of the teeth and limbs. On the other hand, in hominids culture acts as an intermediary between the morphology and the environment. That is, man has adapted culturally to the physical environment, and has adapted morphologically to effectively bearing culture. Thus culture, rather than any particular morphological configuration, is man's primary means of adaptation. His morphological evolution was oriented by selection for a more effective culture-bearing creature. Culture plays a dual role as man's primary means of adaptation, as well as the niche to which man has morphologically adapted. In this sense, all hominids occupy the same adaptive niche.

COMPETITIVE EXCLUSION

Although culture may have arisen as a defensive survival mechanism, once present it opened up a whole new range of environmental resources. Some degree of meat eating and hunting has been observed in the nonhuman primates (Goodall 1964; DeVore and Washburn 1963), and with this background I cannot imagine carnivorous or herbivorous specializations occurring in a culture-bearing hominid lineage, although such specializations have been suggested (Robinson 1961a, 1961b, 1963). Culture acts to multiply, rather than to restrict, the number of useable environmental resources.

Because of this hominid adaptive characteristic, it is difficult to understand how different hominid species could either have arisen or have been maintained sympatrically. The properties that allow sympatry to occur between closely related species are exactly those that an incipient species must acquire in order to complete the process of speciation. These properties are: "(1) mechanisms that guarantee reproductive isolation, and (2) the ability to resist competition from other species that utilize the same or similar resources of the environment" (Mayr 1963:66).

In culture-bearing hominids, the second property makes the interpretation of sympatric hominid speciation doubtful. One of the advantages afforded by culture is the great ecological diversity in the utilization of a broad ecological base it allows. However, because hominids can utilize so many different resources, most of their range consists of areas where only some of them are present at any given time; and, of course, in different places these are different resources. Thus, sympatric hominid species would each be spread over a wide range, in competition for the available resources in each area. The competitive exclusion principle, stating the logical consequence of such competition, does not allow two species with this relationship to coexist for a significant length of time. One or both of the species will either become extinct, or must adapt to a new, less overlapping, niche. Because of the way culture-bearing hominids utilize their environment, subsequent adaptation could not reduce competition. Rather than narrowing the range of utilized environmental resources, such adaptation could only broaden this range, and thus increase the amount of real competition.

Therefore, even if distinct hominid species arose through isolation, one or the other must soon become extinct because of the nature of the hominid cultural adaptation. These views are in complete concurrence with those of Mayr (1950, 1963), Bielicki (1966), Brace (Brace and Montagu 1965),

Campbell (personal communication), and others.

SIGNIFICANCE OF THE PROBLEM

A demonstration of sympatric hominid species would call the whole series of hypotheses about the relation of culture to human evolution into question. This has been recognized by a number of authors who, in defending the proposition of sympatric hominid speciation, have denied the relation of culture to the evolution of at least some bipedal hominids (Leakey 1963b; Tobias 1965a, 1965b; Robinson 1963, 1966). For instance, in discussing his dietary explanation for the adaptive differences between his proposed australopithecine species, Robinson states, "Culture as such cannot be the explanation of the dental differences . . ." (1963:599). Ultimately, by maintaining the interpretation of separate hominid genera, Robinson must reject the hypothesis suggested by Washburn (1951, 1960, 1963) and others of culture as the primary hominid adaptation, responsible for the differentiation of the hominid stock. Thus, in a paper recently read at the Peabody Museum Centennial Meetings, Robinson suggested: "It would seem to be a reasonable hypothesis that agrees well with the facts that hominids came into existence as incompletely erect bipedal herbivores of the *Paranthropus* basic type. But this form does not seem to have been significantly culture-bearing . . ." (1966:8).

Clearly, then, the question of sympatric hominid speciation is more than a mere taxonomic problem. An entire theory about hominid evolution is at stake. Before rejecting the entire theory, it seems reasonable to first make a close examination of the possible refutations. The purpose of this work is to examine one possible refutation, the "Telanthropus" material.

THE STRATIGRAPHIC EVIDENCE AT SWARTKRANS

Some *a priori* reasons for questioning a generic, if not a specific, distinction for the "Telanthropus" specimens, distinguishing them from the other australopithecines, have been discussed. It remains to be seen if the stratigraphic and morphological evidence substantiates the basis of the doubts raised.

In 1950, Broom and Robinson announced the discovery, by the latter, of a mandible in the Swartkrans deposits which was smaller than the other known mandibles of the larger australopithecine type taken from the same site. The new material was given a distinct genus and species name, *Telanthropus capensis*. They offered the following description of the breccia procket in which the mandible was found:

[*The mandible was discovered*] *in a pocket on the edge of the main deposit. . . . The pocket in the main deposit is somewhat different in material and must be of later date, but it may not be geologically much later. There were no bones of mammals associated with the jaw except those of some small rodents which do not help us much* [1950:152].

In addition to the first mandible, the authors go on to describe the position of a second discovery:

We found in the main deposit, and certainly contemporaneous with Paranthropus crassidens, a considerable portion of the lower jaw and a few isolated teeth of man. . . . The jaw is not very different in size from that of Telanthropus capensis, but it seems to differ in a number of characters; owing to the crushing of the latter, it is difficult to make comparisons.

In spite of this early caution, Robinson made such comparisons and assigned the second mandible to *Telanthropus* (1953:446).

In his 1953 publication, Robinson (pp. 446–452) discusses the geology and associations of the Swartkrans deposits in greater detail. The following conclusions can be drawn from this discussion:

1. The first "Telanthropus" mandible was recovered from a "chocolate-colored matrix" on the edge of the main mass of pinkish breccia.
2. The darker breccia differs from the lighter in the degree to which "partial leaching removed some of the calcite which therefore did not so effectively mask the color of the soil. . . . The calcite content dropped from 70% to 50% in the case of the Telanthropus deposit."

3. The second "Telanthropus" mandible, and a maxillary fragment also assigned to this group, were found one-half to two-thirds of the way down from the surface in the main (pinkish) breccia.

Concerning the uniformity of the deposits, and the possibility of their disturbance, he comments:

Although slight traces of stratification have been found in the australopithecine-bearing breccia at Swartkrans, no evidence has yet been found suggesting that the deposit was not a uniform one: there is no evidence of stratification of the fossils. . . . Australopithecine remains have been recovered from the surface layers as well as the deepest ones and the characters of the recovered material are very uniform. While it is clear that in an undisturbed deposit such as this one, the specimens in the surface layers must be younger than those in the deepest levels, in the case of Swartkrans the time lapse between the bottom and the surface was clearly not great enough for it to be detectable in the contained fauna [1953:448–449].

And with regard to the placement of the hominid material:

The greatest concentration of P. crassidens material was found approximately one-half to two-thirds of the way down from the surface, although the concentration here was not markedly greater than elsewhere. All the Telanthropus material was recovered from this same level. . . . some of the specimens were scattered among the P. crassidens specimens.

The fine mandible SK23 is said to have come from the base of the brown breccia (Brain 1958:87). If so, the "Telanthropus" jaws are strictly coeval with "Paranthropus." On the other hand, Brain raises the possibility that this jaw may have originated in a piece of pink breccia embedded within the brown, and recently Oakley and Campbell have also stated that the mandible probably originated in the brown breccia (1967:88). If so, we may reasonably re-examine the claimed coevality of "Telanthropus." However, in order to do so, certain questions concerning the origin of the fossil material in the cave, the nature of the deposits themselves, and the degree

(if any) to which the deposits may have been disturbed, must be considered.

The source of the deposited material is of great interest. How the material got into the cave has a direct bearing upon its distribution within the cave, and hence upon the question of whether or not deposits on the same horizontal level are necessarily coeval. Howell (1959:411) gives five possibilities "as to the manner in which the australopithecines and the associated fauna [could have been] incorporated into the breccias." These possibilities are:

1. The material may simply have fallen in.
2. The material may have been swept in by natural agencies (wind, water, etc.).
3. The site may have been the lair of carnivores, and the animals dragged into the cave as prey or scavenged material.
4. The cave may have acted as a rubbish collector, and thus the deposits may be a rubbish heap left by hominids.
5. The cave may be an actual hominid occupation site.

The nature of the evidence delimits the possibilities for the Swartkrans cave.

Concerning the first two possibilities, collection of the deposits by inanimate means, Howell (1959:411) contends that no evidence at any of the South African australopithecine sites supports them. On the other hand Brain, who has undertaken detailed stratigraphic and geological analyses of all the South African sites, comments on the:

very marked grading trend [in the organic deposits] . . . apparent as one passes from below the position of the original entrance into the further reaches of the cave. . . . It is clear that the finer material has been carried further into the cave, whereas the more normal soil has accumulated close to the entrance [1958:80].

In addition, the pinkish breccia of the main deposit does not appear to be vertically stratified. The evidence implies that the inorganic deposits were swept into the cave by natural agencies.

The possibility that the organic material was deposited in a similar manner cannot be dismissed lightly. A similar analysis of size grading might go a long way toward clarifying this problem. In any event, there is no conclusive evidence denying deposition of the organic material by natural agencies, or even by falling in. These possibilities remain open.

We must also consider possibilities 3, 4, and 5 above: that the animal material was deposited in the cave by a nonhominid animate agent. The presence of stone tools in the deposit argues against these possibilities, for while animals often bring back meat or bones to their lair—which for hyenas, porcupines, and perhaps leopards could be a cave (Brain 1958:11)—it is difficult to imagine these animals also bringing back worked stone tools.

The presence of these tools also argues against the possibility of the Swartkrans cave being a hominid occupation site. The lithic material found at Swartkrans is devoid of any waste material normally found at sites where stone tools are manufactured, such as the occupation levels in Olduvai Bed I (M. Leakey 1966). The use of the Swartkrans cave as a hominid occupation site can be questioned on this basis. In addition, there are other reasons why one would not expect hominids without fire to occupy caves (Coon 1963:236–237). Caves are dark, damp, and often harbor carnivores.

The evidence thus suggests that the hominid material fell, or was thrown, into the cave, rather than deposited in any regular manner by animate agents. Given this manner of deposition, one would not expect vertical strata to appear in the deposits, and no strata appear in the pinkish strata of the main deposit at Swartkrans.

With this manner of deposition, there is no guaranty of temporal uniformity along horizontal layers. Any horizontal area may contain deposits from the entire span of deposition. An examination of Figure 1 shows how this type of unstratified and mixed deposition could have occurred. An object falling into the cave could lodge at any point along the slope. As a result, the deposit of pinkish breccia could have as easily filled from the sides to the middle as from the bottom to the top.

The actual deposition at Swartkrans was probably a combination of filling in both directions. Given this type of filling, there is no determinable temporal ordering within the deposit. In addition, the deposit was

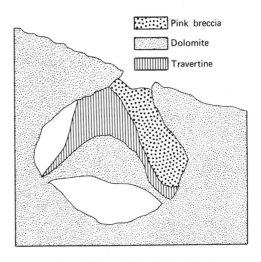

Figure 1. Stage in the evolution of the Swartkrans cave prior to the calcification of the pink breccia deposit. (Adapted from Brain 1958, Fig. 70).

subject to strong shearing and distorting movements for an unknown period after its consolidation (Brain 1958:86–87).

The foregoing would not matter if the deposit was uniform and if the question of temporal ordering within the deposit was not a crucial part of the interpretation of the Swartkrans hominid material. However, Robinson has claimed these deposits clearly demonstrate the coeval existence of two hominid genera; and *if* there are truly two hominid genera within the deposit, then the deposits are not uniform, and the question of temporal ordering is indeed crucial.

The argument that (1) the Swartkrans deposits are uniform, and thus (2) the different hominids mixed within them are sympatric, appears circular. If, on the one hand, the hominids within the deposit are *assumed* sympatric, it is then possible to say that with respect to the fauna, the deposits are uniform. On the other hand, one cannot take the claim of uniform deposits based on this assumption and use this claim to support the conclusion that the hominids found in the uniform deposit are therefore coeval.

A more reasonable, and certainly noncircular, interpretation would be the existence of two different hominid genera mixed in the same deposit indicates the possibility of nonuniformity within the deposit.

Therefore, there are two possible interpretations for the hominid material found within the pink breccia. If the hominid material is all part of the same species, the deposits can be assumed uniform for lack of evidence to the contrary. In this event, the question of coeval species, or genera, never arises. If, on the other hand, we accept Robinson's generic separation of the hominids within the deposit, we cannot assume the deposits to be uniform. Combined with the lack of temporal ordering within this deposit, we are left with no stratigraphic evidence for coeval hominid taxa.

For the hominid material within the pink breccia, neither interpretation justifies Robinson's contention of stratigraphically demonstrated coeval hominid genera.

If the possible stratigraphic interpretations of the "Telanthropus" specimens in the pinkish breccia do not justify Robinson's conclusion, the original "Telanthropus" mandible found in the brown breccia is of even less help. The pink and the brown breccias represent two different deposits with a possible time lapse of unknown length between their depositions:

Evidence favouring a time lapse between the two accumulations is that occasional blocks of pink breccia are found imbedded in the brown. This implies that the pink breccia had been well calcified before the brown material entered. This calcification process is likely to have taken some time [Brain 1958:87].

Thus, the stratigraphic evidence offered at Swartkrans is somewhat ambiguous, and its value must be weighed with this in mind. Dr. F. C. Howell (personal communication) has informed me of new excavations at Swartkrans, uncovering lower layers in the breccia with the remains of (as yet unnamed) smaller australopithecines (see Brain 1967:381–382). However, the discovery of these new specimens does not affect the interpretation of the stratigraphic evidence discussed here.

EVIDENCE OF SKELETAL MORPHOLOGY

We must now consider the question of whether the skeletal morphology of the "Telanthropus" specimens themselves can be used to support this interpretation.

The Swartkrans material attributed to "Telanthropus" consists of a mandible found in the brown breccia, a mandibular fragment found "mixed" with "Paranthropus" specimens in the pinkish breccia along with a maxillary fragment, and the distal extremity

of a radius (Robinson 1953). Isolated teeth at the Sterkfontein Extension site have been attributed by some (Tobias 1965a, 1965b) to *"Homo habilis"* on the basis of size, stratigraphic isolation (they were found in the middle breccia while all other hominid remains come from the lower breccia), and possible association with tools. Because Tobias considers *"Homo habilis"* and "Telanthropus" indistinguishable (Tobias and von Koenigswald 1964), his claim effectively classifies these teeth with "Telanthropus." However, Robinson, while supporting a generic distinction between "Telanthropus" and the other australopithecines at Swartkrans, and a specific distinction between "Telanthropus" and the australopithecines at Sterkfontein, does not separate these teeth from those of the other Sterkfontein australopithecines (1965a). Therefore, I would not be justified in attributing them to "Telanthropus."

POST CRANIAL MATERIAL

Robinson finds the distal end of the radius attributed to "Telanthropus" indistinguishable from that of modern man (1953). However, in the face of an almost complete absence of comparative material (Day 1965), the taxonomic value of this fragment is questionable.

NON-DENTAL CRANIAL DISTINCTIONS

A number of detailed discussions of the "Telanthropus" nondental cranial and mandibular morphology are contained in the literature (Broom and Robinson 1950, 1952; Robinson 1953).

The major features distinguishing the "Telanthropus" mandibles from those of the other Swartkrans specimens are quantitative, rather than qualitative. The "Telanthropus" mandibles are smaller than the other mandibles in the deposit (Robinson 1953:464), falling at the limit, or outside, of the range of variation in both size and proportion of the other mandibles. Robinson makes the following distinctions between the mandibles of his two postulated Swartkrans taxa:

The two mandibles are appreciably smaller than those of P. crassidens, especially with respect to ramus height. . . . The ascending ramus of Telanthropus I *differs in antero-pos-*

terior measurements at the height of the tooth row only slightly from that of P. crassidens, but the height is much greater in the latter. In Telanthropus I, the bicondylar width is geater than the mandibular length, measured in the sagittal plane, while the reverse is the case in P. crassidens [1953:454–455].

On the other hand, the maxillary fragment is quantitatively different from the other Swartkrans specimens, particularly in the nasal area. This fragment has a small nasal spine at the front of the nasal cavity, while in the other specimens the spine is located further inside, its two lateral segments divided by the vomer (Coon 1963:264). The floor of the nasal cavity in "Telanthropus" forms a sharper nasal margin, distinguishable from the more guttered condition in the other Swartkrans specimens. The distance from the nasal spine to the alveolar point is the same as in the other Swartkrans specimens (Robinson 1953:456).

INTERPRETATION OF THE DIFFERENCES

How are we to interpret these differences? While the "Telanthropus" specimens are unquestionably distinct from the other Swartkrans australopithecines, and perhaps from all other australopithecines, we surely do not want to give every distinct specimen a new taxonomic name (Simpson 1961, 1963; Campbell 1963), for every specimen is indeed distinct. Yet, taxonomic nomenclature must not slur over significant differences; a taxonomy ultimately reflects evolutionary relationships (Simpson 1963:3). Features used for classifying must be weighed for both taxonomic relevance (Le Gros Clark 1964) and evolutionary significance (Simpson 1961). The difficulties of a "componential analysis" approach to classification were adequately demonstrated in the development of phonemic theory (Chomsky 1964); there is no indication that a taxonomy for hominids based on such an analysis would be any more successful. Within this framework, we must weigh the distinguishing features of "Telanthropus."

In a summary of his taxonomic arguments, Robinson (1953:500) concludes all characters in which "Telanthropus" differs from the other Swartkrans australopithecines are more "euhominid." However, the differ-

ences in size and structure are not necessarily independent of each other. For instance, some of the structural and proportional differences could be the allometric result of differences in size (Giles 1956). The question remains: are the "euhominid" distinctions the result of evolutionary advancement, or are they the result of small size? And, is the smaller size the result of evolutionary advancement, or does it fit within the australopithecine range of variation? Leakey (1967) recently raised the question of whether size alone can legitimately be considered a taxonomically relevant feature.

Lastly, what constitutes a "euhominid" feature? Surely the similarity between a feature in a fossil hominid and modern man does not necessarily mean a closer relation between them. Robinson (1958) has argued this with respect to cranial cresting patterns in the larger australopithecines. With regard to canine projection, the australopithecines are more similar to modern man than are the Javanese specimens of Homo erectus. Yet, to my knowledge no one has claimed a closer phylogenetic relationship for the australopithecines because of this.

TRENDS IN EARLY HOMINID EVOLUTION

We must look at distinctive features within the framework of the trends that have occurred in human evolution in order to better judge their evolutionary significance. The major trends in hominid evolution from the australopithecine stage to the Homo erectus stage, taking into account the geographic and temporal variation in the known specimens for both stages, are threefold: (1) an increase in cranial capacity (Tobias 1963; Brace and Montagu 1965; Le Gros Clark 1964); (2) a reduction in the size of the face and the posterior dentition (Campbell 1966; Brace 1963; Howells 1966; Frisch 1965; Coon 1963); (3) an increase in the complexity of the material culture (Cole 1963; Oakley 1966; M. Leakey 1966; Howell 1960; Clark 1960; Howell and Clark 1963). These trends are interdependent; the morphological changes were oriented by the changing nature and growing complexity and efficiency of the cultural adaptation (Howell and Clark 1963; Brace and Montagu 1965). They are the significant changes we would expect a creature truly more advanced than the australopithecines to possess.

THE MAXILLARY FRAGMENT

Quite a few of the "euhominid" structural distinctions of "Telanthropus" are exhibited by the maxillary fragment, rather than by the mandibles (Robinson 1953). These include the shortness of the canine socket, the greater depth of the palate, and the well-defined nasal floor and margin with a forward projecting nasal spine (pp. 452–462). However, the distance from the nasal spine to the alveolar point is the same as in the other Swartkrans australopithecines (the *larger* form), and is "greater than the corresponding distance in euhominids" (p. 486). Thus, all of these "euhominid" distinctions occur on a fragment with a face as large as that of the largest australopithecines, and one of the major trends in human evolution between the australopithecines and their successors is the *reduction* of the face!

The appearance of these features on a maxilla otherwise far within the australopithecine range of variation with respect to the most evolutionarily significant characteristics better justifies the extension of the known australopithecine range of variation than the creation of a new genus. Dart concludes: "there is nothing sufficiently distinctive in the palate to separate it even specifically from *Paranthropus*, much less to divorce it generically . . ." (1955:73).

THE MANDIBLES

The remaining distinctions of "Telanthropus" are carried by the mandibles. These deal mainly with size, proportion, and the "U" shape of the dental arcade. Dart (1955) questions the taxonomic relevance of these mandibular features. From a study of the range of variation of these features in both the australopithecines and in samples of *Homo sapiens*, he reaches the following conclusions (pp. 93–95):

1. "The reconstructed ramus of *Telanthropus capensis* is as wide as that of *A. promethus* and probably had the same or approximately similar height (as opposed to that of the reconstruction)."
2. "The height of the body of the *A. promethus* mandible is intermediate between that of *Telanthropus* and extant Nordic European males."
3. "There is a greater range of variation between South African Bantu mandibles than there is between those of *A. promethus* and *Telanthropus*."
4. "The range of variation of form in the mandibles of *Homo sapiens* and their individual parts is relatively far greater than it is in the known Australopithecinae!"
5. "The ranges in variation of 4 mandibular measurements [maximum length, supra-alveolar height, maximular height, and minimum ramus breadth] in living and extinct types of mankind show that there is no more reason for separating the mandibles of all the australopithecines (including *Paranthropus* and *Telanthropus*) from *Sinanthropus* and *Homo heidelbergensis*, than there is for separating the mandibles of Bushmen (or Pygmies) from those of Scotsmen, or New Caledonian and Loyalty Islanders."
6. "The similarity between the mandibles of extinct and extant human beings . . . indicate[s] the impracticability of separating [them] in terms of mandibular structure."
7. Thus "neither the smallness of the mandible, nor the lowness of the body, nor of its ramus in *Telanthropus* can be relied upon as a criterion of generic distinction between *Telanthropus* and other Australopithecinae."

Therefore, the differences in mandibular size and structure that occur between "Telanthropus" and the other Swartkrans australopithecines do not have taxonomic relevance for either the australopithecines or for modern man. The range of variation in hominid mandibular size and structure is so great that it can't even be used to differentiate between *known* hominid species, let alone be used to separate postulated ones.

Moreover, the cusp patterns of the molar teeth and the very large breadth of the ascending ramus in the main "Telanthropus" mandible "appear to demonstrate clearly enough its australopithecine affinities" (Le Gros Clark 1949:39).

SUMMARY

The nondental characteristics of the "Telanthropus" material do not support the claim for either generic or specific distinction from the other australopithecines at Swartkrans, and certainly not from all other australopithecines taken as a whole. It seems far more justifiable to consider the supposedly distinguishing features of these specimens as reasonable extensions of the *estimated* australopithecine range of variation.

DENTAL DISTINCTIONS

The entire case for excluding "Telanthropus" from the Swartkrans sample now rests with the dentition. Indeed, tooth size variation was the strongest argument mustered by Broom and Robinson (1952). Two important facts were brought out in this discussion. First, the lower second molars were as large as, or larger than, the lower third molars. In most australopithecines known at that time, the opposite size progression is found. The "Telanthropus" size progression was then thought to be an important "euhominid" taxonomic characteristic. Second, "Telanthropus" M_1 size was compared with M_1 size for the remaining Swartkrans sample and was found to be significantly different, falling outside of the sample range of variation. At the time, these two taxonomic arguments were quite convincing, and with very few exceptions (Le Gros Clark 1950, 1959, 1964, 1967; Dart 1955), most authors accepted "Telanthropus" as a genus distinct from the remaining Swartkrans population and subsequently as a member of *Homo erectus* (Robinson 1961a, 1961b).

THE ORIGINAL STATISTICAL TEST

In 1952, Broom and Robinson (pp. 116–118) demonstrated the statistical improbability of the "Telanthropus" lower first molars belonging to the remaining australopithecine sample *at Swartkrans*. They chose M_1 for this demonstration because it varied the least of the molars. Thus, they state: "On account of the geater variability of M_2, and the very great variability of M_3 in our *Paranthropus crassidens* samples, it can be shown that the *Telanthropus* samples are not strongly significant for M_2 and are not at all significant for M_3" (1952:117).

Because M_2 and M_3 cannot be used to statistically differentiate "Telanthropus," the test must rest with M_1. If the test for M_1 shows significant difference, M_2 and M_3 can also be assigned to the new taxon as they exist *in situ* in the same mandible.

In their test for the statistical significance of the "Telanthropus" M_1 size difference, Broom and Robinson begin with the necessary assumption that "Telanthropus" was a member of the Swartkrans population (1952:117; Parratt 1961:174–177). They calculated the mean and standard deviation of both M_1 length and M_1 breadth for the entire Swartkrans sample. They could then calculate the distance of the "Telanthropus" measurements from the sample means in units of standard deviations.

If the sample were very large, a separation of more than 2.5 standard deviations would justify the exclusion of the test points ("Telanthropus") from the sample on statistical grounds. A distance of more than 2.5 standard deviations implies that the test points lie a greater distance from the sample means than one would expect due to chance variation within the population.

Broom and Robinson found a separation of 2.8 standard deviations between the sample M_1 mean length and the "Telanthropus" value of 11.9 mm, and a separation of 3.8 standard deviations between the sample M_1 breadth and the "Telanthropus" value of 11.9 mm (p. 117). These values give statistical significance to the hypothesis that the "Telanthropus" molars could not have arisen in the Swartkrans sample. The authors therefore concluded that "Telanthropus" was a demonstrably different hominid on the basis of M_1 size.

THE PROPER COMPARATIVE MATERIAL

The "Telanthropus" first molars lie outside the range of expected sample variation of the Swartkrans sample. However, is the Swartkrans sample the best unit of comparison? As Robinson himself emphasizes (1965a:403), "range of variation" could refer to either the observed sample range or to the calculated population range.

In the human paleontological literature, the word "population" has found many meanings. It has been used to refer to the collection of specimens from a given site, or from a series of sites, or for the entire species concerned (Simpson 1963). None of these uses is correct. A collection of samples from a site, or from sites, is in no way an actual breeding population. Rather, they span an immense temporal, and often geographic, distance. For these early hominids, the most accurate chronological control possible would not allow the assumption that the specimens from a site constitute an actual breeding population. In terms of actual lineage relationship, do we know that the australopithecines from Sterkfontein are more closely related to each other than they are to the specimens from Makapansgat?

We have no way of telling what specimens constituted an actual breeding population. The same problem exists for fossil species. However, in defining fossil species, there is an attempt to include specimens more closely related to each other than to members of other fossil species. Taken as a unit, a fossil species represents a more consistently-related and biologically-meaningful unit than do the specimens from a site.

Thus, "Telanthropus" could be more properly compared with a species, than with the other specimens at Swartkrans alone. Robinson divides the australopithecines into two genera (1965b). Because he includes the Swartkrans australopithecines in *Paranthropus*, a more appropriate comparison for "Telanthropus" would be with the calculated *Paranthropus* range of variation. As Tobias (1965b) points out, the Swartkrans sample is not representative of the *Paranthropus* dental range of variation. The dental coefficients of variation for the Swartkrans sample alone are much smaller than the comparable coefficients of variation in the other australopithe-

cine taxon postulated by Robinson. On the other hand, dental coefficients of variation for all the specimens included in *Paranthropus* by Robinson are almost identical to both those of his other australopithecine taxon, and to those of all australopithecines (Tobias 1965b). For M_1 dimensions, this can be seen in Tables 1 and 2.

SIGNIFICANCE OF M_1 IN HOMINID TAXONOMY

A more serious objection can be raised to the relevance of Broom and Robinson's statistical test. This concerns the use of M_1 in distinguishing hominid species.

One way to determine the taxonomic relevance of a trait is to compare its observed variation within a *known* species to its variation *between* known or postulated species. Concerning the dental variation between the proposed taxa at Swartkrans, Le Gros Clark states: "a similar degree of variation can be demonstrated within the species *Homo sapiens*" (1949:39). Thus, the taxonomic value of M_1 size for distinguishing hominid genera, if not species, is questionable. Indeed when the teeth are slightly worn M_1 size cannot be used to distinguish modern man from the chimpanzee (Schuman and Brace 1954).

A NEW COMPARISON

Even if M_1 size had taxonomic value, it does

Table 1
Comparison of Hominid M_1 Length Measurements to the Australopithecine Population as a Genus and Broken Down into Species

	Australopithecines		
	Smaller Type	Larger Type	All
sample size	9	20	29
mean	14.01	14.57	14.40
standard deviation	1.02	1.23	1.18
coefficient of variation	7.30	8.47	8.23
Distance from mean in units of S.D. of:			
Telanthropus I	2.06	2.17	2.11
Lake Natron (L)	2.34	1.48	1.69
Lake Natron (R)	2.04	1.24	1.44
MNK II	1.28	1.52	1.43
Pithecanthropus B	0.21	0.63	0.51
Australian Aborigine (maximum)	0.01	0.46	0.34
Australian Aborigine (average)	1.67	1.84	1.77

Table 2

Comparison of Hominid M_1 Breadth Measurements to the Australopithecine Population as a Genus and Broken Down into Species

| | Australopithecines | | |
	Smaller Type	Larger Type	All
sample size	9	20	29
mean	12.87	13.74	13.47
standard deviation	0.87	1.14	1.12
coefficient of variation	6.73	8.26	8.23
Distance from mean in units of S.D. of:			
Telanthropus I	1.12	1.62	1.40
Lake Natron (L)	2.81	1.38	1.63
Lake Natron (R)	3.04	1.55	1.81
MNK II	1.46	1.89	1.67
Pithecanthropus B	0.39	0.48	0.24
Australian Aborigine (maximum)	0.73	0.21	0.10
Australian Aborigine (average)	1.12	1.62	1.63

Table 3

Rejection Limits and the Associated Probabilities for the Chauvenet Criterion of Rejection of Unlikely Data

Population size (n)	9	14	20	29
Distance from the mean in standard deviations which must be equaled or exceeded for valid rejection	1.92	2.10	2.24	2.38
Maximum probability of incorrectness of rejection	0.056	0.036	0.025	0.017

not distinguish "Telanthropus" from either the larger australopithecines or from all australopithecines.

Because Robinson includes the other Swartkrans australopithecines in the taxon "Paranthropus," let us compare the "Telanthropus" M_1 values with the range of variation for all specimens that Robinson includes in "Paranthropus." These additional specimens include Kromdraai (Robinson 1956), Lake Natron (Tobias: personal communication), and "Meganthropus" (Tobias and von Koenigswald 1964). The Swartkrans measurements were published by Robinson (1956).

Tables 1 and 2 show the "Telanthropus" M_1 length and breadth distances in standard deviations from three australopithecine samples: from the larger australopithecines (Robinson's "Paranthropus"), from the smaller australopithecines, and from all australopithecines. The standard deviations and coefficients of variation for the three samples are given as estimates of the sample variability.

In addition, the distances of other hominid specimens from these samples are calculated. These additional specimens include Lake Natron, MNK II (Tobias and von Koenigswald 1964), Australian aborigines maximum and mean, and "Pithecanthropus B" (Coon 1963).

In computing the distance values for "Telanthropus," I followed the exact procedure used by Broom and Robinson (1952): that is, in order to make a statistical test for the exclusion of questionable points from a sample, the questionable points must be included in the computation of the sample mean and standard deviation (Parratt 1961:174–177. The metric distance of the "Telanthropus" value from the sample means was divided by the sample standard deviations, resulting in the test statistic: the distances of the questionable point from the sample mean in units of sample standard deviations.

As expected, the variability of all specimens included by Robinson in "Paranthropus" is greater than the variability of the Swartkrans sample alone, even including the

"Telanthropus" material. Thus, while Robinson (1952:118) calculated a standard deviation of 1.01 for M_1 length in the Swartkrans sample including "Telanthropus," the corresponding value for the larger sample is 1.23. However, the variability for the entire "Paranthropus" sample is comparable with both the variability of the other postulated australopithecine taxon, and with that of all the australopithecines.

Using Broom and Robinson's rejection criterion of 2.5 standard deviations, "Telanthropus" cannot be statistically distinguished from the larger australopithecine sample ("Paranthropus") on the basis of either M_1 length or breadth. In terms of M_1 length, "Telanthropus" falls 2.17 standard deviations from the sample mean, and for M_1 breadth, the corresponding distance is 1.62 standard deviations.

Because of the small sample size, 2.5 standard deviations may not be the most appropriate rejection criterion. For an acceptable criterion, it is best to turn to a statistician:

Rejection on the basis of a hunch or general fear is not at all satisfactory, and some sort of objective criterion is better than none. Many objective criteria have been proposed, all of them arbitrary. The one due to Chauvenet seems to be the most widely accepted. This criterion states that a measurement in a set of n trials shall be rejected if its deviation (reckoned from the mean) is such that the probability of occurrence of all deviations equally large or larger does not exceed 1/2n. On this criterion, some rather small deviations are unreasonably discarded if n is not very large [Parratt 1961:176].

The Chauvenet rejection criterion has the disadvantage of rejecting too much if the sample size is small. Thus, it is quite appropriate to test for the exclusion of "Telanthropus."

Table 3 gives the Chauvenet rejection limits in standard deviations for the sample sizes used in this study. These are the limits that must be exceeded in order to reject a questionable point from the sample. The associated probabilities of mistaken rejection are also calculated.

The Chauvenet rejection limits are lower than the 2.5 standard deviation limit used by

Broom and Robinson. Yet, even with a lower rejection criterion, biased toward rejecting too much from small samples, the "Telanthropus" values cannot be excluded from the "Paranthropus" sample, let alone from all the australopithecines.

The rejection limit for a sample size of 20 is 2.24 standard deviations. The "Telanthropus" M_1 length and breadth distances from the "Paranthropus" mean values fall short of this limit. Thus, while the "Telanthropus" molar dimensions fall at the lowest end of the observed range of variation, they fall within the limits of the calculated range. As Robinson points out, this distinction is important:

Observed range and calculated range may differ very significantly, especially where small samples are concerned . . . if attention is confined to observed range where samples are small, distinctions will be frequently found where they do not actually exist . . . what one is really concerned [with is] to estimate and take into account . . . - the range of variation in the species from which the sample came [1965a:403–404].

COMPARISON WITH OTHER HOMINIDS

Indeed, according to Tables 1 and 2, neither the two Homo erectus specimens nor the Australian aborigine mean and extreme value can be used to differentiate these hominids from "Paranthropus" on the basis of the M_1 dimensions. The average aborigine lies no further from the "Paranthropus" mean than does "Telanthropus." The extreme aborigine size is virtually identical to the "Paranthropus" mean, as well as closely resembling the "Paranthropus" pattern and degree of wear (although no one claims the aborigines are restricted to an "essentially vegetarian diet").

Thus, the taxonomic value of M_1 dimensions is questionable. We surely do not wish to base our taxonomic determinations on criteria that cannot be used to distinguish Homo sapiens from the larger australopithecines.

OTHER DENTAL FEATURES

Molar size progression was originally thought to distinguish "Telanthropus" from the other australopithecines. However, recent work has shown that relative molar size has no value in hominid taxonomy (Garn, Lewis, and Kerewsky 1964). From what little is visible in the cusp pattern, there is, again, no basis for separating "Telanthropus" (Le Gros Clark 1950, 1959).

SUMMARY

The dental argument for distinguishing "Telanthropus" from the other australopithecines reduces to a statistical test for M_1 size. However, M_1 has no taxonomic value for distinguishing hominid taxa, and even if it did, this does not justify the separation of "Telanthropus" from either Robinson's proposed taxon "Paranthropus" or from all the australopithecines taken as a group.

RELATION TO THE EAST AFRICAN AUSTRALOPITHECINES

There has been a recent suggestion to include the "Telanthropus" specimens in the postualated species *Homo habilis* (Tobias and von Koenigswald 1964). This, however, has led to unlimited taxonomic confusion. *Telanthropus* is the prior generic name, so if the inclusion is correct *Homo habilis* is an invalid species. Robinson now includes "Telanthropus" with *Homo erectus*. Therefore, in effect there would be no specific distinction between the East African australopithecines (according to Robinson) and *Homo erectus*. On the other hand, other authors find no specific distinction between "Meganthropus" and *Homo erectus*, but Robinson classifies this hominid with *Paranthropus*—a separate genus!

Were we to accept the opinions of only those workers familiar with the material, and choose the appropriate interpretations, we could conclude that while both the larger and the smaller australopithecines can be included in *Homo erectus*, they are generically distinct from each other. Surely someone must be mistaken.

CONCLUSIONS

"Telanthropus" has been offered in rejection of the single species hypothesis. This objection is questionable on both stratigraphic and morphological grounds. Perhaps, if the material were found in another context, the same morphological ambiguities that do not allow its separation from the australopithecines, could be used to argue its inclusion in *Homo erectus*. As things stand, not one piece of evidence stands to distinguish it validly from the other australopithecines. The specimens represent a not unreasonable extension of the estimated australopithecine range of variability.

NOTES

[1] I would like to acknowledge my sincere indebtedness to Dr. Eugene Giles of the Department of Anthropology at Harvard University, Dr. A. Rohn and Dr. F. K. Lehman of the Department of Anthropology at the University of Illinois, and Dr. C. L. Brace of the Department of Anthropology at the University of Michigan, Ann Arbor, for the many invaluable suggestions, criticisms, and corrections they have contributed to this work. I would like to acknowledge my very great debt to Dr. Donald Lathrap of the Department of Anthropology, University of Illinois, for his extensive contribution to the development of the viewpoint implicit in this work, expressing essentially what he has been teaching and saying for the several years that I have known him. I take sole responsibility for the content of this work.

REFERENCES CITED

Bartholomew, G. A., and J. B. Birdsell 1953 Ecology and the protohominids. American Anthropologist 55:481–498.
Bielicki, T. 1966 On "Homo habilis." Current Anthropology 7:576–578.
Brace, C. L. 1962 Comments on "Food transport and the origin of hominid bipedalism." American Anthropologist 64:606–607.
———. 1963 Review of Evolution and hominisation, edited by G. Kurth. American Journal of Physical Anthropology 21:87–91.
———. 1964 The fate of the "classic" Neanderthals: a consideration of hominid catastrophism. Current Anthropology 5:3–43.
Brace, C. L., and M. F. Ashley Montagu 1965 Man's evolution. New York. Macmillan.
Brain, C. K. 1958 The Transvaal ape-man bearing cave deposits. Transvaal Museum Memoir No. 11.
———. 1967 The Transvaal Museum's fossil project at Swartkrans. South African Journal of Science 63:378–384.
Broom, R., and J. T. Robinson 1950 Man contemporaneous with the Swartkrans ape-man. American Journal of Physical Anthropology 8:151–55.
———. 1952 Swartkrans ape-man. Transvaal Museum Memoir No. 6.

Buettner-Janusch, J. 1966 The origins of man. New York, John Wiley & Sons.

Butzer, K. W. 1964 Environment and archeology: an introduction to Pleistocene geology. London, Methuen & Co.

Campbell, B. 1963 Quantitative taxonomy and human evolution. In Washburn, ed. (1963). pp. 50–74.

———. 1966 Human evolution. Chicago. Aldine.

Chomsky, N. 1964 Current issues in linguistic theory. The Hague, Mouton and Co.

Clark, J. D. 1960 Human ecology during pleistocene and later times in Africa south of the Sahara. Current Anthropology 1:307–324.

Cole, S. 1963 The prehistory of East Africa. New York, Mentor.

Coon, C. S. 1962 The origin of races. New York, Alfred A. Knopf.

Coppens, Y. 1966 An early hominid from Chad. Current Anthropology 7:584–585.

Dart, R. A. 1955 Australopithecus prometheus and Telanthropus capensis. American Journal of Physical Anthropology 13:67–96.

———. 1957 The osteodontokeratic culture of Australopithecus prometheus. Transvaal Museum Memoirs No. 10.

———. 1964 The ecology of the South African man-apes. In Ecological studies in southern Africa. D. H. S. Davis, ed. Monographiae Biologicae 14:49–69.

Day, M. 1965 Guide to fossil man. Cleveland, World.

DeVore, I., and S. L. Washburn 1963 Baboon ecology and human evolution. In Washburn, ed. (1963). pp. 335–367.

Frisch, J. E. 1965 Trends in the evolution of the hominoid dentition. Bibliotheca Primatologica, Fasc. 3.

Garn, S. M., A. B. Lewis, and R. S. Kerewsky 1964 Relative molar size and fossil taxonomy. American Anthropologist 66:587–592.

Giles, E. 1956 Cranial allometry in the great apes. Human Biology 28:43–58.

Goodall, J. (See also Lawick) 1964 Tool-using and aimed throwing in a community of freeliving chimpanzees. Nature 201:1264–1266.

Hennig, E. 1948 Quärtarfaunen and Urgeschichte Ostafrikas. Naturwissenschaftliche Rundschau 1:212–217.

Hewes, G. W. 1961 Food transport and the origin of hominid bipedalism. American Anthropologist 63:687–710.

Howell, F. C. 1959 The Villafranchian and human origins. In Ideas on Human Evolution. W. Howells, ed. (1962). Cambridge, Harvard University Press.

———. 1960 European and Northwest African Middle Pleistocene hominids. Current Anthropology 1:195–232.

Howell, F. C., and F. Bourlière, eds. 1963 African ecology and human evolution. Chicago, Aldine.

Howell, F. C., and J. D. Clark 1963 Acheulian hunter-gatherers of Sub-Saharan Africa. In Howell and Boulière, ed. (1963). pp. 458–533.

Howells, W. W. 1966 Homo erectus. Scientific American 215:46–53.

Isaac, G. 1965 The Peninj beds—an early Middle Pleistocene formation west of Lake Natron. Quarternaria 7:101–130.

———. 1967 Stratigraphy of the Peninj group. In Background to evolution in Africa. W. W. Bishop and J. D. Clark, eds. Chicago, University of Chicago Press.

Koenigswald, G. H. R. von 1957 Meganthropus and the Australopithecinae. Proceedings of the 3rd Pan African Congress on Prehistory, pp. 158–160.

———. 1962 The evolution of man. Ann Arbor, University of Michigan Press.

Kurth, A., ed. 1961 Evolution and hominisation. Stuttgart, A. Fischer.

Lasker, G. W. 1961 The evolution of man. New York, Holt, Rinehart, and Winston.

Lawick-Goodall, J. van 1965 New discoveries among Africa's chimpanzees. National Geographic 128:802–837.

Leakey, L. S. B. 1963a East African hominoidea and the classification within this superfamily. In Washburn, ed. (1963). pp. 32–49.

———. 1963b Very early East African hominiodea and their ecological setting. In Howell and Bourlière, eds. (1963), pp. 448–457.

———. 1967 An early Miocene member of Hominidae. Nature 213:155–163.

Leakey, L. S. B. and M. D. Leakey 1964 Recent discoveries of fossil hominids in Tanganyika: at Olduvai, and near Lake Natron. Nature 202:5–7.

Leakey, L. S. B., P. V. Tobias, and J. R. Napier 1964 A new species of the genus Homo from Olduvai Gorge, Nature 202:7–9.

Leakey, M. 1966 Review of the Oldowan culture from Olduvai Gorge. Nature 210:462–466.

Le Gros Clark, W. E. 1949 New palaeontological evidence bearing on the evolution of the hominoidea. Quarterly Journal of the Geological Society 105:7–51.

———. 1950 Hominid characters of the australopithecine dentition. Journal of the Royal Anthropological Institute 80:37–54.

———. 1959 The crucial evidence for human evolution. Proceedings of the American Philosophical Society 103:99–112.

———. 1964 The fossil evidence for human evolution. Chicago, University of Chicago Press.

———. 1967 Man-apes or ape-men? New York, Holt, Rinehart, and Winston.

Marks, P. 1953 Preliminary note on the discovery of a new jaw of Meganthropus von Koenigswald in the Lower Middle Pleistocene of Sangiran, Central Java. Indonesian Journal of Natural Science 109:26–33.

Mayr, E. 1950 Taxonomic categories in fossil hominids. Cold Spring Harbor Symposia on Quantitative Biology 15:108–118.

——. 1963 Animal species and evolution. Cambridge Belknap Press.

Movius, H. L. 1955 Paleolithic archaeology in Southern and Eastern Asia, exclusive of India. Journal of World History 2:257–282, 520–553.

Oakley, K. 1959 Tools makyth man. Smithsonian Report for 1958:431–445.

——. 1966 Frameworks for dating fossil man. 2nd. ed. Chicago, Aldine.

Oakley, K., and B. Campbell 1967 Catalogue of fossil hominids. Part I: Africa. London, British Museum of Natural History.

Parratt, L. G. 1961 Probability and experimental errors in science. New York, John Wiley and Sons.

Pilbeam, D. R., and E. L. Simons 1965 Some problems of hominid classification. American Scientist 53:237–259.

Robinson, J. T. 1953 Telanthropus and its phylogenetic significance. American Journal of Physical Anthropology 11:445–501.

——. 1955 Further remarks on the relationship between Meganthropus and the australopithecines. American Journal of Physical Anthropology 13:429–445.

——. 1956 The dentition of the australopithecinae. Transvaal Museum Memoir No. 9.

——. 1957 Occurrence of stone artifacts with Australopithecus at Sterkfontein. Nature 180:521–524.

——. 1958 Cranial cresting patterns and their significance in the Hominoidea. American Journal of Physical Anthropology 16:397–428.

——. 1961a The australopithecines and their bearing on the origin of man and of stone tool-making. South African Journal of Science 57:3–16.

——. 1961b The origin and the adaptive radiation of the Australopithecines. In Kurth, ed. pp. 120–140.

——. 1963 Australopithecines, culture, and phylogeny. American Journal of Physical Anthropology 21:595–605.

——. 1965a Comment on "New discoveries in Tanganyika" by Tobias (1965b). Current Anthropology 6:403–406.

——. 1965b Homo 'habilis' and the australopithecines. Nature 205:121–124.

——. 1966 The emergence of man. Read at Peabody Museum Centennial Meetings. Xerox version made available by author.

Schuman, E. L. and C. L. Brace 1954 Metric and morphologic variations in the dentition of the Liberian chimpanzee. Human Biology 26:239–268.

Simpson, G. G. 1953 The major features of evolution. New York, Columbia University.

——. 1961 Principles of animal taxonomy. New York, Columbia University.

——. 1963 The meaning of taxonomic statements. In S. L. Washburn, ed. (1963). pp. 1–31.

Tobias, P. V. 1963 The cranial capacity of Zinjanthropus and other australopithecines. Nature 197:743–746.

——. 1965a Early man in East Africa. Science 149:22–33.

——. 1965b New discoveries in Tanganyika: their bearing on hominid evolution. Current Anthropology 6:391–411.

——. 1966 Reply to Bielicki (1966). Current Anthropology 7:579–580.

Tobias, P. V., and G. H. R. von Koenigswald 1964 A comparison between the Olduvai hominines and those of Java, and some implications for hominid phylogeny. Nature 204:515–518.

Washburn, S. L. 1951 The analysis of primate evolution with particular reference to the origin of man. Cold Spring Harbor Symposia on Quantitative Biology 15:67–78.

——. 1960 Tools and human evolution. Scientific American 203:63–75.

——. 1963 Behavior and human evolution. In Washburn, ed. (1963). pp. 190–203.

Washburn, S. L., ed. 1963 Classification and human evolution. Chicago, Aldine.

Weidenreich, F. 1945 Giant early man from Java and South China. Anthropological Papers of the American Museum of Natural History 40:1.

Weinert, H. 1950 Über die Neuen vor- und Frühmenschenfunde aus Africa, Java, China, und Frankreich. Zeitschrift für Morphologe und Anthropologie 42:113–148.

——. 1951 Über die Vielgestaltigkeit der Summoprimaten vor der Menschwerdung. Zeitschrift für Morphologe und Anthropologie 43:73–103.

22

VERTESSZÖLLÖS AND THE PRESAPIENS THEORY
Milford H. Wolpoff

The conviction that a modern form of man must have existed in remote antiquity has been so strong that many specimens have been offered as likely candidates when there really was not enough supporting evidence—for instance, "Telanthropus." Analogous to the French legal tradition in which a suspect is considered guilty until proven innocent, many newly discovered scraps of hominid fossil bone are considered modern until proven otherwise. The Swanscombe skull from England is one of the more famous cases. Nearly three decades after its discovery, it was conclusively shown to be of non-modern form (Weiner and Campbell 1964), but claims concerning its modern status had been repeated so often and with such certainty that it is still considered by many as partial support for the ancient modern hypothesis.

Many other specimens have had similar interpretive histories. One of the most recent to undergo such treatment is the back end of a skull found in a quarry at Vertesszöllös in Hungary in 1965. The deposits, dated by their extinct fauna, are the same age as strata that elsewhere contain the remains of Homo erectus. the interpreters have compared the skull fragment with known erectus material, but have also suggested that the details in which it differs from typical erectus form point in a modern direction (Howells 1966; Thoma 1966). As Dr. Wolpoff shows, however, these suggestions are not supported by the available data.

Howells, W. W. 1966. Homo erectus. Scientific American 215(5):46–53.

Thoma, A. 1966. L'occipital de l'homme mindelien de Vertesszöllös. L'Anthropologie 70:495–534.

Weiner, J. S., and B. G. Campbell. 1964. The taxonomic status of the Swanscombe skull. in C. D. Ovey (ed.) The Swanscombe Skull. Royal Anthropological Institute, London. pp. 175–209.

ABSTRACT. The Presapiens theory, suggesting completely separate lineages leading to Neandertals and to Homo sapiens, has recently received a number of setbacks. However, the discovery of two hominids at Vertesszöllös could be corroborating evidence. The teeth of the first individual were described as those of Homo erectus, as were most features of the second, represented by an occipital. The two main characteristics used to support the Homo sapiens classification of the second individual are the long lambda-opisthion chord and the high cranial capacity, based on a regression using the lambda-opisthion chord. However, the real position of lambda is obscured by the presence of wormian bones, and the regression used to predict capacity was derived from a sample with more Neandertals than Homo erectus specimens. A comparative treatment of the morphological features and recalculation of the regression suggests that separating the occipital from Homo erectus is not justified. Other evidence indicates Homo erectus specimens as big as Vertesszöllös 2. It is unlikely that two hominid lineages occur in the Mid-Pleistocene.

The "Presapiens" theory, as described by Vallois (1958), suggests that Homo sapiens originated as a distinct lineage, completely separate from that which led to the Neandertals. Unlike the "Preneandertal" theory, the presapiens theory holds that this divergence took place before the Mindel/Riss Interglacial, if not before the Mindel glaciation itself.

The theory has suffered a number of

From the American Journal of Physical Anthropology 35:209–215. Copyright by The Wistar Press 1971. Reprinted with permission of the author and the publisher.

serious setbacks, beginning with the demise of Piltdown. (Weiner, Oakley and Le Gros Clark, 1953). The sapient qualities of the Swanscombe cranium have been severely questioned. Stewart (1964) demonstrated that the occipito-mastoid torus is far more like that of Neandertals than it is like anatomically modern *Homo sapiens*, complementing Morant's original description (1938) of the cranium as platycephalic with a low and posterior position for the greatest parietal breadth. Morant also showed that the occipital breadth was completely outside the range of population variation in anatomically modern *Homo sapiens*, and more than three standard deviations from the mean. As both Sergi (1962) and Brace (1964) have indicated, these are distinctive features of *Homo erectus* and Neandertals, and can be used to differentiate these groups from modern man. Finally, Roginskii (1948) used a simple Chi-square test to demonstrate that the combination of Swanscombe features in modern man has a probability of less than 0.001, while these same features fall completely within Neandertal ranges. Thus, Swanscombe evinces characteristics one would expect in a hominid morphologically transitional between *Homo erectus* and Neandertals, and not what one would expect in a hominid transitional between *Homo erectus* and anatomically modern *Homo sapiens*. Surely, the attachment available for extensive nuchal muscles suggests a Mid-Pleistocene sized face.

Using contours, chords, and arcs of Fontéchevade 2 as preserved, Sergi (1962) unambiguously demonstrated its affinities with the Neandertals, rather than with modern men. Brace (1964) showed that the position of the frontal sinus, indicated by a trace on Fontéchevade 2, does not preclude the possibility of a well-developed supraorbital torus, based on the position of the sinus in Krapina frontal number 2, a Neandertal specimen with a well-developed torus. I have studied casts of Fontéchevade 1 and 2. The larger fragment, 2, gives the general appearance of a Neandertal. The contour in *norma verticalis* is teardropped, with the greatest breadth well back on the parietals, close to the position of asterion. The biasterionic breadth is even greater than Swanscombe and is close to the Neandertal mean (Vallois, 1958: 83). In *norma occipitalis*, the cranial contour

is almost perfectly circular, as in the Western European Würm Neandertals. I carefully compared Fontéchevade 1, the small fragment of frontal surrounding the region of glabella, with casts of numerous Neandertal crania. The glabellar area of Fontéchevade 1 is identical to the corresponding areas in Neandertal crania from Gibraltar and Le Moustier. Neither sepcimen from Fontéchevade gives indication of being anything but a Neandertal.

Thus, the separation from Neandertal ancestry or status of the only two "certain Presapiens" accepted by Vallois in 1958 is without compelling substantive basis. Even still, the "Presapiens" Theory has gained new supporters in the last decade. Howell (1960) attempted identification of two hominid lineages during Mindel. More recently, Briggs (1968) suggested separation of the Ternifine mandibles into "paranthropoid" (number 3) and "telanthropoid" (numbers 1, 2) groups. Collins (1969) attempted establishing a number of lineages from Mindel and earlier, based on (apparently somewhat shaky) archaeological and morphological evidence. However, none of these proposals has been generally accepted, even by authors who consider Neandertals a separate lineage (Howells, 1967).

Now, new evidence is available which could support the Presapiens Theory.

Thoma (1966, 1969) has used the two individuals from the site of Vertesszöllös in Western Hungary to argue for the synchronic occurrence of two hominid species: *Homo erectus* and *Homo sapiens*. The taxonomy he suggests for the individuals at this Intermindel site has raised questions of considerable interest (Howells, 1966; 1967; 180). Is it possible that the occipital of the second individual (Vsz. 2) represents an early specimen of *Homo sapiens*? The question has two different meanings. For those who classify Neandertals in *Homo sapiens* this is a simple although somewhat muddled terminological question for, as Eckhardt (1970) has pointed out, we have no unambiguous rules for classifying a specimen which may be a late *Homo erectus* or an early *Homo sapiens*. For Thoma, and some others, the question has an entirely different meaning. Authors who consider *Homo sapiens* and Neandertals parallel but separate lineages would interpret the *Homo sapiens* classification of Vsz. 2 to mean that these lineages had separated by the time of the Mindel glaciation. The second interpretation is questioned here.

Thoma published a detailed comparison of the tooth fragments comprising the individual Vsz. 1 (1967). Two of the fragments, a lower deciduous canine and second molar, proved complete enought for comparisons using diagnostic features. These detailed comparisons, based on both morphology and multivariate statistics, utilized samples of australopithecines, *Homo erectus* from Choukoutien, Neandertals, and a number of *Homo sapiens* groups. Regarding especially the extreme caniniform character of both Vsz. 1 and Choukoutien deciduous canine 120, as well as the lingual cingulum, crown size, and lobated structure of the lingual surface, the Vsz. tooth is identical to the Choukoutien sample and different in these same features from the other groups compared. The molar seems somewhat too large for a Neandertal tooth. Thoma concludes:

. . . comparing the Vertesszöllös teeth with all the other Hominid groups known from homologous teeth, it is possible to find in every case morphological criteria which, combined into discriminative patterns, properly differentiate them from each other—with only the exception of Sinanthropus (1967: 176).

Thus, the first specimen is a *Homo erectus*, while the second, in his view (1966, 1969) is *Homo sapiens.*

The "chopper-chopping tool" industries at Vertesszöllös and at Choukoutien are similar to each other (Kretzoi and Vértes, 1965; Bordes, 1968). This leads to the somewhat bizarre conclusion that two different hominid species are associated with a chopper-chopping tool industry at Choukoutien *(Homo erectus)* and Vertesszöllös *(Homo sapiens)* while the same two species are associated with a hand axe industry at Ternifine *(Homo erectus)* and Swanscombe *(Homo sapiens)*. Because of the similarities between the industries at Vertesszöllös and at Choukoutien where a *Homo erectus* sample from the same time period occurs (Bordes, 1968; Howells, 1966), and because Thoma convincingly demonstrated that Vsz. 1 cannot be distinguished from this *Homo erectus* sample (1967), it is of some interest to examine

his reasons for placing Vsz. 2 in *Homo sapiens* (1966, 1969).

In his most recent analysis, Thoma (1969) states that most characteristics of Vsz. 2, like Vsz. 1, are similar to those in *Homo erectus.* Indeed, he concludes: "The majority of gross morphological features of Vsz. II is Archanthropic in character" (p. 240). Vsz. 2 shares a number of features with both *Homo erectus* and Neandertals. Complexity of the Vsz. 2 sutures at the metasterionic angle and the variations described for the cruciform eminence and the sinus grooves occur in almost all hominid taxa. The small cerebellar fossae compared to the cerebral fossae are also characteristic of the Peking crania (Weidenreich, 1943: 40) and the Solo and other Neandertal crania as well (Weidenreich, 1951; 26). If anything, these fossae seem more nearly equal in size in the Swanscombe occipital. The size relation in anatomically modern *Homo sapiens* is the opposite. Inion is about 25 mm above the internal occipital protuberance. This distance can be matched in other *Homo erectus* crania as well as in Neandertal crania. Weidenreich suggests that the separation occurs because the cerebellar fossae are small (1951; 26), but the height of the nuchal torus, and the very great extent of the nuchal musculature implied, could be another factor. Measurements of thickness are completely within both *Homo erectus* and Neandertal ranges of variation, but often fall outside the range of variation of anatomically modern *Homo sapiens*. The inion angle of the occipital is quite low, falling again within *Homo erectus* and Neandertal ranges of variation.

Other features, however, place the occipital squarely with *Homo erectus*, and distinguish it from Neandertals and other early European crania such as Swanscombe and Steinheim. The occipital torus is prominent and extends laterally across the entire bone in the fashion of almost every other *Homo erectus* specimen, and unlike australopithecines, Neandertals, modern men, and the other two early European crania. This torus is pictured in the excellent series of figures published by Thoma (1966), in which the lateral view, his figure 3, is upside down. The nuchal plane itself is huge, attesting to the presence of a very heavy neck musculature. On the internal surface, the transverse sulcus passes directly to the temporal in Vsz. 2, and in Peking 12 and Java 4 as well. In Swanscombe, however, the sulcus passes to the parietal, as is the case in anatomically modern *Homo sapiens*.

The Vertesszöllös individual was probably quite large, and, based on the robustness of the nuchal muscle attachments, was probably a male. The total morphological pattern is far more similar to that of known large *Homo erectus* specimens than it is to large Neandertals. Unfortunately, the two somewhat later crania, Swanscombe and Steinheim, are quite possibly female. Thus comparisons could be somewhat misleading since gracile features due to grade cannot easily be distinguished from those due to sexual dimorphism.

In contrast, the reasons for placing the occipital in *Homo sapiens*, Thoma's "Palaeanthropus" grade, are few indeed. Thoma (1969) claims only two: a high and fairly curved profile of the upper part of the occipital squama projected in the sagittal plane, and a cranial capacity significantly greater than that of *Homo erectus*.

The sagittal curvature of the upper part of the squama is indicated by the index of the lambda-inion arc to the lambda-inion chord. In Vsz. 2 this index is 108.2; a sample of 9 *Homo erectus* specimens average 105 and range from 102.3 to 108.4 (SD = 1.8). One *Homo erectus* specimen, Olduvai hominid 13, has a greater curvature (108.4). The curvature in Java 1, the specimen with the next highest index (107), is almost as great.

The high profile of the upper part of the squama is misleading. Actually, the angle at inion is not particularly great. Its value, 103°, is equal to or less than those of almost every occipital in the Peking group, and is considerably smaller than the angle in Swanscombe (118°), a more recent European specimen. The upper squama matches Peking crania such as ten quite well in sagittal profile, except for the fact that it extends more anteriorly, and consequently is higher. However, there are wormian bones in the vicinity of lambda which make it impossible to determine exactly where lambda is. Thoma chose the most anterior point whereas Martin (1922: 614) suggests the point where lines smoothly approximating the course of the lamboidal suture cross each other. This point is more posterior, and consequently lower, in the Vsz. 2 occipital. Use of the proper point would diminish the two chords which now fall outside of the *Homo erectus* range by being too large: lambda-inion and lambda-opisthion.

There have been several reconstructions of the lambda-opisthion chord. In the original specimen, deformed in the lambda region, a value of 106 mm was obtained. Thoma's reconstruction of the lambda region yielded a measurement of 102 mm. Tobias's reconstruction of the lambda region, reported in a publication by Thoma (1969), allowed a measurement of 100 mm. When I examined a cast of Vsz. 2 at the Harvard Peabody Museum, I approximated the position of opisthion using the occipital morphology of Swanscombe as a model. This gave a measurement of 99 mm. The value based on Tobias's reconstruction is used throughout this paper.

Thoma estimates the cranial capacity of Vsz. 2 by means of a regression equation relating the lambda-opisthion chord to cranial capacity. Of the 12 specimens he used, only five were *Homo erectus*. With these he mixed five Solo crania, and the Swanscombe and Broken Hill specimens. He conservatively uses the lower 95% confidence limit (1969) concluding that the capacity must be greater than 1400 cm³, using his lambda-opisthion measure of 102 mm, or greater than 1350 cm³, using Tobias's measure of 100 mm.

I separately calculated regressions for *Homo erectus*, Neandertals, and 200 *Homo sapiens* specimens representing a worldwide distribution chosen at random from publications in Biometrika (Benington, 1911; von Bonin, 1936; Fawcett, 1901; Hooke, 1926; Thomson, 1916). Of the seven *Homo erectus* specimens for which the appropriate data are preserved (see table 2), the positions of opisthion were uncertain in Java 1 and 6 and have been estimated in the literature. Regressions were calculated for the *Homo erectus* sample both with and without these specimens. The equations and correlations are given in table 1. The percentage error of regression fit is the average absolute difference between the actual and calculated cranial capacities for the sample, expressed as a percentage of the actual capacity.

The correlation for the regression using the smaller (unestimated) *Homo erectus* sample alone is greater than Thoma's correlation of 0.93 for his entire sample. The correlation value for Neandertals is lower, but this calculation used all of the published Neandertal measurements (n = 14), instead of only a few (n = 6).

Table 2 indicates a test of the regressions by predicting the known cranial capacities in the *Homo erectus* sample. The percentage error for *Homo erectus* both with and without the two approximated specimens is close to 4%. On the other hand, the percentage error of Thoma's equation when used to predict only the capacities for *Homo erectus* is twice as great. The percentage error of Thoma's equation used to predict only the five specimens for which opisthion is known with certainty is greater still, almost 10%.

The archaeological evidence, the morphology of Vsz. 1 from the same site, and, by Thoma's admission, most features of Vsz. 2 suggest the specimen is *Homo erectus*. Thus, it seems reasonable to use a regression based on *Homo erectus* specimens to estimate its cranial capacity. The regression for either sample gives almost identical estimations for Vsz. 2, using Tobias's value of 100 mm for the lambda-opisthion chord. Because the actual value of the chord may be less, the estimation of about 1325 cm³ is a maximum. For instance, if the actual chord were only 1 mm shorter, the calculated capacity for Vsz. 2, using the regression on the larger sample, would be 1305, 23 cm³ less. The estimated value for Vsz. 2 is considerably smaller than the smallest estimate suggested by Thoma, and is even less than the low end of his range. If, instead, the Neandertal regression is used to predict the Vsz. 2 capacity, the result is 1691 cm³—larger

than the maximum of Neandertals used. This appears unlikely.

Is the capacity of Vsz. 2 large enough to be outside of the expected range of *Homo erectus* variation? The range cannot be used because it is too large to be meaningful (± 345 cm³). The estimate is only 100 cm³ greater than the Peking 10 capacity. A *t* test comparing Vsz. 2 to a sample of 12 *Homo erectus* cranial capacities (Tobias, 1967) excluding the Vsz. 2 value itself indicates that Vsz. 2 is *not* significantly different from *Homo erectus* on the 5% level. Of course, along with all of the Peking crania, the capacity is within the *Homo sapiens* range of variation.

Is there reason to expect bigger *Homo erectus* crania than the ones which have already been discussed? The answer seems to be yes. This can be seen in two ways.

First, we may use the relation of mandibular and cranial breadths to estimate the range of breadths in known individuals known from mandibles. The most lateral breadth taken across the mandibular articular area of the cranial glenoid fossae should approximate the bicondylar breadth of the mandible. My own observations indicate that the lateral interglenoid breadth is inevitably larger than the bicondylar breadth in modern apes and man, although the difference is slight. Table 3 gives lateral interglenoid and bicondylar breadths for all appropriate *Homo erectus* specimens. Two out of the five available mandibles are too big to fit any known *Homo erectus* cranium. One of the Peking mandibles is too large to fit any complete cranium from that site, although it is possible that it would fit a reconstruction of the very large skull 5. Ternifine 3 is considerably larger than any other mandible

Table 1

Comparison of regression parameters, correlation, percent error of regression fit, and sample size for the regression of the lambda-opisthion chord on cranial capacity for three hominid groups. The Homo erectus regression was done twice, (1) without the two specimens for which the opisthion position is approximated, and (2) with these two specimens

		Slope	Intercept	Correlation	Percent error of regression fit	Sample size
Homo erectus	(1)	23.77	−1052.4	0.95	3.6	5
	(2)	22.30	− 910.7	0.89	4.1	7
Neandertals		30.36	−1344.3	0.82	6.4	14
Homo sapiens		25.71	−1047.7	0.83	5.8	200

Table 2

Calculation of Homo erectus cranial capacities from regressions with the lambda-opisthion chord. Data for the chord comes from the literature (Weidenreich, 1943, 1945; Jacob, 1966) and from measurements I made on the Harvard Peabody Museum cast set and the Wenner-Gren casts. The cranial capacities were published by Tobias (1967). The calculated values for Vsz. 2 are based on Tobias's lambda-opisthion measurement of 100 mm (Thoma, 1969). Both the absolute and percentage errors of the regressions applied to Homo erectus are given

Specimen	Lambda-opisthion chord	Actual cranial capacity	Calculated cranial capacity by regression:		
			Wolpoff	Wolpoff	Thoma
	mm	cm³	(n = 5)	(n = 7)	
Java 1	78 (est)	850		822	877
2	75	775	731	753	797
4	78	750	802	822	877
6	81 (est)	975		891	957
Peking 3	84	915	944	960	1037
11	86	1015	992	1006	1090
12	87	1030	1016	1029	1117
Average absolute difference of calculated capacities from actual capacities			32	37	68
Percentage average difference			4%	4%	8%
Calculated Vertesszöllös capacity			1325	1328	1463

Table 3

Distribution of three cranial breadth measures in Homo erectus: lateral interglenoid breadth, bicondylar breadth, and biparietal breadth. OH 13 and 16 were measured from scaled photographs published by Leakey (1966). Java 1, 3, and 6 were published by Jacob (1966). OH 9 and Java 2 and 4 were measured from the Wenner-Gren casts. Weidenreich published the Peking crania (1943) and mandibles (1936), as well as Mauer. Ternifine 3 was published by Arambourg (1963). The Ternifine 2 measurement comes from a symmetric reconstruction I prepared from plates in the Arambourg publication, and the reconstructed breadth based on the single Ternifine parietal was published by Krukoff (1967)

Specimen	Lateral Interglenoid breadth	Bicondylar breadth	Biparietal breadth
	mm	mm	mm
Olduvai 16			117
Olduvai 13			113
Olduvai 9	140		133
Java 1			126
Java 2	120		131
Java 3			128
Java 4	116		129
Java 6			128
Peking 2			132
Peking 3	132		133
Peking 10	131		138
Peking 11	128		135
Peking 12	130		139
Peking G1		146	
Peking H1		102	
Ternifine 1			150
Ternifine 2		132	
Ternifine 3		160	
Heidelberg		135	

or cranium. The cranium which fit it was probably broader than Vsz. 2.

Second, we may observe the braincase breadth distribution for all of the complete and fragmentary *Homo erectus* crania. Table 3 gives biparietal breadth distribution. The Ternifine specimen was significantly broader across the parietals than any other *Homo erectus* specimen. Since the breadth is 12 mm less in the Peking cranium with the largest cranial capacity, the Ternifine capacity was probably bigger. Because this parietal belongs to a juvenile, and the Ternifine 3 mandible is adult, at least two large brained *Homo erectus* specimens occur with the others at Ternifine, and one or two (mandible G1 and skull 5) individuals from Peking probably were bigger brained than skull 10.

In sum, both individuals from Vertesszöllös evince a total morphological pattern more like *Homo erectus* than like any other fossil hominid group. In terms of individuals, the specimens show greatest similarities to the crania from Choukoutien, probably the closest in grade, and to the cranium from Swanscombe, a likely member of the same lineage somewhat later in time. The Vertesszöllös material does not provide a good basis for the "Presapiens" Theory. Instead, it supports the interpretation of a single evolving hominid lineage throughout the middle and upper Pleistocene.

ACKNOWLEDGMENTS

I am deeply indebted to W. W. Howells of Harvard University for permission to examine the Peabody Museum cast of Vsz. 2, and to F. C. Howell, University of California, Berkeley, for permission to examine the Fontéchevade casts in his former laboratory at the University of Chicago.

LITERATURE CITED

Arambourg, C. 1963 Le Gisement de Ternifine. Arch. L'Inst. Paléont. Hum., Memoir 32.

Benington, R. C. 1911 A study of the Negro skull with special reference to the Congo and Gaboon crania. Biometr., 8: 292–337.

von Bonin, G. 1936 On the craniology of Oceania. Crania from New Britain. Biometr., 28: 123–148.

Bordes, F. 1968 The Old Stone Age. McGraw–Hill, New York.

Brace, C. L. 1964 The fate of the "Classic" Neanderthals: A consideration of hominid catastrophism. Curr. Anthrop., 5: 3–43.

Briggs, L. C. 1968 Hominid evolution in Northwest Africa and the question of the North African "Neanderthaloids." Am. J. Phys. Anthrop., 29: 377–386.

Collins, D. 1969 Culture traditions and environment of early man. Curr. Anthrop., 10: 267–316.

Eckhardt, R. B. 1970 Bigeneric nomina: A historical and evolutionary perspective. Am. J. Phys. Anthrop., 33: 337–340.

Fawcett, C. D. 1901 A second study of the variation and correlation of the human skull with special reference to the Naqada crania. Biometr., 1: 408–467.

Hooke, B. G. E. 1926 A third study of the English skull with special reference to the Farringdon Street crania. Biometr., 18: 1–55.

Howell, F. C. 1960 European and Northwest African Middle Pleistocene hominids. Curr. Anthrop., 1: 195–232.

Howells, W. W. 1966 Homo erectus. Sci. Amer., 215 (5): 46–53.

———. 1967 Mankind in the Making, revised edition. Doubleday, Garden City.

Jacob, T. 1966 The sixth skull cap of *Pithecanthropus erectus*. Am. J. Phys. Anthrop., 25: 243–260.

Kretzoi, M., and L. Vértes 1965 Upper Biharian (intermindel) pebble-industry occupation site in Western Hungary, Curr. Anthrop., 6: 74–87.

Krukoff, S. 1967 Reconstitution de la largeur bi-parietale totale d'un crane à partir d'un os parietal isolé. C. R. Ac. Sc., Paris, Série D, 264: 1260–1262.

Leakey, L. S. B. 1966 Homo habilis, Homo erectus and the australopithecines. Nature, 209: 1279–1281.

Martin, R. 1928 Lehrbuch der Anthropologie in Systematischer Darstellung. Volume II; Kraniologie, Osteologie. Fischer, Jena.

Morant, G. M. 1938 The form of the Swanscombe Skull. J. Roy. Anthropol. Inst., 68: 67–97.

Roginskii, J. J. 1948 Zur Frage nach dem Alter des heutigen Menschentype (Die Stellung des Schädels von Swanscombe im Hominidensystem). Sovietwis. Gesellschaftwis. Abteil., 1: 114–122.

Sergi, S. 1962 Morphological position of the "Prophaneranthropi" (Swanscombe and Fontéchevade). In: W. W. Howells ed., Ideas on Human Evolution: Selected Essays 1949–1961. Harvard University, Cambridge, pp. 507–520.

Stewart, T. D. 1964 A neglected primitive feature of the Swanscombe skull. The Swanscombe Skull. C. Ovey, ed. Roy, Anthrop. Inst. Occ. Paper, 20: 151–160.

Thoma, A. 1965 The definition of the Neanderthals and the position of the fossil men of Palestine. Yearb. Phys. Anthrop., 13: 137–145.

———. 1966 L'Occipital de l'homme mindelien de Vertesszöllös. L'Anthropologie, 70: 495–534.

———. 1967 Human teeth from the Lower Paleolithic of Hungary. Z. Morph. Anthrop., 58: 152–180.

———. 1969 Biometrische Studie über das Occipitale von Vertesszöllös. Z. Morph. Anthrop., 60: 229–242.

Thomson, E. Y. 1916 A study of the crania of the Moriori, or aborigines of the Chatham Islands, now in the Museum of the Royal College of Surgeons. Biometr., 11: 82–135.

Tobias, P. V. 1967 Olduvai Gorge, Volume II: The Cranium and Maxillary Dentition of *Australopithecus* (Zinjanthropus) *boisei*. Cambridge University, London.

Vallois, H. V. 1958 La Grotte de Fontéchevade. Duxième partie: Anthropologie. Arch. L'Inst. Paleont. Hum., Memoir 29.

Weidenreich, F. 1936 The mandibles of *Sinanthropus pekinensis:* a comparative study. Palaeont. Sinica, ser. D, 7: 1–162.

———. 1940 The torus occipitalis and related structures and their transformations in the course of human evolution. Bul. Geol. Soc. China, 19: 479–558.

———. 1943 The skull of *Sinanthropus pekinensis;* A comparative study on a primitive hominid skull. Palaeont. Sinica, ser. D, 10: 1–486.

———. 1945 Giant early man from Java and South China. Anthrop. Papers Am. Mus. Nat. Hist., 40: 1–134.

———. 1951 Morphology of Solo man. Anthrop. Papers Am. Mus. Nat. Hist., 43: 201–290.

Weiner, J. S., K. P. Oakley and W. E. Le Gros Clark 1953 The solution of the Piltdown problem. Bul. British Mus. (Nt. Hist. Geol., 2: 141–146.

23

THE FATE OF THE "CLASSIC" NEANDERTHALS: A CONSIDERATION OF HOMINID CATASTROPHISM[1]
C. Loring Brace

Until quite recently, many of the students of the hominid fossil record appeared to devote most of their energy to explaining why this or that fossil form could not be a human ancestor. Each feature in which a given fossil differed from typical modern form was labeled a "specialization," which presumably limited the capacity to adapt and therefore disqualified the fossil as a possible ancestor of modern man. At the earliest levels, the Australopithecines were dismissed as a possibility since it was felt that they were too crude to have been capable of making the stone tools found in the same strata. "True man" must have existed somewhere, making the tools for use in hunting Australopithecines, but too clever to leave his own skeletal remains in the same deposits with his presumed victims.

Even before the first Australopithecines had been discovered, the same kinds of arguments were being used in regard to the famed "Neanderthal problem." Immediately prior to the appearance of undoubted moderns in the fossil record, hominid form was characterized by heavier jaws and teeth, more pronounced bony reinforcements and muscle markings on the skulls, and indications of a more rugged and muscular body. For the past two generations, European paleontologists have refused to consider the possibility that modern form could have evolved out of the Neanderthals. Instead, they postulated that moderns, like the Biblical wise men, came out of the East. The vanquished Neanderthals were either exterminated or simply could not compete with the invaders. In any case they became extinct.

The only flaw in this view was the lack of any evidence for a population of ancient moderns in the East. Prior to forty thousand years ago, the more one looks the more one finds only Neanderthals (for an account of some of the looking, see Solecki 1971). And for finds that date between the earliest accepted moderns and the full Neanderthals, the form is a kind of compromise (Suzuki and Takai 1970). The article that follows was one of the first of the recent attempts to turn things around and start thinking about the problems of hominid ancestry from a deliberately evolutionary point of view. In its original form, it was followed by a series of written comments by scholars in the field and published along with a reply by the author. The various expressions of wounded dignity make for interesting reading, and we would like to have reproduced them along with the paper, but we were unable to get permission. The interested reader will find it all in Current Anthropology *(Vol. 5, No. 1, 1964).*

Solecki, Ralph S. 1971. *Shanidar: The First Flower People.* Knopf, New York. 302 pp.

Suzuki, H., and F. Takai (eds.). 1970 *The Amud Man and His Cave Site.* Keigaku Publishing Co., Tokyo. 530 pp.

Were this the skeleton of the oldest man, then the oldest man was a freak, and in antediluvian times, as today, there must have been malformed human beings such as are welcomed by the adhereents of the teaching of the descent of mankind from the apes . . . [Mayer 1864:16].

At the time when Darwin and Huxley first claimed that man evolved from a primate similar to the anthropoids of today, little evidence substantiated by palaeontological *facts was available. In the meantime, however, quite a number of fossil forms have been recovered all of which may justifiably be claimed as "missing links." Yet, strangely enough, the more such intermediate types came to light, the less was the readiness of acknowledging them as ancestors of* Homo sapiens.[2] *in many cases the scepticism apparently was the last bastion from which the final acceptance of Darwin's theory could be warded off with a certain air of scientism* [Weidenreich 1943a:44].

Interpretation of the hominid fossil record has inevitably been colored by the climate of opinion prevalent at the time of the discovery of the major pieces of evidence. What are now recognized as being the earliest known hominids were not the earliest fossil hominids to be known, which may account in large measure for the fact that their essential humanity was not recognized at the time of their discovery. When the first Australopithecine was found in 1924 (Dart 1925:195–99) there already were candidates for all the postulated stages of human evolution, and the suggestion that this was anything more than just another fossil ape was greeted with a notable lack of enthusiasm (Bather 1925:947; Keith 1925c:11; 1925d:462–63; Smith 1925:235; Woodward 1925:235–36: Hooton 1946:288).

At this time the earliest known hominid was *Pithecanthropus erectus* (now properly considered *Homo erectus* by Weidenreich 1940:383; 1943b:246; Mayr 1951:113), and even the most enthusiastic proponents of the human status of this fossil had to concede that if culture had indeed been associated with the population of which it was a member, then that culture must have been of the crudest recognizable sort (Hooton 1946: 298). *Pithecanthropus* was widely hailed as

Reproduced from *Current Anthropology*, Vol. 5, No. 1, 1964. Copyright 1964 by the Wenner-Gren Foundation for Anthropological Research. Reprinted with the permission of author and publisher.

[1]Parts of this paper were read at the 1962 meetings of the American Anthropological Association at Chicago, Illinois, November 18, 1962. I should like to express my gratitude to M. L. Brace and R. V. Humphrey for the illustrations.

[2]This reaches its extreme in the writings of Boule, Osborn, Keith, Hooton, and Vallois who deny human ancestral status to every substantial and well-dated fossil discovery which in any way differs from modern man (Boule 1913, 1921, 1923, 1937; see also Schwalbe 1913:601–3; Keith 1915, 1925a. [1928], 1931; Osborn 1919; Hooton 1931:392–93; 1946:288, 298, 412–13; Boule and Vallois 1957:92, 126, 145, 258).

Haeckel's "missing link" (Haeckel 1899b: 469; Miller 1929) and was considered to exist on the very borderline of human and subhuman stages in evolution. With the bottom-most rung in the scale of human evolution presumably occupied, it took some thirty years and an abundance of evidence (Broom 1939, 1947, 1950; Broom and Schepers 1946; Broom and Robinson 1947a and b, 1949a and b, 1950a, b, and c, 1952; Dart 1948a, b, and c, 1949a, b, c, and d; Broom, Robinson, and Schepers 1950; Robinson 1952a and b, 1953a, b, and c, 1954, 1956; Le Gros Clark 1955a and b; Leakey 1959, 1960a and b) before the hominid status of the Australopithecines became generally acceptable (Bartholomew and Birdsell 1953; Oakley 1959; Brace 1962a). Opinion is still far from being unanimous, and, despite the necessary relationship between Australopithecine anatomy and tool use (Keith 1949:204; Bartholomew and Birdsell 1953; Heberer 1959b:418, 419; Brace 1962a and b), and the clear unbroken sequence of cultural evolution from the Oldowan to the atomic bomb (Leakey 1936: 40–56; 1954:66, 70; Cole 1954:123, 131–38; D. Clark 1959:121 ff.), many authorities prefer to reserve judgment (Chang 1962:5) or to deny the Australopithecines lineal precedence to morphologically more modern hominids on geological grounds alone (Robinson 1954: 196, 197; 1956:172; Boule and Vallois 1957:92; Piveteau 1957:314; Kurtén 1962:490), ignoring the fact that the geological placement of the Australopithecines is so fluid that even absolute dating techniques differ in the age assigned by more than 100% (Emiliani 1955, 1956, 1958, 1961; Evernden, Curtis, and Kistler 1957:15; Curtis, Savage, and Evernden 1961; von Koenigswald, Gentner, and Lippolt 1961:720–21; F. C. Howell, 1962; and Oakley 1962:420).

If the climate of opinion prevalent at the time of discovery has had such a profound and lasting effect upon the interpretation of fossil material found within the last forty years, it should be instructive to consider the effects exerted by the mid-nineteenth century climate of opinion on the interpretation of the first hominid fossils to be discovered more than a century ago. The first publicized discovery of skeletal remains now attributable to an earlier stage in human evolution occurred in Germany in 1856 (Fuhlrott 1857; Schaaffhausen 1857 a and b; 1858; Busk 1861) just three years prior to the publication of Darwin's *Origin of Species* (1859). Even in England where Darwin's influence was relatively stronger than elsewhere, sympathy with an evolutionary viewpoint was far from being unanimous as is evident from the record of the conflicts (Huxley 1860, as reported by Hardin 1960b:25; Huxley 1861). In Germany, where the Neanderthaler was found, evolution, despite the support of Haeckel (1897, 1899a: 487), met with continued scientific opposition and was much longer in being accepted (Potonie 1958:278). In the absence of stratigraphic evidence for antiquity, the Neanderthaler could have been found some years later and still have been given a similar reception. With no proof for its age and no morphologically similar skeletal material available for comparison, these remains, which clearly differed in form from modern man, were judged as being not normal (Mayer 1864; Virchow 1872). The power of this judgment was such that later, when datable remains of clearly similar morphology finally did turn up (Spy, found in 1886; La Chapelle-aux-Saints, found in 1908), the interpretation tended to remain the same although the basis changed markedly and totally different kinds of evidence were offered in its support.

The nineteenth-century view was summarized by Virchow in 1872 when he enumerated the pathological characteristics of the remains. From that point on, Neanderthal was regarded as being peculiar, and the peculiarities were at first thought to be pathological in origin. Circumstantial evidence in favor of Virchow's interpretation was offered by the fact that fossil man was already known to exist (Broca 1868; Rivière 1872) and his form was not radically different from that of modern man. As yet, degrees of antiquity were but dimly perceived, and, in addition, the resemblance of the so-called Old Man of Cro-Magnon to modern man had been enthusiastically stressed with greater confidence than its edentulous condition properly warranted. With a restored set of teeth occluded in characteristic Upper Palaeolithic fashion, his face would have looked far more like that of Combe Capelle and the supposed paradox of its short wide form would have been eliminated. Virchow's final denial of the antiquity of the Neanderthal find was based on the assumed age of the individual. Because of suture closure, it was assumed that he was elderly, and Virchow claimed that no one could live to such an advanced age in a nomadic or hunting-and-gathering society (Potonie 1958:277). He must, therefore, have belonged to a sedentary group and great antiquity would not have been possible (Virchow 1872:163).

By the end of the century, however, much more was known concerning the relative placement of the various subdivisions of prehistory (de Mortillet 1910). At Spy, the two individuals of Neanderthal-like morphology had been found in a Mousterian layer definitely prior to the Upper Palaeolithic (Fraipont and Lohest 1887; Twiesselmann 1958; Bordes 1959), and a calva had been found which differed even more from modern man and which belonged to a geological time far earlier even than Spy (Dubois 1894). Putting these facts together, Gustav Schwalbe tried to support a view of human evolution in three stages starting with Pithecanthropus, developing though Neanderthal into modern man (Schwalbe 1904; 1906a and b: esp. pp. 8 and 166). Schwalbe's views had the advantages of simplicity and logic, although they did run counter to the strong current of thought which was decidedly uncomfortable when suggestions were advanced that man might have evolved from something which looked less manlike than man (cf. Gregory 1949:508).

Furthermore, for the next twenty years the most significant work on fossil man was to come from France because of the fact that relatively extensive remains of Neanderthalers were to be discovered at four different sites: e.g., Le Moustier 1908, La Chapelle-aux-Saints 1908, La Ferrassie 1909, and La Quina 1911. While the Le Moustier skeleton was the first of this group to be found (Hauser and Klaatsch 1909; Klaatsch and Hauser 1909), the somewhat devious activities of the discoverer, the series of unfortunate reconstructions, and the long delay before a description was published combined to deprive it of the notice which it should have received (Weinert 1925). Because the description of the La Ferrassie skeletons was entrusted to Boule, work on them was delayed by his preoccupation with the previously discovered La Chappelle find, and, in fact, a study of the La Ferrassie remains has yet to be published although a half century has elapsed since their discovery. The discovery of the La Quina material (H. Martin 1911) was apparently eclipsed by the simultaneous publication of the first major installment of the desciption of La Chapelle-aux-Saints (Boule 1911). Thus, by chance, the La Chapelle find became the center of attention as the most complete Neanderthal to have been discovered, and, as a result, the work which has long been regarded as definitive for the Neanderthal "type" was a product of French scholarship.

After their discovery on August 3, 1908, the Abbés A. and J. Bouyssonie and L. Bardon sought the advice of their friend and colleague Abbé Henri Breuil who suggested that they give the bones to Professor Marcellin Boule at the Museum d'Histoire Naturelle in Paris for detailed study and description (Breuil 1958:1). Boule with great industry and dispatch produced a series of works culminating in the tomes of 1911, 1912, and 1913 (Boule 1908a and b, 1909a, b, and c, 1911, 1912, and 1913) in which he depicted the Neanderthals in terms which have served journalists and scholars ever since as the basis for the caricature of the cave man. Since he was not prepared to accept such a creature in the human family tree, he settled the question to the general satisfaction by declaring that the Neanderthals as well as the Pithecanthropines—the only other non-modern hominid fossils known—became extinct without issue (Boule 1913:242, 246–49; 1921:242, 245: 1923:244, 247).

At the time when Boule established the view that Neanderthal could not be the ancestor to subsequent forms of men, he offered two points in support of his conclusion (Boule 1913:243; Schwalbe 1913:601). It is instructive to look at these today since they are both accepted without much question, although the evidence involved has undergone marked changes (Vallois 1954, 1959:134–36, 153–56).

1. Modern forms of man already existed at the time of the Neanderthalers.

2. The Mousterian was suddenly replaced by the Upper Palaeolithic and the very suddenness of the change indicated that the bearers of the Upper Palaeolithic must have been developing their cultural traditions elsewhere for a considerable period of time. As a corollary to this, it was claimed that the anatomical differences between the supposed immediately succeeding populations were so great that they precluded the possibility of evolution.

Both of these points are offered in support of his claim that modern forms of Homo sapiens have an antiquity which extends far back into the Pleistocene, but, even at that time, the evidence in their support was very far from being adequate. Curiously enough, both points persist in anthropological writings of recent years, and, while diffeent evidence is offered, it is equally inadequate, as will be discussed shortly.

Boule's candidates for morphologically modern precursors or contemporaries with Neanderthalers were the Grimaldi skeletons—the so-called "Negroids" from the Grotte des Enfants at Menton (Boule 1908b:525)—and later the Piltdown skull (Boule 1913:246; 1921:172; 1923:174; Schwalbe 1913:601–3). These he felt were proof of the early existence of modern forms of man, although he was aware that Cartailhac (1912:231, 252, 265) had already cautioned that the Grimaldi finds were to be associated with Aurignacian cultural material overlying the Mousterian (Boule 1913:213). The reason for Boule's acceptance of Piltdown as valid evidence is not at all clear from the literature, although it may have depended upon the personalities and friendships of the people involved. Previously Boule had examined and rejected the evidence for the antiquity of Galley Hill, Clichy, Denise, Grenelle, Ipswich, Olmo, Bury St. Edmonds, and others (Boule 1913:210, 242; Schwalbe 1913:596, 602), although these could be regarded as at least as reliable as Piltdown.

Boule's position on the replacement of the Mousterian (and hence, Neanderthal man) by the Upper Palaeolithic (and hence, Homo sapiens in the modern sense) is remarkably similar to the theory of catastrophism supported by Cuvier just a century earlier as an explanation for geological successions (Cuvier 1834:107; Boule 1921:9; Dehaut 1945). This should not be surprising since Boule was trained as a palaeontologist in mid-nineteenth century France where palaeontology, comparative anatomy, and geology were taught by Cuvier's disciples and immediate successors who followed in detail the teachings of their late master. Cuvier's explanation for the apparently sudden changes visible in specific stratigraphic sequences was based on his feeling that stratigraphic columns literally recorded *all* the events which had formerly taken place. A sudden change in faunal content indicated that a corresponding sudden change in the animal populations must have taken place at the past time indicated. The appearance of new forms of animals in succeeding superimposed strata did not necessarily signify creation *de novo*, but rather indicated that these animals had previously existed elsewhere in the world, and, following the catastrophe which had eliminated their predecessors in the area under examination, they swept in as an invasion and suddenly occupied the area of their extinct precursors (Dehaut 1945; Eiseley 1958:67).

These views have their roots in the eighteenth and early nineteenth centuries when some sort of explanation was needed for the sequences being discovered in the fossil record and when a theory of evolution was emotionally unacceptable and had not yet been worked out as an encompassing explanatory principle. Cuvier's influence was so strong that many continental scholars, when faced with the development of evolutionary thinking, tried to illustrate every possible way in which it would *not* work instead of examining it rationally and trying to understand how it *could* work. The battle fought by these people has been a defensive one emphasizing negative facets (Vallois 1954:112), and the result has largely been a devious and unproductive delaying action.

Boule, following the tradition in which he had been trained, attempted to show that the morphological gap between Neanderthal and modern man was so large and the temporal gap was so small that the former could not have been the ancestor of the latter. The extinction of the one and the invasion of the other was postulated, and the result was the development of what could be labeled the theory of hominid catastro-

phism—still vigorously advocated by Boule's disciple Vallois (1946, 1949b, 1954, 1959) and echoed by many others (W. W. Howells 1942, 1944, 1959; Heberer 1944, 1949, 1950, 1951, 1956, 1959a and b; F. C. Howell 1951, 1952, 1957; Breitinger 1952, 1955; Le Gros Clark 1955a; Patte 1955; and Gieseler 1959; to name a few). In his efforts to give his arguments the greatest possible effect, Boule claimed that Neanderthals exhibited many characters which subsequent unbiased research has failed to substantiate. Thus, despite Boule's claims, there is not trace of evidence that Neanderthalers had exceptionally divergent great toes or that they were forced to walk orang-like on the outer edges of their feet (Morton 1926:314); there is no evidence that they were unable fully to extend their knee joints (this should have been settled by the excellent work of Manouvrier 1888 and 1893, but was dismissed by Boule 1912:140); there is no evidence that their spinal columns lacked the convexities necessary for fully erect posture (Straus and Cave 1957); there is no evidence that the head was slung forward on a peculiarly short and thick neck (Stewart 1962:152); and there is no evidence that the brain was qualitatively inferior to that of modern man (Montagu 1960:196; Comas 1961:307—8).

One could logically ask, then, in what ways, if any, the Neanderthals do differ from modern men. In general, they convey the impression of skeletal rugosity including the wide epiphyses of the long bones, the relative thickness of the hand and foot bones, and the relative stoutness of the ribs (see the general listing of characteristics by F. C. Howell 1957:335–36), but primarily their distinctiveness occurs in the size of the face (Morant 1927:339; F. C. Howell 1951:387; 1952:403) involving gross tooth dimensions and supporting architecture (c.f. Brace 1962b:349). No one of these differences is outside the range of variation of modern man, but taken together, the face dimensions, especially, indicate a population noticeably distinct from any *populations* existing today, yet there is no good reason why such a population could not have been ancestral to modern man (Hrdlička 1929:620; 1930:348; Weinert 1925:53; 1936:515; 1944b:231; Weidenreich 1943a;46–48; 1947a:190, 196; 1949:156; Le Gros Clark 1955a:45). In fact, given the aggregate human fossil material form the Australopithecines through the Pithecanthropines and presumably on up, it would be most extraordinary if something like Hrdlička's Neanderthal phase had *not* occurred just prior to the development of more modern forms (Weidenreich 1949:156).

Since the time of Boule's analysis, very few attempts have been made to compare Neanderthals as a group with other human populations. One of these (Morant 1927) compares individual (mainly La Chapelle-aux-Saints) measurements with the range of modern population means, and, however correct the conclusions may be, this remains highly dubious as a statistical procedure (Abbie 1952:81). Another study (Thoma 1957–58) does not even use measurements but relies on subjective appraisal of morphological features, arbitrarily designated as single gene traits, and does not allow for any population variability at all (see analysis by Brace 1962c). These works, as did that of Boule, are not concerned with how the characteristics of modern man developed and what they developed from, since their primary purpose is a negative one—to demonstrate that Neanderthal man could not have had any descendants.

While the morphology and particularly the functional significance of morphological differences has been left largely unstudied (for an attempt to reverse this trend see Brace 1962a and b), there has on the other hand been much interest in the question involving the possible contemporaneity of modern man with the Neanderthals. The idea has been that if evidence of a morphologically modern population could be found at the same time as, or earlier than, the Neanderthals, then this would serve as the logical ancestor to modern man, and we need never fear that anything so "brutish" as a Neanderthal would show up in our family tree. The popularity of this approach has been enormous in spite of the fact that over the years the candidates offered to represent this supposed population have proved to be a shadowy lot, impossible to pin down (Stewart 1951:102–3; F. C. Howell 1957:341–42).

Boule himself offered the Grimaldi skeletons as contemporaries of Neanderthals (1913:213, 243) although Cartailhac had already noted that they should be considered Aurignacian and hence subsequent to the

Mousterian (Cartailhac 1912:252, 265, 297). Boule also regarded Piltdown as a possible early stem from which modern man arose (Boule 1913:246; 1921:172). The famous exposure of the Piltdown remains as fraudulent (Weiner, Oakley, and Clark 1953) means that both of the pieces of evidence which he offered in favor of this view must be discarded. Curiously enough, Schwalbe in his extensive review of Boule's work on La Chapelle noted the Aurignacian status of Grimaldi and the questionable nature of Piltdown but still was so impressed by Boule's weighty scholarship that he partially changed his former assertion (1906a:5, 8, 25, 31) that Neanderthals had been the direct precursors to later forms of men (Schwalbe 1913:602).

Following the capitulation of Schwalbe in 1913, the standard interpretation of the European Neanderthals was that they were a curious and peculiar group of "specialized," squat, clumsy, and unadaptable men doomed to sudden extinction following the first stadial of the Würm glaciation when faced with the invasion of a population of "noble," "handsome," "clean-limbed," fully modern men of superior form and culture (Keith 1915:136, 505; 1925a (1928): 198–99; 1946: 141; Osborn 1919:272; Boule 1921:242–45; 1923:244–47; Burkitt 1921:90; de Morgan 1921:55; Capitan 1922:18; MacCurdy 1924:Vol. 1:209–10; Sollas 1924:254; Hooton 1931:357, 393; 1946:412; W. W. Howells 1942:192–93; 1944:170, 207; 1959: 205–7; Knight 1949:156; F. C. Howell 1951:406, 410; 1952:402; 1960:224; Mayr 1951:113, 116; Leakey 1953:205; Clark 1955a:57, 63, 71, 74; Boule and Vallois 1957:255–58; Piveteau 1957:598; Place 1957:80, 84, 90; Hibben 1958:34, 39; von Koenigswald 1958:21; Potonie 1958: 283–85; Bates 1961:34; Lasker 1961:101; Dobzhansky 1962:180; and many others).

In one of the most thoughtful considerations of the mistakes commonly made when appraising human fossil material, Le Gros Clark (1955a:39–45) considers the implication of the frequent use of the term "specialized" in reference to fossil man (1955a:40), noting that on morphological grounds alone such arguments are inapplicable to Neanderthal man and his possible relations to what he distinguishes as *Homo sapiens*. Yet Clark himself subsequently uses "specialized" (p.

71) and "specialization" (p. 74) to characterize the Neanderthals and presumably to exclude them from *sapiens* ancestry—this in spite of his caution that it is not legitimate to use in this way, as arguments against ancestral relationships, characters which are not, among other things, "related to any marked degree of *functional* specialization" (1955a:41, italics Clark's). Despite his excellent advice, neither he nor any other recent author follows it, and there is no mention of the functional significance of those facets of Neanderthal morphology which serve to distinguish it from that of more recent man. (For an attempt to view these features from the point of view of changes in selective pressures, see Brace 1962*b*:347–49). Properly speaking, the only real human "specialization" is culture, and, since culture is not a product of the human gene pool, arguments claiming cultural specialization as a reason for failure to survive are dubious to say the least. Any such argument claiming anatomical specialization as a reality, let alone as a significant reality, must be more carefully worked out than that offered by Vallois (1959:134) who simply follows Boule in offering a sterile repetition of the features wherein Neanderthal differs from modern man, labels them specializations, and assumes thereby that he has proven the inability of modern form to have arisen from anything called Neanderthal. The authors cited above have preferred to rely on the tentative time estimates advanced by Quaternary geologists, whose work they were unable to appraise competently, as proof that there was insufficient time for the Australopithecines, Pithecanthropines, Neanderthals, and modern men to be related in any direct sense, and in this way they have perpetuated what Gregory calls "the anachronism of demanding that the remote ancestors of any line must already possess all the habitus and features of its distant descendants" (Gregory 1949:508). For instance, not one of the well-preserved Western European Neanderthals can be given a date with a possible plus or minus variation of much less than 20,000 years, which means that there is a 40,000 year time span within which they could occur. Any statement claiming a sudden transition in the form of the inhabitants of Europe at or before 35,000 or so years ago assumes a knowledge of

Neanderthal dating which we simply do not possess.

The widespread certainty that a gap in the stratigraphic sequence necessarily indicated a break in the continuity of the local population—catastrophism in the best pre-Darwinian tradition—was momentarily upset by the find of a population at Skhul (Mount Carmel, Palestine) in 1931–32 which was morphologically intermediate between Neanderthal and modern peoples (Keith and McCown 1937; McCown and Keith 1939). Thus there was geat relief among the proponents of Neanderthal extinction when Mount Carmel was presumably demonstrated to have been Third Interglacial (Garrod and Bate 1937; Garrod 1958:183; F. C. Howell 1958:186; 1959; 1961:10) and hence necessarily prior to the more primitive Neanderthalers. With *sapiens* occurring earlier than Neanderthal, then the likelihood was considered eliminated that Neanderthal was the ancestor to modern man, and the relief of those who were manifestly uneasy about the possibility of discovering a Neanderthal skeleton in a *sapiens* closet was apparent. But it was an uneasy relief, and the attempt to grasp at early *sapiens* straws continued (Vallois 1949a:357–58; 1954:123; McCown 1951:92; W. W. Howells 1959:233; Montagu 1960:230–50).

With the existence of fossil skeletal material from various places exhibiting a complete graduation from fully Neanderthal to fully modern morphology, former efforts to deny the Neanderthals ancestral status on the grounds that they were too "specialized" or "peculiar" or just plain "different" have lost their force, although remnants of such arguments still exist (Kälin 1946:284; Heberer 1949:1472; 1955a:88; Vallois 1954:114–16; 1959:134–35). Whereas "thirty years ago it almost became a sport of a certain group of authors to search the skeletal parts of Neanderthal Man for peculiarities which could be proclaimed as 'specialization', thereby proving the deviating course this form had taken in evolution" (Weidenreich 1943a:44), this has now been abandoned by most scholars and the case has been reduced to one of dating—for instance the primary concern exhibited by F. C. Howell for geological relationships rather than for morphological change and the factors influencing it (F. C. Howell 1951, 1952, 1957, 1958,

1959, 1960, 1961, 1962). As Le Gros Clark says, "On purely morphological grounds (and without reference to paleontological sequence), there is no certain argument why *H. neanderthalensis* could not be ancestral to *H. sapiens*. But, in this particular instance, the fossil record shows clearly that such was not the case" (Clark 1955a:45).

Interestingly enough, in his various works Clark himself apparently has been guilty of three "fallacies," all of which he warns against. He refers to *sapiens* skulls in Europe prior to the last major glaciation on what he calls "reasonably sound" geological evidence (Le Gros Clark 1959:34). Since in this particular instance he refers to no specific fossil, one cannot appraise what he means by "reasonably sound," but if as he implies elsewhere his reference is to the dating of such finds as Fontéchevade (Clark 1955a:67), Mount Carmel (Clark 1955a:69), and Krapina (Clark 1955a:70), then he has been guilty first of the fallacy of relying on tentative and inadequately documented dating procedures (Bordes 1961; Higgs 1961a:139; 1961b:153). Clark himself has recognized the "equivocal" nature of the dating of many hominid fossils (1955a:37) but this does not deter him from using such equivocal data to support his previously drawn conclusions. For instance, despite Clark's claim that the Fontéchevade remains were found *in situ* (1955a:67; see Movius 1948:367), the circumstances surrounding the discovery are anything but clear. The remains were apparently discovered in a block of material in the laboratory (Vallois 1959:7), documentation remains inadequate, no stratigraphic section remains as a check, and from the conflicting accounts it is difficult to discover just what the circumstances surrounding the discovery really were (Bordes 1961). In this instance, Clark appears to be following the tradition established in British anthropological circles of being so anxious to prove the great antiquity of *sapiens* forms that any such indication, no matter how tenuous, will be accepted until proven false.

As far as the dating of Krapina is concerned, he states that "it is now generally agreed that the deposit belongs to the last interglacial period" (1955a:70), basing his statement on the faunal associations. Since he quotes no sources, it is not possible to discover how this general agreement is made. It should be noted, however, that Krapina was not dug stratigraphically and the exact faunal associations of the human skeletal material are still unknown (Vukovič 1959). Furthermore, *Dicerorhinus merkii* survived beyond the last interglacial in southern Europe and would be no necessary time marker for Krapina even if it were conclusively indicative of the layers in which the human remains occurred (Vallois 1959:88) and, finally the most recent reappraisal would be inclined to place it in a Würm interstadial, the Göttweiger. (Guenther 1959:205, 208). The recent discussion of the removal of Skhul from the Riss-Würm interglacial needs no more comment here (Higgs 1961b:153).

Second, Clark is guilty of another fallacy to which he alludes (1959:35)—that of inferring form and taxonomic affiliation on the basis of fragmentary and inadequate evidence. Thus he offers the Fontéchevade fragments as being not demonstrably different from *Homo sapiens* (1955a:67), yet, problems of dating aside, the uncertainties surrounding the form of the major fragment (Fontéchevade II) are clearly apparent despite the extraordinarily poor quality of the illustrations in Vallois' monograph (Vallois 1959: p. 15, Fig. 4; p. 35, Fig. 12 and Plate XV). When tracings are made of these, enlarged to the same size, and superimposed for comparison, the differences between the form of the vault prior to restoration (see Figs. 1 and 2) and that claimed following restoration (Figs. 3 and 4) are so great that the only hint that the subject is the same skull is in the rough similarity in outline of the broken margin on the right. With such gross disagreement apparent in the work of the only author who has made a close study of the original, the claim that the reconstruction of the frontal width indicated a lack of brow ridge (Vallois 1959:35–36) becomes simply a statement unsupported by any evidence. Figure 5 shows Figure 2 superimposed on Figure 4 and reveals width discrepancies of 20%, leaving the reader quite unable to see the factual basis for Vallois' conclusions.

Vallois' claims concerning the significance of the placement of the supposed trace of frontal sinus must be taken on faith since it fails to show in the poor photographs. Apparently it is in a part of the frontal devoid of the external bony table (Vallois 1949a:348; 1954:125; 1959:60–65), and any cranial con-

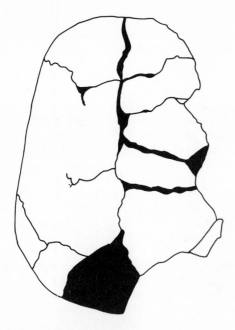

Figure 1. Enlarged tracing of a photograph of Fontéchevade II, *norma verticalis*, before restoration. From Vallois 1959:15, Fig. 4.

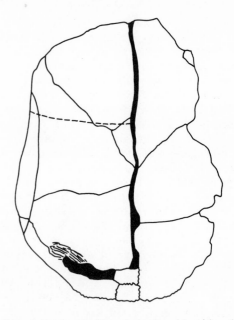

Figure 3. Tracing of a diagraph drawing of Fontéchevade II, *norma verticalis*. From Vallois 1959:35, Fig. 12.

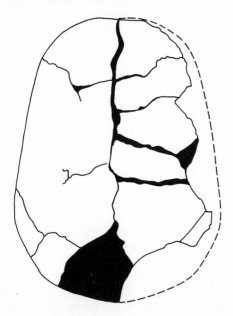

Figure 2. The same tracing shown in Fig. 1 with the outline completed.

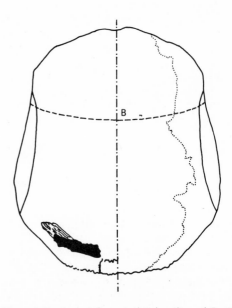

Figure 4. Tracing of the completed outline of Fontéchevade II, after restoration. From Vallois 1959: 36, Fig. 13.

tour based on diploë alone—even in a skull which has not spent any time in the ground—is not something which can be used with much confidence. The simple presence of sinus in an otherwise undistinguished piece of frontal is not in itself evidence either

for or against the existence of a brow ridge, as can be seen from Krapina frontal number 2 in which the sinus extends 27 mm. above the top of the naso-frontal suture and a good 15 mm. above the maximum swelling of a well-developed brow ridge at glabella (Fig.

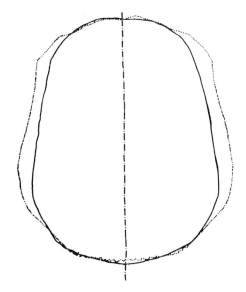

Figure 5. Fig. 4 superimposed on Fig. 2, with the superimposed lengths set equal.

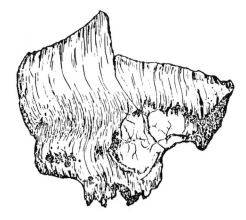

Figure 6. Krapina frontal number 2, *norma frontalis.* Drawn from the original.

6). The top of the sinus is above any trace of the start of the brow ridge.

Furthermore, the assertion that the presence of a sinus precludes the juvenile status of Fontéchevade I implies a knowledge of the age of development of the frontal sinus in possible Neanderthal populations which we do not possess, in spite of Vallois' reference to the eight-year-old La Quina child (1954:124). When it suits their convenience, authors frequently refer to the supposed fact that distinctive Neanderthal morphology develops early in life (F. C. Howell 1951:406; Boule and Vallois 1957:233–24; W. W. Howells 1959:202–3), yet when an undoubted

Neanderthaler is found, such as Le Moustier, which lacks the supposedly typical brow ridge, then there is no hesitation to refer this to the relative youth of the bearer (Weinert 1925:16), conveniently ignoring the fact that at age sixteen the Le Moustier "youth" had relatively little growing left to do.

It appears that in accepting the Fontéchevade remains as representative of a presumed population, many recent authors, including Le Gros Clark himself, have not heeded the warning which Clark advances against utilizing individuals for comparison where size, sex, and particularly age are in doubt (Clark 1955a:33). F. C. Howell has repeatedly urged caution in relying too heavily on such fragmentary pieces of evidence as Fontéchevade for the primary prop supporting radical theories (F. C. Howell 1951; 1957:342; 1958:194), and despite Montagu's somewhat indignant expostualations (Montagu 1952) it would seem that Howell's comments should have had more influence.

In connection with this same fallacy of inferring from inadequate data, Le Gros Clark (1955a:64) and many others (Hooton 1946:333; Stewart 1951:102; Boule and Vallois 1957:185–86; Piveteau 1957:533–34; W. W. Howells 1959:217; Montagu 1960:202) have stressed the mixture of neanthropic and primitive features in the Steinheim skull, but few such commentators (excepting W. W. Howells 1944:171 [not repeated in 1959]; and F. C. Howell 1951:399–401) have even mentioned the fact stressed in the descriptive monograph that the skull had undergone a considerable amount of post-mortem deformation (Weinert 1936:466–68). This is clearly visible in the cast as can be seen from Figure 7. The presence of a canine fossa claimed by Boule and Vallois (1957:185) is not conclusive in either cast or photographs, the claimed absence of prognathism could just as easily be due to the fact that the incisor-bearing part of the face is missing, and furthermore the whole facial skeleton has been badly warped post-mortem. The "laterally compressed" aspect of the skull supposedly indicating *sapiens* form (Hooton 1946:333) should be taken literally since the whole left side of the skull has been deformed toward the midline (Weinert 1936:469) as can be seen from the fact that the width of the palate between the third molars is only 35 mm. (versus 40 mm. for the minimum mean

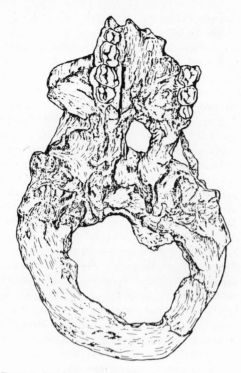

Figure 7. Steinheim *norma basalis*. Drawn from the cast with the aid of a camera lucida.

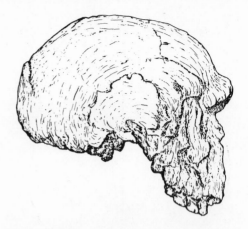

Figure 8. Steinheim *norma lateralis*. Drawn from the cast with the aid of a camera lucida.

modern figure listed in Martin 1928:931, although Martin mentions an individual minimum of 33 mm.), and the biauricular breadth is only approximately 82 mm. (compared with the minimum modern individual dimension of 100 mm. recorded in Martin 1928:765). (These measurements were taken from the cast). The occipital has apparently been slightly warped underneath creating the supposedly *sapiens* "rounded back and neck region" (W. W. Howells 1944: 171). Finally, the brow ridges and the forehead, as noted in Weinert's description (1936:478, 500) and recently recognized only by Montagu (1960:202) are reminiscent of Pithecanthropus rather than Neanderthal or *sapiens* (see Fig. 8). The presumably "neanthropic" features of Steinheim, then, would seem to occur mainly in the reconstructions of those who would have them appear that way.

Finally, in considering inferences made from incomplete remains, one must refer to the famous Swanscombe skull. Reference could also be made to Ehringsdorf and Quinzano where the face is likewise missing (Calrk 1955a:66–68), but since, excluding the fragmentary and dubious Fontéchevade remains, the greater part of the case for *sapiens*

antiquity rests on Swanscombe, it will be considered by itself. Unlike the Fontéchevade finds, there can be no doubt concerning the late second interglacial age of the Swanscombe remains (Oakley 1953:44; F. C. Howell 1960:195–98). If the form of the vault were indistinguishable from modern man this would be most suggestive, although by itself not conclusive. The original detailed report found no measurements or proportions wherein the remains could be considered distinguishable from recent *Homo sapiens* (Morant 1938: 71, 95) despite the Neanderthaloid biasterionic breadth. Yet on the other hand it could not be distinguished from the warped and distorted Steinheim skull (Morant 1938:78, 97).

In connection with the appraisal of unquantifiable characters, Clark quite properly warns against overemphasis of "primitive" features of fossil remains simply because the material is old (Le Gros Clark 1959:35); however he neglects to warn against the overemphasis of "modern" features by authors whose desire to find clear evidence for the pre-Würm existence of morphologically modern man is so strong that some have expressed it as a "need" (McCown 1951:92; Weckler 1954:1022). Still, with Clark's caution against inferring from inadequate data 1955a:64) and his emphasis on the consideration of total morphological pattern (1955a:15–17), and despite his admission that further finds might show that Swanscombe was quite distinct from modern form (Le Gros Clark 1959:35), yet he concludes that it is indeed indistinguishable from modern man (1955a:66). He feels that if the face were of a form comparable to the "extreme Neanderthal type" this would be reflected in the anatomy of the preserved vault parts. Since he indicates that this is not the case, he believes that the brow ridges could not have been more pronounced than those of the Steinheim skull (1955a:66), although, as has been indicated above, the Steinheim brow is so far from being *sapiens* in form that it is better compared with Pithecanthropus than with the Neanderthals, and yet as Morant has indicated the Steinheim vault differs less from the modern "type" than does the Swanscombe (Morant 1938:78).

To contrast with Clark's confidence in the sapient form of Swanscombe, Weidenreich felt that attempts to classify it were doubtful until proof could be brought forward of the characters of the brow and face (Weidenreich 1943b:273; 1947a:194; note a similar cautious view offered by Keith 1949:264). This was a logical recognition of the fact emphasized by Morant that the greatest distinction between Neanderthals and subsequent forms of men occurs in the development of the face (Morant 1927:339, 374–75; F. C. Howell 1951:387; 1952:403; Brace 1962b:349). In spite of his good morphological caution and the other solid theoretical reasons for insisting on full documentation before a fossil be accepted which would contradict most of the evidence for human evolution, Weidenreich has been criticized for possible "morphological dating" (Stewart 1951:98) and for "preferring morphological to geological evidence in the dating of fossils" (Straus and Cave 1957:359). In retrospect, however, his cautions were well founded. The association of Piltdown fragments, in which he refused to believe (1936:117–19), has been proven fraudulent, and, after some thoughtful skepticism regarding the morphology of the Swanscombe skull (Sergi 1953; Breitinger 1952:132–33; 1955:38; Drennan 1956), one of the very people who questioned Weidenreich's motives in urging such caution has himself observed that the occipito-mastoid crest of the Swanscombe skull looks much more like that of the known Neanderthals than that of modern man (Stewart 1960:363; 1961:210, 216). These observations, showing that the anatomical evidence for pre-Neanderthal *sapiens* is far from secure, suggest the final fallacy which

weakens the case of the proponents of such views.

This fallacy might be called that of establishing broad and far-reaching theories of human evolution on poorly documented samples—in many cases single dubious specimens. This has been clearly warned against by F. C. Howell (1957:342; 1958:194), and although it has been recognized by Le Gros Clark (1959:35), in this as in the other instances cited he has failed to follow his own very good advice.

A brief listing of the major authors and their candidates for ancient *sapiens* should show how the evidence has changed since 1908 without becoming any less nebulous.

Boule 1908	Grimaldi
Boule 1913	Grimaldi and Piltdown
Keith 1915	Galley Hill (Piltdown)
Osborn 1919	No evidence except sheer faith
Osborn 1922	Piltdown
Hooton 1931	Piltdown (Galley Hill)
Howells 1944	Mount Carmel (Galley Hill and Swanscombe)
Hooton 1946	Piltdown, Galley Hill, and Swanscombe
Keith 1949	Abandons the view
Le Gros Clark 1955	Swanscombe and Fontéchevade
Boule and Vallois 1957	Fontéchevade
Montagu 1960	Swanscombe and Fontéchevade

This should suffice to show that the evidence has undergone a complete change while the argument has remained substantially the same. The words of Samuel Butler, uttered in protest to the triumph of Darwinian views but now peculiarly appropriate in their support, complained that "no matter how much any one now moves the foundations, he cannot shake the superstructure, which has become so currently accepted as to be above the need of any support from reason" (Butler 1878:276).

Evidently the theoretical framework has not altered since the influential works of Boule on La Chapelle-aux-Saints, and a great majority of the students of human evolution have been primarily concerned with the attempt to demonstrate that various non-modern hominids were the contemporaries of modern forms of man. The aim was to prove thereby that these non-modern hominids could not be the forerunners of truly modern men.

Despite this clearly anti-evolutionary bias, fully realized twenty years ago by an interested sociologist (Gillette 1943), no modern work goes so far as to deny that human evolution occurred (although Boule and Vallois 1957 would deny almost all of the fossil evidence for it). It would seem rather to be a case of "out of sight, out of mind" since the crucial events in the development of *sapiens* morphology are generally pushed back in time to a point where "the fossil record dwindles into obscurity" (Brace 1962c:730) and people are not likely to be disturbed by the sight of a human ancestor who looks rather less than human.

The effect of Boule's work and the immediate and continuing influence which it has had (Keith 1915, 1925a, 1928, 1931, 1946; Osborn 1919; MacCurdy 1924; Hooton 1931, 1946; W. W. Howells 1944, 1959; Montagu 1945, 1951, 1960; Vallois 1954, 1959; Clark 1955a; Patte 1955; Piveteau 1957; Lasker 1961) was so powerful that F. C. Howell has recently commented that he knew of no "thoughtful worker in the field in the past half century" who has advocated a view involving the evolution of men of modern form from the European Neanderthals (F. C. Howell 1957:341). Actually he is forgetting the views of Hrdlička (1926, 1927, 1930), Weidenreich (1928, 1940, 1943a, 1946, 1947a, 1949), Weinert (1925, 1932, 1936, 1944a, 1944b, 1951, 1955) and others (see Vallois 1954:113) who must be accounted as thoughtful workers however much one may disagree with them on some points. As far as the effect which their opposition to the picture painted by Boule has had, they might just as well have never existed.

It is interesting that the fundamentally anti-evolutionary, or at least non-evolutionary, tone of palaeoanthropology as represented in the writings of the majority of western European and American authors has been clearly recognized by Russian and Polish anthropologists (Roginski 1947, 1951; Wierciński 1956; Dambski 1957). The willingness of eastern European students to accept the fossil record as indicative of the evolution of man may stem in part from the prestige which Hrdlička continued to enjoy in the country of his birth and neighboring areas (Dokládal and Brožek 1961:456), although it would seem that at least part of the reason may be based on sociopolitical ideology and not on basic biology—witness the pointless pregenetic insistence on typology (Wierciński 1962; esp. the comment by Michalski on pp. 32–35) and the continued fruitless attempts to view the issues of human biological variation as revolving around the long dead conflict of polyphyletism with monophyletism. In the "conflict" it is claimed that "it is the Soviet students who now stand in the van" and exhibit "the correct attitude" (Dambski 1957:179). It appears however that the "van" stalled before a concern was developed for natural selection and the mechanisms involved in heredity, and it would seem to have remained stationary ever since. This criticism, while primarily directed at the purposeless typologies of the living, can also be made of the great majority of the attempts to interpret the human fossil record. It is hoped that this paper will serve as a preliminary effort to reverse the trend.

In the desire to prove Neanderthal extinction, it would appear as though many recent authors have rejoiced in chronological indications, however shaky, which would tend to confound a logical view of human evolution (Le Gros Clark 1955a:38, 45; Place 1957:76; Hibben 1958:27, 36–37; F. C. Howell 1958:187; W. W. Howells 1959:226). Thus both Hrdlička and Weidenreich have been taken to task for putting more reliance on the morphological developments, which they were professionally competent to evaluate in their thinking about evolutionary development, than in the tentative orderings which the very incomplete geochronological studies sought to assign to certain fossil specimens (Stewart 1949:15; 1951:97–98; Le Gros Clark 1955a:72; Straus and Cave 1957:359). Admittedly the concept of morphological dating, as applied by Hrdlička to the New World, thoroughly deserved the criticism which it received, but condemnation was pushed beyond the specific to the general with the implication that the morphological assessment of evolutionary development and hence possible age is *never* a legitimate procedure (Stewart 1949:16). As an indication that the criticism was carried too far, the same source deplored the fact that by 1948 Sir Arthur Keith had finally wavered in his former blind acceptance of the geological appraisal of the Galley Hill skeleton (Stewart 1949:14; 1951:97). Ironically, in a publication which appeared at the same time as the criticism, it was finally and unassailably demonstrated that the supposedly objective evidence for the antiquity of Galley Hill was worthless (Oakley and Montagu 1949).

Interestingly enough, Keith's original reasons for claiming great antiquity for modern forms of man were not based primarily on geological indications of the great age of *sapiens* skeletal material, but rather were founded on the inverted application of the principal of morphological dating itself. In Keith's mind, anything so unique as modern morphology must have required a great extent of time in which to develop, and, therefore, on form alone, he judged modern man to be very ancient (Keith 1925a [1928], I:x, 265–66, II:711). This is not only "very close to morphological dating," this in fact *is* morphological dating. Thus while Keith is generally credited with the staunch defense of Galley Hill and Piltdown as proof of sapient antiquity, in his writings he maintained proper caution by noting the morphological problems of Piltdown and the legitimate question concerning the geological authenticity of Galley Hill (1925a [1928], II:713). His basic thought was that "the proof that man of a modern build of body was in existence by the close of the Pliocene period is presumptive, not positive" (Keith 1925a [1928], II:711), and his presumption was based on his feeling that immense time was necessary for evolution to work—time which he then believed the Pleistocene could not offer.

This, of course, brings up the real source of Keith's troubles. In 1915 he had felt daring in offering a stretch of 400,000 years as the duration of the Pleistocene, and by 1925 he felt compelled to reduce this to 200,000 years and was unhappily contemplating the presumed necessity of further reducing it to little more than 100,000 years (Keith 1925a [1928], I:xiv–xv). It seems to have been the fate of Sir Authur Keith to have been the victim of other people's mistakes—witness Piltdown. In 1925 he recognized the strain to which his reliance on extant geological estimates had forced him to subject the fossil evidence and compared his position to that of Huxley when Kelvin, by the "precise" methods of physics, had reduced the age of

the earth to 24 million years (Chamberlain 1901:225; Keith 1925a [1928], I:xv; Eiseley 1958:233–44). Although Keith said in despair, "there must be a mistake somewhere" (1925a, I:xv) yet he persisted in using a date for the Pleistocene which would not allow an evolutionary explanation for the known hominid fossils (1931:34). When at last he became aware of a Pleistocene date in the neighborhood of 1 million years (1949:164, 208), he modified his former interpretations and abandoned the attempt to prove great relative antiquity for modern forms of men (Keith 1949:265), reluctantly admitting Neanderthal man into the ancestry of "the proud Caucasian" (1949:263) although he persisted in refusing to admit that this could have taken place in Europe (1949:244).

Clarifying the doubts cast on some of Weidenreich's views, subsequent events have shown that his suspicion of the validity of Piltdown and the sapient form of Swanscombe, while certainly "very close to morphological dating" (Stewart 1951:98), was suspicion well founded (Weiner, Oakley, and Clark 1953; Stewart 1960, 1961). Other facets of Weidenreich's work, such as his claim for giant hominid ancestors (1945:115), his failure to recognize the significance of the Australopithecines (1943b:268–69; 1945:121), and his approach to orthogenesis (1941:435; 1947b:407, 416) will draw few defenders now.

Whatever the weaknesses in the works of Weidenreich, Hrdlička, and Weinert, their similar approaches to the Neanderthal question deserve careful consideration, which so far has not been given them. Because Hrdlička published his views extensively before Weidenreich, he will be considered first, while Weinert, as the last major living representative of such an interpretation, will be considered after Weidenreich.

The full development of Hrdlička's ideas can be seen in his Huxley Memorial Lecture for 1927 reprinted in the Annual Report of the Smithsonian Institution for 1928 (Hrdlička 1929:593–621) and repeated and emphasized in 1930 (Hrdlička 1930:328–49). It is not surprising that the perspective of more than thirty years should reveal that Hrdlička cannot be substantiated in some of his ideas, but what *is* surprising is that these turn out to be remarkably few and do not affect his major thesis.

Thus he refused to accept geological indications for a succession of four glacial maxima in Europe during the Pleistocene (Hrdlička 1927:271; 1929:617–18; 1930:346; cf. Keith's similar views 1925a [1928], I:x, 265–66; 1931:34–36), although, since he did recognize the evidence for the onset of peri-glacial conditions at the time of the Neanderthals, he was able to view evolutionary problems where early Würm populations are concerned from the point of view of changes in selective factors. Hrdlička's question (1930:345) concerning the motivation of a supposed *sapiens* population to invade a Europe in the grip of a most unappealing climate might be parried by the postualation that the Neanderthal—*sapiens* change took place during the Göttweiger interstadial, although both the skeletal and the geological evidence is still not even adequate to frame the question let alone answer it and hence such an answer must be in the nature of an evasion.

While Hrdlička made a conscientious effort to view the human evolutionary changes he observed in terms of changes in selective pressures, he did not have a sufficient grounding in evolutionary genetics, and, consequently, he misinterpreted the significance of the great morphological variability which his extensive familiarity with the skeletal material had led him to appreciate. Noting Neanderthal skeletal variability and postulating increasing stringency of selective pressures, he inferred that the two were connected in a cause-and-effect relationship, although he did not tackle the problem of why the ultimate change resulted in a reduction of general muscularity and a reduction in size of the facial skeleton (1929:619; 1930:347). Weidenreich, faced with similar problems in later years, likewise could see no logical rationale for such reductions and concluded by assigning them in some cryptic way to the enlargement of the brain (Weidenreich 1941:343–435). It is interesting to note that F. C. Howell goes no further than to assign "classic Neanderthal" form to "severe selective pressures" (1951:409; 1952:403; 1957:337) but does not say how this works and makes no effort to view *sapiens* evolution from this point of view. Le Gros Clark, for his part, is simply content to quote F. C. Howell (1955a:61).

In speaking of an increase in population variability, Thoma (1957:496, 502) noted that according to sound evolutionary theory (Simpson 1944) this should indicate a *decrease* in selective pressures, but since he, like the other authors cited, feels certain that Palaeolithic conditions call for strong selection, he explains the variability (for the Mount Carmel populations) as a result of hybridization. Actually, all of these authors have failed to appreciate the fact that culture, rather than climate, has been the prime factor to be reckoned with in assessing the selective pressures operating on man. If Neanderthal and Neanderthaloid (e.g., Mount Carmel) actually do show unusual variability, then it seems logical to view this as a reduction in the former adaptive significance of the traits in question. With the clear indications of the increase of special tools for special purposes beginning in the Mousterian and continuing without break through the Upper Palaeolithic in Europe and the Middle East (Bordes 1958; Smith 1961), the extreme rounding wear seen on the anterior teeth of earlier populations, indicative of extensive use of the dentition as a tool, gradually reduces, and it can be inferred that developing culture has reduced the adaptive significance of the huge Middle Palaeolithic dentition and its supporting facial architecture (Brace 1962b:348–49). In conjunction with principles recently elaborated (Brace 1963), the ultimate result of the reduction of the adaptive significance of a structure will be the reduction of the structure itself. This provides the final reason for the transformation of a Neanderthal into a *sapiens* population which Hrdlička, Weidenreich, and Weinert postulated but could not quite account for.

Aside from these weak points in Hrdlička's reasoning, the rest is quite sound in spite of the fact that it has been almost completely ignored. First of all, he recognized that a view calling for Neanderthal extinction demands that there should be a demonstrable sudden replacement in Europe of one population by the other which had been developing elsewhere. While Hrdlička did not observe, as he might have done to some effect, that this in miniature was precisely the type of stratigraphic explanation which Darwin was up against nearly a century before in refuting the prevailing views of Cuvier and catastrophism, yet he did note that there are a number of problems which views involving extinctions and invasions must face.

1. Invasion and replacement presupposes a long double line of evolution which is so unlikely as to require solid proof before it could be rendered acceptable. Furthermore, an invasion to be successful in the face of an established population presupposes a large invading force, and a large invading force presupposes a still larger mother population elsewhere. As Hrdlička noted, there is no clear evidence for any such large non-Neanderthal population in Europe, and there certainly is none in Asia or Africa. To this one might add that, despite the efforts of a whole subsequent generation of students all anxious to prove *sapiens* antiquity, there is neither cultural nor skeletal evidence for these phantom *sapiens* populations, and the few individuals offered as such (for instance Steinheim, Swanscombe, Fontéchevade, and Kanjera) are either distorted, fragmentary, of dubious date, or downright un-*sapiens*.

   F. C. Howell (1951, 1952, 1957, 1959) has sought to provide a reason for a long independent period of evolution for two hominid lines by claiming the climatic isolation of Europe during the early Würm, but the marked cultural similarities between Europe and the Middle East as opposed to either one and other parts of the Old World (Africa or eastern Asia) would seem to indicate that the ecological zone stretching from Iran across the northern Mediterranean border to southwest Europe, far from being broken up into cultural isolates, was a zone in which similar cultural elements maintained circulation—i.e., a kind of Middle Palaeolithic or Mousterian culture area. Evidence for claimed isolation is going to have to come from human cultural/physical data and not exclusively from speculations based on climatological information.

2. Differential rates of evolution for postulated different human groups, as Hrdlička noted, need to be justified. Why should one group, the European Neanderthals, cease to evolve? Hrdlička's question might be strengthened by noting that selective pressures must have been quite similar in their operation on human populations throughout the then north temperate areas of the Old World during the Pleistocene. Certainly the cultural parallels archeologically evident between Europe, southern Russia, and the Near East are striking evidence that the cultural solution to environmental problems has been quite similar from the time of the third interglacial on up. If, as has been suggested (Brace 1962b:343) culture is a major determiner of the selective forces operating on human populations, then there is no reason to regard the selection in Europe as having been different in nature from that to the East, and the supposed evolutionary stagnation of the European inhabitants is still unexplained.

3. If invasion and population replacement did occur, presumably due to the superiority of the invading population, Hrdlička asks:

   (a) Why did the invading population not prevail sooner?

   (b) Why did they take over the precise caves and sites formerly occupied by the Neanderthals?

   (c) Why did this supposedly superior population live exactly the same kind of life their predecessors had? Since evidence is accumulating to indicate that the European Upper Palaeolithic may be largely the product of cultural evolution *in situ*, it might be added that the superior newcomers must have arrived culture-less or have abandoned their own so-far undiscovered culture to take over that of the Neanderthalers whom they presumably displaced. This in fact comes close to being the argument used in one of the most strained explanations yet produced (Weckler 1954:1015–16).

   (d) What example can one give from contemporary and historical knowledge of the complete extinction of a whole group of humanity by the action of another one?

Of all the sound and compelling questions asked by Hrdlička, only the last facet of this one, which is relatively trivial, seems to have drawn any response. W. W. Howells (1944:208) and Vallois (1954:120) offer the American Indians as an example of the presumed extinction of a whole group of humanity, noting that they will never noticeably affect the physical type of the United

States, and, for the purposes of future excavators, they might as well be extinct. This of course assumes that the future anthropologists can ignore the accumulation of evidence from the 60 million inhabitants of Mexico and the countries further south (*Encyclopaedia Britannica World Atlas* 1960:39) where Pre-Columbian genes represent a substantial proportion of the common pool. The previous requirement noted by Hrdlička, of a large invading population and an even larger parent population, would of course have been met, rendering Howells' and Vallois' example inappropriate even if it were true.

Of all the major figures still actively concerned with problems in human evolution, only Vallois still frankly champions a picture of separate human lines evolving in parallel fashion in neighboring or even the same geographical areas (1959:155). This he believes is solidly consistent with the concepts developed by vertebrate palaeontology and evolutionary theory since the beginning of the century, and he considers the supposed parallel lines to indicate hominid adaptive radiation. Nowhere, however, does he consider what is adaptive about such presumed parallel developments, nor does he make any effort to consider the primary hominid adaptive mechanism, which is not to be seen in the lists of traits on which he relies. The mechanism, of course, is culture. One can even view the adaptive niche inhabited by man as a cultural niche. Conceived in this way, the "competitive exclusion principle" which Hardin used to explain the existence, in the long run, of only one species in each ecological niche (Hardin 1960a) clearly shows why only one hominid species has existed at any one time during the Pleistocene. Such an approach combined with what is known about the distribution of the Mousterian simply will not allow the long time separate development of *sapiens* and Neanderthal lines. Symbolic of Vallois' failure to consider the relationship between human morphology and the primary adaptive factors influencing it is Vallois' statement, when describing the Fontéchevade remains, that his concern is chiefly with the "anthropology," and for that reason he leaves out the archaeology (Vallois 1954:114). To be sure, "anthropology" in France means "physical anthropology," but perhaps one of the reasons for the consistently anti-evolutionary position taken by French physical anthropology is that, in relegating all concern for culture to ethnologists and archaeologist, they have eliminated human adaptation from their thinking, and without an understanding of this it is of course difficult to interpret the hominid fossil record from an evolutionary point of view.

It would seem that any view which attempts to picture the Neanderthalers as "aberrant," "extreme," "special," or "specialized," and as having been a blind end in evolution which became extinct without descendants would have to be able to answer in convincing fashion the points raised by Hrdlička, yet, although such views are practically unanimous among the students of fossil man today, none has attempted such answers.

While Hrdlička was thoroughly familiar with the early human skeletal remains prior to 1930 and had made one of the most significant attempts to interpret them, he does not seem to have been as familiar with the literature as he was with the bones. While he quoted from the published works of five of the most influential scholars of his day (Hrdlička 1930:326–27) and remarked with what should have been devastating effect that "they give us *H. sapiens*, without showing why, or how, and where he developed his superior make-up" (Hrdlička 1930:345; see also 1927:270), yet he apparently believed that "all these opinions can probably be traced, directly or indirectly, to the authoritative notions arrived at during the earlier years of this century, on material less ample than at present, by one of the foremost students of Neanderthal man, Gustav Schwalbe" (Hrdlička 1927:250; 1929:594; 1930:327). He cites no reference to back up this accusation, but, in a recent although much milder version of the same view, F. C. Howell lists as sources Schwalbe's publications in 1901, 1906, and 1923 (F. C. Howell 1957:340). A check of these and others (Schwalbe 1897, 1899, 1901a and b, 1902, 1904, 1906a and b, 1913, 1923 [actually written in 1916 just before his death]) has not only failed to reveal any evidence for this (cf. Weidenreich 1928:9) but has clearly shown that quite the reverse was true. Prior to this yielding to the influence of Boule in 1913, he had arranged the available fossil men as stages in a linear sequence—Pithecanthropus, Neanderthal, and modern—which he believed represented the course of human evolution (Schwalbe 1906a:25; 1913: 602). Rather than Schwalbe, whose views apparently were basically the same as Hrdlička's, the latter should properly have implicated the views of Boule and the fundamentally anti-evolutionary ethos of French palaeontology which, via the subsequent espousals by Keith and Osborn and others, have delayed the acceptance of the human fossil record from an avowedly evolutionary point of view from that day to this.

A proper appreciation of the position of Schwalbe is raised since it gives a clue to the background of his pupil and, later, colleague Franz Weidenreich, one of the very few scholars besides Hrdlička to have attempted to view the Neanderthals as a normal facet of human prehistoric development. Weidenreich's views, reflecting the years he spent in China, are less oriented toward the specifically European fossil record, and his attempts to interpret the position of the Neanderthals were always made from the point of view of his larger view of human evolution. As a result, his general thinking was a little more sophisticated, while his specific treatment of European Neanderthal problems is much more sketchy than the above recounted views of Hrdlička.

In general, Weidenreich maintained that no more than one species of man existed at any one time during the Pleistocene (1943b:253). While he recognized that long-standing differences in the selective factors prevalent in different geographical areas would result in local differentiations yet he believed that interpopulation contact involving inevitable genetic exchange had always been sufficient to maintain specific unity within the genus Homo. This view receives considerable confirmation from the Lower Palaeolithic archaeological record which shows the broad spread of similar culture traits over wide areas of the Old World (Oakley 1950; Braidwood 1957). Where culture traits have spread, genes must have spread also.

Yet despite Weidenreich's clear reasoning concerning prehistoric population dynamics, one recent work presents a diagram of "the Polyphyletic or Candelabra school, modified

(and exaggerated)" purporting to represent Weidenreich's views of human evolution (W. W. Howells 1959:236). In this diagram, vertical lines are used to represent evolutionary continuity in four areas of the world, but the horizontal and diagonal lines of Weidenreich's own original diagram indicating genetic interchange between adjacent populations have been eliminated (Weidenreich 1947a:210). After decreeing that Weidenreich's areal populations must follow rigid separate grooves, Howells expresses incredulity that these four lines should converge to produce "the same kind of man everywhere" (W. W. Howells 1959:235; see also similar sentiments expressed by Vallois 1959:154). The scheme is then rejected as being too rigid.

This, however, has not done justice to Weidenreich's intent. To take a specific instance, Weidenreich regarded the Pekin group, with which he was most familiar, as a direct ancestor to Homo sapiens with a closer relationship "to certain Mongolian groups—than to any other races. . . . This statement does not mean that modern Mongols derived exclusively from Sinanthropus or that Sinanthropus did not give origin to other races" (Weidenreich 1943b:253, italics added). Certainly the inhabitants of a given area have a larger proportion of genes derived from the previous inhabitants of that same area than of those from any other area, but there is always going to be a certain amount of genetic interchange with adjacent populations as Weidenreich has indicated, and he has regarded this interchange as sufficient to have maintained the unity of the human species at any given time level during the Pleistocene. To picture his scheme of evolution as consisting of rigid separate grooves is not to exaggerate it; it is to misrepresent it.

The views of Weidenreich, while expressed in the terms of a morphologist and human palaeontologist, correspond quite closely to those expressed by a population geneticist (Dobzhansky 1951:1067) which should not be surprising since in fact both types of scholar are concerned with the same problem—human evolution. While they approach it from different directions, they can be expected to agree with each other as they converge.

While Weidenreich, being less familiar

with the European stratigraphic and skeletal records than Hrdlička, accepted the view of the supposed stratigraphic break between the Neanderthal and *spaiens* inhabitants of Europe which the proponents of hominid catastrophism have advanced, yet he notes that this still does not deny the possibility that evolution from a Neanderthal population to a *sapiens* one did not occur in another part of the world (1943a:47). Recognizing this as a possibility, he was careful to note in relation to Neanderthal man in Europe that "in no case, however, can the capability of his advancing into *Homo sapiens* be denied" (Weidenreich 1943a:48; cf. Le Gros Clark 1955a:45).

Weidenreich clearly accepted Hrdlička's Neanderthal Phase of Man (Weidenreich 1928:59; 1943a:40) noting in effect that it is much more reasonable for human palaeontologists to explain evolution in terms of the fossils already on their desks rather than to engage in the perpetual pursuit of phantom populations of supposedly sapient form (Weidenreich 1949:153). In one of the last things he wrote, Weidenreich, like Hrdlička (1930:348) asks the question, "If Neanderthal Man, for example, was not an ancestor of modern man, who was this ancestor?" (Weidenreich 1949:156).

With such substantial views and challenging questions offered by two of the major figures in American physical anthropology in the twentieth century, it is legitimate to wonder why they have received no serious consideration, why the views find no supporters, and why the questions remain unanswered. Certainly it cannot be due exclusively to the demonstrable discrepancies in some of the other issues supported by Hrdlička and Weidenreich, for one can cite the example of Sir Arthur Keith whose conviction of *sapiens* antiquity sails on without him (Stewart 1951:98) despite the fact that the major issues for which he stood on race, eugenics, and Piltdown have had to be abandoned.

It would seem that at least part of the failure of the ideas of Hrdlička and Weidenreich to have their deserved impact can be assigned to the positions occupied by both men. Weidenreich, following his introductions to a similar viewpoint by Schwalbe, taught for one third of a century as an

anatomist and physiologist, but the final phase of his career, where he was specifically dealing with fossil man and human evolution and where his evolutionary thinking reached its published expression, was spent in connection with the museum world. Hrdlička's entire career was spent in a museum, and however much a museum environment may encourage research, it does not guarantee the general recognition of the knowledge thus gained.

Meanwhile, Hooton was attempting to build American physical anthropology in the image of Sir Arthur Keith, and the success which he had can be seen in the almost unanimous acceptance of Keith's general evolutionary views in spite of the demise of Galley Hill and Piltdown and in spite of the fact that Keith himself abandoned them at the end of his life. Weidenreich and Hrdlička had no students, and, as a result, their thinking is unrepresented in the current generation of anthropologists. It is an interesting commentary on the strength of academic tradition to note that these two men were among the few physical anthropologists of their generation not specifically trained in the concepts of hominid catastrophism—one having been specifically trained to view the hominid fossil record from an evolutionary viewpoint, and the other having acquired his anthropological training largely by himself and independent of any established scholar or school of thought.

No discussion of Neanderthal interpretations would be complete without some consideration of Hans Weinert, the only living anthropologist who has actively maintained that the known Neanderthals represent a previous stage in human evolution. Weinert has represented this point of view since the 1920's but has, if anything, drawn even less notice in the French- and especially the English-speaking worlds than has either Hrdlička or Weidenreich. Part of the tendency to overlook his work may be due to the language barrier, although his views have been translated into French (1944a). While he wrote the section on fossil man in the widely read compendium *Anthropology Today* (1953), it remains in German and one fears that this only serves as an exercise for graduate students boning up for their language exams.

The disruptions suffered by German anthropology as a result of two world wars and the stifling influence of the Nazi regime have meant that few German anthropologists have achieved much recognition since the 1920's. Writers on fossil man such as Breitinger, Gieseler, and Heberer accept the predominant views of the significance of the Neanderthals advocated by French (and derived English and American) anthropology (Heberer 1955b). In this area, Weinert is the sole perpetuator of German evolutionary views dating from prior to the First World War, and some of the failure of his position to receive recognition may be traceable to the general eclipse of German anthropology.

The other possible reason for his failure to attract serious consideration is his insistence, almost amounting to an obsession, that the human ancestor was a chimpanzee (1944b:204–5, 208–11, 228–29, 243–44, 263; 1953:102, 104). This, however, should have been put in its proper perspective by his clear recognition that both men and chimpanzees have been pursuing long independent courses of evolution since the Tertiary (Weinert 1951:28, 54–55). Perhaps his acceptance of Piltdown (1944b:223), despite the suspicion of German anatomists from Schwalbe (1913:602) to Weidenreich (1936:117–19), can be traced to this early confusion. In any case, if one reads Australopithecine or even prehominid for chimpanzee wherever it occurs in his earlier writings, then his reasoning makes quite good sense.

If the Pithecanthropus-Sinanthropus skulls can be taken as morphologically intermediate between the immediate prehominids and modern man and if they do represent a stage in the prehistoric development of the genus *Homo* (denied by Boule 1913:263; 1921:109; 1923:109, 1937:20; Vallois 1946:370; and implicitly denied by Boule and Vallois 1957:145, 191, 257), then the rest of Weinert's arguments must be given serious attention.

At the outset, he noted the frequent lack of a clear correspondence between the record of archaeology and the geological time scale and the untrustworthiness of absolute time designations. Thus his position is less dependent upon the accuracy of premature time estimates than is the position of those who prefer a catastrophic to an evolutionary explanation for the hominid fossil record. His major arguments run as follows:

1. Neanderthal morphological characteristics fit nicely in between those of Pithecanthropus and those of modern man, and it would be difficult on morphological grounds alone to deny the existence of a Neanderthal stage in the line which developed into modern man (1944b:245).

2. "Everywhere we meet Middle Palaeolithic forms of men, only the Neanderthaler and nothing else is to be found" (1944b:248). If in fact the Neanderthals became extinct without issue, this would mean that "up to now we have always found in the Middle Palaeolithic only the remains of extinct side lines but never individuals of our own ancestral line." (1944b:244; also 1947:105).

3. The frequency of Neanderthaloid features visible in Upper Palaeolithic skeletal remains, particularly among those of the earliest known Upper Palaeolithic, is particularly marked in comparison with their evident descendants, the later Neolithic and modern peoples. Especially notable in this respect are the finds at Brünn, Brüx (noted in this same context by Schwalbe 1960b), Chwalynsk, Combe Capelle, Lautsch, Mount Carmel (actually a late Mousterian population), Podbaba, Podkumok, and Prédmost (Weinert 1944b:243–61; 1947:103–4, 136–38; 1951:177–91).

Not since before the last world war has any other established authority specifically recognized the morphological intermediacy of the earliest Upper Palaeolithic populations between the earlier Mousterian and more recent peoples (Coon 1939:37), although a number of authors have apparently been aware of the possible implications since they have taken pains to explain that, in these cases, there is nothing really reminiscent of Neanderthal morphology or that for reasons of dating this could not be linked in an evolutionary series with the Neanderthals (Vallois 1959:93, 135–37). On the other hand, the recognition of this morphological intermediacy has led a number of authors to seek some sort of explanation, and, being unwilling to concede that "pure" *Homo sapiens* did not exist in remote antiquity, they have suggested varying degrees of hybridization between a "classic" Neanderthal and one or another sort of "modern" form of man (Coon 1939:38–44, 51; Montagu 1940:521; Hooton 1946:337–38; Thoma 1957–58; W. W. Howells 1959:228). This, however, becomes exceedingly vague when the "modern" element in the mixture is described as "primitive sapiens" (W. W. Howells 1944:202–3; Thoma 1958:43), which in turn is considered as differing irrevocably from Neanderthal form by nuances in the degree of brow ridge division, of canine fossa, and relative chin development. Since the functional significance of these features is not considered, it is not at all clear why so much importance should be attached to them—particularly when it is realized that the range of variation amongst modern peoples greatly exceeds the difference between for instance Skhūl V and La Ferrassie I (cf. brow ridges in Australian versus Chinese, canine fossa in Negro versus Eskimo, chin in Tasmanian versus European).

There is no doubt that the available evidence is insufficient to constitute proof in the sense of "highly significant" statistical probability for any given hypothesis as was realized by Hrdlička (1930:345), although this should not be taken to indicate, as Vallois does (1945:113 ff.), that a catastrophist hypothesis is therefore more likely than an evolutionary one. Before a defense of the evolutionary point of view is undertaken, it should be briefly mentioned that two schools of hominid catastrophism exist at the present. The first is represented solely by Vallois who still maintains the position established by Boule that, if there is any relation between Neanderthal and modern forms of man, it was due to common ancestry at a time so remote that there is no fossil evidence for it. This view, entitled "Présapiens" by Vallois (1959:97 ff., 144–56), might be called the position of extreme (or "classic") catastrophism, in opposition to the modified (or "progressive") catastrophism of Sergi, Heberer, F. C. Howell, Breitinger, Le Gros Clark, and others (entitled the "Préneanderthal" theory by Vallois (1959:139–44). This latter view has relied heavily on the third interglacial status of the Skhūl remains as an indication that a population existed prior to the European Neanderthals of the early Würm whose morphological features were

closer to those of modern man. The removal of Skhūl from the third interglacial (Higgs 1961a and b) and the discovery of early Würm Neanderthals of "classic" form in the Middle East (Solecki 1955, 1960, 1961; Stewart 1959, 1962) indicate that the sequence and timing of hominid developments in southwest Asia was not significantly different from the picture derived from the European record. This leaves primarily Saccopastore as support for the views of modified hominid catastrophism, and an appreciation of the expression of sexual differences in the Neanderthals (Weinert 1947:96–98) and the great but generally ignored range of variation of the "classic" Neanderthals themselves (Brace 1963c:731) should remove the arguments built on this basis.

Recently F. C. Howell has stated in reference to the possibility of a Neanderthal phase in human evolution that, "unfortunately, this point of view has still to be meaningfully stated in terms of modern evolutionary theory" (1957:331), although he regards such a concept as "no longer useful since there was marked variability from one such group to another" (Howell 1957:343). This, of course, implies that Hrdlička's definition of Neanderthal was conceived in terms of physical characteristics which, in fact, it was not. Since I believe that some concept of Neanderthal Phase *can* prove useful, it should be worthwhile to restate it—I hope meaningfully—and see whether the "marked variability" correctly noted by Howell is indeed a fatal flaw.

While quantities of writing exist on the subject of the Neanderthals, almost no concise definition is offered. Hrdlička's definition, however, is not only concise, it is the only one offered in conjunction with clear evolutionary principles. It is worth quoting it here.

The only workable definition of Neanderthal man and period seems, for the time being, to be, the man and period of the Mousterian culture. An approach to a somatological definition would be feasible but might for the present be rather prejudicial. [Hrdlička 1930:328, differing trivially from Hrdlička 1927:251; Hrdlička 1929:595; italics Hrdlička's.]

Contrary to what one might have expected, Hrdlička's definition, then, was primarily a cultural definition. If culture is "the principal adaptive mechanism employed by man in his so far successful bid for survival," (Brace 1962b:343), then it makes good sense to view the major stages of human evolution in terms of major changes which culture has undergone. Since major cultural changes have in each case altered the selective pressure operating on the human physique, then there is good reason to expect a correlation between the cultural and the physical changes in the human fossil record, and we should be able to fill in the somatological part of the definition left blank by Hrdlička.

Necessarily the sequence of stages so discovered will depend upon the completeness of the information which we possess, and inevitably our information is sketchy for the earlier part. Here, again, culture shows an advantage over skeletal material alone as a guide since the archaeological record, whatever its defects, is far more complete than the record of hominid fossils. Fortunately there are just enough of the latter to make, tentatively, some of the correlations necessary in the construction of such a scheme.

Utilizing the cultural and skeletal evidence available, four stages in human evolution can usefully be postulated which simply constitute a redefinition, with the addition of an Australopithecine stage, of the scheme offered by Schwalbe (1906a:8) and defended by Weinert (1932; 1951:57–59; 1955:304) and Weidenreich (1904:381; 1946:29)—realizing of course that future increases in information will show that these are really arbitrary points chosen in what is actually a continuum. The four stages are presented diagramatically in Figure 9, with an indication of the cultural-biological interactions designated by the arrows. Since this paper is primarily concerned with the Neanderthal problem and since these designated relationships have been discussed elsewhere (Brace 1962a and b), it need only be added that the biological consequences of the cultural changes indicated in stages 1 and 2 probably were delayed in much the same way that the general facial reduction of stage 4 is the consequence of the cultural elaboration of stage 3.

Specifically, reliance on tools for defense, characterizing the difference between the Prehumans and the Australopithecine stage, meant that projecting canines were no longer necessary equipment and hence free to vary. With the cumulative effect of random mutation inevitably resulting in the reduction of those structures whose adaptive significance has been reduced or suspended (Brace 1963), the canines of the first tool users could be expected to reduce after a sufficient period of reliance on tools (and hence culture in the larger sense) as the primary means for defence. The same kind of delay can be expected before the reduction of the

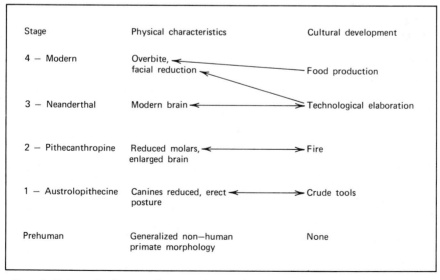

Stage	Physical characteristics	Cultural development
4 — Modern	Overbite, facial reduction	Food production
3 — Neanderthal	Modern brain	Technological elaboration
2 — Pithecanthropine	Reduced molars, enlarged brain	Fire
1 — Austrolopithecine	Canines reduced, erect posture	Crude tools
Prehuman	Generalized non–human primate morphology	None

Figure 9. The postulated stages in human evolution with the related selective pressures indicated by the associated cultural developments.

molars followed the regular utilization of fire (and perhaps the addition of significant and regular quantities of protein to the diet as a result of the development of effective hunting techniques. Meat does not have to be chewed as much as other foods since protein digestion is primarily in the stomach and there is less requirement to be mixed with salivary enzymes).

Among the bearers of the Mousterian cultural traditions assigned to stage 3, "the post-cranial skeleton is basically modern human in over-all morphology" (F. C. Howell 1957:335). The brain has reached its modern size and, despite the attempts of Boule to characterize its supposed "structural inferiority" (Boule and Vallois 1957:246; see also Boule 1912:182–206; surviving in Patte 1955:500), there are no indications that the brain was functionally different from that of modern man (Weidenreich 1947b; Montagu

1960:196). Clear differences can be seen only in the metric and morphologic characters relating to the face (Morant 1927:333–40, 374; F. C. Howell 1951:387; Brace 1962b:347–49). With much of the organization of the human face concerned with the supporting role it plays in regard to the dentition, any change in selective factors affecting the teeth will ultimately have effects on total facial morphology. According to published figures, there is no evident difference between the gross tooth dimensions and little between the tooth forms of the Pithecanthropine and the Neanderthal stages shown in Figure 9. See Figure 10. (Pithecanthropine and Neanderthal tooth measurements compiled from Weinert 1925:32, 37, 39; Weidenreich 1937:17, 24, 29, 38, 81, 82; Dahlberg 1960:245; and Brace unpublished.) It is evident that the greatest difference in the teeth of the Middle Palaeolithic and those of

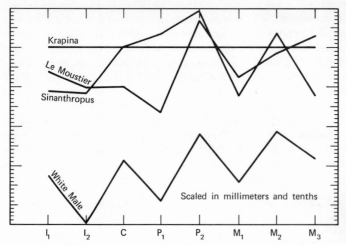

Figure 10. Middle Pleistocene, Neanderthal, and modern tooth-crown size (M.D. + B.L.), with Krapina taken as the line of reference. See Table 1 for figures.

Table 1
Crown Size Measurements (M.D. + B.L.) [a]

	Krapina	LeMoustier	Sinanthropus	White ♂
I^1	19.13	18.5	18.02	15.88
I^2	17.53	16.5	16.35	13.10
C	19.21	18.2	19.25	16.31
PM^1	19.95	18.3	20.30	16.05
PM^2	18.34	19.0	19.28	16.11
M^1	25.26	24.5	23.73	21.86
M^2	23.45	23.3	23.63	21.32
M^3	22.53	22.8	21.31	19.72

aThese are the measurements from which Fig. 10 was constructed. Adapted from Brace, unpublished; Weinert, 1925; Dahlberg, 1960; and Weidenreich, 1937, respectively.

modern man occurs in the anterior part of the dental arch.

In the absence of any other reliable evidence pertaining to the facial morphology of the Pithecanthropine stage (where no complete face is preserved), it can be tentatively assumed that this was not significantly different from that of the Neanderthal stage except in the area of the brow ridge where the face is hafted onto the skull. Selective factors pertaining to the dentition, then, can be presumed to have changed little between the Pithecanthropine and the beginning of the Neanderthal stages, but following the Neanderthals, the reduction amounting to the transformation into the modern face, is clear evidence of such a change (see comments by Keith 1925b:318–19). It has been suggested elsewhere that technological elaboration starting in the Mousterian and proceeding on through the Upper Palaeolithic introduced specialized tools to perform the variety of tasks formerly handled by the teeth—especially the front teeth (Brace 1962b:347–49). The adaptive significance of a large dentition having been thus reduced, it is free to vary, and the probable effect of accumulating random mutations is reduction (Brace 1963).

With such an explanation for the significance of the difference between Pithecanthropine, Neanderthal, and modern form, I suggest that a morphological corollary be added to Hrdlička's cultural definition of Neanderthal as a stage or Phase of human evolution.

Neanderthal man is the man of the Mousterian culture prior to the reduction in form and dimension of the Middle Pleistocene face.

This view of human evolution in general and of the problems represented by the interpretation of Neanderthals in particular is offered in place of the views of hominid catastrophism generally held, which apparently had their theoretical bases in the early nineteenth-century doctrines of Georges Cuvier and which have dominated anthropological thinking for the past fifty years following their application to the extensive French Neanderthal material by the palaeontologist Marcellin Boule. Such views reach their extreme with Weckler's curious formulation which pictured hypothetical populations tramping to and fro over vast distances "for reasons not as yet ascertained" (Weckler 1954:1013), but perhaps the clearest expression of this view is in the writings of the French prehistorian Teilhard de Chardin who believed that the phases of human development "displace each other rather than pass into each other directly, . . . neither Peking Man, . . . nor Neanderthal Man have any direct offspring left today in the living world: they have been swept away by *Homo Sapiens*" (Teilhard de Chardin 1943:25–26; also quoted by Weidenreich 1947a:197).

To eliminate the headache concerning the origin of modern man by claiming that he sprang full blown from the mind of a troubled palaeontologist into an early Pleistocene stratum is to propose an explanation which borders on mythology. Instead, it is urged that the orientation based on standard evolutionary theory as developed by Schwalbe, Hrdlička, Weidenreich, and Weinert be re-examined and a systematic attempt be made to view the known hominid fossil record in these terms as modified by more recent theoretical advances in the thinking of genetics and ecology.

Finally, in keeping with the promise inherent in the title of this paper, I suggest that it was the fate of the Neanderthal to give rise to modern man, and, as has frequently happened to members of the older generation in this changing world, to have been perceived in caricature, rejected, and disavowed by their own offspring, *Homo sapiens*.

ABSTRACT

The current view that the "Classic" Neanderthals were an aberrant, specialized, or otherwise peculiar side branch which eventually became extinct without descendants has its origins in anti-evolutionary interpretations placed upon the available hominid fossils by the French palaeontologist Marcellin Boule in the early part of the current century. The theoretical bases of Boule's thinking stem from the early nineteenth century position of Georges Cuvier who attempted to explain sequence in the fossil record by a series of catastrophes with their attendant extinctions and subsequent invasions.

Without specifically labelling it as such, Boule applied the concept of catastrophism to explain the sequence of forms in the hominid fossil record, assuming that none of the fossil men discovered which differed from modern man could be regarded as ancestral to modern man. The proof of this assumption lay in the claim that modern forms of man already existed as exemplified by the Grimaldi skeletons. Although these skeletons were shown to be more recent than the Neanderthals, the conviction remained that ancient moderns would be found, and, guided by the ideals of what is here labelled hominid catastrophism, a disproportionate amount of the efforts of subsequent prehistorians has been devoted to their discovery. In fact, far more time has been expended in the attempt to deny the evidence for human evolution than in trying to show how man could have evolved.

Attempts to interpret the available hominid fossils from a frankly evolutionary point of view have been offered by Schwalbe, Weinert, Weidenreich, and Hrdlička, but because of the eclipse of German anthropology as a result of the First World War and subsequent political history, both Schwalbe's and Weinert's views have been ignored. Hrdlička and Weidenreich were museum men and failed to have the impact on anthropological thinking which was enjoyed by the views of Boule via Keith, Hooton, Vallois, and their numerous students. As a result, the Neanderthals are denied any role in the ancestry of modern man despite the fact that all of the candidates for ancient moderns are open to serious doubts—either of date or morphology or both.

Recognizing the Australopithecines as the earliest ancestors of modern man, this paper suggests that the initial three stage scheme of Gustav Schwalbe be expanded to four stages with the Australopithecines as the first stage, the Pithecanthropines as the second, the Neanderthals as the third, and finally modern man as the result. Changes in brain size are related to the supposed selective advantage conferred by cerebral increase, while progressive reduction of the dentition and hence the entire facial skeleton is related to the suspension of the advantage in possessing a large face which occurred as a result of increasingly effective cultural adaptation —particularly refinements in cutting tools in the later part of human cultural and physical evolution.

REFERENCES CITED

Abbie, A. A. 1952. "A new approach to the problem of human evolution." *Transactions of the Royal Society of South Australia* 75:70–78.

Absolon, K. 1957. Recherches d'ethnographie préhistorique dans les stations diluviales de Moravie. *Mélanges Pittard*. Brive (Corrèze): Chastrusse et Cie. pp. 5–12.

Ackerknecht, Erwin H. 1953. *Rudolph Virchow: Doctor, Statesman, Anthropologist*. Madison: University of Wisconsin Press.

Arambourg, Camille. 1957. Les Pithecanthropiens. *Mélanges Pittard*. Brive (Corrèze): Chastrusse et Cie. pp. 33–41.

———. 1958. Les stades évolutifs de l'humanité. *The Leech* (Raymond A. Dart Commemorative Number) 28:106–111. [PVT*]

Arambourg, C., M. Boule, H. Vallois, and R. Verneau. 1964. Les grottes paléolithiques des Beni-Ségoual, Algérie. *Archives de l'Institut. de Paleontologie humaine*. Mem. 13.

Asmus, Gisela. 1943. Die menschlichen Skelettfunde Mährens als Mittler zwischen Alt- und Jungpaläolithikum. *Zeitschrift der Mährischen Landesmuseums*. N.F. 3:46–66. [KJN*]

———. 1951. Zur Stellung des Neandertalers in der Menschheitsgeschichte. *Eiszeitalter und Gegenwart* 1:176–185. [KJN*]

———. 1952. Zur Frage der jungpaläolithischen Brünn-Rasse. *Homo* 132–134. [KJN*]

Bartholomew, G. A., and Birdsell, J. B. 1953. Ecology and the proto-hominids. *American Anthropologist* 55:481–98.

Bates, Marston. 1961. *Man in nature*. Englewood Cliffs, N.J.: Prentice-Hall, Inc.

Bather, F. A. 1925. The word "Australopithecus" and others. *Nature* 115:947.

Berckhemer, F. 1937. Bemerkungen zu H. Weinert's Abhandlung "Der Urmenschen-Schädel von Steinheim." *Verhandlungen der Gesellschaft für Physische Anthropologie* 8:49–58. [KJN*]

Bordes, Francois. 1950. L'évolution buissonnante des industries en Europe occidentale. Considérations théoriques sur la Paléolithique ancien et moyen. *L'Anthropologie* 54:393–420.

———. 1958. "Le passage du Paléolithique moyen au Paléolithique superiéur," in *Hundert Jahre Neanderthaler* (editor G. H. R. von Koenigswald), pp. 175–81.

———. 1959. Le contexte archéologique des hommes du Moustier et de Spy. *L'Anthropologie* 63, Numbers 1–2.

———. 1961a. Personal communication, June 9.

———. 1961b. Mousterian cultures in France. *Science* 134:803–10.

Boule, M. 1904. La paléontologie au muséum et

*The references followed by initials indicate the sources used in the comments that followed the original article.

l'oeuvre de M. Albert Gaudry. *Revue Scientifique* 22:676–84.

―――. 1908a. L'homme fossile de La Chapelle-aux-Saints (Corrèze). *Comptes Rendus Academie des Sciences, Paris*, pp. 1349–52.

―――. 1908b. L'homme fossile de La Chapelle-aux-Saints. *L'Anthropologie* 19:519–25.

―――. 1908c. Albert Gaudry. Notice necrologique. *L'Anthropologie* 19:604–11.

―――. 1909a. L'homme fossile de La Chapelle-aux- Saints. *L'Anthropologie* 20:257.

―――. 1909b. Le squelette du tronc et des membres de l'homme fossile de La Chapelle-aux-Saints. *Comptes Rendus Academie des Sciences, Paris*, pp. 1554–56.

―――. 1909c. Sur la capacité cranienne des hommes fossiles du type dit de Néanderthal. *Comptes Rendus Academie des Sciences, Paris*, pp. 1352–55.

―――. 1911–13. L'homme fossile de La Chapelle-aux-Saints. *Extrait Annales de Paléontologie* (1911) VI:111–72 (1–64); (1912) VII:21–192 (65–208); (1913) VIII:1–70 (209–78).

―――. 1921. *Les hommes fossiles: Éléments de paléontologie humaine.* Paris: Masson et Cie.

―――. 1923. 2d edition. *Les hommes fossiles: Éléments de paléontologie humaine.* Paris: Masson et Cie.

―――. 1937. Le Sinanthrope. *L'Anthropologie* 47, Numbers 1–2.

Boule, M., and H. V. Vallois. 1957. *Fossil men.* Translated by Michael Bullock. New York: Dryden Press.

Brace, C. L. 1962a. Comments on: Food transport and the origin of hominid bipedalism. *American Anthropologist* 64:606–7 (Part 1).

―――. 1962b. "Cultural factors in the evolution of the human dentition," in *Culture and the evolution of men* (editor M. F. A. Montagu), pp. 343–54. New York: Oxford University Press (Galaxy Books).

―――. 1962c. Refocussing on the Neanderthal problem. *American Anthropologist* 64:729–41.

―――. 1963. Structural reduction in evolution. *The American Naturalist* 97:39–49.

Braidwood, Robert J. 1957. 3d edition. *Prehistoric men.* Chicago: Chicago Natural History Museum.

Breitinger, Emil. 1952. Zur Morphologie und systematischen Stellung des Schädelfragmentes von Swanscombe. *Homo* 3:131–33.

―――. 1955. Das Schädelfragment von Swanscombe und das "Praesapiens-problem." *Mitteilungen der Anthropologischen Gesellschaft in Wien* 44–45:1145.

Breuil, Henri. 1906. Les gisements présolutréens du type d'Aurignac. *Congrès International d'Anthropogie et d'Archéologie Préhistorique* 13, No. 1:323–333.   [KJN*]

―――. 1907. La question aurignacienne. *Revue préhistorique* 2:158–162   [KJN*]

―――. 1909. L'Aurignacien présolutreen. *Revue préhistorique* 4:229–265.   [KJN*]

―――. 1912. Les subdivisions du paléolithique supérieur et leur signification. *Congrès International d'Anthropologie et d'Archeologie Préhistorique* 14:165–233.   [KJN*]

―――. 1958. "Soixante ans de découvertes d'hommes primitifs et leur influence sur les idées," in *Hundert Jabre Neanderthaler* (editor G. H. R. von Keonigswald), pp. 1–6. Utrecht, Netherlands: Kemink en Zoon N.V.

Broca, Paul. 1868. Sur les crânes et ossements des Eyzies. *Bulletin Societé d'Anthropologie de Paris*, 3:350–92 (2d series).

Broom, Robert. 1939. The dentition of the Transvaal Pleistocene anthropoids, *Plesianthropus* and *Paranthropus*. *Annals of the Transvaal Museum* 19:303–14.

―――. 1947. Discovery of a new skull of the South African ape-man, *Plesianthropus*. *Nature* 159:672.

―――. 1950. The genera and species of the South African fossil ape-man *American Journal of Physical Anthropology* 8:1–3 (new series).

Broom, Robert and C. W. H. Schepers. 1946. The South African fossil ape-man: The Australopithecinae. *Transvaal Museum Memoirs* 2:1–272. Pretoria.

Broom, Robert and J. T. Robinson. 1947a. Further remains of the Sterkfontein ape-man, *Plesianthropus*. *Nature* 160:430–31.

―――. 1947b. Two features of the Plesianthropus skull. *Nature* 159:809–10.

―――. 1949a. A new mandible of the ape-man *Plesianthropus Transvaalensis*. *American Journal of Physical Anthropology* 7:123–27 (new series).

―――. 1949b. A new type of fossil man. *Nature* 164:322–23.

―――. 1950a. Man contemporaneous with the Swartkrans ape-man. *American Journal of Physical Anthropology* 8:151–55 (new series).

―――. 1950b. Note on the skull of the Swartkrans ape-man *Paranthropus crassidens*. *American Journal of Physical Anthropology* 8:295–300 (new series).

―――. 1950c. Notes on the pelves of the fossil ape-men. *American Journal of Physical Anthropology* 8:489–94 (new series).

―――. 1952. Swartkrans ape-man *Paranthropus crassidens*. *Transvaal Museum Memoirs*, Number 6. Pretoria.

Broom, Robert, J. T. Robinson, and G. W. H. Schepers. 1950. Sterkfontein ape-man *Plesianthropus*. *Transvaal Museum Memoirs*, Number 4. Pretoria.

Brothwell, D. R. 1960. Upper Pleistocene human skull from Niah Caves. *Sarawak Museum Journal* 9:323–49.   [DRB*]

―――. 1961. The people of Mount Carmel. A

reconsideration of their position in human evolution. *Proceedings of the Prehistoric Society* 27:155–9. [DRB*]

———. 1963a. When and where did man become wise? *Discovery* 24:10–14. [DRB*]

———. 1963b. Evidence of early population change in Central and Southern Africa: doubts and problems. *Man* 63:101–4. [DRB*]

du Brul, E. Lloyd and Charles A. Reed. 1960. Skeletal evidence of speech? *American Journal of Physical Anthropology* 18:153–56 (new series).

Büdel, Julius. 1951. Die Klimazonen des Eiszeitalters. *Eiszeitalter und Gegenwart* 1:16–26. [KJN*]

Burkitt, M. C. 1921. *Prehistory*. Cambridge (England); Cambridge University Press.

Busk, George. 1861. On the crania of the most ancient races of man, by Professor H. Schaaffhausen, of Bonn. *The Natural History Review, a Quarterly Journal of Biological Science* 1:155–76.

Butler, Samuel. 1878. 2d edition. *Life and habit.* London: Trübner and Co., Ludgate Hill.

Capitan, Dr. L. 1922. *La Préhistoire.* Paris: Payot et Cie.

Cartailhac, Émile. 1912. Archéologie. *Les Grottes de Grimaldi (Baoussé-Roussé)*, Tome II, Fascicule II. Monaco.

Chamberlain, T. C. 1901. "On Lord Kelvin's address on the age of the Earth as an abode fitted for life." *Annual report of the Board of Regents of the Smithsonian Institution for the year ending June 30, 1899,* pp. 233–46. Washington.

Chang, Kwang-Chih. 1962. New Evidence on Fossil Man in China. *Science* 136: 749–60.

Clark, J. Desmond. 1959. *The prehistory of Southern Africa.* Harmondsworth, England: Penguin Books, Ltd.

Clark, W. E. Le Gros. 1955a. *The fossil evidence for human evolution: An introduction to the study of paleoanthropology.* Chicago: University of Chicago Press.

———. 1955b. The os innominatum of the recent Ponginae with special reference to that of the Australopithecinae. *American Journal of Physical Anthropology* 13:19–27 (new series).

———. 1959. Reason and fallacy in the study of fossil man, in *Readings in Anthropology* (editor Morton H. Fried), I, 27–45. (Reprinted from *The Advancement of Science,* Number 43 (1954), pp. 280–92).

Cole, Sonia. 1954. *The prehistory of East Africa.* Harmondsworth, England: Penguin Books, Ltd.

Comas, Juan. 1961. Scientific racism again? *Current Anthropology* 2:303–40.

Coon, Carleton Stevens. 1939. *The races of Europe.* New York: Macmillan Co.

———. 1962. *The origin of races.* New York: Alfred A. Knopf. [CSC, MFF, WWH*]

Coon, Carleton Stevens, S. M. Garn, and J. B.

Birdsell. 1950. *Races.* Springfield, Ill: Chas. C. Thomas. [JEW*]

Curtis, C. H., D. E. Savage, and J. F. Evernden. 1961. Critical points in the Cenozoic. *Annals of the New York Academy of Sciences* 91:342–51.

Cuvier, Georges. 1834. Discours sur les révolutions de la surface du globe, in *Récherches sur les ossmens fossiles.* 5th edition, 1:93–417.

Dahlberg, Albert A. 1960. The dentition of the first agriculturists (Jarmo, Iraq). *American Journal of Physical Anthropology* 18:243–56.

Dambski, Jerzy. 1957. Wspolczesne poglady na jadnosc rodzaju udzkiego (Contemporary views on the unity of the human species). *Przeglad antropologiczny* 23:160–81. (English summary.)

Dart, Raymond A. 1925. *Australopithecus: africanus:* The man-ape of South Africa. *Nature* 115:195–99.

———. 1948a. The adolescent mandible of *Australopithecus prometheus. American Journal of Physical Anthropology* 6:391–409 (new series).

———. 1948b. An Australopithecus from the Central Transvaal. *South African Science* 1:200–1.

———. 1948c. The Makapansgat proto-human *Australopithecus prometheus. American Journal of Physical Anthropology* 6:259–81 (new series).

———. 1949a. The first pelvic bones of *Australopithecus prometheus:* preliminary note. *American Journal of Physical Anthropology* 7:255–57 (new series).

———. 1949b. The cranio-facial fragment of *Australopithecus prometheus. American Journal of Physical Anthropology* 7:301–32 (new series).

———. 1949b. The predatory implemental technique of *Australopithecus. American Journal of Physical Anthropology* 7:1–16 (new series).

Darwin, Charles. 1859. *On the origin of species by means of natural selection, or the preservation of favoured races in the struggle for life.* London: John Murray, Albemarle Street. (See reprint of 1st edition, New York: Philosophical Library, 1951).

Dehaut, Émile-Georges. 1945. "Les doctrines de Georges Cuvier dans leurs rapports avec le transformisme," in *Encyclopédie Biologique.* Paul Lechevalier (Ed.) pp. 1–33. Paris: Libraire pour les Sciences Naturelles.

Dobzhansky, T. 1951. Comment on the paper by T. D. Stewart. *Cold Spring Harbor Symposia on Quantitative Biology* 15:106–7.

———. 1962. *Mankind evolving.* New Haven, Conn.: Yale University Press.

Dokládal, Milan, and Josef Brožek. 1961. Physical anthropology in Czechoslovakia: Recent developments *Current Anthropology* 2:455–77.

Drennan, M. R. 1937. The Florisbad skull and brain cast. *Transactions of the Royal Society of South Africa* 25:103–114. [PVT*]

———. 1956. Note on the morphological status of

the Swanscombe and Fontéchevade skulls. *American Journal of Physical Anthropology* 14:73–83 (new series).

Dreyer, T. F. 1935. A human skull from Florisbad, Orange Free State. *Proceedings of the Royal Academy of Sciences, Amsterdam* 38:119–128. [PVT*]

Dubois, Eugene. 1894. *Pithecanthropus erectus, eine menschenähnliche Übergangsform aus Java* Batavia Landes Druckerei. Reprinted by G. E. Stechert, New York. (Pamphlet.)

Eiseley, Loren C. 1958. *Darwin's century: Evolution and the men who discovered it.* Garden City, N.Y.: Doubleday and Co.

Emiliani, C. 1955. Pleistocene temperatures. *Journal of Geology* 63:538–78.

———. 1956. Note on absolute chronology of human evolution. *Science* 123:924–26.

———. 1958. Ancient temperatures. *Scientific American* 198:54–66.

———. 1961. Cenozoic climatic changes as indicated by the stratigraphy and chronology of deep-sea cores of Globigerina-ooze facies. *Annals of the New York Academy of Sciences* 96:521–36.

Encyclopaedia Britannica World Atlas. 1960. Chicago: Encyclopaedia Britannica. Inc.

Evernden, J. F., G. H. Curtis, and R. Kistler. 1957. Potassium-argon dating of Pleistocene volcanics. *Quaternaria* 4:13–17.

Fraipont, Julien, and Max Lohest. 1887. La race humaine de Neanderthal ou de Canstadt en Belgique. *Archives de Biologie* 7:587–757.

Frenzel, Burkhard. 1959, 60. *Die Vegetations- und Landschaftszonen Nordeurasiens während der letzten Eiszeit und während der postglazialen Wärmezeit.* Mainz Akademie der Wissenschaften und der Literatur, Abhandlungen des Mathematische-naturwissenschaftlichen Klasse, Jahrgang 1959, No. 13 und Jahrgang 1960, No. 6:165–67. Wiesbaden, Germany: Franz Steiner Verlag. [KJN*]

Fuhlrott, J. C. 1857. Theilen des menschlichen skelettes im Neanderthal bei Hochdal. *Verhandlungen des naturhistorischen Vereines der preussischen Rheinlande und Westfalens* 14:50.

Garrod, D. A. E. 1958. The ancient shorelines of the Lebanon, and the dating of Mt. Carmel Man, in *Hundert Jahre Neanderthaler* (editor G. H. R. von Koenigswald), pp. 182–83. Utrecht, Netherlands: Kemink en Zoon, N.V.

———. and D. M. A. Bate. 1937. *The Stone Age of Mount Carmel Vol. I: Excavations at the Wady el-Mughara.* Oxford: Clarendon Press.

Gaudry, Albert. 1878 (reprinted 1895). *Les Enchainements du Monde Animal dans le Temps Géologiques: Mammifères Tertiaires.* Paris: Masson et Cie.

———. 1903. Contribution à l'histoire des hommes fossiles. *L'Anthropologie* 14:1–14.

Genovés T., S. 1960. *Prólogo, notas, recopilación, bibliografica y traducción de "Lugar que ocupa el hombre de Neandertal en la evolución humana" de F. Clark Howell.* Suplemento de Tlatoani, No. 2, 62, pp. [SGT*]

———. 1962. Sobre unos comentarios en el campo de la Antropologiá Física a un trabajo del arqueologo Ibarra Grasso. *Khana* 1, Nos. 36, 37:165–8. [SGT*]

Gieseler, W. 1959. 2d edition. Die Fossilgeschichte des Menschen, in *Die Evolution der Organisme* (editor G. Heberer), pp. 951–1109. Stuttgart. (1st edition, 1943. G. Fischer, Jena.)

Gillette, J. M. 1943. Ancestorless man: The anthropological dilemma. *Scientific Monthly* 57:533–45.

Golding, William. 1955. *The inheritors.* New York: Harcourt, Brace and World. [MFF*]

Goodman, Morris. 1961. The role of immunochemical differences in the phyletic development of human behavior. *Human Biology* 33:111–31. [SGT*]

Greenblatt, Milton, and Harry C. Solomon. 1958. Studies of lobotamy, in *The Brain and Human Behavior* (edited by Harry C. Solomon, Stanley Cobb, and Wilder Penfield), pp. 19–34. Baltimore: Williams and Wilkins Company.

Gregory, W. K. 1949. The bearing of the Australopithecinae upon the problem of man's place in nature. *American Journal of Physical Anthropology* 7:485–510 (new series).

Guenther, E. W. 1959. Zur Alters datierung der diluvialen Fundstelle von Krapina in Kroatien. *Bericht über die 6. Tagung der Deutschen Gesellschaft für Anthropologie.* Gottingen: pp. 202–9.

Haeckel, Ernst. 1897. *The evolution of man: A popular exposition of the principal points of human ontogeny and phylogeny.* New York. D. Appleton and Co.

———. 1899a. 4th edition. *The History of creation or the development of the earth and its inhabitants by the action of natural causes.* Translated and revised from the 8th German edition by E. Ray Lankester. London: Kegan Paul, Trench, Trübner and Co., Ltd.

———. 1899b. On our present knowledge of the origin of man. *Annual report of the Board of Regents of the Smithsonian Institution for the year ending June 30, 1898,* pp. 461–80. (Discourse delivered at the 4th International Congress of Zoologists at Cambridge, England, August 26, 1898.) (Translated from author's edition in German printed at Bonn, 1898.)

Hardin, Garrett. 1960a. The competitive exclusion principlè. *Science* 131:1292–98.

———. 1960b. Science is heresy. *Think* 26:23–26.

Hauser, O., and H. Klaatsch. 1909. Der neue Skelettfund Hausers aus dem Aurignacien. *Praehistorische Zeitschrift* 2:180–82.

Heberer, G. 1944. Das Neanderthal problem und die Herkunft der heutigen Menschheit. *Jenaische Zeitschrift für Medezin und Naturwissenschaft* 77:262–89.

——. 1949. Die unmittelbaren Vorfahren des *Homo sapiens. Universitas: Zeitschrift fur Wissenschaft, Kunst, und Literatur (Stuttgart)* 4:1465–77.

——. 1950. Das Präsapiens-Problem, in *Moderne Biologie, Festshrift zum 60. Geburtstag von Hans Nachtsheim* (editors H. Grüneberg and W. Ulrich), pp. 131–62. F. W. Berlin: Peters.

——. 1951. Der phylogenetische Ort des Menschen. *Studium Generale* 4:1–14.

——. 1955a. Die geographische Verbreitung der fossilen Hominiden (ausser Eusapiens) nach neuerer Gruppierung. *Die Naturwissenschaften* 42:85–90.

——. 1955b. Pierre Marcellin Boule, in *Forscher und Wissenschaftler im Heutigen Europe* (editors H. Schwerte and W. Spengler), pp. 288–95. Vol. 4 of *Gestalter unserer Zeit.* Hamburg: Gerhard Stalling Oldenburg.

——. 1956. Die Bedeutung des Fundes im Neanderthal vor 100 Jahren. *Die Naturwissenschaften* 43:409–14.

——. 1959a. The descent of man and the present fossil record. *Cold Spring Harbor Symposia on Quantitative Biology* 24:235–44.

——. 1959b. War die Hominisation ein adaptivselektiver oder ein orthogenetischer Prozess? *Naturwissenschafter Rundschau* 12:414–19.

Hibben, Frank C. 1958. *Prehistoric man in Europe.* Norman, Okla.; University of Oklahoma Press.

Higgs, E. S. 1961a. North Africa and Mount Carmel: Recent developments. Some Pleistocene fauna of the Mediterranean coastal areas. *Man* 61:138–39.

——. 1961b. Some Pleistocene faunas of the Mediterranean coastal areas. *Proceedings of the Prehistoric Society* 27: 144–54 (new series).

Hooton, Earnest Albert. 1931. *Up from the ape.* New York: Macmillan Co.

——. 1946. 2d edition, revised. *Up from the ape.* New York: Macmillan Co.

Howell, F. Clark. 1951. The place of Neanderthal in human evolution. *American Journal of Physical Anthropology* 9:379–416 (new series).

——. 1952. Pleistocene glacial ecology and the evolution of "Classic Neandertal" man. *Southwestern Journal of Anthropology* 8:377–410.

——. 1957. The evolutionary significance of variation and varieties of "Neanderthal" man. *Quarterly Review of Biology* 32:330–47.

——. 1958. Upper Pleistocene men of the Southwest Asian Mousterian, in *Hundert Jahre Neanderthaler* (editor G. H. R. von Koenigswald), pp. 185–98. Utrecht, Netherlands: Kemink en Zoon N.V.

——. 1959. Upper Pleistocene stratigraphy and early man in the Levant. *Proceedings of the American Philosophical Society* 103:1–65.

——. 1960. European and Northwest African Middle Pleistocene hominids. *Current Anthropology* 1:195–232.

——. 1961. Stratigraphie du Pleistocène Supérieur dans l'Asie du Sud-ouest: Age absolu de l'homme et de ses industries. *L'Anthropologie* 65:1–20.

——. 1962. Pottasium-argon dating at Olduvai Gorge. *Current Anthropology* 3:306–8.

Howells, W. W. 1942. Fossil man and the origin of races. *American Anthropologist* 44:182–93.

——. 1944. *Mankind so far.* Garden City, N.Y.: Doubleday and Co.

——. 1959. *Mankind in the making.* Garden City, N.Y.: Doubleday and Co.

Howells, William, editor. 1962. *Ideas on Human Evolution: Selected Essays 1949–1961.* Cambridge: Harvard University Press.

Hrdlička, Aleš. 1926. The peopling of the earth. *Proceedings of the American Philosophical Society* 65:150–56.

——. 1927. The Neanderthal phase of man. *Journal of the Royal Anthropological Institute.* 67:249–69.

——. 1929. The Neanderthal phase of man. *Annual Report of the Board of Regents of the Smithsonian Institution, for 1928,* pp. 593–621. Washington, D. C. (The Huxley Memorial Lecture for 1927. Reprinted by permission, with minor alterations by the author, from the *Journal of the Royal Anthropological Institute* 67:249–69).

——. 1930. *The skeletal remains of early man.* Smithsonian Miscellaneous Collections, Whole Volume 83. Washington, D. C.

Hulse, Frederick S. 1962. Race as an evolutionary episode. *American Anthropologist* 64:929–45.

——. 1963a. Objectives and methods. *American Anthropologist Memoir* 94:69–79.   [RDG*]

——. 1963b. Review of *The Origin of Races,* by C. S. Coon (New York: Alfred A. Knopf, 1962). *American Anthropologist.* 65:685–87.

Huxley, Thomas Henry. 1861. On the zoological relations of man with the lower animals. *The Natural History Review, a Quarterly Journal of Biological Science* 1:67–84.

Jacobshagen, E. 1957a. Der Schädelrest der Frau von Rhünda (Bezirk Kassel). *Anatomischer Anzeiger* 104:64–87.

——. 1957b. Zur Lösung des morphologischen Neandertaler-Problems. *Zeitschrift für Morphologie und Anthropologie* 48:254–67.

Jelinek, J., J. Pelišek, and K. Valoch. 1959. Der Fossile Mensch Brno II. *Anthropos* 9 (new series).   [KJN*]

Kälin, J. 1946. Zum Problem der menschlichen

Stammesgeschichte. *Experientia* 2:272–87.

Keith, A. 1915. *The antiquity of man*. London: Williams and Norgate.

———. 1925a. 2d edition. *The antiquity of man*. London. (Also, 1928: Philadelphia: J. B. Lippincott Co.)

———. 1925b. Concerning the rate of man's evolution. *Nature* 116:317–20.

———. 1925c. The Taungs skull. *Nature* 116:11.

———. 1925d. The Taungs skull. *Nature* 116:462–63.

———. 1931. *New discoveries relating to the antiquity of man*. New York: W. W. Norton and Co.

———. 1946, 1947. *Evolution and ethics*. New York: G. P. Putman's Sons.

———. 1949. *A new theory of human evolution*. New York: Philosophical Library.

Keith, A., and T. D. McCown. 1937. "Mount Carmel Man: His bearing on the ancestry of modern races," in *Early Man* (editor G. G. MacCurdy), pp. 41–52. London: J. B. Lippincott Co.

King, W. 1864. The reputed fossil man of Neanderthal. *Quarterly Journal of Science* 1:88–97.
[SGT*]

Klaatsch, Hermann. 1923. *The Evolution and Progress of Mankind*. Edited and enlarged by Adolf Heilborn (Translated by Joseph McCabe). London: T. Fisher Unwin Ltd.

Klaatsch, H., and O. Hauser. 1909. Homo Mousteriensis Hauseri. Ein altidiluvialer Skelettfund im Department Dordogne und seine Zugehörigkeit zum Neanderthaltypus. *Archiv für Anthropologie* 7:287–97 (Vol. 25 of the whole series).

———. 1910. Homo Aurignacensis Hauseri, ein palaolithischer Skelettfund aus dem unteren Aurignacien der Station Combe-Capelle bei Montferrand (Périgord). *Praehistorische Zeitschrift* 1:273–338.

Knight, Charles R. 1949. *Prehistoric man: The great adventurer*. New York: Appleton-Century-Crofts.

Koenigswald, G. H. R. von. 1958. "Der Solo-Mensch von Java: ein Tropischer Neanderthaler," in *Hundert Jabre Neanderthaler* (editor G. H. R. von Keonigswald), pp. 21–26. Utrecht, Netherlands: Kemink en Zoon, N.V.

Koenigswald, G. H. R. von, W. Gentner, and H. J. Lippolt. 1961. Age of the basalt flow at Olduvai, East Africa. *Nature* 192:720–21.

Kulp, J. Laurence. 1961. Geologic time scale. *Science* 133:1105–14.

Kurtén, B. 1957. Mammal migrations, Cenozoic stratigraphy and the age of Peking man and the australopithecines. *Journal of Paleontology* 31:215–27.

———. 1962. "2. The Dating of the Earliest Hominids," in "Pleistocene Dating and Man: A World-wide Dating by Means of Fauna." *Advancement of Science* 18: 489–90.

Lasker, Gabriel Ward. 1961. *The evolution of man*. New York: Holt, Rinehart and Winston.

———. 1963. Advanced courses. *American Anthropologist Memoir* 94:111–21. [RDG*]

Laughlin, William S. 1963. Concepts and problems. *American Anthropologist Memoir* 94:81–97. [RDG*]

Leakey, L. S. B. 1935. *The stone age races of Kenya*. London: Oxford University Press. [PVT*]

———. 1936. *Stone Age Africa*. London: Oxford University Press.

———. 1953. 4th edition, revised. *Adam's ancestors*. London: Methuen and Co.

———. 1954. Olduvai Gorge. *Scientific American* 190:66–71.

———. 1958. Problems relating to fossil man. *The Leech* (Raymond A. Dart Commemorative Number) 28:116–19. [PVT*]

———. 1959. A new fossil skull from Olduvai. *Nature* 184:491–93.

———. 1960a. The discovery by L. S. B. Leakey of *Zinjanthropus boisei*. *Current Anthropology* 1:79.

———. 1960b. Recent discoveries at Olduvai Gorge. *Nature* 188:1050–52.

———. 1961a. New finds at Olduvai Gorge. *Nature* 189:649–50.

———. 1961b. The juvenile mandible from Olduvai. *Nature* 191:417–18.

McCown, Theodore D. 1951. The genus Palaeoanthropus and the problem of superspecific differentiation among the Hominidae. *Cold Spring Harbor Symposia on Quantitative Biology* 15:87–96.

McCown, Theodore D., and A. Keith. 1939. *The Stone Age of Mount Carmel, Vol. 2: The fossil human remains from the Levalloiso-Mousterian*. Oxford: Clarendon Press.

MacCurdy, George Grant. 1924. *Human origins: A manual of prehistory*, Volumes 1 and 2. New York: Appleton.

Manouvrier, L. 1888. Mémoire sur la platycnémie chez l'homme et chez les anthropoïdes. *Mémoires de la Societe d'anthropologie de Paris* 3:469–550.

———. 1893. Étude sur la Rétroversion de la tête du tibia et l'attitude humaine à l'epoque quaternaire. *Memoires de la société d'anthropologie de Paris* 4:219–64.

Martin, Henry. 1911. Sur un squelette humain de l'époque moustérienne trouvé en Charente. *Comptes rendus de l'Academie des Sciences*, pp. 728–30.

Martin, Rudolf. 1928. *Lehrbuch der Anthropologie*, Volume 2. Jena: Gustav Fischer.

Matiegka, J. 1934. Homo Předmostensis: Fosilní

Člověk z Předmostí na Moravě. *Publications of the Czechoslovakian Academy of Science and Art.* (French summary, pp. 105–45).

Mayer, A. F. J. C. 1864. Über die fossilen Überreste eines menschlichen Schädels und Skelettes in einer Felsenhöhle des Düssel- oder Neander-Thales. *Archiv für Anatomie, Physiologie und Wissenschaftliche Medecin* 1:1–26.

Mayr, Ernst. 1951. Taxonomic categories in fossil hominids. *Cold Spring Harbor Symposia on Quantitative Biology* 15:108–18.

———. 1963. *Animal species and evolution.* Cambridge: Belknap Press of Harvard University Press. [MFF, WWH*]

Miller, Gerrit S., Jr. 1929. The controversy over human "missing links." *Annual Report of the Board of Regents of the Smithsonian Institution for 1928,* pp. 413–65.

Montagu, M. F. Ashley. 1940. Review of: *The Stone Age of Mount Carmel, Vol. 2,* by T. D. McCown and A. Keith (Oxford: Clarendon Press, 1939). *American Anthropologist* 42:518–22.

———. 1945. *Introduction to Physical Anthropology.* Springfield: C. C. Thomas.

———. 1951. 2d. edition. *Introduction to Physical Anthropology.* Springfield: C. C. Thomas.

———. 1952. Neanderthal and the modern type of man. *American Journal of Physical Anthropology* 10:368–70 (new series).

———. 1960. 3d edition. *Introduction to physical anthropology.* Springfield: C. C. Thomas.

Morant, G. M. 1927. Studies of Palaeolithic man II: A biometric study of Neanderthaloid skulls and of their relationships to modern racial types. *Annals of Eugenics* 2 (Parts 3 and 4) :318–80.

———. 1938. The form of the Swanscombe skull. *Journal of the Royal Anthropological Institute* 68:67–97.

Morgan, Jacques de. 1921. *L'humanité préhistorique: Esquisse de préhistoire générale.* Paris: La Renaissance du Livre.

Mortillet, Gabriel de, and Adrien de Mortillet. 1910. (Reprint of the 3d edition, 1900. 1st edition, 1883). *La préhistoire.* Paris: Librairie Schleicher Frères.

Morton, D. J. 1926. Significant characteristics of the Neanderthal foot. *Natural History* 26:310–14.

Movius, Hallam L. Jr. 1948. Tayacian man from the cave of Fontéchevade (Charente). *American Anthropologist* 50:365–67.

Narr, Karl J. 1951, 53. Formengruppen und Kulturkreise im europäischen Palaölithikum (Stand und Aufgaben der Altsteinzeitforschung). *Ber. d. Römisch-German. Komm.* 34:1–40. [KJN*]

———. 1956. "Die Steinwerkzeuge aus der Zeit des Neandertalers," in *Der Neandertaler und seine Umwelt.* Edited by K. Tackenberg, pp. 49–67. Bonn: Rudolf Habelt Verlag. [KJN*]

———. 1957a. Der Neandertalfund und die Ab-stammungslehre. *Forschungen und Fortschritte* 31:321–25. [KJN*]

———. 1957b. "Vorderasien, Nordafrika und Europa," in *Oldenbourgs Abriss der Vorgeschichte.* Edited by W. D. von Barloewen, pp. 1–48 Munich, Germany: R. Oldenbourg. [KJN*]

———. 1962a. *Urgeschichte der Kultur.* Stuttgart: Kröners Taschenausgabe 213. Stuttgart, Germany: A. Kröner Verlag. [KJN*]

———. 1962b. "Menschenfunde an der Grenze von Mittel- und Jungpälaolithikum (einige chronologische Aspekte)," in *Evolution und Hominisation.* Edited by G. Kurth, pp. 221–28. Stuttgart, Germany: G. Fischer Verlag. [KJN*]

———. 1963. *Kultur, Umwelt und Leiblichkeit des Eiszeitmenschen (Studien zu ihrem gegeseitigen Verhältnis).* Stuttgart: G. Fischer Verlag. [KJN*]

Neufeld, John O. 1958. Changes in the trabecular pattern of the mandible following the loss of teeth. *Journal of Prosthetic Dentistry* 8:685–97.

Newell, Norman D. 1963. Crisis in the history of life. *Scientific American* 208:77–92. [SGT*]

Oakley, Kenneth P. 1950. 2d edition. *Man the tool-maker.* London: British Museum (Natural History).

———. 1953. "Dating fossil human remains," in *Anthropology Today* (editor A. L. Kroeber), pp. 43–56. Chicago: University of Chicago Press.

———. 1959. Tools makyth man. *Smithsonian Report for 1958,* pp. 431–45. Washington, D.C. (Reprinted from *Antiquity,* Volume 31, 1957).

———. 1962. Dating the emergence of man. *The Advancement of Science* 18:415–26.

———. and M. F. Ashley Montagu. 1949. A reconsideration of the Galley Hill skeleton. *Bulletin of the British Museum (Natural History) Geology* 1:27–46. London.

Osborn, Henry Fairfield. 1919. 3d edition. *Men of the Old Stone Age.* New York: Charles Scribner's Sons.

———. 1922. The Dawn Man of Piltdown, Sussex. *Natural History* 21:577–90.

Patte, Étienne. 1955. *Les Néanderthaliens: Anatomie, Physiologie, comparisons.* Paris: Masson et Cie.

Piveteau, J. 1957. *Traité de paléontologie: Tome VII: Primates paléontologie humaine.* Paris: Masson et Cie.

Place, Robin. 1957. *Finding fossil man.* New York: Philosophical Library.

Post, Richard H. 1962. Population differences in red and green color vision deficiency: a review, and a query on selection relaxation. *Eugenics Quarterly* 9:131–46.

Potonie, R. 1958. Zur allgemeinen Bedeutung des Neandertal-Fundes, in *Hundert Jahre Neanderthaler* (editor G. H. R. von Koenigswald), pp. 277–86. Utrecht, Netherlands: Kemink en Zoon N.V.

Rivière, Émile 1872. Sur le squelette humain trouvé dans les cavernes des Baoussè-Rousse (Italie), dites Grottes de Menton, 1e 26 mars 1872. *Comptes Rendus de l'Academie des Sciences,* Paris 74:1204–7.

Robinson, J. T. 1952a. The Australopithecine-bearing deposits of the Sterkfontein area. *Annals of the Transvaal Museum* 22:1–19.

——. 1952b. Some hominid features of the ape-man dentition. *J. Dent. A. South Africa* 7:102–13.

——. 1953a. Meganthropus, australopithecines and hominids. *American Journal of Physical Anthropology* 11:1–38 (new series).

——. 1953b. The nature of *Telanthropus. Nature* 171:33.

——. 1953c. *Telanthropus* and its phylogenetic significance. *American Journal of Physical Anthropology* 11:445–501. (new series).

——. 1954. The genera and species of the Australopithecinae. *American Journal of Physical Anthropology* 12:181–200 (new series).

——. 1956. The dentition of the Australopithecinae. *Transvaal Museum Memoirs,* Number 9. Pretoria.

Roginskii, J. J. 1947. K voprosoo drevnosti cheloveka sovremennogo tipa; mesto svanscombskogo tcherepa v sisteme hominid. *Sovietskaaia Etnografiia* 3:33–40.

——. 1948. Zur Frage nach dem Alter des heutigen Menschentype (Die Stellung des Schädels von Swanscombe im Hominiden-system). *Sowietwissenschaft, Gesellschaftwissenschaftliche Abteilung* 1:114–22.

——. 1951. Osnovnye anthropologischeskie voprosy v probleme proiskhozhdeniia sovremennogo cheloveka. *Trudy Inst. Etnografii* 16:153–204.

Schaaffhausen, H. 1857a. Theilen des menschlichen skelettes im Neanderthal bei Hochdal. *Verhandlungen des naturhistorischen Vereines der preussischen Rheinlande und Westfalens* 14:50–52.

——. 1857b. Theilen des menschlichen skelettes im Neanderthal bei Hochdal Sitzungsberichte der niederheinischen Gesellschaft für Natur- und Heilkunde in Bonn. *Verhandlungen des naturhistorischen Vereines der preussischen Rheinlande und Westfalens* 14:38–42.

——. 1858. Zur Kentniss der ältesten Rassenschädel. *Archiv für Anatomie, Physiologie und Wissenschaftliche Medecin in Verbindung mit Mehreren Gelehrten.* Edited by Johannes Müller, pp. 453–78.

Schwalbe, Gustav. 1897. Über die Schädelformen der ältesten Menschenrassen mit besonderer Berücksichtigung des Schädels von Egisheim. *Mittheilungen der Philomathischen Gesellschaft in Elsass-Lothringen* 3:72–85.

——. 1899. Studien über *Pithecanthropus erectus Dubois. Zeitschrift für Morphologie und Anthropologie* 1:1–240.

——. 1901a. Der Neanderthalschädel. *Bonner Jahrbüch.* Number 106:1–72. Bonn.

——. 1901b. Über die specifischen Merkmale des Neanderthalschädels. *Verhandlungen der Anatomische Gesellschaft: Ergänzheft zur Anatomische Anzeiger* 19:44–61.

——. 1902. Der Schädel von Egisheim. *Beiträge zur Anthropologie Elsass-Lothringens,* Heft 3. Strassburg.

——. 1903. Über die Vorgeschichte des Menschen. *Verhandlungen der Gesellschaft der Deutschen Naturforscher und Arzte.* 75 Versammlung zu Cassel: 163–83.

——. 1904. *Die Vorgeschichte des Menschen.* Braunschweig: Friedrich Vieweg und Sohn.

——. 1906a. *Studien zur Vorgeschichte des Menschen: I. Zur Frage der Abstammung des Menschen.* Stuttgart: E. Scheizerbart, pp. 11–80.

——. 1906b. *Studien zur Vorgeschichte des Menschen: II. Das Schädelfragment von Brüx und verwandte Schädelform.* Stuttgart: E. Scheizerbart, pp. 83–182.

——. 1913. Kritische Besprechung von Boule's Werk: "L'homme fossile de La Chapelle-aux-Saints" mit eigenen Untersuchungen. *Zeitschrift für Morphologie und Anthropologie* Band XVI, Heft 1, pp. 527–610.

——. 1923. (Actually written in 1916). Die Abstammung des Menschen und die Ältesten Menschenformen, in *Die Kultur der Gegenwart: ihre Entwicklung und ihre Ziele* (editor Paul Hinneberg), pp. 223–338. Leipzig and Berlin: B. G. Teubner Verlag.

Senyürek, Muzaffer. 1955. A review of the order of eruption of the permanent teeth in fossil hominids. *Türk Tarih Kurumu Belleten* 19:407–44.

Sergi, S. 1953. I Profaneranthropi di Swanscombe e di Fontéchevade. *Rivista di Antropologia Roma* 40:65–72.

——. 1958. "Die Neanderthalischen Palaeanthropen in Italien," in *Hundert Jahre Neanderthaler.* Edited by G. H. R. von Koenigswald, pp. 38–51. Utrecht, Netherlands: Kemink en Zoon, N.V.

[AT*]

——. 1962. L'extinction des Paléanthropes néandertaliens et l'origine des Phaneranthropes. *Atti del VI Congrosso Internazionale delle Scienze Preistoriche e Protostoriche. I. Relazioni generali:* 287–296. Florence, Italy: G. C. Sanzoni. [KJN*]

Simpson, G. G. 1944. *Tempo and mode in evolution.* New York: Columbia University Press.

——. 1953. *The Major Features of Evolution.* New York: Columbia University Press.

Skerlj, B. 1958. Were Neanderthals the only

inhabitans of Krapina? *Bulletin Scientifique* 4:44.

Smith, G. Elliot. 1925. The fossil anthropoid ape from Taungs. *Nature* 115:235.

Smith, Philip E. L. 1961. The origins of the Solutrean. Paper presented to the Annual Meetings of the American Anthropological Association, Philadelphia, November 16.

——. 1963. The Abbé Henri Breuil and prehistoric archaeology. *Anthropologica* 4:199–208.

Solecki, R. S. 1955. Shanidar Cave, a Paleolithic site in Northern Iraq. *Sumer* 11:14–38.

——. 1960. Three adult Neanderthal skeletons from Shanidar Cave, Northern Iraq. *Smithsonian Report for 1959*, pp. 603–35. Washington, D. C.

——. 1961. New anthropological discoveries at Shanidar, Northern Iraq. *Transactions of the New York Academy of Sciences* 23:690–99 (series 2).

——. 1963. Prehistory in Shanidar Valley, Northern Iraq. *Science* 139:179–93. [MFF*]

Sollas, W. J. 1924. 3d edition, revised. *Ancient hunters and their modern representatives*. New York: Macmillan Co.

Stewart, T. D. 1949. The development of the concept of morphological dating in connection with early man in America. *Southwest Journal of Anthropology* 6:1–16.

——. 1951. The problem of the earliest claimed representatives of *Homo sapiens*. *Cold Spring Harbor Symposia on Quantitative Biology* 15:97–107.

——. 1952. Wishful thinking in the reconstruction of skulls. *American Journal of Physical Anthropology* 10:520–54.

——. 1959. The restored Shanidar I Skull. *Smithsonian Report for 1958*, pp. 473–80. Washington, D.C.

——. 1960a. Form of the pubic bone in Neanderthal Man. *Science* 131:1437–8. [SGT, DRB*]

——. 1960a. Indirect evidence of the primitiveness of the Swanscombe skull. Abstract of a paper presented to the Annual Meeting of the American Association of Physical Anthropologists. *American Journal of Physical Anthropology* 18:363 (new series).

——. 1961. A neglected primitive feature of the Swanscombe skull, in *Homenaje a Pablo Martinez del Rio en el XXV aniversario de la edición*, pp. 207–17.

——. 1962. Neanderthal cervical vertebrae. *Bibl. primat.* 1:130–54. (Basel/New York: S. Karger).

Straus, W. L., Jr., and A. J. E. Cave. 1957. Pathology and the posture of Neanderthal man. *Quarterly Review of Biology* 32:348–63.

Teilhard de Chardin, Pierre. 1943. *Fossil Man: Recent discoveries and present problems*. Peking: Henri Vetch.

Thoma, A. 1957, 1958. Métissage ou Transformation? Essai sur les hommes fossiles de Palestine.

L'Anthropologie (1957) 61:470–502: (1958) 62:30–52.

——. 1962. Le déploiement évolutif de l'Homo sapiens. *Anthropologia Hungarica* 5:1–111. [AT*]

Tobias, P. V. 1955. Physical anthropology and somatic origins of the Hottentots. *African Studies* 14:1–22. [PVT*]

——. 1955, 1956. Les Bochimans Auen et Naron de Chanzi. Contribution à l'étude des Anciens Jaunes Sud-africains. *L'Anthropologie* 59:235–52, 429–61; 60:22–52, 268–89. [PVT*]

——. 1956. Evolution of the Bushman. *American Journal of Physical Anthropology* 14:384. [PVT*]

——. 1957. Bushmen of the Kalahari. *Man* 57:33–40. [PVT*]

——. 1959. Some developments in South African physical anthropology 1938–1958. Epilogue to A. Galloway, *The skeletal remains of Bambandyanalo*. Johannesburg: Witwatersrand University Press. [PVT*]

——. 1960. The Kanam Jaw. *Nature* 185:946. [PVT*]

——. 1961a. New evidence and new views on the evolution of man in Africa. *South African Journal of Science* 57:25–38. [PVT*]

——. 1961b. "A re-examination of the Kanam mandible." *Proccedings of the Fourth Pan-African Congress on Prehistory, Leopoldville, August, 1959*, pp. 341–60. [PVT*]

——. 1962. "Early members of the genus *Homo* in Africa," in *Evolution and Hominisation*. Edited by G. Kurth, pp. 191–204. Stuttgart: Gustav Fischer Verlag. [PVT*]

Topinard, P. 1888. Review of *Les ancêtres de nos animaux dans les temps géologiques* by Albert Gaudry. In *Revue d'Anthropologie* 3:472–74 (third series).

Trevor, J. C., and D. R. Brothwell. 1962. The human remains of Mesolithic and Neolithic date from Gua Cha, Kelantan. *Federation Museums Journal* 7:6–22. [DRB*]

Twiesselmann, F. 1958. Les Néanderthaliens découverts en Belgique, in *Hundert Jahre Neanderthaler* (editor G. H. R. von Koenigswald), pp. 63–71. Utrecht, Netherlands: Kemink en Zoon, N.V.

von Uslar, Rafael, and K. J. Narr. 1956. "J. C. Fuhlrott und der Neandertaler," in *Der Neandertaler und seine Umwelt: Gedenkschrift zur Erinnerung an die Auffindung im Jahre 1856*. Edited by K. Tackenberg, pp. 9–31. Bonn Germany: Rudolf Habelt Verlag. [KJN*]

Vallois, H. V. 1946. Les nouveaux Pithécanthropes et le problème de l'origine de l'Homme. *La Nature* 3125:367–70.

——. 1949a. The Fontéchevade fossil man. *American Journal of Physical Anthropology* 7:339–62.

——. 1949b. L'origine de *Homo sapiens*.

Comptes Rendus de l'Academie des Sciences 228:949–51.

——. 1952. Néanderthal . . . Néandertal? L'Anthropologie 55:557–58. [SGT*]

——. 1954. Neanderthals and Praesapiens. Journal of the Royal Anthropological Institute 84:111–30.

——. 1957. Fossil men. New York: Dryden Press. [PVT*]

——. 1959. La Grotte de Fontéchevade. Deuxième Partie: Anthropologie. Archives de l'Institut de Paléontologie Humaine, Mémoire 29. Paris.

Vallois, Henri V., and Hallam L. Movius. 1952. "Catalogue des Hommes Fossiles." Proceedings of the 19th Session of the International Congress of Geologists, Algiers, 1952. Vol. 5. [KJN*]

Verneau, Rene. 1924. La race de Néanderthal et la race de Grimaldi: leur rôle dans l'humanité. Journal of the Royal Anthropological Institute 54:211–30.

Verworn, M., R. Bonnet, and G. Steinman. 1919. Der diluviale Menschenfund von Obercassel bei Bonn. Wiesbaden: J.F. Bergmann.

Virchow, Rudolf. 1872. Untersuchung des Neanderthal-Schädels. Verhandlungen der Berliner Gesellschaft für Anthropologie, Ethnologie und Urgeschichte 4:157–65.

Vuković, S. 1959. Verbal information. Varaždin, Yugoslavia.

Washburn, Sherwood L. 1963. The curriculum in physical anthropology. American Anthropologist Memoir 94:39–47. [RDG*]

Weckler, J. E. 1954. The relationships between Neanderthal man and Homo sapiens. American Anthropologist 56:1003–25.

Weidenreich, F. 1928. Entwicklungs- und Rassentypen des Homo primigenius. Natur und Volk 58:1–13; 51–62.

——. 1930. Lamarck, seine Persönlichkeit und sein Werk: zur 100 Wiederkehr seines Todestages. Natur und Museum 60:326–33, 363–69.

——. 1932. "Lamarckismus." Natur und Museum 62:298–300.

——. 1936. The mandibles of Sinanthropus pekinensis: a comparative study. Palaeontologia Sinica 7:1–132 (series D).

——. 1937. The dentition of Sinanthropus pekinensis: A comparative odontography of the hominids. Palaeontologia Sinica 101:1–180.

——. 1940. Some problems dealing with ancient man. American Anthropologist 42:375–83.

——. 1941. The brain and its role in phylogenetic transformation of the human skull. Transactions of the American Philosophical Society 31:321–442 (Part 5) (new series).

——. 1943a. The "Neanderthal Man" and the ancestors of "Homo sapiens." American Anthropologist 45:39–48.

——. 1943b. The skull of Sinanthropus pekinensis: A comparative study on a primitive hominid skull. Palaeontologia Sinica. 127:1–484.

——. 1945. Giant early man from Java and South China. Anthropological Papers of the American Museum of Natural History Volume 40: (Part I). New York.

——. 1946. Apes, giants and man. Chicago: University of Chicago Press.

——. 1947a. Facts and speculations concerning the origin of Homo sapiens. American Anthropologist 49:187–203.

——. 1947b. Some particulars of skull and brain of early hominids and their bearing on the problem of the relationship between man and anthropoids. American Journal of Physical Anthropology 95:387–418 (new series).

——. 1947c. The trend of human evolution. Evolution 1:221–36.

——. 1949. Interpretations of the fossil material, in Early man in the Far East (editor W. W. Howells). Studies in Physical Anthropology, Number 1. The American Association of Physical Anthropologists, pp. 149–57.

Weiner, J. S. 1961. The East African fossil men. New Scientist 9:534–36. [PVT*]

Weiner, J. S., K. P. Oakley, and W. E. Le Gros Clark. 1953. The solution of the Piltdown problem. Bulletin of the British Museum (Natural History) Geology 2:141–46.

Weinert, H. 1925. Der Schädel des eiszeitlichen Menschen von le Moustier in neuer Zussammensetzung. Berlin: J. Springer.

——. 1932. Ursprung der Menschheit Stuttgart: Ferdinand Enke.

——. 1936. Der Urmenschenschadel von Steinheim. Zeitschrift für Morphologie und Anthropologie 35:463–518.

——. 1944a. L'Homme préhistorique. Paris: Payot.

——. 1944b. 2d edition, revised, Ursprung der Menschheit: Über den engeren Anschluss des Menschengeschlechts an die Menschenaffen. Stuttgart: Ferdinand Enke.

——. 1947. 2d edition, revised. Menschen der Vorzeit: Ein Überblick über die altsteinzeitlichen Menschenreste. Stuttgart: Ferdinand Enke.

——. 1951a. Stammesentwicklung der Menschheit. Braunschweig: F. Vieweg.

——. 1951b. Über die neuen Vor- und Frühmenschenfunde aus Afrika, Java, China und Frankreich. Zeitschrift für Morphologie und Anthropologie 42:113–48.

——. 1953. Der fossile Mensch, in Anthropology Today (editor A. L. Kroeber), pp. 101–19. Chicago: University of Chicago Press.

——. 1955. Die Neanderthaler-Gruppe und die Praesapiens-Funde. Forschungen und Fortschritte 29:297–304.

Wells, L. H. 1952. Fossil man in Southern Africa. *Man* 52:36–37. [PVT*]

———. 1956. The place of the Broken Hill skull among human types. *Proceedings of the Third Pan-African Congress on Prehistory, Livingstone,* pp. 172–74. [PVT*]

———. 1959. The problem of Middle Stone Age man in South Africa. *Man* 59:158–60.

[PVT*]

Wierciński, Andrzej. 1956. Zagadnienie wystepowania form *Homo sapiens* we wczesnym i srodkowym plejstocenie. (The problem of the appearance of forms of *Homo sapiens* in the early and mid-Pleistocene.) *Przeglad anthropologiczny* 22:267–85. (English summary).

———. 1962. Racial analysis of human populations in relation to their ethnogenesis. *Current Anthropology* 3:2, 9–20.

Woo, J. K., and J. T. Peng. 1959. Fossil human skull of early paleoanthropic stage found at Hapa, Shaquan, Kwangtung Province. *Vertebrata Palasiatica* 3:175–82.

Woodward, Sir Arthur Smith. 1925. The fossil anthropoid ape from Taungs. *Nature* 115:235–36.

24

ENVIRONMENT, TOOTH FORM, AND SIZE
IN THE PLEISTOCENE
C. Loring Brace

To the casual reader, it must seem that students of animal evolution devote an inordinate amount of time to the contemplation of fossil teeth. The teeth of prehistoric animals do get a good deal of attention and for good reasons. As the hardest parts of the skeleton, they are the most often preserved. In many instances, fossil creatures are known only from the evidence of their teeth, none of the rest of the skeleton having been preserved or discovered. Teeth, as much or more than any other part of the skeleton, reflect directly the genetic potential of the organism. Their growth is less subject to alterations caused by environmental factors. Finally, teeth relate rather directly to that for which they are adapted, being the only portion of the skeleton that literally comes in direct contact with the environment. Teeth, then, should be a sensitive indicator of evolutionary change—changes in selective forces, diet, life-way, and resultant genetic response.

This article was written before Brace had had a chance to examine the original Australopithecine material in Africa. For data on these specimens, he was dependent on the incomplete accounts that had already been published. Since that time, the author has studied all the available Australopithecine specimens, and more have been discovered. Consequently, the reader will note that the treatment of the Australopithecines is less developed and more in line with traditional views than is the case in selection 20.

Operating on the assumption that changes in selective forces will produce changes in organisms previously in a state of adaptive equilibrium, it should be possible to reverse the process and, by an examination of structural modifications that have occurred through time, make inferences concerning the nature of alterations in the forces of selection. An examination of the available evidence allows one to generalize concerning the morphological changes that have taken place in the hominid line during the Pleistocene. If the available hominid skeletal material is treated as belonging to a single evolutionary line—an assumption that is far from being universally accepted[12] [14]—the most distinct changes that have occurred are largely limited to the cranium. Postcranial changes are to be observed, not the least of which is a major increase in gross bodily bulk between the early and the late Australopithecines but, other than noting that this has allometric implications when specific features are considered, it is possible to relegate

From *Journal of Dental Research* 46 (1967):809–816. Reprinted with permission of author and publisher.

such matters to a status of secondary importance and to defer their treatment until the cranial aspects have been examined.

Restricting our attention to the skull, variations that can be readily discerned from the preserved hard parts allow us to focus attention on changes that have taken place in two major organs. Changes in brain size and their implications are relatively obvious and call for little further comment, whereas changes in the masticatory apparatus and their implications for evaluating related parts of the face and braincase involve the would-be analyzer in an area of perhaps unexpected complexity. Some of the aspects of this area will be considered.

To compare the various hominid groupings and to appraise their dental changes through time, quantitative criteria are desirable. Preferably, these criteria should reflect functional aspects of the dentition and should be under genetic control, although it does not matter whether the genetic background is simple (single gene locus) or complex (polygenic and pleiotropic involvement). Regarding the amount of dental material that can be brought into action as being functionally important and almost entirely under genetic control, it is clear that gross tooth measurements are of prime concern for the student of dental evolution. Where aspects of crown morphology contribute to effective tooth size in ways that are not reflected by gross measurements, rating scales for their assessment can contribute to the evaluation of effective dental bulk although, however valuable these may be as additional confirmation of what is metrically demonstrable, they are always subject to the limitations that their divisions are subjectively established. Hypocone, hypoconulid, and hypoconid development for molars, and lingual margin elevation and lingual tubercle development for incisors, among other features, have been used with great effectiveness in evaluation and comparison.[6-8]

Measurements are the most graphic means of assessing functional tooth size. Evidently, a full treatment would require that measurements of three dimensions be represented. Ideally, mesial-distal, buccal-lingual, and cervical-occlusal (or incisal) measures would be needed to demonstrate tooth bulk, but in practice this means of measurement is impossible to use for more than selected individuals of prehistoric populations because of the generally heavy wear to which the teeth were subjected immediately after eruption. Cervical-occlusal measurements exist for some teeth and add to the general appraisal that can be made of dental evolution in much the same way as for morphological assessment. Where anything like population representation can be suggested, however, dental size appraisals are mainly restricted to mesial-distal and buccal-lingual measurements. These too—especially mesial-distal measures—are influenced by wear[7] but, if extremely worn teeth are rejected, these measurements can yield the most reliable quantitative estimate of the amount of tooth area that can be brought into action.

The mesial-distal diameter has frequently been used as a general indicator of gross tooth size, although it should be noted that interproximal wear, universal wherever there is heavy tooth use, and simple occlusal wear of incisors will both diminish mesial-distal dimensions. Although the buccal-lingual diameter is a better indicator of tooth size, the use of both mesial-distal and buccul-lin-

gual measurements can be expected to have a certain damping effect on the impact that individual or idiosyncratic variation may have on the attempt to portray the course of evolution. The reliance on either measurement alone, especially on the mesial-distal measurement, may produce a biased picture of tooth size for the earlier stages of human evolution since, for these populations, only few individuals are known and, for these, the number of measurable teeth per category is well below a figure that could give one confidence in their representative nature. This is particularly true where teeth from the forward end of the dental arch are concerned, although this should not justify their exclusion from consideration as has occasionally been advocated.

For purposes of this paper, then, a figure approximating tooth cross-section area will be used; this figure is composed of the product of the mesial-distal and the buccal-lingual and the dimensions of each tooth.[1] The maxillary dentition was chosen for purposes of comparison since, with the relatively smaller size of the lower canines and incisors, the same amount of interproximal attrition has a relatively greater effect and would make it more difficult to appraise genetically based population differences.

The course of human evolution can be portrayed by comparing four arbitrary stages plus a number of substages or phases: the Australopithecine stage with an early or Australopithecus phase and a late or Paranthropus phase, the Pithecanthropine stage, the Neanderthal stage, and the modern stage.

These stages, of course, are simply arbitrary points on what would actually be a continuum if there were sufficient evidence, but they serve as convenient reference points for appraising the nature of the

[1]I am grateful to Mr. Milford Wolpoff of the Department of Anthropology, University of Illinois, for insisting that comparisons be made in terms of area rather than some modification of the old crown module, since the latter, despite dividing the sum of the mesial-distal and buccal-lingual measures by the constant 2, most closely reflects perimeter. Area, on the other hand, can be looked on as the significant trait where matters of selection and adaptation are under consideration.

changes that have occurred. Burial practices and increasing population density in the late Pleistocene present enough evidence so that the nature of the continuum is more readily apparent.

Table 1 shows the average mesial-distal times buccal-lingual crown area measurements for each tooth category for populations representing the various stages and substages of human evolution. The various populations and sources quoted were chosen as being the only populations representing the various stages where measurements from more than one individual are available.

Based on these figures, a quick review of the major trends in the evolution of hominid dental dimensions can be expressed graphically. Figure 1 shows that the major changes between the early and the middle Pleistocene involved a reduction of the postcanine teeth and an increase in the size of the precanine teeth. One could suggest that the precanine dimensions of *Australopithecus* do not actually represent a condition intermediate between *Paranthropus* and *Sinanthropus* since an allometric correction for gross body size differences would elevate them to a bulk exceeding even that of *Paranthropus*.

From the Pithecanthropines to the Neanderthals—a time span of about half a million years—relatively little change in gross dental

Table 1

Average Tooth Cross-Section Areas (Mesial-Distal x Buccal-Lingual)
for the Maxillary Teeth of Populations Representing the Various Stages
and Substages of Human Evolution

Stage or Substage	I¹	I²	C	P¹	P²	M¹	M²	M³
Australopithecus	78.02	40.92	88.36	112.14	116.59	171.94	211.63	202.49 (1)a
Paranthropus	71.44	48.96	82.65	140.58	163.24	199.95	233.61	254.82 (1)
Sinanthropus	79.52	66.82	92.36	100.03	89.97	140.46	138.76	112.42 (2)
Krapina	91.10	76.74	91.88	97.52	81.40	159.50	137.07	126.60 (3)
Skhūl	78.65	51.48	74.57	84.80	72.20	134.41	122.44	104.81 (4)
Prědmost	66.9	50.25	66.32	68.64	71.29	134.43	129.90	125.87 (5)
Australian Aborigine	74.26	53.13	75.60	80.34	72.72	145.92	142.79	123.00 (6)
Chicago White	61.86	42.85	66.42	63.14	63.13	119.31	113.25	96.24 (7)

[a]Figures computed from (1) Robinson, 1956; (2) Weidenreich, 1937; (3) Krapina as measured by Brace; (4) McCown and Keith, 1939; (5) Matiegka, 1934; (6) Campbell, 1925, and (7) Dahlberg, 1960.

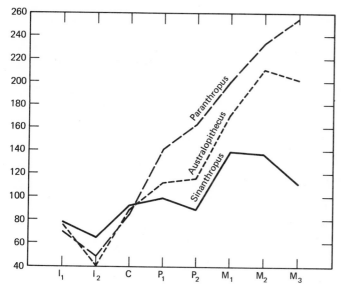

Figure 1. Average tooth cross-section areas for the maxillary teeth of *Australopithecus*, *Paranthropus* and *Sinanthropus*.

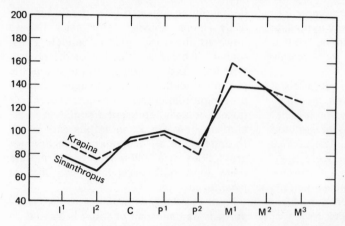

Figure 2. Average tooth cross-section areas for the maxillary teeth of *Sinanthropus* and *Neanderthals* as represented by Krapina.

dimensions occurred (Fig. 2). About the only consistent trend that can be observed is a still further increase in the size of those teeth at the very front end of the dental arch, and this may in fact be the result of sampling problems.

Ever since their discovery, the Neanderthaloids of Skhūl, Mount Carmel, have been recognized as being intermediate in form between the full Neanderthals and modern men (by which is usually meant Europeans or populations of European extraction). Among the various groups of living men, the Australian aborigines have long been regarded as preserving the most primitive facial morphology and, although there has been some reluctance to compare this with Neanderthaloid form, it is interesting to note that the similarity in gross dimension between the teeth of the Skhūl Neanderthaloids and modern Australian aborigines are almost identical until the molars are reached. The molars from Skhūl are unaccountably smaller

(Fig. 3). In fact, they are smaller than Upper Paleolithic Europeans, and this variation may simply be an illustration of the problems inherent in relying on small-sized samples.

When populations from the last 40,000 years are measured and their dental dimensions plotted (Fig. 4), it is evident that, with the sole exception of the Skhūl molars, the relative position of the line on the graph corresponds well with the relative age of the population in question. In fact, it might be claimed that this is the most consistent measurable change to have occurred in man since the Neanderthal stage. Reduction in size has been consistent, particularly at the forward end of the dental arch and, if the modern population figures had not been derived from males only, the apparent reduction would have been even greater.

If generalizations are made about the dental changes that have occurred during the course of hominid evolution, it is apparent that the anterior portion and the posterior

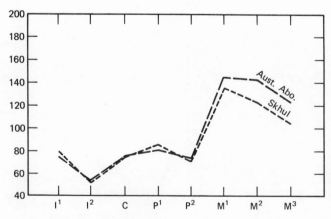

Figure 3. Average tooth cross-section areas for the maxillary teeth of the Skhūl Neanderthaloids and modern Australian aborigines.

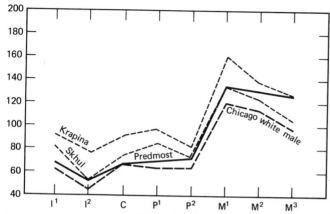

Figure 4. Average cross-section areas for the maxillary teeth of Neanderthals as represented by Krapina, Neanderthaloids as represented by Skhūl, the Upper Paleolithic population from Predmost, and modern man as represented by Chicago white males.

portion of the dental arch have changed at different times, at different rates of speed, and for different reasons. When the function of the anterior teeth is regarded as one of holding and nipping and that of the posterior teeth as specifically to crush food, there is some justification in lumping the measurements of the anterior and posterior teeth separately and attempting to discuss the metric changes in terms of changes in their assumed functions.

Table 2 gives the average cross sections for incisors and canines summed (canines have functioned as incisors throughout the known course of hominid evolution) separately from those summed for premolars and molars. Plotting the figures so acquired (Fig. 5) it is clear that, although there has been a consistent trend toward postcanine tooth reduction

since the Neanderthal stage, the most distinct change has been the sharp reduction between the Australopithecines and Pithecanthropines (even without attempting to correct allometrically for early Australopithecine body size).

When the same procedure is followed for the anterior dentition, a different pattern is revealed (Fig. 6). The anterior teeth increased in size up to the Neanderthal stage after which, considering the short period of time involved, there has been a pronounced reduction. It is interesting to note that although Australian aboriginal teeth are the largest among living men—their molars are scarcely smaller than Neanderthal molars —their incisors are not even half way up the scale between the modern and Neanderthal levels.

Table 2
Average Maxillary Tooth Cross-Section Areas for Incisors
and Canines Summed and for Premolars and Molars Summed

Tooth	Australo-pithecus	Paran-thropus	Sinan-thropus	Krapina	Skhūl	Předmost	Australian Aborigine	Chicago White
I^1	78.02	71.44	79.52	91.10	78.65	66.9	74.26	61.86
I^2	40.92	48.96	66.82	76.74	51.48	50.25	53.13	42.85
C	88.36	82.65	92.36	91.88	74.57	66.32	75.60	66.42
Total	207.30	203.05	238.70	259.72	204.70	183.47	202.99	171.13
P^1	112.14	140.58	100.03	97.52	84.80	68.64	80.34	63.14
P^2	116.59	163.24	89.97	81.40	72.20	71.29	72.72	63.13
M^1	171.94	199.95	140.46	159.50	134.41	134.43	145.92	119.31
M^2	211.63	233.61	138.76	137.07	122.44	129.90	142.79	113.25
M^3	202.49	254.82	112.42	126.60	104.81	125.87	123.00	96.24
Total	814.79	992.20	581.64	602.09	518.66	530.13	564.77	455.07

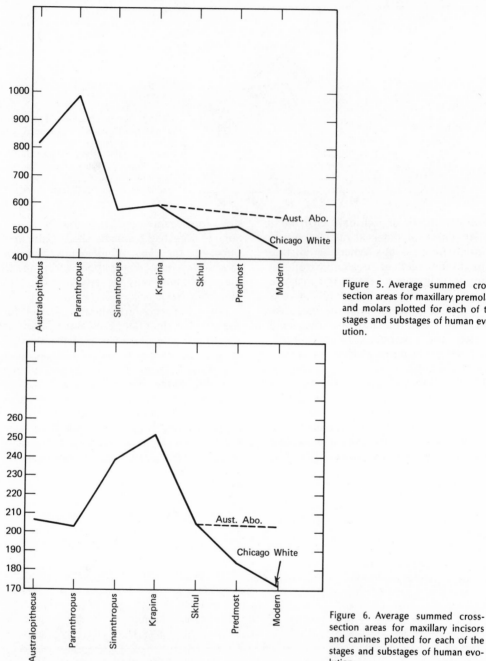

Figure 5. Average summed cross-section areas for maxillary premolars and molars plotted for each of the stages and substages of human evolution.

Figure 6. Average summed cross-section areas for maxillary incisors and canines plotted for each of the stages and substages of human evolution.

As suggested previously in this paper, major modifications in structure should allow us to make inferences about the nature of alterations in the forces of selection. One of the achievements of modern anthropology has been the demonstration that the cumulative effect of man's traditions and activities—his culture—greatly alters the na-ture of the operation of selective forces. Consequently, one would suspect that any pronounced alteration of selective forces, as demonstrated by a distinct structural modification, should correspond to a major change in man's cultural adaptive mechanism.

On the basis of this assumption, Figure 7

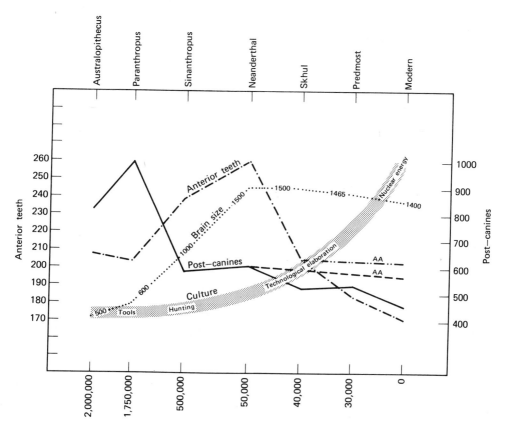

Figure 7. The major hominid cranial changes plotted opposite the major adaptive changes that have occurred in the cultural dimension throughout the course of human evolution.

portrays the significant major cranial changes that have occurred in hominid evolution along with the developments in culture which may be at least partially responsible (Table 3).

At the beginning of hominid evolution, the very existence and use of tools must have constituted a major change in the circum-

Table 3

Estimated Cranial Capacities for the Various Stages and Substages of Human Evolution

Stage or Substage	Cranial Capacity
Australopithecus	? 500
Paranthropus	? 600
Pithecanthropus	±1,000
Neanderthals	±1,500
Skhūl	±1,500
Předmost	1,465
Modern man	±1,400

stances of adaptation. Although Figure 5 shows an increase in molar size between Australopithecus and Paranthropus, it must be remembered that this is an expression of the measurements themselves before any attempt is made to adjust allometrically for the differences in body size. Such an allometric adjustment could raise the dimensions of Australopithecus molars at least to Paranthropus size. At the same time, the anterior segment of the dental arch would also have to be adjusted upward. This means that our explanation would have to account for a hypothetical decrease in the relative size of the front teeth between Australopithecus and Paranthropus. Speculating that the use of tools and weapons for defense early in hominid evolution reduced the selective advantage formerly inherent in the possession of large front teeth (especially canines), one would expect to find hominids with relatively enlarged front teeth as one moves back in time toward the point at which they actually played a defensive role. As time went on, tools progressively preempted the function of defense, reducing the adaptive advantage inherent in the possession of large front teeth. With the forces of selection relaxed,[11] the operation of the "probable mutation effect"[2,3] would follow, and dental reduction would be the result.

By the middle Pleistocene, there is a secondary rise in front tooth size and a sharp drop in molar size. It is tempting to correlate these changes with the evidence revealed by archeology that systematically practiced big game hunting becomes a major facet of human existence for the first time—constituting a change of considerable magnitude in the cultural dimension. The addition of regular quantities of meat protein to the diet presumably reduced the amount of uncooked vegetable matter requiring mastication and, since meat requires substantially less chewing than starch and carbohydrate-type foods, it is possible to suggest that the amount of compulsory mastication required of middle Pleistocene hominids was substantially reduced. The relaxation of selective pressures maintaining large molar size would allow the probable mutation effect to operate, and a reduction in molar size would be expected.

The secondary increase in incisor size is a little less simply accounted for. The number of Pithecanthropine incisors (confined almost entirely to *Sinanthropus*) is so small that it is perhaps easier to make assessments from the Neanderthal material, which is considerably more abundant. From the heavy rounded wear that characterizes Neanderthal incisors, it is evident that they were being used for more than just eating. It would seem that Neanderthal incisors were regularly used as a convenient all-purpose tool for cutting, tearing, holding, and shaping a variety of objects. Certainly, as culture increased in effectiveness as an adaptive mechanism, the importance of imposing human control on the environment increased. Since a specialized technology was lacking, the means of effecting such control devolved on the human physique. The muscularity of Upper and particularly Middle Pleistocene hominids may be a general indication of this, and it is possible that the great size and morphological development of the anterior teeth may be a specific manifestation.

Starting with the beginning of the last glaciation, the pace of cultural change underwent great acceleration. The band designated "culture" in Figure 7 reflects a crude subjective appraisal of this acceleration which continues at the present at an ever-increasing rate. During the Mousterian and even more in the Upper Paleolithic, a variety of specialized tools appeared which reduced the hitherto increasingly important manipulative role played by the front teeth. This relaxation of selection allowed the probable mutation effect to produce a sharp reduction in incisor size along with great morphological simplification. If the horizontal axis of the chart were anything like an approximation of proper scale, this decrease in incisor size would be even more dramatic. Improvement of food preparation and cooking technics could be the reason for similar if less dramatic changes in the molar region.

If the scheme developed so far has any justification, and if the emphasis placed on specific functional groups of teeth are related to the history of tooth development, then there are some implications for the interpretations of variations in dental and facial size and form as seen in modern man. For instance, it is no surprise to discover that the technologically most primitive representatives of modern man—the Australian aborigines—have the largest teeth in the world.[4] It is also no surprise to discover that the inhabitants of the Middle East, where technological elaboration has an antiquity equal to or greater than anywhere else in the world, have the smallest teeth (corrected for body size) found among modern men.[5] Between these extremes lie all sorts of stages and manifestations of dental reduction. One could venture to predict that many if not all of these can be associated with backgrounds where technological elaboration occurred at specific predictable degrees of antiquity. Archeologists could be induced to supply us with such estimates for various areas, but now we run up against a surprising and rather unexpected obstacle. Perhaps because of the bad name that old-fashioned physical anthropology acquired for the exercise of measuring, perhaps because the problem was never cast in these terms before, or perhaps for some other reason, there is a woeful lack of studies recording the simple tooth measurements of the various groups of modern man. Australian aborigines and Eskimo (albeit weak on incisors) have been studied, and tooth size for Lapps, Kalihari Bushmen, and S.E. Bantu are known but, when the dental measurements of people of western European extraction have to be referred to as those for a group of white males from Chicago, then it is apparent that much needs to be done. At present, there is no published information on the dental dimensions of the inhabitants of the Congo, West Africa, Ethiopia, India, wherever Pygmies occur (except for a small sample from European museums[1]), most of the countries of western Europe, Russia, China, Tibet, New Guinea, or anywhere in Middle and South America, or for North American Indians (except Pecos Pueblo).

If the ideas presented in the first part of this paper are to be tested anywhere, they must be tested on the living peoples of the world. What with the increasing blurring of population boundaries, to say nothing of the political obstacles to field research, it seems urgent to point out the great need for a program that could generate such studies. The technics are simple and the time and expense required are not beyond the means of many students and scholars. I hope that some readers will be sufficiently stimulated to undertake such work or direct students toward the systematic quantitative appraisal of the teeth of modern *Homo sapiens*.

REFERENCES

[1]Brabant, H. Observations sur la Denture des Pygmees de l'Afrique Centrale, *Bull. Group. Int. Rech. Sci. Stomat.*, 8:27–49, 1965.

[2]Brace, C. L. Structural Reduction in Evolution, *Amer. Naturalist*, 97:39–49, 1963.

[3]———. The Probable Mutation Effect, *Amer. Naturalist*, 98:453–455, 1964.

[4]Campbell, T. D. *Dentition and Palate of the Australian Aboriginal*, Adelaide, Australia, The Hassell Press, 1925.

[5]Dahlberg, Albert A. The Dentition of the First Agriculturalists (Jarmo, Iraq), *Amer. J. Phys. Anthropal.*, 18:243–256, 1960.

[6]Frisch, John Ernest, *Trends in the Evolution of the Hominoid Dentition*, Bibliotheca Primatologica, Fasc. 3., Basel, Switzerland, S. Karger, 1965.

[7]Goose, Denys H. Dental Measurement: an Assessment of its Value in Anthropological Studies. In Brothwell, D. R., editor, *Dental Anthropology*, London, Pergamon Press, 1963, p. 125–148.

[8]Gregory, W. K. *The Origin and Evolution of the Human Dentition*, Baltimore, Williams and Wilkins, 1922.

[9]McCown, T. D., and Keith, A. *The Stone Age of Mount Carmel*, vol. II: The Fossil Human Remains from the Levalloiso-Mousterian, Oxford, England, Clarendon Press, 1939.

[10]Matiegka, J. *Homo Predmostensis, Fosilni Clovek z Predmosti na Morave*, Prague, Czechoslovakia. Publications of the Czechoslovakian Academy of Science and Art, 1934.

[11]Post, Richard H. Population Differences in Vision Acuity: a Review, with Speculative Notes on Selection Relaxation, *Eugenics Quart.*, 9:189–212, 1962.

[12]Robinson, J. T. *The Dentition of the Australopithecinae*, Pretoria, Republic of South Africa, Transvaal Museum Memoir no. 9, 1956.

[13]———. Adaptive Radiation in the Australopithecines and the Origin of Man. In F. C Howell and F. Bourliere, editors. *African Ecology and Human Evolution*, New York, Viking Fund Publications in Anthropology no. 36, Wenner-Gren Foundation for Anthropological Research, Inc., 1963, p. 385–416.

[14]Vallois, H. V. Neanderthals and Praesapiens, *J. Roy. Anthropol. Inst.* 84:111–130, 1954.

[15]Weidenreich, Franz. The Dentition of Sinanthropus pekinensis: a Comparative Odontography of the Hominids, *Palaeontol. Sinica* 101:1–180, 1937.

[16]The Origin of Man. *Current Anthrop.*, 6:34–431, 1965.

25

POST-PLEISTOCENE CHANGES IN THE HUMAN DENTITION[1]
C. Loring Brace and Paul E. Mahler

From *American Journal of Physical Anthropology*
34:191–203, 1971. Reprinted with permission of the author
and publisher.

Many scholars have assumed that once modern man appeared, following the Neanderthals, evolution effectively stopped. Students of the human fossil record generally focus on the period from thirty thousand years ago on back, while students of "ongoing human evolution" focus on living people in the twentieth century. Evolution, however, did not stop simply because we called a particular fossil population "modern." Selective forces continued to change as human technology developed. To an increasing extent man has imposed a cultural filter between the forces of the environment and his previously unprotected physique. Following the logic of the PME (selections 2 and 3), we would expect resulting reductions in formerly important structures.

Not only has a burgeoning technology altered the way in which we manipulate things, but the food-producing revolution of ten thousand years ago has drastically altered human dietary practices. Both factors should have significantly reduced the selective pressures that had long operated to maintain large and healthy teeth. If our predictions are correct, there should have been significant reductions in the human dentition in the recent past. Furthermore, since the impact of the food-producing revolution has been in effect for very different lengths of time in different parts of the world, we should expect to find that the extent of dental reduction in a given population is in direct proportion to the length of time that the population in question had enjoyed (?) the benefits of this life-way.

Despite the quantity of potentially available evidence many people have not felt that there was any merit to this approach. As a result, data and support have been hard to obtain. The following article, then, must be regarded as a tentative and preliminary effort in an area that remains largely unexplored.

ABSTRACT. Published evidence indicates sharp reductions in the hominid dentition following the end of the Pleistocene. These reductions, both in size and in morphological complexity, have proceeded farthest in those areas where culture change has occurred most rapidly. The model proposed here suggests that post-Pleistocene dental reduction may be the result of the change in selective forces consequent from the invention and use of pottery and the changes in food-preparation techniques after the end of the Pleistocene. Models for testing this hypothesis are discussed.

". . . if it is undeniable that since the Paleolithic dental evolution has occurred in the sense that there has been a diminution in the number of teeth, a reduction in their volume, a simplification in their form and an approximation of their roots, it is no less doubtful that the occurrence of mutations at times has come to complicate and influence the general manner of that evolution." (translated from Brabant and Twiesselmann, 1964:55).

There is an assumption in many quarters that human form has remained essentially unchanged since what is called "modern" man first appears in the fossil record. In part this view is a survival from the era when the very idea of human evolution was viewed with something less than enthusiasm and when fully modern form was identified as far back in time as possible despite the exceedingly fragmentary and inconclusive evidence (Brace, '64). More recently the idea that man did in fact evolve from something that looked distinctly less than modern has gained increasing acceptance, but a vestige of the former attitude has tended to linger on in the belief that once "modern" form was achieved in the Upper Paleolithic, human evolution effectively came to a halt. Textbook accounts consistently portray Cro-Magnon man as being indistinguishable from 20th century Europeans. To be sure, there has been a growing interest in human microevolutionary change and what has been called the processes of ongoing human evolution, but there has been relatively little concern for and almost no research devoted to understanding recent trends in human biological change where the time span is measured in thousands of years rather than known generations.

Admittedly some care is needed in the approach to such questions, given the considerable effects which environment can have on human form. Genetically similar populations can appear phenotypically quite different as the result of differences in nutrition, disease, and the effects of exercise during the growth process. Keeping this in mind, however, one should be able to choose for study some traits where change must be basically genetic and where concomitant changes in selective forces can be suggested or observed.

In a previous paper it was suggested that,

[1]Earlier versions of this paper were presented before the American Association of Physical Anthropologists in the symposium *Teeth as Tools*, organized by Dr. Stephen Molnar, Washington, D.C., March, 1970; and at the meetings of the American Anthropological Association in San Diego, November, 1970.

". . . major modifications in structure should allow us to make inferences about the nature of alterations in the forces of selection. One of the achievements of modern anthropology has been the demonstration that the cumulative effect of man's traditions and activities—his culture—greatly alters the nature of the operation of selective forces. Consequently, one would suspect that any pronounced alteration of selective forces, as demonstrated by a distinct structural modification, should correspond to a major change in man's cultural adaptive mechanism." (Brace, 1967a:813),

Evidence for the coincidence of brain and tooth size changes with changes in cultural dimensions was then presented. The focus, however, was principally directed toward events which took place during the Pleistocene itself. The concern of the present paper, in contrast, is with late Pleistocene and post-Pleistocene changes. Even though the time depth is short as evolutionary time is usually considered, nevertheless if the principles elaborated earlier (Brace, 1963, 1967a), have any validity, recent events should be expected to proceed in predictable fashion.

The most dramatic and easily measured changes in human form observable in the late Pleistocene are associated with the dentition and, in the section that follows, evidence will be presented which shows that changes of this nature have continued in a predictable manner after the end of the Pleistocene. It was earlier suggested that the development of specific tools for specific purposes reduced the adaptive value in the possession of a large and well-developed dental apparatus, and it was further suggested that, as a consequence, dental reduction was produced by the Probable Mutation Effect (Brace, 1963).

Extending the argument, the prediction which underlies the efforts reported here suggests that the greatest amount of post-Pleistocene dental reduction should have occurred in those populations where cultural developments related to tooth use have been in effect for the longest period of time. However much the dentition may be used as an auxiliary manipulating device, its primary function has been connected with the processing of food. Throughout most of human evolution, the loss of the dentition would have severely reduced the chances of survival, simply because adequate alternate food-processing techniques did not exist. By 6,000 B.C., however, the widespread use of pottery in the Middle East (totally absent only a few hundred years earlier) completely changed the significance of the human dentition. (For a detailed treatment of a crucial archeological sequence from the pre-ceramic on, see Hole, et al., 1969.) Cooking pots make possible the reduction of food items to drinkable consistency which means that the teeth are no longer really necessary for survival. Given these conditions of selection relaxation (Post, 1962), one can guess that the biological consequences will be dental reduction, the mechanism being the Probable Mutation Effect (the "PME"). The operation of the PME suggests that through random mutation, the developmental processes controlled by complex genetic mechanisms will be disrupted with the final result being an incomplete or simplified structure (Brace, 1963). This suggests that the most likely results of the most likely mutations—the probable mutation effect—will be structural reduction. Obviously such an "effect" can only be of importance where the forces of selection are relaxed or suspended.

The validity of the PME as a change-producing mechanism has been challenged by some, and we do not intend to use this occasion to produce a detailed defense. In passing, however, it should be mentioned that, if the universal pleiotropy critique of Wright (1964) and Holloway (1966) were valid, then the increase in frequency of a beneficial trait under the impetus of natural selection would be just as impossible as the decrease following selection relaxation. The objection has been offered that a trait is not free to vary when selection for it is reduced because the adaptive value of the other traits controlled by the same genetic background probably will not also be reduced. In reply, it should be noted that the development of a particular advantageous trait would be similarly inhibited because, in like fashion, it is unlikely that the other traits influenced by the controlling gene would also be advantageous. The assumption of universal pleiotropy, then, is just as great a stumbling block to maintaining an orthodox view of evolution by means of

natural selection as it is to reduction following selection relaxation as suggested by the PME. Recent work in molecular biology has demonstrated that mutations can and do occur without being subjected to the forces of selection (King and Jukes, 1969), and that frequently they can have such specific effects that pleiotropy is not involved (Auerbach, 1967). This bolsters the logic initially used to propose the PME.

Of course it is always possible that particular reductions are in fact advantageous and are the direct result of selection pressure. But if, after prolonged and careful investigation, an observed trend toward reduction cannot be associated with any accruing benefits, it would be an abdication of scientific responsibility to declare that natural selection must be operating even if the mechanics are undiscoverable. Reductions have been documented in such human traits as vision, nasal septum form, and tear duct size where conditions of selection relaxation have been noted (Post, 1962, 1965, 1969a,b), and it is possible to suggest that the mechanism has been the PME.

In some instances the attempt to invoke "ordinary natural selection" is supported by somewhat unconvincing explanations as for instance the claim that dental arch size "in the later stages of man's evolution" is reduced because the lessened angular momentum of the craniofacial mass increases possible head-swivelling speed (Brues, 1966). We suspect that the small but consistent dental reduction which distinguishes modern Europeans from their Mesolithic ancestors cannot be accounted for by suggesting that it represents the survival value of being able to look back over one's shoulder with significantly greater speed.

Post-Pleistocene reduction in the human dentition has been recognized by a few scholars, notably by the late Sir Arthur Keith (1920, 1923, 1924, 1928), with impressive documentation by Brabant and Twiesselmann (1964), by D. A. Lunt (1969), and by D. L. Greene (1970). The following section presents quantitative evidence which bolsters the picture of post-Pleistocene dental reduction and adds support to suggestions concerning why these changes have occurred where and when they did. It is obvious that the evidence that has been collected here is far from conclusive. Normally such a poorly supported case would not justify presentation, but in this instance we feel that presentation of the model itself will allow others who have access to more data to perform the tests which are indicated. One thing that has become evident as a result of these efforts is the extremely limited amount of information available in the published literature. If this attempt has no other result, at least we hope that we shall have stimulated work on the collection and publication of quantitative information on the dentitions of living and prehistoric human populations.

THE EVIDENCE

Since the present concern is with late and post-Pleistocene dental reductions, the condition which preceded the reductions should be initially specified. As a point of departure, the procedure previously discussed (Brace, 1967a) of using the Neanderthal dentition as a model has been followed. There may well have been local differences, but the remarkable metric similarity between the Krapina Neanderthal teeth and those of the *Homo erectus* ("Sinanthropus") population of Choukoutien (Brace, 1967a: Fig. 2) suggests that the forces of selection had remained approximately the same for about half a million years, at least as far as the teeth were concerned. The Neanderthal dentition then should serve as a better general model for the condition from which all modern forms evolved than blind chance alone would have predicted.

The Krapina collection, measured by the senior author, includes the greatest number of known Neanderthal teeth, and, although all the other Neanderthal teeth for which measurements are available (Patte, 1962) have been added to the sample on which our graphs are based, the Krapina teeth obviously are numerically the most important. The additions in fact make little change in the mean figures.

Because a good portion of our information concerning the Neanderthal dentition comes from loose teeth, there is no way to identify sex. Even among more recent archeological collections where skeletons are more likely to be complete, the problem of identifying sex is difficult. Consequently we have followed general practice and made no attempt

to separate the data by sex. The measurements—mesial-distal (MD) and buccal-lingual (BL)—whether taken by ourselves or by those whose data we use, were done according to the convention described by Goose (1963). Some of the Neanderthal teeth and most of those in the more recent populations remain implanted in mandibles and maxillae. To facilitate their measurement, the tips of a standard Boley gauge were ground fine enough so that they could slip between adjacent teeth, allowing a proper MD measurement to be taken from contact facet to contact facet. Data were collected only on permanent teeth which had not been worn to the point where one would suspect serious alteration in the measurements. Our experience corroborates Goose's observation that the accuracy of independently repeated measurements is not greater than one-tenth of a millimeter. Consequently we recorded our individual tooth measurements (MD and BL) to a single decimal place.

As in the earlier paper (Brace, 1967a), these graphs present a kind of profile of cross-sectional areas, tooth by tooth, for visual ease of comparison. Admittedly the product of the MD and BL crown dimensions is not an exact representation of cross-sectional area since crown form is not precisely parallel-sided, but it is the best approximation that can be quickly produced, and since it is constructed from measurements most frequently recorded in the literature, it is the most convenient basis for comparing dental wear potential in various populations. As conditions of selection change, variation in cross-sectional area should be a good indicator of the biological response.

The data on which our graphs (Figs. 1–2) are based are presented (in square millimeters) in Tables 1 and 2. Where our published sources reported MD and BL means instead of individual measurements, we multiplied these means (mean MD x mean BL) to provide our approximation of cross-sectional area. In these cases, no estimate of variance was possible. Where we had access to data on individual teeth, we could calculate cross-sectional area for each, plus means and standard deviations for the populations. The measurements included are uncorrected for body size since, for the time being, we are accepting the evidence which suggests that

Table 1

MEAN CROSS-SECTIONAL AREAS IN SQUARE MILLIMETERS OF MAXILLARY TEETH

	I^1	I^2	C	p^1	p^2	M^1	M^2	Ma_3
Neanderthal[1]	89.19(41)[9] ±12.60	72.94(42) ±8.66	86.90(52) ±12.18	85.38(36) ±20.66	80.36(51) ±12.23	142.44(52) ±21.51	133.98(53) ±15.91	119.94(49) ±17.39
Up. Paleo.[2]	67.76(26) ±13.84	47.61(22) ±11.69	68.12(26) ±10.39	67.32(28) ±9.74	66.12(27) ±13.62	129.45(31) ±14.62	127.37(30) ±18.27	117.00(22) ±19.97
Mesolith.[3] (France)	61.06(9)	46.23(7)	61.42(8)	62.79(11)	61.10(7)	122.72(7)	113.68(6)	98.98(8)
12–16th C.[4] (Europe)	58.93(98)	39.68(103)	63.08(108)	55.90(108)	55.44(106)	112.00(104)	95.23(102)	83.83(89)
Wadi Halfa[5]	71.54(5)	51.68(5)	64.60(4)	73.72(9)	74.00(8)	138.99(8)	136.53(9)	110.92(10)
Natufians[6]	64.97(8)	45.56(8)	66.22(9)	65.80(13)	65.55(15)	134.07(14)	127.05(11)	105.09(8)
Jarmo[6]	58.08(2)	40.20(4)	69.72(5)	71.25(2)	76.44(2)	123.12(5)	116.28(5)	89.88(1)
Dickson Mound[7]	65.44(107) ±7.14	50.64(107) ±6.03	71.87(112) ±7.97	73.32(99) ±7.90	68.32(106) ±9.11	129.08(136) ±14.51	121.49(117) ±16.52	102.29(88) ±17.14
Aztec[8]	63.15(13) ±5.07	45.25(18) ±7.26	67.25(19) ±8.01	68.25(23) ±5.58	62.97(21) ±6.70	116.90(16) ±10.84	111.61(18) ±8.70	88.42(15) ±9.95

[1]Principally based on the Krapina dentition as measured by Brace with additional data from Patte ('62).
[2]Principally from Matiegka ('34), but see footnote 2, page 330.
[3]From Sahly et al. ('62).
[4]From Twiesselmann and Brabant ('60).
[5]From Greene et al. ('67).
[6]From Dahlberg ('60).
[7]Courtesy of M. H. Wolpoff.
[8]Courtesy of T. H. Charlton.
[9]The figure in parentheses indicates the number of individuals from which the mean was calculated; ± indicates the standard deviation wherever it can be computed.

Table 2
MEAN CROSS-SECTIONAL AREAS IN SQUARE MILLIMETERS OF MANDIBULAR TEETH

	I1	I2	C	P1	P2	M1	M2	M3
Neanderthal[1]	44.94(36)[9] ±8.48	53.39(41) ±7.85	72.69(40) ±11.66	71.63(49) ±11.91	70.50(57) ±12.50	128.59(54) ±18.83	134.63(65) ±19.51	130.00(65) ±17.49
Up. Paleo.[2]	34.69(31) ±8.46	41.49(31) ±8.65	56.48(32) ±11.08	57.48(35) ±8.02	61.11(41) ±7.73	125.48(58) ±15.22	121.69(52) ±17.15	117.53(34) ±20.33
Mesolith.[3] (France)	31.72(11)	37.05(9)	54.40(11)	51.06(6)	55.30(13)	123.17(12)	107.10(11)	97.92(5)
12–16th C.[4] (Europe)	30.60(102)	35.91(107)	51.48(109)	46.72(108)	52.14(109)	110.21(107)	97.00(109)	95.00(99)
Wadi Halfa[5]	35.91(4)	40.92(3)	59.94(4)	67.64(5)	70.84(5)	139.15(9)	135.70(8)	135.70(6)
Natufians[6]	33.48(10)	39.60(13)	55.30(13)	55.38(16)	59.04(14)	124.20(16)	116.60(16)	113.36(13)
Jarmo[6]	30.74(3)	36.60(3)	54.67(4)	59.20(3)	71.38(3)	119.70(6)	111.10(6)	119.88(2)
Dickson Mound[7]	32.10(95) ±4.30	41.30(99) ±3.88	58.81(121) ±7.19	58.60(126) ±6.19	64.57(119) ±9.08	130.85(132) ±12.58	125.42(116) ±15.05	120.79(100) ±17.95
Aztec[8]	30.39(18) ±4.63	38.78(19) ±3.58	55.72(24) ±6.42	53.71(24) ±4.33	59.51(26) ±15.46	115.58(19) ±15.66	111.32(23) ±9.11	97.90(20) ±16.56

1–9 See footnotes 1–9 in Table 1.

Table 3

Probability that the X^2 figure could occur by chance alone. The cells above the diagonal contain significance figures which refer to the comparison of the maxillary dentition. The figures below the diagonal refer to the mandibular dentition. Blank cells indicate no significance.

	Neand.	Wadi Hal.	Upper Pal.	Natuf.	Jarmo	Meso.	Euro.
Neand.		0.02	0.001	0.001	0.001	0.001	0.001
Wadi Hal.	—		—	–	0.05	—	0.001
Upper Pal.	0.05	—		–	—	—	0.001
Natuf.	0.01	—	—		—	—	0.001
Jarmo	0.001	—	—	—		—	0.05
Meso.	0.001	0.001	—	—	—		—
Euro.	0.001	0.001	0.05	—	0.05	—	

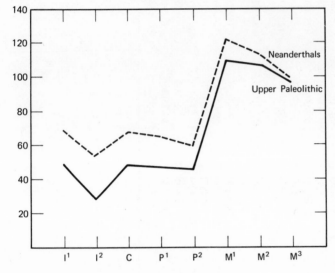

Figure 1. Cross-sectional areas in square millimeters for the maxillary teeth of Neanderthals, represented principally by Krapina, but with everything else available added (from Patte, 1962) compared with the Upper Paleolithic, represented principally by Predmost, but, again, with everything else available added (see footnote 2).

the relationship between tooth size and body size in populations of the genus *Homo* is "effectively nil" (Garn and Lewis, 1958:878).

The between-population differences in cross-sectional area visible in these graphs are not large, and only a few are "significant" by simple statistical tests such as Student's *t* (and this cannot even be done for most of the Old World examples because variance figures are lacking). The comparisons can be checked by using X^2 tests, the results appearing in Table 3. Evidently there are significant differences between the largest (Neanderthal) dentition and most of the others. The smallest (12–16th century Europeans) also differs significantly from most of the others. More interesting than the significance of the difference of the most widely separated populations, however, is the consistency of the *direction* of the change through time in a given geographical area.

Figure 1 (maxilla) and Figure 2 (mandible) show how size is reduced for each tooth between the Neanderthals and the European Upper Paleolithic. Proceeding in time, Figure 3 and Figure 4 show that there was a further drop in tooth size among the Mesolithic populations of post-Pleistocene Europe and that, during the last 5,000 years, this has continued in the same direction. The Upper Paleolithic figures were principally derived from the Predmost material (Mateigka, 1934) to which other available measurements were added.[2] While Predmost is in East-Central

[2]The additional measurements were taken from a wide variety of sources. Rather than cite each one, we refer the reader to the list in Wolpoff (1969, and 1971). To be absolutely sure of the accuracy of our figures, however, we used only those that we could check in numerical form in the cited original sources, omitting those that were taken from scaled photographs.

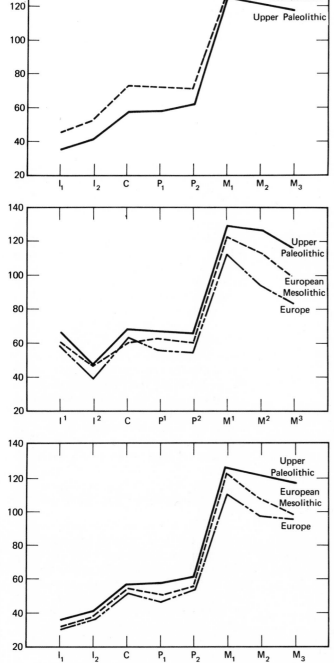

Figure 2. Cross-sectional areas in square millimeters for the mandibular teeth of the Neanderthals compared with the Upper Paleolithic.

Figure 3. Cross-sectional areas in square millimeters for the maxillary teeth of the European Upper Paleolithic Western European Mesolithic (Rouffignac), and "modern" Europeans (12th to 16th century French.)

Figure 4. Cross-sectional areas in square millimeters for the mandibular teeth of European Upper Paleolithic Mesolithic, and modern populations.

Europe rather than Western Europe, it provides the only relatively complete data on Upper Paleolithic teeth. From the scattered comparative evidence available, the teeth appear to be representative of dental size throughout Europe at that time. The Mesolithic data were taken from material excavated at Rouffignac in southwestern France (from Sahly et al., 1962), and the "modern European" information came from skeletal material in a twelfth to sixteenth century graveyard on the Belgian-French border (from Twiesselmann and Brabant, 1960).

While there is little or no significance by χ^2 test in the difference between each group and its temporal successor, the existence of non-random changes is shown by the use of the Wilcoxon matched-pairs signed-ranks test. The probabilities that the differences are due to chance alone are presented in Table 4. Actually these probability figures (as is true also in Table 5) assume that two-tailed test logic is being pursued; that is the mere existence of difference is being tested, whether consistently larger or consistently smaller. Since we have predicted that change should occur in a given direction—reduction—through time, we could justify using the significance levels for a one-tailed test. This would convert 0.02 to 0.01 and 0.01 to 0.005 giving even stronger support to our hypothesis.

Table 4

Probability that differences are due to change alone based on the Wilcoxon matched-pairs signed-ranks test. The cells above the diagonal contain significance figures which refer to the comparison of the maxillary dentition. The figures below the diagonal refer to the mandibular dentition.

	Neand.	Upper Pal.	Meso.	Euro.
Neand.		0.01	0.01	0.01
Upper Pal.	0.01		0.01	0.01
Meso.	0.01	0.01		0.01
Euro.	0.01	0.01	0.02	

Table 5

Wilcoxon matched-pairs signed-ranks test probability figures. Cells above the diagonal refer to maxillary tooth-size comparisons; below to mandibular. Blank cells indicate no significance

	Neand.	Wadi Hal.	Natuf.	Jarmo
Neand.		0.02	0.01	0.01
Wadi Hal.	—		0.02	0.01
Natuf.	0.01	0.01		—
Jarmo	0.01	0.02	—	

There are no data on skeletal or dental form from the Middle Eastern Upper Paleolithic; the nearest thing that could be used as a substitute was the information from the Mesolithic population from Wadi Halfa in the Sudan (Greene et al., 1967). Geographically this falls right at the edge of, or slightly outside, (Wendorf et al., 1970) what has been called the "Mousterian Culture Area" (Brace 1967b; and see discussion in Bordes, 1968:126). Since the Wadi Halfa region lacked the relatively long history of technological elaboration which grew from the Mousterian and flowered in the Upper Paleolithic in the core of this area, one would expect that the selective forces operating on the dentition of the Sudanese Mesolithic population would be roughly equivalent to those in effect further north and northwest during the Upper Paleolithic. In fact, the tooth measurements of the Wadi Halfa population (6,000 to 9,000 B.C.) are of about the same size as those of the European Upper Paleolithic as is shown in Figures 5 and 6. The differences are not significant by χ^2

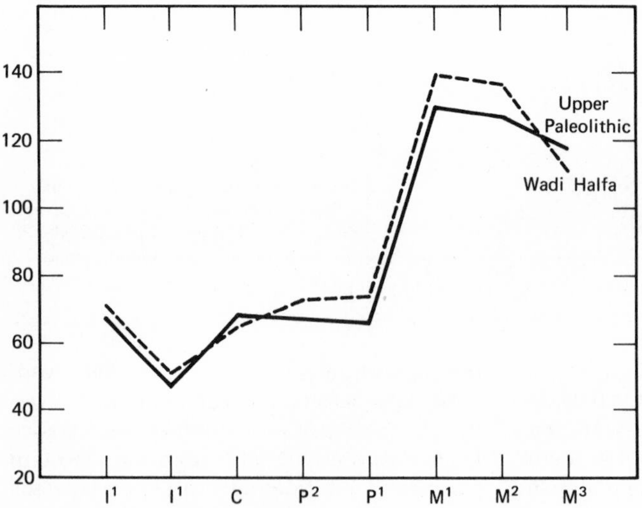

Figure 5. cross-sectional areas in square millimeters for the maxillary teeth of the Mesolithic population from Wadi Halfa (Sudan) compared with those from the European Upper Paleolithic.

test (see Table 3), although the larger average size of the Wadi Halfa posterior dentition accounts for the fact that the mandibular teeth are not significantly different from the Neanderthal dentition either by X^2 or by the Wilcoxon matched-pairs signed-ranks test (see Tables 3, 5).

Pottery was not present at the beginning of the phase represented at Jarmo, although it did appear during that phase (see Braidwood and Howe, 1962), and the selective pressures on the dentition must have been nearly the same as for a Mesolithic population. Note in Figures 9 and 10 that the Jarmo measure-

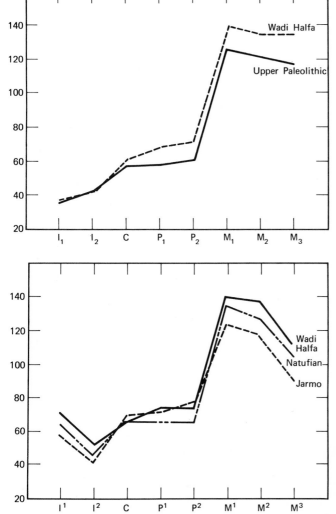

Figure 6. Cross-sectional areas in square millimeters for the mandibular teeth of Wadi Halfa compared with the European Upper Paleolithic.

Figure 7. Cross-sectional areas in square millimeters for the maxillary teeth of the late Pleistocene and post-Pleistocene sequence of the Middle East, using Wadi Halfa as the equivalent to the European Upper Paleolithic, the Natufians of Palestine for the Mesolithic, and Jarmo (Iraq) as Neolithic.

Plotting the Middle Eastern sequence in analogous fashion to the Western European sequence of Figures 3 and 4, one can see a representation of post-Pleistocene change in Figures 7 and 8. Note that the teeth from the Neolithic population of Jarmo (Iraq) average out to be only slightly smaller than the Mesolithic Natufian population from Palestine (Dahlberg, 1960) and that the difference is not statistically significant (see Tables 3, 5).

ments fit into the Western European sequence in very much the same way as did the French Mesolithic population shown in Figures 3 and 4. The Mesolithic and Jarmo dentitions do not differ significantly by either of the statistical tests used.

Predicting from this evidence, one might expect that still more recent populations should have yet smaller teeth, but here we run into an embarrassing lack of data and we

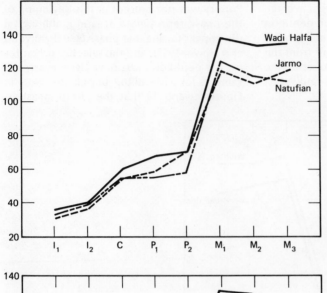

Figure 8. Cross-sectional areas in square millimeters for the mandibular teeth of the late Pleistocene and post-Pleistocene sequence of the Middle East.

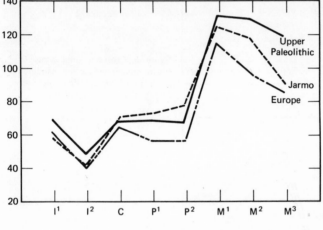

Figure 9. Cross-sectional areas in square millimeters for the maxillary teeth of the late Pleistocene and post-Pleistocene of Western Europe compared with the Jarmo Neolithic population from the Middle East.

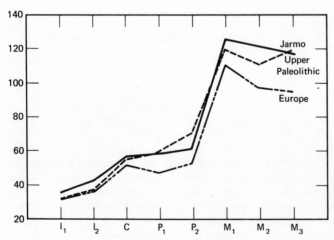

Figure 10. Cross-sectional areas in square millimeters for the mandibular teeth of the late Pleistocene and post-Pleistocene of Western Europe compared with Jarmo.

cannot use the graphic form of our previous examples. Incomplete evidence (lacking incisors, canines and third molars) from modern descendants of these earlier Middle Eastern populations does indeed support the predictions (Rosenzweig and Zilberman, 1967). This same problem—lack of sufficient published data—prevents our doing much more than suggesting one of the more interesting predictions that comes from this model. It is mentioned here in hopes that others who have access to data can put it to the test.

We have suggested that dental reduction was accelerated in the post-Pleistocene as a result of the major changes which occurred in subsistence technology, particularly food preparation techniques. These, however, did not occur everywhere at the same time. In the area that has been the principal concern in this paper, the food-producing revolution occurred first in the Middle East, spreading west and north rapidly at first and, at the end, relatively slowly (Waterbolk, 1968:1101). The biological impact of this change in the nature of selective forces has been in operation at least twice as long for the populations of the Middle East and adjacent areas as it has at the northwestern margin. Consequently, the existence of a tooth-size cline in modern Europe would be predicted, starting with minimum measurements in the Middle East and reaching a maximum in Scandinavia and the northwestern edges of the British Isles. What incomplete evidence there is (compare Dockrell, 1956, and Lysell, 1958a,b, for the northern and western extremes with Rosenzweig and Zilberman, 1967, for modern Middle Eastern figures) does not contradict this suggestion; personal observation of face and jaw size reinforces it, although we are again thwarted by an embarrassing lack of basic data.

If this interpretation has any merits, it should work in other parts of the world as well. It could be applied for East and Southeast Asia, Africa, and India, but again, data simply have not been collected. Even though time depth is quite short, this prediction should also be testable on New World skeletal material, and here we have

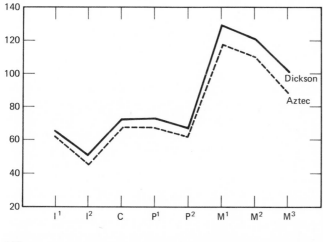

Figure 11. Cross-sectional areas in square millimeters for the maxillary teeth of a late Aztec population at San Juan Teotihuacan, Mexico, compared with the Middle Mississippian Indians of Dickson Mound, Illinois.

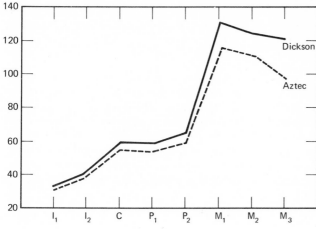

Figure 12. Cross-sectional areas in square millimeters for the mandibular teeth of Aztec compared with Middle Mississippian Indians from Illinois.

just enough information to suggest that it does indeed work. Figures 11 and 12 show the tooth size profiles of the inhabitants of San Juan Teotihuacan at the point of contact with the Spanish (but before intermarriage) compared with the Middle Mississippian people of Dickson Mound, Illinois. Since the food-producing revolution and the use of pottery have been factors in the life of the populations of the Valley of Mexico for a longer period of time than has been the case further north, one would expect the maximum amount of dental reduction among the aboriginal inhabitants of the New World to have occurred there. One would also expect the least amount of reduction to be found in those peoples who were north of the boundary of New World agriculture. Unfortunately the specimens of these latter available to us displayed such heavy wear, particularly on the incisors, that we could not use them for comparative purposes, although the few relatively less worn teeth do tend to confirm our expectations. Instead, we have used information from the northernmost population available. The contrast between San Juan Teotihuacan and Dickson Mound is not dramatic and not significant by X^2, but it is consistent and in the direction of our prediction; and it is highly significant by the Wilcoxon matched-pairs signed-ranks test (0.005).

From a quick visual inspection one retains the impression that morphological reduction has also, predictably, gone to a greater extent in the Aztec teeth. Specifically, reductions in hypocone (upper molars), hypoconulid (lower molars), shovelling (incisors), missing third molars and lateral incisor reduction all appear more pronounced than in the teeth of Middle Missippian Indians. This, however, is a superficial impression and should be checked by conventional comparative methods.

NON-GENETIC CHANGES

Crown morphology and actual dental dimensions are clearly under direct genetic control. Changes in these traits represent genuine biological evolution, but there are other changes in the dentition and its supporting structure that are non-genetic. Shape of the palate, cheek-bone development, gonial angle size, and the form of occlusion can be greatly altered by different environmental stresses that impinge on the dentition during the growth process (Hunt, 1960). One of the striking changes that has recently taken place in the human dentition appears to be of this nature and deserves some comment here. This is the appearance of the overbite.

Some years ago, the somewhat simplistic suggestion was advanced that this was a functional mechanism which was developed to promote a distal wedging action (Brace, 1962). The overbite did not appear with the food-producing revolution, however, and did not come to characterize the European occlusion until after the Middle Ages (see comments by Keith, 1920:85 and 1924:136). The parallel between the adoption of the table fork (including the gastronomic habits implied) and the appearance of the overbite is too striking to be coincidental. The diffusion of the fork from Italy to northwest Europe in the 17th century (Montagné, 1961; Deetz, 1969) drastically altered "civilized" eating habits. Henceforth food items were held down on the plate for cutting instead of being clamped between the incisors to be torn or cut into chewable size.

As always when one believes he has thought of something original, someone else inevitably said it before. So it is in this case. The statement, in a report on the "mound-builders" who fascinated the literate a century ago, is explicit enough to warrant quoting.

"This form of the teeth (edge-edge bite, flat wear) is not peculiar to the mound-builders but is characteristic of savage races generally. This disuse of the front teeth for the purpose of severing mouthfuls of food from the mass, consequent upon the use of the knife and fork, materially modified the process of mastication and the form of the teeth." (Henderson, 1882:711).

Actually wear is not necessary to produce an edge-to-edge bite since this form of occlusion can be observed in individuals where no wear is present. The simple habit of using the incisors to hold food while it is being cut apparently prevents the over-eruption of both maxillary and mandibular incisors which creates the overbite. The issue of the overbite is raised, not because this suggestion is necessarily correct, but because it, like many other questions that have been with biological anthropology for a long time, could easily be solved with a little problem-oriented research.

CONCLUSION

The evident conclusion which emerges from this survey is that the data which could be used to test the hypotheses which have been tendered here have yet to be collected. Attempts to interpret the significance of human variation by noting the coincidence between clines in putative selective forces and accompanying variation in inherited (although undoubtedly polygenic) traits have been regarded with "despair" as examples of "soft thinking" and dismissed with the words, "The viewpoint is modern, but the methodology so very old" (Harrison, 1965:295). One could reply that the speculative nature of papers such as this is due to the fact that so few have actually done the work of acquiring the necessary data. If teeth are measured, incisors or perhaps third molars are not reported. More frequently, only mesial-distal measurements are taken in spite of the fact that, particularly in populations where wear is heavy, they alone are not an adequate measure of tooth size. Attempts to gather information to test hypotheses of the kind proposed are rejected as "unlikely to produce significant new knowledge." Yet on the other hand, mountains of information continue to be collected on traits of unknown biological significance. Sometimes one suspects that if it requires precipitation or, better yet, electrophoresis, it is supported as "Science." When we see support being given to the collection of data principally because the technique is sophisticated while it is being denied where the rationale calls for techniques that are simple, then we feel that it might be appropriate to rephrase Harrison's complaint to express our own, to wit: "the methodology is modern, but the viewpoint so very old."

We suggest that the study of post-Pleistocene changes in the human dentition is a legitimate and important enterprise. At the moment, it is being pursued by altogether too few scholars. It is our hope that, if this paper has no other effect, at least it will have stimulated the collection of usable information which can be applied towards the solution of some of the issues raised.

ACKNOWLEDGMENTS

The research on which this paper is based was accomplished despite refusals of support from the National Science Foundation and the National Institutes of Health.

For measurements on the Aztec population of San Juan Teotihuacan, we are greatly indebted to their excavator, Dr. Thomas H. Charlton, of the Department of Sociology and Anthropology at the University of Iowa. For the measurements on the Dickson Mound teeth, we are equally indebted to Dr. Milford H. Wolpoff of the Department of Anthropology, Case Western Reserve University. We are grateful to Dr. Richard G. Wilkinson of the Department of Sociology and Anthropology at the State University of New York at Albany, and to Dr. Stephen Molnar of the Department of Anthropology at Washington University in St. Louis for their aid in bringing certain information to our attention. We thank Dr. James E. Harris and Dr. Melvyn J. Baer of the University of Michigan School of Dentistry for critical comments and advice as we wrestled with the revisions of this paper.

LITERATURE CITED

Auerbach, C. 1967 The chemical production of mutations. Science, *158*: 1141–1147.

Bordes, François 1968 The old Stone Age. McGraw-Hill, New York.

Brabant, H., and F. Twiesselmann 1964 Observations sur l'évolution de la denture permanente humaine en Europe occidentale. Bulletin du Groupement Internat. pour la Rech. scient. en Stomatologie, 7: 11–84.

Brace, C. L. 1962 Cultural factors in the evolution of the human dentition. In: Culture and the Evolution of Man. M. F. Montagu, ed. Oxford University Press (Galaxy Book), New York. pp. 343–354.

———. 1963 Structural reduction in evolution. Amer. Naturalist, *97:* 39–49.

———. 1964 The fate of the 'classic' Neanderthals: a consideration of hominid catastrophism. Current Anthropology, *5:* 3–43.

———. 1967a Environment, tooth form and size in the Pleistocene. J. Dent. Res., 46 (Supplement to No. 5): 809–816.

———. 1967b The Stages of Human Evolution.

Prentice-Hall, Inc., Englewood Cliffs, New Jersey.

Braidwood, R. J., and B. Howe 1962 Southwestern Asia beyond the lands of the Mediterranean littoral. In: Courses Toward Urban Life. R. J. Braidwood and G. R. Willey, eds. Aldine, Chicago. pp. 132–146.

Brues, A. M. 1966 "Probable Mutation Effect" and the evolution of hominid teeth and jaws. Am. J. Phys. Anthrop., 25: 169–170.

Dahlberg, A. A. 1960 The dentition of the first agriculturalists (Jarmo, Iraq). Am. J. Phys. Anthrop., 18: 243–256.

Deetz, J. 1969 The reality of the pilgrim fathers. Nat. Hist., 78: 32–45.

Dockrell, R. B. 1956 Tooth size in Irish (Aran Island) families. Europ. Orthodont. Soc. Reports, 32: 200–216.

Garn, S. M. and A. B. Lewis 1958 Tooth size, body size, and 'giant' fossil man. Amer. Anthrop., 60: 874–880.

Goose, D. H. 1963 Dental measurement: an assessment of its value in anthropological studies. In: Dental Anthropology. D. R. Brothwell, ed. Pergamon Press, N.Y., pp. 125–148.

Greene, D. L. 1970 Environmental influences on Pleistocene hominid dental evolution. Bioscience, 20: 276–279.

Greene, D. L., G. H. Ewing and G. J. Armelagos 1967 Dentition of a mesolithic population from Wadi Halfa, Sudan. Am. J. Phys. Anthrop., 27: 41–56.

Harrison, G. A. 1965 Review of M. F. A. Montagu, ed. The Concept of Race. Race, 6: 288–297.

Henderson, J. G. 1882 Aboriginal remains near Naples, Ill. Smithson. Inst. Ann. Rep., pp. 686–721.

Hole, F., K. V. Flannery and J. A. Neely 1969 Prehistory and Human Ecology of the Deh Luran Plain: An Early Village Sequence from Khuzistan, Iran. Mem. of the Mus. of Anthrop., Univ. of Mich., No. 1.

Holloway, R. L., Jr. 1966 Structural reduction through the "probable mutation effect": a critique with questions regarding human evolution. Am. J. Phys. Anthrop., 25: 7–11.

Hunt, E. E., Jr. 1960 The continuing evolution of modern man. Cold Spring Harbor Symp. on Quant. Biol., 24: 245–254.

Keith, A. 1920 Comment on L. H. D. Buxton, The Teeth and jaws of savage man. Trans. Brit. Soc. for the Study of Orthodont., 1916–1920, pp. 85–86.

————. 1923 The adaptational machinery concerned in the evolution of man's body. Nature (Supplement) No. 2807: pp. 257–268.

————. 1924 Concerning certain structural changes which are taking place in our jaws and teeth. In' The Growth of the Jaws, Normal and Abnormal, in Health and Disease. The Dental Board of the United Kingdom, London, pp. 133–147.

————. 1928 The Antiquity of Man. J. B. Lippincott, Philadelphia, Vol. II.

King, J. L., and T. H. Jukes 1969 Non-Darwinian evolution. Science, 164: 788–798.

Lunt, D. A. 1969 An Odontometric Study of Mediaeval Danes. Acta Odontolog. Scandinav. Supp. 55, 27, Glasgow.

Lysell, L. 1958a A biometric study of occlusion and dental arches in a series of Medieval skulls from N. Sweden. Acta Odontolog. Scandinav., 16: 177–203.

————. 1958b An odontological examination of the remains of Erik XIV. Transac. Roy. Sch. Dentist, Stockholm. No. 1, pp. 1–16.

Matiegka, J. 1934 Homo Předmostensis: Fosilní Človek z Předmostí na Moravé. Publicat. Czech. Acad. Sci. and Art, Prague.

Montagné, P. 1961 Larousse Gastronomique: The Encyclopedia of Food, Wine and Cookery. C. Turgeon and N. Froud, eds. Crown Publishers, Inc., New York.

Patte, E. 1962 La Dentition des Néanderthaliens. Masson et Cie., Paris.

Post, R. H. 1962 Population differences in red and green color vision deficiency: a review, and a query on selection relaxation. Eugen. Quart., 9: 131–146.

————. 1965 Notes on relaxed selection in man. Anthrop. Anz., 29: 186–195.

————. 1969a Deformed nasal septa and relaxed selection, II. Social Biol., 16: 179–196.

————. 1969b Tear duct size differences of age, sex and race. Am. J. Phys. Anthrop., 30: 85–88.

Rosenzweig, K. A. and Y. Zilberman 1967 Dental morphology of Jews from Yemen and Cochin. Am. J. Phys. Anthrop., 26: 15–22.

Sahly, A., H. Brabant and M. Bouyssou 1962 Observations sur les dents et les maxillaires du Mésolithique et de l'âge du fer trouvé dans la grotte de Rouffignac, département de la Dordogne, France. Bull. Group. Internat. Rech. scient. Stomatol., 5: 252–285.

Twiesselmann, F., and H. Brabant 1960 Recherches sur les dents et les maxillaires d'une population d'âge Franc de Coxyde. Bull. Group. Internat. Rech. scient. Stomatol., 3: 99–171; 355–400.

Waterbolk, H. T. 1968 Food production in prehistoric Europe. Science, 162: 1093–1102.

Wendorf, F., R. Said and R. Schild 1970 Egyptian prehistory: some new concepts. Science, 169: 1161–1171.

Wolpoff, M. H. 1969 Metric Trends in Hominid Dental Evolution. Unpublished Doctoral Dissertation, Department of Anthropology, The University of Illinois.

————. 1971 Metric Trends in Hominid Dental Evolution. Case Western Reserve University Studies in Anthropology, No. 2. Cleveland.

Wright, S. 1964 Pleiotropy in the evolution of structural reduction and dominance. Amer. Naturalist, 98: 65–69.

4
HUMAN DIVERSITY

26

A NONRACIAL APPROACH TOWARDS THE UNDERSTANDING OF HUMAN DIVERSITY
C. Loring Brace

Folk knowledge provides effective guidelines for many of the situations that people encounter. Judicial and political systems based on faith in the common sense of the average person have stood the test of time. There are limitations, however, to the insights that unaided common sense can provide. For example, until the end of the fifteenth century, everybody simply "knew" that the earth was a flat place, bounded by oceans and deserts, and that the sun, moon, planets, and stars revolved around it. Earth was the center of a universe created specifically for the benefit of mankind.

Renaissance exploration and astronomy effectively changed this. Darwin and Einstein later showed the flaws in other major areas of what was traditionally regarded as common knowledge. At present we can point to another area where traditional views are not only wrong, they are responsible for some of the more unsavory aspects of current social practice. The area to which we refer is human variation and how it is traditionally perceived. It is a matter of common knowledge that mankind is divided into a number of "races." Political and social activities simply assume the reality of human races and proceed from there.

Over the past two decades, however, zoologists have come to realize that the race or subspecies concept, is not the most effective way of coming to grips with the reality of variation in an increasing number of animals. It has been recognized that traits in widely distributed populations vary in the strength of their development from one area to another, but, whereas one trait may have a north-south gradient (or cline), another may have an east-west gradient, a gradation from the center to the periphery of the range and so forth. With few if any traits co-varying, it becomes meaningless to choose a particular region of the species distribution and label it a race.

While this view has not been without opposition, it has been proposed seriously for meadow frogs (Moore 1949), butterflies (Gillham 1956), pine martens (Hagmeier 1958), and zebras (Mettler and Gregg 1969). It appears to describe wolf variation in the wild better than the subspecies approach (Mech 1970), and it has led one zoologist to suggest that "the feeling is growing that geographical variation of animals is best expressed in terms of the individual variant characters themselves, rather than as subspecies" (Brown 1958). Looking at human variation with this in mind, one anthropologist concluded that "there are no races, there are only clines" (Livingstone 1962). With this we heartily concur. The concept of race is a facet of the folklore of Western civilization that is inadequate to account for the facts of human biological variation, to say nothing of the brutal behavior that is practiced in its name.

The following article is a preliminary attempt to deal with the reality of human variation, without using the race concept.

Brown, W. L., Jr. 1958. General adaptation and evolution. *Systematic Zoology* 7:157–168.

Gillham, N. W. 1956. Geographical variation and the subspecies concept in butterflies. *Systematic Zoology* 5:110–120.

Hagmeier, E. M. 1958. Inapplicability of the subspecies concept to the North American marten. *Systematic Zoology* 7:1–7.

Livingstone, F. B. 1962. On the non-existence of human races. *Current Anthropology* 3:279–281.

Mech, L. David. 1970. *The Wolf.* Natural History Press. Garden City, New York. 348 pp.

Mettler, L. E., and T. G. Gregg. 1969. *Population Genetics and Evolution.* Prentice-Hall, Englewood Cliffs, N.J. 212 pp.

Moore, J. A. 1949. Geographic variation of adaptive characters in *Rana pipiens* Schreber. *Evolution 3*:1–24.

It is the task of Physical Anthropology to further the understanding of human evolution. Of course the investigation and interpretation of the hominid fossil record is clearly one of the ways in which this is accomplished, but another and equally important approach is through the consideration of physical diversity among the living peoples of the world. Superficially it might seem as though it would be easier to deal with the abundant evidence present in the form of living peoples, but actually this turns out to be somewhat more difficult.

The paleoanthropologist's approach starts with the arranging of the known fossil record in time, after which the causal mechanisms postulated to produce the changes so observed can be discussed. To many, the analogous procedure on the part of the student of the living is to arrange the peoples of the world according to geographical location, and then to attempt an explanation for the population differences observed. In practice this is far less easy since a number of problems immediately arise which greatly complicate the issues.

First of all, it is extremely difficult to say where one population ends and another begins. An arrangement of world populations based on such characteristics as stature and head form would differ radically from an arrangement based on hair form and skin color. The criterion for the delineation of living human groups is considered to be their breeding behavior, and a population is then considered to be that group of people who habitually choose their mates from among themselves. This approach to the identification of meaningful human groups enjoys considerable following at the present time since, following the insights which have come from that branch of the biological sciences called population genetics, the unit which is significant for the evolutionary survival of a species has been recognized as the breeding population. This works quite well in delineating meaningful groups in nature such as, for instance, field mice or

fruit flies. Zoologists have used the term "races" to designate breeding populations which share identifiable characteristics, and it has been assumed that a similar practice could be followed in dealing with human groups. When races are delineated for mankind by modern biologically oriented physical anthropologists, they are usually defined along these lines.

The use of such an approach as an attempt to discover biologically meaningful human groups usually does not take complete consideration of the fact that human breeding populations are determined by the dictates of culture, rather than by specifically physical features. Certainly the most valid groupings of human beings are based upon cultural criteria. This puts the physical anthropologist in the awkward position of having to base the analysis of human physical diversity upon groupings which are not primarily based upon morphological characteristics.

The result is that "race" has always been a troublesome issue for human biologists, aside from the social and political problems that have been involved. This accounts for the fact that there is such widespread disagreement among anthropologists concerning the definitions of race and the identification of the races of man. Definitions range all the way from the denial that races exist at all to the attempt to define race on an exclusively morphological basis, and, for the majority of anthropologists who recognize some division of *Homo sapiens* into constituent races, the number recognized has ranged all the way from two or three up into somewhere in the hundreds. Finally, once a given anthropologist has settled on a definition which suits him, he then discovers that there is relatively little that he can do with his races except to list them.

This is all in marked contrast to the convenience which the social scientist finds in the term race. While individual sociologists may hold slightly differing definitions, the differences are not significant and, in fact, disappear in practice. There is virtual unanimity among professionals in the applications and uses of the term. Even those anthropologists who have attempted to define race on biological grounds alone are forced to admit that the sociologist is quite properly within his own province when he studies the problems engendered by race relations. Obviously the concept of race is used in the same way by people concerned with a theoretical as well as an applied interest in politics, i.e., by political scientists as well as politicians.

The definition of race which is offered here is essentially that of the social scientist and is based upon the perception of physical traits which are assumed to characterize human groups. Race is defined as being:

a group of mankind, members of which can be identified by the possession of distinctive physical characteristics.

The inclusion of the word "distinctive" in this definition is crucial since the importance of race is primarily in human perception, and, of course, in the attitudes and actions of the perceivers. Unless differences are clearly and easily perceived, consistent attitudes and practices cannot be pursued, and the race in question loses its identity as far as the people under consideration and also the social scientists are concerned. In some cases, what are perceived as racial differences are in fact primarily cultural differences between people whose genetically based physical characteristics are not markedly distinguishable. For instance, if one were to send a Sikh man to a barber, give him a shave and a haircut, and dress him in a business suit, he would be indistinguishable from, say, someone of Italian or any other Mediterranean origin. The same thing would be true for a Sikh woman in, for instance, a bikini and a bathing cap. However, the man in beard and turban, and the woman in her sari are immediately recognizable as being racially distinct from people of European origin.

Because human breeding populations are delineated by culturally established boundaries, and because of the inhumanity which has been practiced in the name of race, it occasionally has been advocated that the term be entirely abandoned. In the past, certain authors (for instance Huxley 1941 [1926] and Montagu 1951) have noted that since culture determines the criteria by which human groups are delimited, the proper unit to be considered in discussing human breeding populations is the "ethnic group," and that the term race be given up for these purposes.

On the face of it, it might seem that race as it has been defined above, being breeding populations with the addition of perceived physical differences, would be the most desirable grouping for the exploration of human physical differences. Actually, as was perceived some time ago and recently re-emphasized (Hogben 1931; Huxley and Haddon 1936; Montagu 1941; Livingstone 1962), neither the use of breeding population (ethnic group) nor race, no matter how it is defined, is sufficient for the understanding of human diversity. It has become apparent that the assumption that there is something significant in the association of traits in a single group of people is an assumption which obscures the factors influencing the occurrence and distribution of any single trait. *The most important thing for the analysis of human variation is the appreciation of the selective pressures which have operated to influence the expression of each trait separately.* Since in many important cases the crucial selective factors have no reference to ethnic or population boundaries, obviously an approach which takes population as its unit for study will fail to produce an understanding of whatever is influencing the distribution of the characteristics in question.

At this point it should be noted that the biggest changes in the human fossil record occurred as a result of changes in the selective pressures affecting particular features, and the changes in the selective pressures in turn followed improvements in the primary adaptive mechanisms in question (Brace 1964). Since the primary human adaptive mechanism is culture, it may be legitimately asked why a culturally defined group should not be the proper unit for the study of adaptively determined human variation. The answer is that for some purposes the presence or absence of the crucial adaptation may indeed coincide with culturally determined population boundaries, but for most characteristics, the adaptations, while cultural, are quite unrestricted by the boundaries of specific cultures. For instance, metal cutting utensils are as much the property of the Congolese pygmy as they are the property of the Viennese or the Roman or the New Yorker. Clearly, many adaptively important cultural features are not limited by the boundaries of specific cultures, any more than are the genetic characteristics of particular populations limited by their preferred but not exclusively practiced breeding habits.

Human physical variation can best be understood by relating the distributions of specific morphological features to the distribution and history (also the prehistory) of the relevant selective and adaptive forces. In the section which follows, a few of the most obvious characteristics of mankind will be discussed where the distribution parallels the known or postulated distribution of the selective factors involved. Because of the stress which has been placed on characteristics controlled by single genes, it has been assumed by many recent authorities that only the study of such traits could produce any precise insight into human diversity. It is apparent, however, that most of the traits by which human races can be easily recognized are not single gene traits, and yet, as we shall see, their distribution is just as logical as that of the traits which are relatively simpler in their genetic background.

The traits which will be considered first are those which have been traditionally most important for racial recognition (or discrimination, depending on the purpose behind making the distinction). The first such trait which will be examined is skin color.

SKIN COLOR

Figures 1a and 1b show the probable distribution of skin color throughout the world just before European exploration and colonization so radically changed human distributions on the face of the earth. It can be seen that dark pigmentation is found only among people who live within fifteen to twenty degrees of the equator, although not all people who live in the tropics are dark. Furthermore, some people who are generally accounted as being very dark may be partially exhibiting the effects of heavy sun tanning. The aboriginal inhabitants of Australia—particularly those who did not live in the extreme norther part—frequently bear testimony to the fact that their dark color is sometimes due to living out in the sun without any clothing.

In some areas, however, it is clear that people living within twenty degrees of the equator are definitely not noticeably dark, as is the case with the inhabitants of Indonesia and northern South America. In these cases, the people in question apparently have not been there for a sufficient period of time to have developed pigmentary protection.

The pigment in the human skin is a complex organic molecule called melanin. Its exact function is still a matter of dispute (Baker 1958), and, as with many of the other physical differences between men, its importance is based on presumptive rather than proven evidence, but the presumptions appear reasonable and must be given thoughtful attention.

Where the ultraviolet component of solar radiation is strong, as it is in the tropics, the possibility of damage to the living cells in the

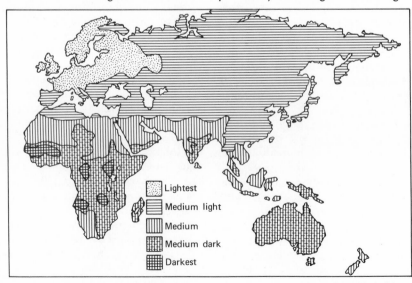

Figure 1a. Skin color distribution. Condensed and redrawn after Biasutti 1959. Old World.

Figure 1b. Skin color distribution. Condensed and redrawn after Biasutti 1959. New World.

dermis of the human skin is always present. Melanin in the outer layer of skin absorbs the harmful ultraviolet radiation and does not allow it to penetrate the living skin. As a result, physicians have long noted the much higher frequency of tissue injury and resultant skin cancer in relatively depigmented as opposed to relatively heavily pigmented peoples where the skin of both has been subjected to excessive amounts of sunshine (Keith 1949). Apparently dark skin has survival value in the tropics as people have suspected for many years.

Against this it has been argued that many dark-skinned tropic dwellers do not in fact have to contend with much strong sunlight. The Congo negro or the pygmy of the Ituri forest spend large parts of their lives sheltered by jungle, and yet they are quite well endowed with melanin. The answer is that neither of these people has been there for very long. While this at first seems unexpected in view of the widespread certainty that the Negro comes from the jungles of Africa, yet it turns out that this certainty is largely a

piece of modern folklore. For one thing, the tropical rainforest is relatively restricted in extent, covering far less area than either dry grassland with scattered scrub trees or full desert. For another thing, survival in the rainforest depends on the possession of iron tools and suitable jungle-adapted crops, both of which are relatively recent in Africa. Apparently the Congo area has only recently sustained the populations which now live there, and a consideration of the selective pressures which were important in determining the skin color of the Congolese inhabitants at the present and in the recent past must look instead to the areas from which these people came. There are no historic records placing their origins, but linguistic and cultural evidence all indicates that they came from the area where the grassland merges with the forest to the north and west of the Congo basin and just south of 20⁰ north latitude. The assumption that dark skin has value for people who have been adapting for a long time to an environment characterized by an abundance of tropical sunlight is not contradicted by the inhabitants of Africa, despite their present distribution.

While the equator passes several degrees south of the southernmost parts of India and Ceylon, yet the whole southern half of the Indian subcontinent from Bombay on down is below the twentieth parallel, and one would expect if our assumptions are correct, that the peoples who have inhabited these regions for the longest period of time, and hence who have been longest exposed to the selective effects of the environment, would show the greatest amount of pigmentation in their skins. As is expected, the peoples whom present cultural and linguistic evidence suggest were the most ancient inhabitants of the area are indeed the darkest in color (this is supported by the myths, legends, semihistorical and historical writings of the ancient Aryans). For instance, the Munda speaking people, as relatively northerly outposts in central India, but most particularly back-woods "hill tribes" such as the Kadar of southern India and the Vedda of Ceylon. In general, there is a north-south color gradient with the darkest people in the south. India, then, supports the generalizations which have been made on the basis of skin color distribution in Africa.

In southeast Asia, Indonesia, and the western Pacific again the initial impression is one of a great confusion of different colors. The equator runs right through the middle of the big islands of Sumatra and Borneo, just south of the tip of the Malay peninsula, and just north of New Guinea, and the area bracketed by 20° N and 20° S, includes mainland Southeast Asia, the northern quarter of Australia, and all of the islands in between extending far east into the Polynesian part of the Pacific. There are no really dark-skinned people in Sumatra or Borneo or the parts of Indonesia right on the equator, and it is not until one gets farther away from mainland southeast Asia, such as into parts of the Philippines, New Guinea, Melanesia, and northern Australia, that one finds the kind of really dark brown skin which for purposes of social discrimination is called black. A few peoples in the refuge of the Malay jungles and the inhabitants of the out-of-the-way Andaman Islands, between the Malay peninsula and India, also show very dark skins, but with these exceptions the bulk of the people in Indonesia and southeast Asia range from brown in the

south to yellow-brown up near the Chinese border.

The reason why there is so little evidence for dark skin among the inhabitants of the western and northern parts of this area is tied up with the history of population movements during the recent past. On the basis of the remnant peoples such as the Semang and Sakai of the Malay peninsula, the Andaman islanders, the Aeta of the Philippines and other less adequate hints, it is reasonable to regard the original inhabitants of the whole area as having been dark. Population was not dense because the basic means of subsistence was hunting and gathering which requires large areas to support limited numbers of people. The development of efficient farming techniques farther north allowed these northern peoples to spread south into what must have been for them relatively unoccupied country, absorbing and/or eliminating the few darker people who had formerly had the country to themselves.

Historical records amply confirm the north-south movements of the last 2000 years, and the decrease in both cultural and physical resemblances to the mainland becomes more marked the farther east one goes, until one reaches New Guinea. For a variety of reasons, the inhabitants of New Guinea and Australia are clearly the most ancient people of the area under consideration and consistently have dark skins. It seems reasonable to regard the Polynesians, who now spread far to the east of New Guinea, as being the end product of the first great push from mainland southeast Asia, having passed north of New Guinea itself. If we are correct in regarding the whole area as having been thinly populated with dark skinned peoples before the migrations, then the present remains of the first light skinned people to come from the mainland should show the effects of having absorbed darker elements on the way. This certainly is supported by the appearance of the present Polynesians.

In our consideration of the distribution of the various shades of human pigmentation, no mention has been made of the western hemisphere. In general, it appears that the Indians had not been across the Bering Straits for a long enough time for selection to have had much effect on skin color, even in the most tropic parts of Central and South

America. The color of the Indians then, like that of the Indonesians, betrays their eastern Asiatic origin.

So far, this presentation has been concerned with light skinned people moving down into tropic areas where dark people had prevailed. Of course, in Africa the formidable barrier of the Sahara desert and the swamps of the upper Nile prevented any such population movements, and in the New World there were no preceding dark tropic dwellers, but this picture holds true for Arabia, India, and Southeast Asia-Indonesia. This southern expansion of light colored peoples has been recognized by many generations of geographers, historians, and anthropologists, but very few have grappled with the question of why it happened.

There are two basic problems involved. First, what made these people light skinned in the first place, and second, why did they press south. The problem of their southerly movement has been treated from time to time, but it will be deferred here until after the discussion of the problem of depigmentation. Some authorities have simply assumed that "white" was the original color for all mankind, although this still evades the question of what adaptive advantage it must have conferred in order to have originally become established.

Another suggestion has been advanced claiming that the reduction in epidermal melanin allows more ultraviolet radiation to penetrate the skin and aid in the formation of vitamin D. This presumably is an advantage in those parts of the north temperate zone where year around cloud cover so reduces the available amount of sunshine that every bit absorbed is of value. This view runs into difficulty when one realizes that at the time of year when sunlight is at its rarest and weakest, the greatest amount of depigmented skin is securely covered with quantities of clothing. By the same token, the fur covered members of the animal world should all be showing the effects of a severe vitamin D deficiency.

The mention of clothing brings us to what appears to be the real source of the reduction in skin pigment which is so apparent in peoples whose remote origins were in the neighborhood of 50° north latitude. From the foregoing discussion it seems apparent that a relatively great amount of skin pigment has been of value to a hairless animal living in the sunnier parts of the tropics, and since the fossil record points to just this area as the remote home for all mankind, there is some basis to assume that the remote human ancestors were dark in color. This being the case, our problem is to understand how some eventually became light.

While there can be no proof for it, this is offered as the most likely means by which it happened. The archeological record shows that relatively successful and extensive human occupation of the north temperate zone as a permanent habitat did not occur until the last glaciation. During the previous glaciations, the onset of cold conditions had forced people back south, but by the end of the third interglacial, the technological facets of developing human culture had just reached the point where, with some refinement, they would allow people to adapt to the cold instead of having to flee it. People stayed in the north, then, taking abundant advantage of the quantities of big game which lived there.

The archeological record shows an abundance of scrapers appearing in Europe and the Middle East at the onset of the Würm glaciation, and this clearly shows an increasing preoccupation with the preparation of animal skins. Equally clearly the Neanderthals did not tramp through the snows in the loin cloth type of garment pictured in the standard cartoon. One of the things which allowed them to survive was the use of adequate clothing. Now for the first time man presented something besides his own skin to the outer world, which meant that the presence or absence of melanin no longer had any importance.

With the adaptive significance of melanin substantially reduced starting with the onset of the last glaciation approximately 70,000 years ago, the genetic background for melanin production was free to vary, and the inevitable result was that mutations detrimental to melanin production occurred. Since these were not selected against because of the reduction in importance of the protective function formerly played by melanin, such mutations accumulated in these populations with the eventual result that melanin ceased to be produced with the same efficiency. Thus the cultural factors which allowed human survival in the north temperate zone greatly reduced the survival value of a particular trait—pigmentation—and the resultant accumulation of random mutations meant that the trait was eventually reduced, a process which has been termed "the probable mutation effect" (Brace 1963).

The degree of human depigmentation, wherever it is found, should indicate the length of time and the extent to which skin pigment has been reduced as an adaptive feature. This is borne out by observation since the people with the palest coloring in the world today are those who can trace their ancestry back to the zone stretching from western through eastern Europe and on into southern Russia where the archeological record gives evidence that human survival depended on the use of clothing for a longer period of time than anywhere else in the world. It is tempting to suggest that perhaps this may also be related to the reason why peoples stemming from northern Europe have always been so stuffy about the idea of human nudity, but this is going a bit beyond the realm of physical anthropology.

It might be asked why the inhabitants of northern China (Manchuria) and Mongolia are not as light-skinned as the Europeans of the same latitude. The answer must be that they have not been there for quite so long, and their ancestors therefore were not dependent upon clothing for survival purposes for as far back in time. The archeological record does not provide the same kind of confirmation for this view as it does for the interpretation advanced for the West since the artifacts assignable to the early Würm are notably meager, although this is actually what one would expect if the area were not permanently inhabited at this time. The near absence of evidence for human habitation at this time in the northern parts of the far East (see Chang 1962) is in marked contrast to the abundance of Mousterian remains in the West and must indicate that the depigmentation process in Asia started substantially more recently.

Eventually the cultural mechanism was developed which allowed the inhabitants of eastern Asia to spread north, and which at the same time allowed for a reduction in their epidermal melanin. In this northward spread during the final stages of the Würm, they encountered the Bering Strait land bridge which then was up to 1300 miles wide (Haag 1962), and as a result, populated the Western Hemisphere. With this background, the depigmentation of the inhabitants of eastern Asia and the New World should have started at the same time, and it is no surprise to discover that they are now approximately the same color.

Only two areas of the world suggest that the south temperate zone was inhabited back into the Pleistocene for any length of time, one being south Africa and the other being the southern half of Australia. While neither area shows evidence that clothing was ever used to the extent where it would reduce the significance of extensive skin pigmentation, yet both areas are south of the tropics and the intensity of ultraviolet radiation is substantially reduced. We should expect that peoples who can be regarded as long-time inhabitants of these zones would show at least a partial reduction in pigmentation from the condition associated with the descendants of the ancient dwellers in the tropics proper, and this is indeed the case. The aborigines of the southern part of Australia are not so dark as the "blackfellow" in the north, and the South African Bushmen and Hottentots are lighter still, being a sort of yellow-brown which accords with the suspicion based on archeological evidence that they have inhabited the southernmost parts of Africa for a longer period of time than the aborigines have lived in southern Australia.

Having thus accounted for the forces which produced differences in human skin color, it is now appropriate to make brief mention of the reasons why the recent past has seen such extensive movements on the part of the relatively depigmented peoples south into India and southeast Asia. The explanation runs like this. The technological and cultural changes which allowed men to survive in the temperate latitudes during the cold of the last glaciation, and which led to their eventual depigmentation, started trends in cultural adaptation which culminated in the discovery of methods of controlling the food supply after the Pleistocene was over. The Neolithic revolution was a cultural development which was distinguished by the beginning of human efforts to control the propagation of plants and animals.

The success of this food producing way of life, in contrast to the previous hunting and gathering kind of existence, can be seen in the vast increase in numbers of the peoples whose cultural heritage stems from this source. The food producing revolution occurred earliest in the Middle East starting approximately 10,000 years ago (Flannery 1961), and before long the area had about as many people as the existing subsistence techniques could support. Cultural elaboration including the improvement of farming was one result, but another was the actual movement of populations into areas where existing farming techniques could be applied and where the indigenous population was too sparse to provide an obstacle. Climate was a limiting factor to the north, although technological advances eventually mitigated this, but to the south the opportunities for expansion were somewhat less restricted, and the result was the kind of color distributions which we can see in the world today.

HAIR

The form and color of the hair of the head is often given an importance second only to skin color by those who feel impelled to make racial discriminations. The geographical distribution of hair follows the distribution of skin color without exception, and, in spite of the numerous individuals where the two appear to be unrelated, it is apparent that this is the one instance where what is regarded as two traits vary together for a biological reason. Pigment in hair itself has no particular significance, but hair is a structure derived from the epidermis and will necessarily share facets of the same system for melanin production.

For individuals whose forebears had become adapted to survival in areas of strong sunlight, the well developed melanin production system of the epidermis will certainly ensure that the hair too has its fair share of melanin. Because of the structure of hair and the arrangement of the melanin granules within it, hair with only a moderate amount of melanin will appear black, which is why so many people in the world whose forebears underwent slight to moderate epidermal depigmentation still have predominantly black hair. Where depigmentation has been allowed to become advanced, the hair becomes affected, and, depending on the degree, all shades can be seen from brown through blond.

Red hair is something else, the existence of red pigment in the skin and hair being not well accounted for as yet. It seems most

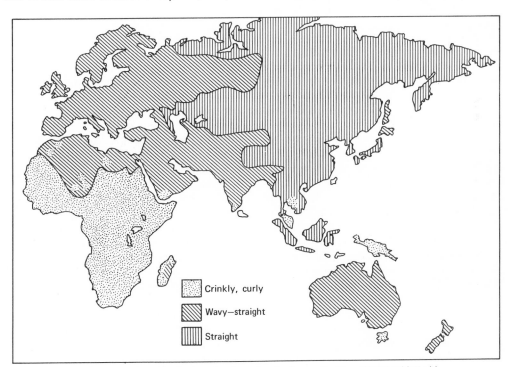

Figure 2a. Hair form distribution. Condensed and redrawn after Biasutti 1959. Old World.

Crinkly, curly

Wavy—straight

Straight

Figure 2b. Hair form distribution. Condensed and redrawn after Biasutti 1959. New World.

likely, however, that redness in hair and skin arose as the result of random changes in a different part of the enzymatic substrate normally responsible for melanin production, but this must be accounted an educated guess.

Unlike hair color, hair form apparently has had definite adaptive significance. The human head is one of the few parts of the body where the skin is underlain by a rather thinner than usual protective cushion of subcutaneous fat. A good hair covering can serve as protection against mechanical injury to bone and that rather vital organ, the brain.

The most striking thing about the distribution of hair form is the tendency for the extremely kinky forms of hair to occur among the same people where the very darkest skin pigmentation is to be found. There is no direct correlation between skin color and hair form as is shown by the presence of the most extreme hair form among the only moderately pigmented Bush-

men of South Africa, so the suspicion is raised that tightly spiral hair may be an adaptive feature, and the reason why its distribution parallels that of dark skin color is that both traits may be responses to related conditions. If dark skin is the adaptive response to high levels of ultraviolet radiation, and the insulation provided by woolly head hair is a response to high levels of solar heat radiation, then it is obvious that both adaptations are responses to different challenges evoked by living in an area characterized by an excessive amount of sunlight.

In the past, observers have noted the presence of dark skin and kinky hair in Africa, traces of it in southern Arabia, stronger traces among the hill tribes of India, the jungle peoples of the Malay Peninsula, the Andaman and Philippine pygmies, and finally its full development in the inhabitants of Melanesia, and have offered a number of theories involving vast migrations for obscure reasons. It is much easier, however, to regard these instances of the simultaneous occurrence of extremes of human variation in both skin color and hair form as the logical adaptive responses to similar selective pressures.

One more thing can be added in considering variations related to the hair. If our argument relating to depigmentation is generally applicable, then among those people who have provided cultural means for the protection of the head for the longest period of time, we should find the greatest amount of reduction in the biological adaptations normally associated with such protection. The same people who were the first to use clothing extensively may be assumed to have provided protection for the head, i.e., hats, and this assumption receives support from the fact that it is among their descendants today that we observe the highest proportion of deficiencies in the normal head protective mechanism—hair. Not surprisingly, it is among people of European derivation that the highest frequencies of gray hair and baldness occur.

So far, this discussion of human physical variation has dealt with extremes in adaptation which are responses to purely environmental selective forces. To be sure, these forces are limited by latitude instead of by specific geographic province or breeding population which means that no nice explanation can be offered which starts with the breeding population as the significant unit. The next facet of human variation to be considered also clearly shows the futility of starting one's analysis with "races" or breeding populations, since it cuts right across population and even geographic boundaries, again, as in the previous characteristic discussed, following the dictates of selection or its absence.

FACE FORM

Besides general pigmentation and hair form, the characteristics long considered of greatest importance for racial diagnosis are connected with the form of the face. While the previously discussed characteristics are not merely controlled by single genes or even by the various alleles of a single locus, yet they are genetically much simpler than the complex of anatomy which we call the face. Nevertheless, despite the complexities and

unknowns which surround the genetic background of face form, an investigation of the variations in the human face shows that the differences can be associated with relatively clear differences in selective factors.

There are two aspects of the face each associated with a different major function subject to important differences in selective forces affecting human survival. These are the parts particularly associated with the respiratory passages and those associated with the whole chewing apparatus. It might be argued that the face is also the locus for the organs of sight which of course is true, but on the other hand the microscopic complexity of the visual machinery does not allow any gross anatomical differences to occur. Variations in the color of the eye, in color vision, visual acuity, and even in the size of the eyeball can occur without affecting the skeletal housing called the eye socket and without any influence on the anatomy of adjacent areas. This cannot be said for variations in the nose area and in the jaws and teeth, and it is the intent here to consider such variations and the selective pressures which produce them.

Because variations in the dental apparatus are most clearly related to differences in selective pressures and because they have not been considered from this point of view previously, these will be considered first. Apart from the existence of an edge-to-edge bite in some peoples but not in others, which is partially but not entirely a matter of the characteristic mode of usage and hence wear, the primary differences in the human masticatory apparatus are simple differences in size. Some peoples have big teeth and some peoples have small teeth, and of course the whole tooth-bearing part of the face is related to the size of the teeth themselves. Not surprisingly, the people in whom the growth process produces large teeth also tend to have large jaws, large chewing muscles, and other evidences of exuberant bone growth associated with the skull and face.

Good studies on the dimensions of human teeth are surprisingly rare in scientific literature, but enough information is available to be able to arrive at a quite satisfactory understanding of the relationship between the size of the dentition and the selective factors influencing it. The smallest teeth are to be found among the peoples of Central and Eastern Europe and the Middle East, and the largest teeth are those of the Australian aborigines. Not only are Australian teeth the largest in the world, but under pre-European conditions they regularly showed the most extreme degree of wear (Campbell 1925).

This amount of abrasion points in a direct and simple manner to the selective forces operating to maintain large teeth. With the largest of human teeth being worn to the gums by middle age, it is easy to imagine what would happen if the teeth had been any smaller. Obviously, smaller teeth would wear down at an earlier age leaving the possessor effectively toothless in the prime of life. A toothless person in the Australian "outback" before the advent of European technology had a relatively reduced chance of surviving, and, if these circumstances occurred before the normal end of the reproductive life, the opportunities for transmitting the traits involving small tooth size to the next generation are materially decreased. The operation of the forces which maintained large teeth in pre-British Australia offers one of the clearest pictures of natural selection at work influencing human form and survival.

Since there are great differences in the amount of tooth wear to be seen among the different peoples of the world, and since extremes of tooth wear can influence the chances for survival, it is instructive to consider the causes for wear in its most pronounced form. Clearly the most important function of the masticatory apparatus is to reduce food to the appropriate form and size for swallowinng. The teeth, as the bearing surfaces of this crushing machine, are worn, at least in part, by the abrasive content of the food they chew. In the case of the Australian aborigines, the game which they catch is singed by being rolled in the ashes of an open fire, briefly roasted, and then eaten—ashes, grit, and all—with a minimum of assistance from a manufactured cutlery. Of course the products of the hunt provide only a portion, and at that not even the major portion, of the aboriginal diet, although it was certainly large enough to account for a substantial amount of dental abrasion. The rest of the diet included varying amounts of seeds, nuts, fruits, berries, insects, roots and vegetable products most of which were eaten without any further preparation. Obviously the eating of the proverbial peck of dirt was an annual phenomenon for the Australian aborigines and not something which took a whole lifetime to accomplish.

While the immense variety of their diet might not qualify the Australians as a literal example of grinding poverty, yet there can be no question that such a regimen can produce a great deal of tooth wear. There is, however, another important source of tooth wear to be considered which has nothing to do with the diet, and this involves the observation, also made on other peoples who show similar kinds of tooth wear, that the aborigines use their mouths like a third hand. When first discovered, the Australian aborigines possessed a culture whose technological poverty was greater than that of any other people in the world, being on a par with what we believe the most advanced human technology was like some time during the third interglacial. With such a rudimentary tool kit, they frequently avail themselves of the convenient all-purpose tool which heredity had provided in the form of their large and powerful jaws and teeth. As vise, clamp, or pliers, the dentition is frequently used to hold objects which are then manipulated with the hands. The wear thus produced occurs in most pronounced form on the front teeth in contrast to wear produced by heavy duty food chewing which affects the molars, and it is interesting to note that it is the front teeth which show the most extreme degrees of wear by early middle age.

This being the case, one would expect an inverse correlation between the amount of wear on the front teeth and the level of technological development among the peoples of the world, and to a degree this holds true. The simplicity of the picture is somewhat spoiled by the discovery that a people such as the Eskimo, with a relatively complex technology for a nonliterate, nonindustrialized culture, show a quite similar degree of wear on the incisors, definitely limiting the chances for survival of the aging Eskimo. The special problems which survival in the Arctic raise mean that, despite the greater technological development, the Eskimo use their teeth extensively in manipulating their environment—untying knots, chewing frozen boots, and most important of all, tanning skins for clothing. Among most of the peoples of the world, however, the greater the technological complexity of their culture, the less the front teeth are worn and the smaller these teeth tend to be.

It is apparent that where the teeth are extensively used as tools, a premium is placed on large incisors. Small front teeth are distinctly disadvantageous and are actively selected against by the early deaths and failures of their possessors to reproduce. There is no problem, then, in explaining the existence of large teeth wherever they are found. The existence of small teeth at first seems somewhat less easy to account for, but a little reflection will show that their occurrence obeys the same principle which lies behind the distribution of depigmentation. Specifically, where technological development has resulted in the production of tools which are designed to perform the tasks formerly performed by the teeth, then the presence of large front teeth is no longer important for human survival. Random mutations affecting the teeth can occur without disadvantage, and since random mutation in reference to any structure eventually results in its reduction, the teeth in question are reduced (Brace 1963). As would be expected,

the people with the smallest teeth in the world are those whose remote ancestors first developed a complex technology.

Technological complexity, however, is not limited by race, and, as a result, that part of face size which is contributed by the dentition varies across population boundaries in a way which would be quite inexplicable if racial group were taken as the starting point for analysis. Any chart attempting to trace the distribution of differences in human dentition size is plagued with two problems. First of all, published information exists for only a few human populations, and second, despite conflicting evidence (Garn and Lewis 1958), some correlation should exist between gross body size and tooth size. Figure 3 is an admittedly subjective picture based on the available information crudely corrected for body size by showing the relative size of the teeth in proportion to body bulk. For instance, the Bushmen of South Africa have always been cited as having small teeth since their dimensions are approximately the same as those of Europeans, but then no consideration is taken of the fact that Bushmen are noticeably smaller in gross bulk. In proportion to their body size, Bushmen teeth are actually relatively large, although not in the

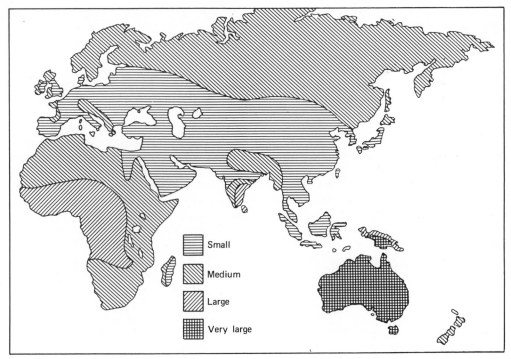

Figure 3. Face form distribution as indicated by relative tooth size.

same category as those of the Australian aborigines.

A few words of interpretation are in order for Figure 3. The smallest teeth belong to those people whose forebears first enjoyed the technological benefits made possible by the food producing revolution. Food producers with their sedentary existence generally accumulate more possessions and can therefore have a more elaborate technology than hunters and gatherers. Reasonably enough, then, there is a broad band extending from central Europe through the Middle East, across northern India into the Far East and Southeast Asia which corresponds with the areas where the food producing revolution had had its effects for the longest period of time.

Actually, plotting the distribution of relative gross tooth size in this manner obscures the fact that there is something of a West-East gradient in effective incisor size in the small tooth zone which is not expressed by simple length-width dimensions alone. This is due to a change in the form of the front teeth. Shovel-shaped incisors, dating from the observations of Hrdlička, 1920; 1921), have been assumed to characterize the inhabitants of eastern Asia, and, in an era when human morphological characteristics were assumed to have no functional significance, resemblances were supposed to indicate historic relationships between populations or races, and wherever shovel-shaped incisors were found, whether in American Indians or in Asiastic Pithecanthropines, it was presumed that this indicated some sort of relation to modern Asians. Re-examination of material found before the shovel shape was recognized as significant shows that not only the European Neanderthalers but also their Upper Paleolithic descendants had shovel-shaped incisors, although most modern Europeans do not.

The problem is less the explanation of the origin of shovel shaped teeth than explaining why they ceased to exist in the areas where they are now absent. Following the principle of trying to understand the reason for the existence of specific traits rather than taking the recognition of difference as being sufficiently important by itself, the significance of incisor form takes on a different aspect. Instead of being simply an indication of ancestry as it was formerly believed, the raised lingual margins of the incisors are an indication that the teeth were formerly (or still are) subjected to heavy usage and great wear. Adding to the total amount of incisor enamel by the raising of the lingual borders is a simple adaptive way in which the potential for wear is increased without the necessity of increasing overall tooth size and hence increasing jaw size (Brace 1962).

Although the evidence is not sufficient, it seems likely that all middle Pleistocene hominids had large shovel-shaped incisors. As technology developed and the value of large incisors decreased, particularly in that part of the temperate zone where the food-producing revolution took place, then the teeth were free to vary with the inevitable result that reduction occurred. There are two ways in which a shovel-shaped tooth can reduce, one is to reduce the overall dimensions which Figure 3 shows occurred all the way across the middle latitudes of the Old World. The other method of reduction is the elimination of the extra enamel in the form of the raised lingual margins. As a reflection of the fact that technological elaboration, in the form of Upper Paleolithic cultures and subsequently the earliest food producers, occurred earliest in the area from the Middle East through central Europe, it is understandable why the absence of shovelling makes the effective amount of enamel less among the peoples of these areas than among the people farther east whose teeth are actually the same size in gross dimensions.

A comparison of the tooth dimension chart with that representing the distribution of variations in pigmentation shows that the two distributions do not correspond. In fact, starting in the Middle East where teeth are smallest and going north and west it can be seen that teeth actually increase in size while pigment decreases, with the largest teeth in Europe occurring at the extreme north and west fringes. Evidently while clothing was an ancient feature of cultural adaptation in these areas, the kind of technological complexity which goes with a food producing type of subsistence came much later—a statement which is supported by an abundance of archeological evidence.

The extent of a band of medium dentitions down the east part of Africa reflects the spread of effective stone cutting tools, of the sort which allowed the Neanderthal face to change into a more modern form, which occurred at about the same time that the Upper Paleolithic flourished in the north. This form of technological advance did not penetrate the edges of the forest region in West Africa and around the Congo basin——perhaps because of a lack of sufficient suitable raw materials—and the effect was that the dentitions of these peoples remained relatively larger. People with these larger teeth then multiplied in great quantities following the acquisition of farming techniques and suitable food crops which allowed them to spread into the previously unoccupied African rain forests. These people expanded to the south and east, spreading out into the area where only a moderately large lower face was characteristic, thus creating a somewhat confused picture for this trait in the southern parts of East African and the eastern parts of South Africa. The relative size of the lower part of the face in Africa evidently remains the same acrosss boundaries of skin color, hair form, subsistence economy, and geographic province while at the same time varying within each of these. Clearly hair form or skin color or geographic province has no particular biological or adaptive tie with the size of the dentition so that any appraisal of human facial variations which starts with sociologically defined races as its basic units will fail to understand the distribution or the meaning of such variations. It is only by plotting the distribution along with that of the relevant selective factors that one can appreciate the problems involved.

Dental variation in the rest of the world follows the same principles. The parts of India and Southeast Asia in which remnants of hunting and gathering populations are to be found show a relative enlargement of the lower face. When New Guinea and Australia are added to the area considered, the results are just what one would expect, with the relative increase in face size showing a close correlation with the areas in which technological elaboration has been present for the shortest period of time.

Much less information is available for the Western Hemisphere so it has been left out of Figure 3, but every indication shows that it follows the same principles. Judging from photographs of Indians from all over both North and South America, it would appear that the smallest faces in the New World are confined to an area running from the highlands of Peru in western South America, north through Middle America to somewhere just south of the boundaries between Mexico and the United States. Reasonably enough, this corresponds with the area where food producing cultures have been in existence for the longest period of time in the Western Hemisphere.

The distribution of variations in the size of the human dental apparatus apparently follows the distribution of the relevant influencing factors in a reasonable fashion despite the sketchy nature of our information for many populations. Skin color also behaves in a similarly predictable manner, but the distribution of dental size bears no relation to that of skin color since the important influencing forces vary quite independently.

With two of the most outstanding characteristics by which people can be seen to vary evidently showing no relation to each other, it is not surprising to find that other areas of human variation which can be traced in terms of their influencing selective factors are also independent. While the shape of the lower part of the human face is determined by the development of the masticatory apparatus, variations in the upper face are dominated by the shape of the nose.

The history of human face form, starting with the pre-human ancestors of man and proceeding up to the present day, has been one of varying degrees of reduction. The dental apparatus has been greatly reduced as its defensive and manipulative functions have decreased, and the whole supporting facial skeleton has decreased along with it, with the exception of the part which has served as housing for the respiratory apparatus. Apparently it would have been detrimental to human survival to further reduce the air intake passages. The result has been the preservation of a relict of the former extent of facial development which we now identify as the human nose.

To a certain extent, then, the degree of nasal prominence is a reflection of the amount of reduction of the rest of the face. Part of nasal shape also is determined by the relative degree of development of the immediately adjacent parts of the face. For instance, the peoples who are noted for the possession of particularly broad noses all have particularly large incisors, meaning that the whole facial skeleton in the area where the nose is widest is noticeably spread. People such as the Australian aborigines and various other peoples from New Guinea to western Africa where, for the reasons mentioned above, the incisors are particularly large evidently show a widening of the whole lower face including the external form of the nose.

In addition to the differences in the width of the lower part of the nose, there remain outstanding differences in the length of the nose and in the height of the nasal bridge which cannot simply be explained by citing different degrees of reduction in the rest of the face. The distribution of nose form in the world is shown in Figures 4a and 4b by the various values recorded for the nasal index. A low index indicates a long narrow nose while a high index describes a relatively short wide nose, but since, as we have seen, nasal width is at least partially accounted for by another trait which is distributed according to its own selective pressures, it is evident that the nasal index is not the best criterion of nasal length and height. It is the best measure available, however, and will have to

serve as the basis for tentative interpretations.

Like dental size, the form of the nose does not correspond very closely to population boundaries, and, apart from the portion of its variation which is directly related to the size of the lower face, it appears that nose form responds to another set of influencing forces. A quick glance at Figures 4a and 4b will show that the relatively shortest noses occur only in the tropics, and observation confirms the fact that the nasal bridges of the peoples in question are low as well as being short. At first it seems as though no consistent sense could be made from such an observation since such people as the inhabitants of East Africa right on the equator have appreciably longer, narrower, and higher noses than the people in the Congo at the same latitude. A former generation of anthropologists used to explain this paradox by invoking an invasion by an itinerant "white" population from the Mediterranean area, although this solution raised more problems than it solved since the East Africans in question include some of the blackest people in the world with characteristically woolly hair and a body build

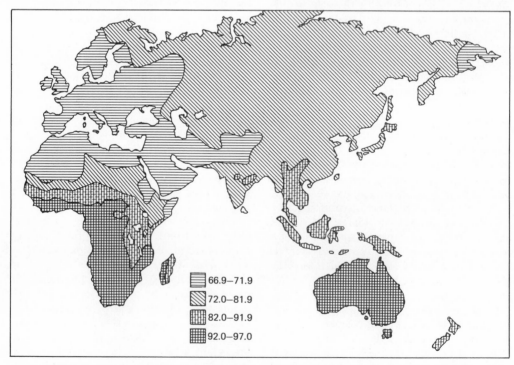

Figure 4a. Nose form distribution as seen in the nasal index. Condensed and redrawn after Biasutti 1959. Old World.

66.9–71.9
72.0–81.9
82.0–91.9
92.0–97.0

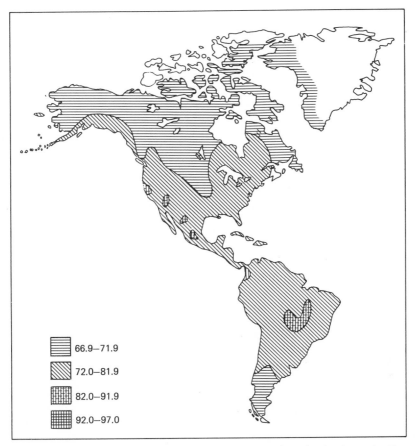

Figure 4b. Nose form distribution as seen in the nasal index. Condensed and redrawn after Biasutti 1959. New World.

▦	66.9–71.9
▨	72.0–81.9
▦	82.0–91.9
▦	92.0–97.0

unique among the world's populations for its extreme linearity and height.

While the full answer to nose form distribution is yet to be given, a good attempt supported by some significant research has been made (Weiner 1954). The point of departure, as with the other traits for which distributions have been sensibly explained, has been the consideration of the possible functions which differences in nose shape might serve. While Weiner's results seem to indicate that the major function of a lengthened nasal passage is the moistening of dry inspired air, it is still possible that a part of the significance of variation in nose shape may be related to the need to warm incoming air in extremely cold climates, as was suggested in earlier studies (Thomson and Buxton 1923; Davies 1932).

If there is merit to these suggestions the distribution of big noses should indicate the areas where people have had to cope with either extreme dryness or extreme cold, and by and large the actual distribution more or less fits expectations. The relatively long noses of East Africa become explicable then when one realizes that much of the area is extremely dry for parts of the year. The long noses of the dry Middle East and those of the cold northwest fringes of Europe fit expectations, but there are a number of cases which seem less obvious at first glance.

The Bushmen of the extremely dry Kalahari desert in southern Africa possess greatly reduced noses in seeming contradiction to their habitat. This becomes less of a paradox when it is realized that the Bushmen have only recently been forced to take refuge in the desert by the settlement of the temperate southernmost parts of Africa by peoples possessing more efficient subsistence techniques and weapons. Likewise, the inhabitants of the dry central Asiatic plains have only been there for the last few millennia.

The Eskimo, too, can be viewed as a relative newcomer to the Arctic, and although they do indeed possess long narrow nasal passages, the nasal bridge is not so high as might be expected—perhaps in part due to the fact that the heavy stress put upon the dentition has meant that the rest of the face has undergone relatively less reduction than among the cold-adapted peoples of northern and western Europe.

The Australian aborigines are the final apparent exception to the presumed association of nasal length with lowered humidity. The Australian desert is one of the driest areas inhabited by man, yet the nasal index is relatively high. In this case, the actual length of the nose is over-shadowed by its great width, and this width is simply a reflection of the fact that the whole lower face is greatly broadened to accommodate the biggest incisors possessed by modern *Homo sapiens*. Within Australia itself, however, nose form varies in conjunction with humidity just as one would expect. The longest and highest noses occur in the central desert, while the shortest and lowest noses occur in the tropical and humid north.

A final comment on nose form concerns the explanation for the tendency for short low noses to occur among peoples who dwell in the humid parts of the tropics. This again appears to be a case of the reduction of a character which confers relatively little benefit on the possessors. Long nasal passages are of no particular advantage where the inspired air needs to be neither moistened nor warmed, and any variation arising in relation to nose form would be equally likely to survive. Since most naturally occurring variations will tend to reduce the size of the structure in question, the accumulation of their effects in time results in the reduction of the noses of the long-time denizens of the moist tropics.

BODY BUILD

While the facets of morphology discussed above are those most commonly used in making racial distinctions, major differences have also been observed to occur in body build which make sense when considered in adaptive terms. Obviously in a cold climate it is desirable to use the heat generated by metabolic activity as efficiently as possible.

Conversely it is equally apparent that for people to sustain activities in very hot climates, the major concern is the the development of some kind of mechanism which promotes the dissipation of the heat generated in metabolising enough fuel to produce the activity in the first place. Since heat loss occurs at the surface of the body, it is clear that bodies which have different relative amounts of surface area will differ in the speed with which heat dissipation occurs as a simple example demonstrates. If one hundred pounds of copper is shaped into a sphere and heated, it will hold its heat for a much longer period of time than one hundred pounds of copper stretched out in a wire a half mile long and heated to the same temperature. Not only does shape influence the relationship between surface area and bulk, but differences in gross size can also play a part. Changes in surface area vary in proportion to the square of linear dimensions while changes in volume vary as their cube, so it is obvious that as the object in question gets bigger the volume increases more rapidly than the surface area even when the shape is held constant. Adaptive variations in both size and shape have been recognized for man (Coon, Garn and Birdsell 1950; Newman 1953).

Although there are many individual and group exceptions, it can be said that, on the average, human bulk decreases in the hotter and increases in the colder areas inhabited by man, and the inference has been made that this is related to the greater heat-conserving properties of larger bodies (Roberts 1953). But not only are there size differences, there are also differences in shape. Long slender arms and legs are clearly associated with desert-living peoples while short limbs and heavy bodies can be seen in the arctic. A number of objections have been raised to considering the short limbs of arctic peoples as adaptive, but it seems quite clear that the danger of frostbite makes long arms and legs considerably less desirable in cold climates.

Against the adaptive value of specific body form in the tropics, it has been pointed out that the tallest as well as the smallest people in the world live very close to each other right on the equator in east central Africa. Actually, whether such a view is adequate or not, it can be argued that both extremes in body build are different ways of handling the heat dissipation problem. One way of presenting a maximum amount of surface area to the air is to stretch a given mass into an elongated shape, and certainly the immensely tall East Africans of the Upper Nile area are about as linear and elongated as people get. The other way of influencing the mass-surface area ratio is to change the size. Increasing gross size without changing form was seen to increase mass in proportion to surface area. This being true, the converse evidently is that a decrease in size will decrease the mass (proportional to the cube root of any linear dimension) in relation to the surface area thus accomplishing the same thing that shape modification can do.

The pygmy, simply by being small, acquires the same surface-mass ratio which is achieved by the Nilotic African who is normal in bulk but greatly elongated in shape. Since both are equally efficient heat dissipating mechanisms, the factors influencing which adaptation will occur stem from other sources than a simple concern for heat regulation. The tall East Africans generally are food producers whose subsistence is derived from their cattle. This means that the food supply is relatively assured and that they get regular amounts of protein in their diets. Pygmy subsistence, however, is less assured, and there may be long periods when food is not plentiful and little protein is eaten. This kind of problem would be particularly hard on people who are large enough so that they need a regular and substantial food intake, and of course, would be especially severe for the rapidly growing child. A people who have low nutritional requirements as adults and who grow less rapidly during the critical phases of development will have a better chance of surviving as marginal hunting and gathering populations in the fringes of tropical forests.

With small size being both efficient for heat dissipation and the best assurance for survival in an area afflicted with periodic nutritional bottlenecks, it becomes possible to understand why peoples within the pygmy stature range exist in such places as the eastern edge of the Congo basin, southern India and Ceylon, the Andaman Islands, Malaya, the Philippines, and the remote parts of New Guinea. With the limited amounts of big game in these areas and before the recent advent of iron tools and weapons in

many of them, the survival value of being small is quite evident.

Former explanations for the distribution of pygmies relied on vast postulated migrations of a single stock of small-statured people throughout the tropics of the Old World, but it makes much better evolutionary sense simply to regard the pygmies, wherever they occur, as size adaptations made in situ by the local populations of the areas in question. The Congo pygmy is simply the small end and remnant of a distribution of hunting and gathering peoples which extended, prior to the diffusion of an agricultural subsistence base into sub-Saharan Africa, around the edges of the Congo forest and on through the edges of the West African forest where it merges with the savannah. In southern India, Ceylon, and Southeast Asia the peoples of pygmoid stature are the remnants of hunting and gathering populations which, because of the great southward push of food producing techniques and peoples into the more desirable areas, are confined to the more inaccessible and heavily forested refuges. Only in the Andaman Islands did pygmies remain unaffected by the unequal competition with food-producing peoples, although here the only choice for habitat was necessarily tropical forest with no big game and the same sort of occasional nutritional bottlenecks which plague hunting and gathering peoples in the tropical forests elsewhere.

For the reasons discussed under skin color and hair form, the remnants of the ancient inhabitants of southern India and Southeast Asia are all very dark in color and possess very tightly curled hair. In contrast to this, some of the jungle inhabitants of central Borneo and the Philippines have the reduced coloring and reduced hair curl which is more characteristic of the peoples who have arrived from the north in relatively recent times. At the same time, they are of extremely small size illustrating the selective effect which the problems of survival in such an environment exerts on the human physique regardless of the differences in other traits which may have developed in diverse geographical areas. In the highlands of New Guinea, as well, there are people of pygmy stature but, again, with very different faces from those of the short peoples of either Africa, Southeast Asia, or Borneo since they come closer to resembling smaller versions of the faces of the aborigines of Australia. Again, the effects of this kind of environment have determined the pygmy physique despite the differences in technological selective factors which have resulted in marked facial differences in the areas considered.

Central New Guinea is a particularly interesting case since there has been no overwhelming invasion by peoples whose characteristics developed in response to selective pressure elsewhere as was true for Southeast Asia and Indonesia, nor have new subsistence techniques been in effect for a long enough time for a substantial change in the distribution of local groups to have been distorted beyond the possibility of recognizing its original form, as has been the case in Africa. As a result, the New Guinea pygmy is not an abrupt isolated phenomenon, either culturally or physically, as is now general for the small peoples elsewhere in the world. Because New Guinea has been less overwhelmed either by invading peoples or by the effects of diffusing cultural features than anywhere else in the world, it is interesting to note that only here is there the completely gradual cline from the local normal sized peoples to the pygmies without break in just the manner which can be assumed to have once been the case for all the regions that now have isolated pygmy populations.

Before leaving the subject of the significance of variations in human physique, another set of influencing factors must be considered. While the pygmies appear to be a response to problems stemming from both periodic food shortages and the necessity for the efficient dissipation of metabolically generated heat, and other differences in physique appear to be adaptive, there seems to be another factor affecting human survival in parts of the temperate zone. A belt of chronic overpopulation and undernourishment extends from Egypt through India and into southern China and Southeast Asia, but the people, while small, have not become pygmoid in size. While it is impossible to do anything more than suggest the answer, it would appear that any further reduction in size would decrease the potential for the amount of labor which the people must sustain in order to survive. These people seem to be able to produce a maximum amount of work on the smallest possible

number of calories per day. If they were larger, they would eat more than they could grow, and if they were smaller they could not sustain the amount of effort necessary to support a family, so a close adjustment is made, and, despite the different origins of the peoples in this belt, there is remarkable similarity in gross size and bodily proportions.

Enough has been said about the gross morphological variations visible in mankind. Others exist which have not been treated, and much of what has been said has been obvious but undocumented by the kind of solid proof which is usually demanded of biological interpretation. The object in presenting it has been not only to touch on the major observable variations in man, but also to demonstrate that the various traits in which people differ are distributed according to the selective factors responsible for their expression and not because of any association with socially delimited boundaries such as the perception of race. Where the selective factors are related or happen to vary together, then the traits they influence will likewise vary together, but, as has been shown, it is commoner to see the selective forces and their corresponding traits varying more or less independently of each other and crossing geographical and population boundaries without regard to the supposed limits of human gene pools or areas of mating preference.

TRAITS WITH KNOWN MODES OF INHERITANCE

If this approach to understanding human variation is clear when gross morphology is the subject for consideration, it is at least as obvious when characteristics are investigated for which a precise knowledge exists concerning the genetic background. In fact, in much recent biological thinking there has been the feeling that morphological variation is difficult to appraise since the precise mode of inheritance of morphology is so poorly known and the result has been the abandonment of morphology as a valid area for investigation by many recent students (see Livingstone 1961). This explains the reason why the data on which this present appraisal of human morphological variation is based was collected primarily a generation or more ago and remains so incomplete.

With the last two to three decades there has been a belief among biologists and particularly biological anthropologists that the simple understanding of the genetics of a trait was sufficient reason for collecting information about the occurrence of the traits in question in many human populations. Consequently the energy which had gone into morphological trait gathering in generations gone by has been recently poured into genetic trait gathering. The result has been the collection of an enormous amount of information relating to human characteristics with a simple mode of inheritance. Recalling the role of the basic genetic material in the production of protein molecules (Crick 1958), it is not unexpected that many of the features which are inherited as single gene characters turn out to be proteins or closely related molecules (Harris 1959). Within the last few years, the realization has grown that the distribution of some of these traits corresponds with the distribution of recognized and important selective factors. Now at last some evolutionary sense can be made out of what formerly seemed to be merely biochemical oddities.

A significant attempt has been made in the interpretation of the distribution of deficiencies in color vision (Post 1962). While the exact biochemical deficiency which produces failures to see colors is unknown, the mode of inheritance is clear and simple. Contrary to popular assumptions, failure to see red and failure to see green are not due to the same genetic deficiency, although the genes controlling each type of vision occur at loci on the X chromosome and hence are examples of the phenomenon of ordinary genetic linkage as well as sex-linkage. While genetically these are actually two separate traits, yet as far as the individual possessing either is concerned, failure to see colors, whatever the genetic source, is subject to the same kind of selection, and, for purposes of distribution studies, there is some justification in lumping the two. Furthermore, many studies have failed to recognize the differences and have lumped them anyway. It seems obvious that visual acuity, including color vision ability, is highly desirable for a people depending on hunting and gathering as their chief mode of subsistence. Post has noted that any deficiency in vision among such a group should be detrimental and

should be selected against. For people at a food producing level of subsistence, the penalties for poor color vision should be less severe, and one would expect mutations affecting vision to accumulate in time, eventually resulting in a reduction of visual efficiency in the same manner whereby skin pigmentation undergoes reduction following the suspension of the significant selective factors.

Theoretically, then, one would expect the highest percentage in deficiencies of color vision to occur among people whose forebears were the first to forsake a foraging for a food producing mode of subsistence, and therefore one would further expect the distribution of increasing color vision deficiency to correspond with the cline of dental reduction. The expectation is fulfilled in most instances with the highest percentages of colorblindness occurring among the peoples of European and Middle Eastern origin, followed closely by Chinese. This is reasonable since, as with the the slightly lesser degree of dental reduction in Asia, the food producing revolution occurred slightly later in China than it did in the Middle East.

The lowest percentages of color vision deficiency occur among modern hunting and gathering populations, although there is some confusion in the evidence where the samples tested are too small to be reliable. Clearly, then, the distribution of colorblindness frequencies, in cutting across boundaries of socially perceived racial differences, behaves in the same manner that has already been demonstrated for morphological features. Again, the most important criterion to consider is the distribution of the selecting force.

One of the clearest cases of the relation between selective forces and the distribution of the associated trait has been presented in Livingstone's classic work on the distribution of abnormal hemoglobins (1958). This is too well known to be repeated here, although it should be noted that as a result of his careful study, we now have a well documented picture of the spread of a trait not only by actual population movement but across population boundaries as a result of the inevitable genetic exchange which adjacent populations practice. Since the genetics of this trait are simple and the selective forces involved are so strong, it can be quantified in a way which is not possible for the morphological traits which have previously been discussed. Because of this, Hemoglobin S can serve as a model for understanding the mechanisms behind the distribution of any trait whose expression is subject to natural selection in man, whether it be a single gene character or one controlled by an unknown number of genes and loci. Livingstone, despite his reluctance to deal with trait distributions where the mode of inheritance is not clear, has fully appreciated the significance of his discoveries in the undermining of the standard anthropological use of the concept of race (Livingstone 1962), and his position would appear to be substantially the same as that being advocated in this present paper.

With the insights gained from the successful interpretation of the various facets of the abnormal hemoglobins, it is now becoming possible to foresee the explanation of some other characteristics which have been known but not understood for quite some time. For instance, as long as human blood groups were considered to be nonadaptive (Boyd 1950), it was impossible to make any sense out of their distributions. Because of the clearly inherited nature of serological phenomena, they were siezed upon with enthusiasm as the best racial markers known. There were two consequences of this approach to the study of human diversity. First, the fact that biologists started with the assumption that racial groups (breeding populations) were the significant units for analysis provided fuel to those people who wished for their own profit to believe that human races are of different innate worth, hence justifying existing practices of racial discrimination. The second consequence was that by restricting consideration to breeding populations, it was difficult to appreciate the covariation of selective factors and the respective human adaptations where these crossed population boundaries as they do in so many cases. This means that a full understanding of human variation and how it arose was not possible.

Recently, however, there has been a change in the orientation of the people interested in human diversity. It has been realized that a simple naming of human groups or races has no particular significance as a biological aim, although the study of

human group relations and hence group identification has real significance for the sociologist and for other social scientists. In addition, human biologists have increasingly realized that their primary task is the explanation of how human variations arose, and it is obvious that the assumption that human differences are nonadaptive defeats any such effort before it is begun. If man's form is the product of evolution, then man's differences must be evolutionary responses to different selective pressures, and it should be possible to explain differences in what were once considered the least adaptive of nonadaptive characters, the various blood types.

With this revitalized evolutionary view in mind, some effort has been made to discover what selective factors could account for the marked differences in allelic frequencies which the A B O system exhibits in the various parts of the world. With the different alleles showing some association with disorders of the digestive system (gastric ulcer and intestinal carcinoma), suspicion has arisen that A B O differences may be related to characteristic differences in diet (Kelso and Armelagos 1962). With the immunological techniques, by which blood types are recognized, testing primarily for incompatibilities in closely related proteinoids, it seemed probable that the various blood types may have something to do with adjustment to other complex organic molecules which are frequently encountered during daily life—for instance in eating. The preliminary research of Kelso and Armelagos shows that there is indeed a suggestive association between various frequencies of the A B O system and major population differences in characteristic amounts of fat, carbohydrate, and protein intake. Further work may show that different kinds of protein may correspond to particular A B O frequencies—for example, some peoples derive most of their proteins from animals while others get the greater quantity from such vegetable foods as beans or lentils.

While this is not to be regarded as proven, yet for the first time it is apparent that investigation is proceeding along fruitful lines, and vast increases in the understanding of known facets of human·diversity can be foreseen in the near future. For instance, despite the association of various manifestations of the Rh blood group system with problems of pregnancy, the reasons for the existence of differences in the system in the first place remain entirely unknown. Likewise no sense has yet been made out of the distributions within the NMS system and many others. One thing seems certain: as with the understanding of variations in human morphology, the solution to such problems in the distribution of simple genetic traits will only come when the concept of race is abandoned as the starting point for biological analysis.

REFERENCES

Baker, Paul T. 1958. Racial difference in heat tolerance. *American Journal of Physical Anthropology* 16: 287–306.

Biasutti, Renato. 1959. *Le Razze i Popoli Della Terra.* Third edition revised I: 721. Unione Tipografico—Editrice Torinese.

Boyd, William C., 1950. *Genetics and the Races of Man.* Boston, Little, Brown and Company.

Brace, C. L. 1962. "Cultural Factors in the Evaluation in the Human Dentition." *Culture and the Evolution of Man,* M. F. A. Montagu, ed. New York, Oxford University Press.

———. 1963. Structural reduction in evolution. *The American Naturalist,* 97:39–49.

———. 1964. The Fate of the "Classic" Neanderthals: A Consideration of Hominid Catastrophism. *Current Anthropology* 5:3–38.

Campbell, T. D. 1925. *Dentition and Palate of the Australian Aboriginal,* Ph.D. Thesis, University of Adelaide, The Hassell Press, Adelaide.

Chang, Kwang-chih. 1962. New evidence on fossil man in China. 1962. *Science,* 136:749–760.

Coon, Carleton S., Garn, S. M. and Birdsell, J. B. 1950. *Races.* Springfield, Thomas.

Crick, F. H. C. 1958. On protein synthesis. *Symposia of the Society for Experimental Biology* XII:138–163.

Davies, A. 1932. A Re-survey of the morphology of the nose in relation to climate. *Journal of the Royal Anthropological Institute* 62:337–359.

Flannery, Kent V. 1961. Early village farming in southwestern Asia (Mimeographed manuscript).

Garn, Stanley M. and Arthur B. Lewis. 1958. Tooth-size, body-size and "giant" fossil man. *American Anthropologist,* 60:874–880.

Haag, William G. 1962. The Bering Strait land bridge. *Scientific American* 206:112–123.

Harris, H. 1959. *Human Biochemical Genetics.* New York, Cambridge University Press.

Hogben, Lancelot. 1931. *Genetic Principles in Medicine and Social Science.* London, Williams and Norgate Ltd.

Hrdlička, Aleš. 1920. Shovel shaped teeth. *American Journal Physical Anthropology* 3:429–465.

———. 1921. Further studies on tooth morphology. *American Journal Physical Anthropology* 4:141–176.

———. 1924. New data on the teeth of early man. *American Journal Physical Anthropology* 7:109–132.

Huxley, Julian S. 1941. *Man Stands Alone,* New York, Harper.

Huxley, Julian S. and A. C. Haddon. 1935. *We Europeans: A Survey of 'Racial' Problems.* London, Jonathan Cape.

Keith, Arthur. 1949. *A New Theory of Human Evolution.* New York, Philosophical Library.

Kelso, J. and G. Armelagos. 1962. Nutritional Factors as Possible Selective Agencies in the Determination of A B O Blood Group Frequencies. (Paper read at the annual meeting of The American Anthropological Association, November 18, 1962).

Livingstone, Frank B. 1958. Anthropological implications of sickle cell gene distribution in west Africa. *American Anthropologist* 30:533–562.

———. 1961. More on middle pleistocene hominids: comments. *Current Anthropology* 2:117–118.

———. 1962. On the non-existence of human races. *Current Anthropology* 3:279.

Montagu, M. F. Ashley. 1941. The concept of race in the human species in the light of genetics. *The Journal of Heredity* XXXII:243–247.

Newman, M. T. 1953. The application of ecological rules to the racial anthropology of the aboriginal new world. *American Anthropologist* 53:311–327.

Post, Richard H. 1962. Population differences in red and green color vision deficiency. *Eugenics Quarterly* 9:131–146.

Roberts, D. F. 1953. Body weight, race and climate. *American Journal Physical Anthropology* 11:533–558.

Thomson, Arthur and L. H. Dudley Buxton. 1923. Man's nasal index in relation to certain climatic conditions. *Journal of the Royal Anthropological Institute of Great Britain and Ireland* 53:92–122.

Verneau, Le Dr. René. 1906. Anthropologie, *Les Grottes de Grimaldi* (Baoussé Roussé) Tome II, Fascicule I, Imprimerie de Monaco, pp. 1–212.

Weidenreich, F. 1937. The dentition of *Sinanthropus pekinensis:* A comparative odontography of the hominids. *Palaeontologia Sinica* 101:1–180.

Weiner, J. S. 1954. Nose shape and climate. *American Journal Physical Anthropology* 12:1–4.

27

RACIAL CLASSIFICATIONS: POPULAR AND SCIENTIFIC
Gloria A. Marshall*

The folkloristic origin of race concepts, accepted by the scientific community, and fed back in reinforced form to the general public is discussed by Marshall in the following article. This subject has recently been considered in even greater detail by John S. Haller, Jr. (1971), who shows the pernicious consequences of this kind of feedback. Socially and politically prominent elements in the American northeast, threatened by Irish, eastern, and southern European immigration, made common cause with the remnants of Southern aristocracy toward the end of the nineteenth century. The Northerners supported Southern efforts to disenfranchise the American black population, and the Southerners supported Northern efforts to establish immigration quotas based on the principle of Aryan supremacy.

But, as Marshall notes, racial thinking can be changed. Not only have the Irish achieved respectability in America, but to some extent have come to epitomize it to the exclusion of the previous criteria for the elite. For example, a turn-of-the-century Boston Brahmin would come close to apoplexy at hearing the Boston Irish speech of the late President John F. Kennedy described as a "Harvard accent," but the American public in the second half of the twentieth century accepts this without question. Although the change in racial attitudes seems agonizingly slow from the point of view of the current victims of the misuse of the concept, it has nonetheless been rather remarkable from the perspective of units of time measured in generations. In fact, there is hope.

Allport, Gordon W. 1954. *The Nature of Prejudice.* Addison-Wesley, Cambridge. 537 pp.

Daniels, Roger, and Harry H. L. Kitano. 1970. *American Racism: Exploration of the Nature of Prejudice.* Prentice-Hall, Englewood Cliffs, N.J. 155 pp.

Haller, John S., Jr. 1971. *Outcasts from Evolution: Scientific Attitudes of Racial Inferiority, 1859–1900.* University of Illinois Press, Urbana. 288 pp.

Higham, John. 1963. *Strangers in the Land: Patterns of American Nativism, 1860–1925.* Atheneum, New York. 431 pp.

Myers, Gustavus. 1960. *History of Bigotry in the United States.* Edited and revised by Henry M. Christman. Capricorn, New York. 474 pp.

I

Many scholars in the biological sciences agree that all typological divisions of mankind into discrete racial groups are to some extent arbitrary and artificial. Despite this widespread agreement, there appear to be two divergent views regarding the utility of the concept of race in studies of human biology. On the one hand, there are scholars who maintain that race as a statistically defined unit can and should be utilized in the description and analysis of intraspecific variation (I). According to this view, the concept of race is applicable to clusters of populations, each of which can be genetically defined.

*I wish to thank Karen Kerner for her assistance in the research on which this paper is based. I also wish to thank Miss Kerner, along with Robert LeVine, Joyce Riegelhaupt, Edward Riegelhaupt, Harold Conklin, Marvin Harris, Samuel Sutton, and David Feingold for their helpful comments at various stages in the preparation of this paper.

From Mead, Dobzhansky, Tobach, and Light (eds.): *Science and the Concept of Race,* New York: Columbia University Press, 1968. Reprinted with the permission of the author and publisher.

On the other hand, there are scholars who argue that in view of the arbitrariness of racial classifications, there can be little or no justification for the continued use of the race concept. Scientists who hold this view consider that the analysis and description of intraspecific variation in human and nonhuman populations can be most fruitfully pursued without reference to the concept of race (2). Jean Hiernaux (3) has stated this position as follows:

If any racial classification is arbitrary, for what purpose can it be of any use? Why spend so much time and effort building a classification, knowing that many others, not any worse, could be opposed to it, and that it runs the risk not only of being useless but also harmful by conveying the erroneous impression that it makes generalization possible?

Some of the anthropologists and biologists who favor continued use of the race concept have maintained that racial classifications are useful if they reflect the phylogenetic development of the species (4). That such a purpose is not necessarily served by *any* racial classification is noted by Ehrlich and Holm (5), who caution that "there is no basis for assuming, without extensive genetic study, that any population or any taxonomic group is an evolutionary unit." On the same issue, Hiernaux (6) has argued that it would be extremely difficult to derive a phylogenetic tree from data on contemporary human populations since the species did not split into groups which were "exposed to different evolutionary forces and events under complete or effective genetic isolation," and he goes on to state:

The general picture [of human evolution] is not one of isolated groups differentiating in circumscribed areas. Mixture occurred many times in many places between the most various populations brought into contact by human mobility. The tendency toward high adaptive specialization was balanced again and again by migration, and by man's power to transform his environment. Even if we could reconstruct the intricate succession of mixtures that contributed to each living population, the final picture would look like a reticulum more than a tree, and a reticulum defies dichotomizing subdivision.

It is not only the study of human variation that has led to a reappraisal of the utility of the concept of race for the analysis of intraspecific variation. Examination of the characters used in subspecific classifications of butterflies led N. W. Gillham (7) to conclude:

In view of the prevailing discordance of geographical patterns followed by different variates, racial partition of butterfly species is not only arbitrary, but it must also necessarily weight some variates and ignore others, without regard for the biological significance of any of them. The best that can be hoped for now is an analysis of variation by individual characters, avoiding arbitrary subdivision of the species. Such analysis will eventually yield a less distorted picture of species formation than that to which the artificial subspecies now inevitably leads.

The debate regarding the relevance of the concept of race for the analysis and description of intraspecific variation has important implications for all sciences concerned with the study of mankind. However, it does not appear that this debate has had widespread impact on professionals in the fields of medicine, psychology, sociology, history, or political science. Moreover, the investigations and publications of many scholars in these and other fields often deal with populations that are termed "races" even though the distinctive attributes of these populations have no proven biological significance.

What is often unrecognized or ignored is the fact that the "races" about which many scientists speak and write are those perceived and delineated by particular groups of people who interact in given sociopolitical contexts. Comparative studies of these popular racial typologies show them to vary from place to place; studies of popular racial classifications also show them to vary from one historical period to another. In no instance are these classifications referable to competent genetic studies; rather, they are "concocted by human beings to explain or render intelligible their observations" (8). Whereas most scholars today acknowledge that it is necessary to make a distinction between popular and technical conceptions about human biology, they do not necessarily avoid confusion of the two. Hence, many scientists persist in the use of the term race to describe groups whose racial statuses are determined, and whose racial characteristics are defined, by sociopolitical expediencies.

This paper attempts to document the variability in the criteria upon which popular racial classifications are based and to show that scientific discussions of race often reflect and reinforce popular notions about human variation. It also intends to show that both scientific and popular conceptions about race are usually influenced by socio-political considerations. Many of the points raised in this paper have been discussed in various contexts by anthropologists and by scholars in other fields. That they must be repeated here indicates the difficulties involved in communicating on the subject of race.

II

Most laymen and many scientists in the United States hold that there are three "major races": Caucasian (white), Negro (black), and Mongolian (yellow). This typology has a scientific basis; it is a revision of that proposed by J. F. Blumenbach, a distinguished anatomist and physician of the eighteenth century (9). But in some parts of the country Chinese Americans and other peoples from Asia are sometimes classed as "white" (10). However, almost nowhere in the United States is there any doubt that there are at least two "major races": namely, the Negro race and the white race.

In the United States, it is popularly held that descent is the basis upon which individuals are assigned to racial groups. However, Marvin Harris (11) has argued that it is a rule of *hypodescent* which governs the assignment of many individuals to the two major races distinguished by Americans. A rule of hypodescent operates when individuals whose parents belong to different "races" are assigned to the one that is politically subordinate. In America, individuals who have no known or acknowledged African ancestry constitute a politically and economically superordinate group. From this group has come the rule that individuals of both European and African parentage must be assigned to the politically subordinate group

that is referred to as the Negro race.[1] "Thus, first generation children of interracial marriages in the United States are uniformly Negroes, when it is absolutely certain that such children have received half of their hereditary endowment from one parent and half from the other" (11).

Even though the operation of the rule of hypodescent results in the application of the term Negro to American populations any of whose ancestors came from Africa, there is considerable ambiguity regarding the racial classification of peoples whose ancestors were European and Asian or African and Asian. Moreover, there does not appear to be popular consensus concerning the racial affiliation of people whose ancestors were African and European but who speak a language other than English. In New York, populations who speak Spanish are not usually referred to as belonging to the "Negro race" or to the "white race," but are simply designated as "Spanish," "Cuban," "Puerto Ricans," or "peoples of Puerto Rican descent." In many contexts, these appellations are used as if they were equivalent to the racial designations currently in use. Were the same people to speak only American English, they would be classed as Negro or as white, depending on the particular observer's perception of physical and behavioral "racial" cues.

Clearly, the popular racial typologies in America are not based on any competent genetic studies. It is also evident that observable phenotypical characteristics are often totally irrelevant in the assignment of individuals to the racial groups. There are Negroes who "can pass for white"; there are whites who "could pass for Negroes."

The popular American conceptions about race contrast sharply with those of contemporary Brazil, where descent plays a negligible role in establishing racial identity. Marvin Harris (12) has shown that full siblings whose phenotypes are markedly different are assigned to different racial categories. Harris's studies also indicate that more than forty

[1]In fact, it might be more accurate to say that it is known or demonstrable sub-Saharan African ancestry or "black African" ancestry which governs the assignment to the "negro race," since the populations of North Africa are not usually termed Negro.

racial categories are utilized in Brazil and that there are hundreds of racial terms constructed of combinations of these. In addition, there are alternative meanings for the same term, as well as a lack of consensus concerning the assignment of any particular term to a given individual (13). Moreover, Harris points out that there is "a high frequency of passing out to other categories in conformity with the achievement of socio-economic success" (12). Phenotypical attributes such as skin color, hair form, and nose or mouth shape enter into Brazilian racial classifications, but no combination of these variants is predictive of the "race" to which a person will be assigned since socio-economic position is one important determinant of racial status.

In Japan, skin color does not necessarily enter into popular racial classifications. The Burakumin or "outcastes" are popularly believed to be racially distinct from ordinary Japanese. They were formerly termed Eta—a word written with the characters for "defilement abundant"—and were officially emancipated in 1871 but remain a minority group set apart from other Japanese by low socio-economic status and by residential segregation.

The Eta are Japanese who descended from the lowest stratum in a hierarchical social system which existed in the earliest known period of Japanese history and was formalized by edict in the seventh century A.D. (14). At that time, the Imperial House created two major categories: the free and the base. Included in the latter category were peasants, certain artisan guilds, and slaves. By the tenth century, most of the formalized class distinctions had become meaningless; social differences between the free and the unfree were no longer observable, and most of the base guilds were free.

It was during this period that Buddhism became accepted throughout Japan, and the Buddhist beliefs fused with indigenous Shinto beliefs concerning the avoidance of impurity. According to Donoghue (14):

The syncretic religious concepts that evolved associated the taking of life with ritual impurity, and the guilds whose livelihood depended upon animal slaughtering were physically and morally isolated from the "legitimate" society. The outcastes became known as Eta.

The Eta formed small enclaves on the outskirts of towns and villages, where they were joined by other marginal social groups such as beggars, criminals, vagabonds, and entertainers.

In Japan, some theories on the history of the outcastes suggest that they originated from a people different from the ancestors of the socially acceptable Japanese. One theory holds that the outcastes are descendants of the aboriginal inhabitants of the Japanese isles. Another theory maintains that they are descendants of Korean war captives brought to Japan in the late sixteenth century; a third considers the Eta to be the offspring of Negritoes of the Philippines (15).

Most Western scholars regard the outcastes as physically identical to other Japanese. However, in the 1920s and 1930s a number of Japanese scholars described the Eta as a distinct race, and today many laymen still regard the outcastes as racially distinct from other Japanese. The outcastes' "distinctive racial heritage" is allegedly manifest in their behavior and appearance. Outcastes are popularly considered to be dirty; they are likened to hoodlums and gangsters. They are said to be afflicted with venereal diseases, tuberculosis, and leprosy (14). They are said to have one rib bone missing, to have distorted sexual organs, and to have defective excretory systems. Since they are animals, dirt does not stick to their feet when they walk barefooted (16).

The data on popular racial classifications current in the United States, in Brazil, and in Japan indicate that any expedient set of physical and/or behavioral attributes may be taken as the basis for such classifications. In these and other popular racial taxonomies, there often is a fusion and/or confusion of behavioral and physical attributes, leading to the perpetuation of the notion of the inheritance of cultural characteristics.

The assignment of individuals to the various racial categories recognized in different societies is often based on perceived behavioral differences rather than on demonstrable physical differences. Even where physical differences exist between the "races" delineated, laymen usually make no attempt to ascertain the biological significance of these differences! Moreover, the physical and behavioral attributes which are perceived as characteristic of a group are usually "explained" as being racial in origin.

Despite the recognition by many scholars that popular racial classifications should not serve as a basis for scientific discussions of human variation and related topics, many scientific studies are based on these classifications. Moreover, many scholars provide support for these nonscientific classifications by stating or implying that the popularly and/or politically defined "races" can be distinguished on the basis of biologically relevant criteria.

"Scientific" justification for the classification of the Eta as a race was provided by Kikuchi Sanya, whose book on the outcastes was written "from an anthropological point of view." Ninomiya (17) summarizes Kikuchi's thesis as follows:

There are many peculiarities of the Eta, *such as* (a) *practice of eating meat when the Japanese proper despise it;* (b) *reddish tinge in eye color;* (c) *prominence of the cheekbone;* (d) *non-Mongolian type of the eyes;* (e) *dolichocephalic head;* (f) *shortness of stature; and* (g) *shortness of the neck.*

In the 1930s, a professor of anthropology at Tokyo Imperial University also was of the opinion that "the Eta are not of the Mongolian type," although he did not "make this as a definite conclusion" (17).

It is hardly necessary to document the fact that many scholars in the United States conduct research and write books which imply that the "White race" and the "Negro race" are genetically defined entities. It will suffice to point out that virtually all scholars who write about "race and intelligence" assume that the "races" which they study are distinguished on the basis of biologically relevant criteria. So accepted is this fact that most scholars engaged in such research never consider it necessary to justify their assignment of individuals to this or that "race" (18).

Even when scholars in the biological sciences devise or utilize racial classifications, these are generally no more than refinements of typologies used by laymen. Scientific racial typologies are usually based on presumptions about or intuitions regarding the distribution of genetic characteristics. The manifest bases for these typologies are variations in arbitrarily chosen phenotypical characteristics. Yet it is well known that the relationship between genotype and phenotype is not simple and that the effects of the operation of environmental forces on the phenotype are not genetically transmitted. Moreover, even when scientists make a serious attempt to base their racial typologies on genetic variants, they do not squarely face the problem that there should be some biologically relevant justification for the choice of the characters on whose variation the "races" are defined (19).

It cannot be expected that the difficulties inherent in the construction of racial classifications will be appreciated by laymen when these problems are not often acknowledged by the scientists themselves. Normally, the layman who reads the literature on race and racial groupings is justified in assuming that the existent typologies have been derived through the application of theories and methods current in disciplines concerned with the biological study of human variation. Since the scientific racial classifications which a layman finds in the literature are not too different from popular ones, he can be expected to feel justified in the maintenance of his views on race.

It is not surprising, therefore, that scientific discourses on race serve to buttress the popular belief that discrete racial groups exist among mankind or that scientific racial typologies serve to legitimize popular racial classifications. On the one hand, scientists often base their studies of "racial differences" on popularly and/or politically defined races. On the other hand, they often take popular racial classifications as a point of departure for the construction of their own typologies, which, on close examination, appear just as spurious as those utilized by laymen (20).

III

The literature on racial typologies of earlier historical periods in America further indicates that both scientific and popular racial classifications reflect prevailing sociopolitical conditions. Significant changes in the political status of some ethnic groups in America have led to reappraisals of their "racial" statuses and of the "racial" characteristics by which they were defined.

In contemporary America, there are a number of populations of European origin who comprise the "white race." Even though some laymen subdivide this race on the basis of the national origin or religious affiliation, most Americans agree that there is essentially one "white race." That scientists concur in this opinion is illustrated by the fact that no present-day study that proposes to compare races would compare Americans who came from Ireland with those who came from England. But this was not always the case. Barbara Solomon's book, *Ancestors and Immigrants* (21), which deals with racial ideologies in New England between the 1850s and 1920s, demonstrates that "white" people who are now regarded as members of one "race" were formerly divided into several "races." In the second half of the nineteenth century and the early decades of the twentieth century, various American scholars published works which divided and redivided peoples now termed white or Caucasian into the following "races": Anglo-Saxons, Celts, Teutons, Jews, and southern Europeans or "brownish races." Scandinavians were regarded as a branch of the Teutonic "race," and Teutons and Anglo-Saxons were regarded as cousins, "racially" speaking.

Between the 1830s and 1870s the industrial expansion of New England brought waves of immigrants from Europe to Boston and the surrounding areas. Most were from Ireland. In the early phases of immigration, the self-styled Brahmins, who comprised the New England aristocracy, decried the "racial inferiority" of these Irish immigrants. In the 1840s and 1850s many prominent New Englanders shared C. E. Norton's apprehensions about the "sudden influex of people so long misgoverned . . . [and] of a race foreign to our own" (22). Charles F. Adams, Jr. remarked that "the Irish race," being "quick of impulse, sympathetic, ignorant, and credulous . . . have as few elements in common with native New Englanders as one race of men well can have with another" (23).

By the 1870s, the Irish, representative of the so-called Celtic race, gained dominance in some service industries in Boston and nearby mill towns; by the 1880s, they wrested the political leadership of Boston from the old New England aristocracy. The political supremacy of the Brahmins having been challenged, various academicians from this aristocracy sought to prove that the increased influx of members of the Celtic and other "inferior races" undermined the chances for the survival of democratic institutions which were Teutonic in origin and transmitted "through the blood."

During the 1870s, Francis A. Walker, a noted social scientist who was to become a university president, was a leading spokesman for those who were alarmed by the rising power of the alien Celts. The census of 1880 confirmed Walker's suspicions that the birth rate among the urbanized immigrant populations was exceeding that of the native Anglo-Saxons, and he became obsessed by the "fecundity of the foreign elements in the United States." During the 1880s Walker wrote many articles on the evils of immigration and used his academic affiliations to appeal to younger scholars to support his thesis that the arrival of foreigners in the United States had caused a "shock to the principle of population among the native element." By the end of the 1880s, "the happy ideal of assimilation, which [John] Fiske had spread over the land, disintegrated under Walker's cogent proofs, and, for old New Englanders, immigration became a matter of racial preservation" (24).

Support for New England raciology had come from academic circles in Europe. During the latter half of the nineteenth century one of the most influential books was *The Races of Men*, written in 1850 by Robert Knox, a professor of anatomy at the Edinburgh College of Surgeons, which proclaimed that all of civilization depended on race. To the Celts, Knox attributed the following characteristics: "furious fanaticism; a love of war and disorder; a hatred for order and patient industy; no accumulative habits; restless, treacherous, uncertain; [one need only] look at Ireland" (25). Knox saw the American Know-Nothing riots as a prelude to the inevitable conflict between Saxons and Celts. He said that "the war of race will some day shake the Union to its foundation. They never will mix—never commingle and unite" (25).

Edward A. Freeman, an Oxford historian, was another scholar who favored racial explanations of history. In 1881 when Freeman made a lecture tour of the United States, he proposed that "the best remedy for whatever is amiss in America would be if every Irishman should kill a Negro and be hanged for it" (26).

During the late nineteenth and early twentieth centuries, the appeals to limit European immigration were increasingly based on racial as well as economic arguments. The Immigration Restriction League of Boston, founded in 1894, was in the forefront of the battle to ensure that the Anglo-Saxon-Teutonic racial strains would not be overwhelmed by "Slav, Latin, and Asiatic races, historically down-trodden, atavistic, and stagnant" (27).

Solomon points out that historians, economists, sociologists, and physical scientists synthesized the earlier diffuse Teutonist sentiments into a pseudoscientific ideology of racial superiority. These academicians were influenced by the League's opinions; in turn, Brahmin restrictionist views were reinforced by the scholars' presentations. The Eugenics movement, which crystallized in America in the early twentieth century, argued that the influx of alien races had increased the rate of "insanity, imbecility, and feeblemindedness" in the population of the United States.

By the early twentieth century, however, less attention was being paid to the inferiority of the Celts than to that of the south-eastern Europeans, who, according to the Eugenicists, "had hereditary passions which were unalterable, regardless of public schools and economic opportunities in the United States" (28). Restrictions on the immigration of these undesirables would be the initial step in the creation of a race of supermen in America.

The Anglo-Saxon, Teutonic, southern European, Jewish, and other "races" defined during this period of American history were considered immutable; the characteristics which distinguished them were endowed by heredity. As might be predicted, these "racial" characteristics were as often behavioral as physical. Despite the alleged immutability of these "races" and of the characteristics attributed to them, New Englanders did in fact change their evaluation of the so-called "races of Europe."

Between the 1830s and 1890s, the Celts were described as ignorant, shiftless, credulous, impulsive, and mechanically inept; they were inclined toward drinking and related crimes. By the 1890s, when the Irish were the political leaders of the hub of New England and large numbers of southern Europeans were coming to the United States, the Irish had become tolerated aliens. The shift in attitude toward the Celtic race reflected the change in the political situation. The Irish were said to have "a remarkable race trait of adaptability which explained the achievement of the more intelligent and prosperous of the Boston group." Moreover, the Irish "above all races [had] the mixture of ingenuity, firmness, human sympathy, comradeship, and daring that [made them] the amalgamator of races" (29).

That there were no proven biologically significant differences among the "races of Europe" did not prevent New Englanders from perceiving European immigrant populations as separate races. So-called racial differences were said to be manifest in life-styles; racial affiliation could be determined by listening to individuals speak or by hearing their names. In any case, even without perceptible clues, the relative backwardness of the immigrants was "proof" of their inferior intellectual capabilities and characters, both of which were reputedly determined by "racial" heritage.

IV

Solomon's *Ancestors and Immigrants*, Gossett's *Race: the History of an Idea in America*, Stanton's *The Leopard's Spots* (30), and Curtin's *Image of Africa* (31) provide abundant documentation for the statement that at various historical periods, racial typologies and/or ideologies have reflected prevailing sociopolitical conditions. Historically, both scientific and lay concepts of race have served to support the economic and political privileges of ruling groups who regarded themselves as superior by virtue of phylogenetic heritage rather than because of the accidents of culture history.

From the preceding discussion it should be apparent that popular racial classifications are based on a wide range of emotional, political, and other evaluative criteria that are not relevant to the biological study of human variation. The differences in popular racial typologies become apparent when one shifts in time or place from one society to another. Therefore, it is obvious that there can be no justification for the elevation of any popular racial classification to the status of an analytic system in science.

Studies which purport to demonstrate the genetic basis for this or that behavioral characteristic observed among persons who make up popularly defined races are essentially nonscientific and should be labeled as such. Hence, to presume to study the genetic basis for some behavioral attribute of the "Negro race" in America is to ignore the fundamental difficulty of defining that "race." It is entirely probable that any biogenetically significant division of Americans would include some groups comprised of *both* so-called Negroes and so-called whites. But to isolate such groups would violate the folk theory that there is a pure white race and a Negro race which includes some so-called racial hybrids.

In conclusion, it must be made clear that this paper is not aimed at the deprecation of the study of human variation. The directions for future research into the genetics of human variation have been indicated by various writers, including the contributors to the volume entitled *The Concept of Race*, edited by Ashley Montagu. The isolation of those genetic characters that constitue the most variable array of features in mankind, the determination of the characters that admit of biologically significant clustering of breeding populations, the study of the relationship between genotype and phenotype, including the investigation of genetic characters as they are represented in different life stages of individuals—these are some of the problems which have to be pursued.

These problems can and should be studied without reference to race, which has never been and never will be a primarily biological concept. The history of the use of the race concept by scientists and laymen alike makes it apparent that race could probably never be accepted as a purely statistical concept. Race is a biopolitical concept, the continued use of which will serve only to obfuscate the problems entailed in the study of human variation. As Livingstone (32) has pointed out:

Just as Galileo's measurements and experi-

ments paved the way for Newton's laws of motion, which totally replaced the Aristotelian laws of motion concerned as they were with describing the nature of bodies and their "essences," our newer genetic knowledge and the measurement of gene frequencies will replace the studies on the nature or essence of race and the mathematical theory of population genetics will replace the Linnaean system of nomenclature.

NOTES AND REFERENCES

[1]This is the position taken by a number of contributors to this symposium. It is exemplified by Theodosius Dobzhansky in *Mankind Evolving* (New Haven, Yale University Press, 1965), 266–69. It also appears to be the view of William Boyd, *Genetics and the Races of Man* (Boston, Little, Brown and Co., 1950), and of C. S. Coon, S. M. Garn, and J. B. Birdsell in *Races* (Springfield, Ill., C. C. Thomas, Publisher, 1950).

[2]This point of view is represented by a number of contributors to the volume *The Concept of Race*, edited by Ashley Montagu (New York, The Free Press, 1964). For a critical examination of the theoretical and methodological problems involved in racial classifications, see especially the articles by Jean Hiernaux, "The Concept of Race and the Taxonomy of Mankind," 29–45; Frank B. Livingstone, "On the Nonexistence of Human Races," 46–60; Paul R. Ehrlich and Richard W. Holm, "A Biological View of Race," 153–79; and Nigel A. Barnicot, "Taxonomy and Variation in Modern Man," 180–227.

[3]Hiernaux, in *The Concept of Race*, 40.

[4]See, for example, S. L. Washburn, "The Study of Race," in *The Concept of Race*, 242–60.

[5]Ehrlich and Holm, in *The Concept of Race*, 175; see also 154–55, 161–62, and 177–78.

[6]Hiernaux, in *The Concept of Race*, 41–42.

[7]N. W. Gillham, "Geographic Variation and the Subspecies Concept in Butterflies," *Systematic Zoology*, 5 (1956), 110–20, quoted by Ehrlich and Holm in *The Concept of Race*, 167.

[8]Livingstone, in *The Concept of Race*, 56.

[9]See Thomas F. Gossett, *Race: The History of an Idea in America* (Dallas, Southern Methodist University Press, 1963), 37–39, 69–70, and 80.

[10]*New York Times*, October 20, 1966, p. 21, reported that "Chinese-American public school children in Boston have been officially declared white by the School Committee ['the official city agency in charge of Boston's public schools'] in the latest phase of the controversy over racial imbalance in schools." One week later, it was reported that the Massachusetts State Board of Education had rejected the ruling of the Boston School Committee, and that Chinese-American

children who had been classed as white would be reclassified as nonwhite. *New York Times*, October 27, 1966, p. 40.

[11]Marvin Harris, *Patterns of Race in the Americas* (New York, Walker and Co., 1964), 56.

[12]Marvin Harris, "Race," in *International Encyclopedia of the Social Sciences* (forthcoming edition).

[13]Marvin Harris and Ruth Martinez, "Referential Ambiguity in the Calculus of Brazilian Racial Identity," unpublished manuscript.

[14]This account of the history of the Eta is based upon John Donoghue, "An Eta Community in Japan: The Social Persistence of Outcaste Groups," *American Anthropologist*, 59 (1957), 1000–17. For additional data on this group, see George DeVos and Hiroshi Wagatsuma, eds., *Japan's Invisible Race: Caste in Culture and Personality* (Berkeley, The University of California Press, 1966).

[15]See Shigeaki Ninomiya, "An Inquiry Concerning the Origin, Development, and Present Situation of the *Eta* in Relation to the History of Social Classes in Japan," *Transactions of the Asiatic Society of Japan*, Second series, Vol. 10 (1933), 47–154.

[16]Kikuchi Sanya, *Eta-Zoku ni Kansuru Kenkyù* (A Study Concerning the *Eta* Race, Tokyo, 1923), cited in Ninomiya, *An Inquiry*, 56.

[17]Ninomiya, *An Inquiry*, 56.

[18]This is exemplified by the comments of Audrey M. Shuey in her book, *The Testing of Negro Intelligence* (Lynchburg, Va., J. P. Bell Co., 1958), and by comments of the authors whose studies are reviewed by Shuey.

[19]For a discussion of the methodological problems involved here, see Hiernaux, 30–40 and Ehrlich and Holm, 160–61 and 163–64 in *The Concept of Race*.

[20]For a sample of scientific racial typologies, see those summarized in Dobzhansky, *Mankind Evolving*, 256–66.

[21]Barbara Solomon, *Ancestors and Immigrants* (Cambridge, Harvard University Press, 1956).

[22]Charles Eliot Norton, "Goldwin Smith," *North American Review*, 205 (1864), 536, quoted in Solomon, *Ancestors*, 12.

[23]Charles Francis Adams, *Three Episodes of Massachusetts History* (Boston, Houghton Mifflin and Co., 1892), Vol. II, 957, quoted in Solomon, *Ancestors*, 29.

[24]Solomon, *Ancestors*, 69–79.

[25]Robert Knox, *The Races of Men* (Philadelphia, 1850), 26–27 and 177, quoted in Gossett, *Race*, 96.

[26]Edward A. Freeman, *Lectures to American Audiences* (Philadelphia, 1882), quoted in Gossett, *Race*, 109.

[27]Solomon, *Ancestors*, 111.

[28]*Ibid.*, 151.

[29]*Ibid.*, 154.

[30]William Stanton, *The Leopard's Spots* (Chicago, University of Chicago Press, 1960).

[31]Philip D. Curtin, *The Image of Africa* (Madison, University of Wisconsin Press, 1964).

[32]Livingstone, in *The Concept of Race*, 55.

28

THE DISTRIBUTIONS OF THE ABNORMAL HEMOGLOBIN GENES AND THEIR SIGNIFICANCE FOR HUMAN EVOLUTION
Frank B. Livingstone

Our understanding of the nature of human variation is so heavily conditioned by the race concept that we learn in childhood as part of the folklore of our society, and it is so governed by the emotionally charged aspects of our visual perceptions, that the first serious attempt to deal with the nature of human difference from a clinical and nonracial point of view came as a result of the study of a trait that is not visible. This attempt was the classic article by Livingstone (1958), dealing with the distribution of an abnormal hemoglobin in West Africa and the reconstruction of past events and selective forces that account for the distribution.

The genetic control of the hemoglobin molecule is accomplished by a pair of genes at a single chromosomal locus. A person with normal hemoglobin will have two normal genes (AA). In some populations, the frequency of the abnormal hemoglobin that Livingstone studies (hemoglobin S) reaches 15 percent, which is extraordinary when one considers that virtually all the individuals whose hemoglobin is controlled by two abnormal genes (SS) fail to live to reproductive age. The question of what maintains the high frequency of the S gene was answered when it was realized that the heterozygote—the individual with one gene of each kind (AS)—was better able to survive the effects of infection from the malaria parasite Plasmodium falciparum.

Livingstone worked out the cultural, historical, and ecological factors that influenced the distribution of malaria and then showed how the distribution of abnormal hemoglobin corresponded. Because his work was done in Africa and because many Americans who suffer from the anemia caused by a double dose of the S gene are of African descent, it has been widely assumed that sickle-cell anemia is an African disease. Such is the grip of racial thinking that this is accepted by much of the medical profession and a growing part of the American black community at the present time. For this reason, we chose not to reprint Livingstone's classic study but rather to use a later one in which he gives maps showing the distribution of hemoglobin S in Sicily, Greece, the Middle East, Arabia, and India, as well as in Africa. Hemoglobin S in fact follows the distribution of falciparum malaria right across the Old World, crossing political, ethnic, breeding population, skin color, and face form boundaries wherever the selective force does.

Much more information is now available (Livingstone 1967—and a revision now in preparation), and it is clear that other traits have different kinds of distributions (see, for example, Livingstone 1969). As Livingstone concludes in the following article, his work was done without using the concept of race. In fact, we can add that the implications of his work run squarely against the utility of the race concept. One could predict that the more traits are analyzed, the more independent clines there will appear to be. For example, recently evidence has been found that the enzyme responsible for the breakdown of the milk sugar lactose is missing from adults in much of the world. It is hardly needed since most people drink no milk after they are weaned in childhood. In the absence of lactase, milk cannot be digested, and digestive upsets and diarrhea result. Some populations, however, do use milk as a part of the adult diet and most of these adults have lactase. Since the people responsible for the study come from an area (Western Europe and its derivatives in North America) in which many adults consume milk and tend to possess the enzyme, they judge the non-possessors as "deficient" even though this is the average human condition. Using the gene for adult lactase possession to assess population relationships, one would find that the herding peoples of East Africa seem to have more in common with northwest Europeans than with their agricultural neighbors (McCracken 1971). But adult lactase is just another cline dependent on the long-term effects of the selective force. Again, the concept of race obscures the nature of human trait variation.

Livingstone, Frank B. 1958. Anthropological implications of sickle cell gene distribution in West Africa. *American Anthropologist 60:533–562.*

———. 1967. *Abnormal Hemoglobins in Human Populations: A Summary and Interpretation.* Aldine, Chicago. 482 pp.

———. 1969. An analysis of the ABO blood group clines in Europe. *American Journal of Physical Anthropology 31:1–10.*

McCracken, Robert D. 1971. Lactase deficiency: an example of dietary evolution. *Current Anthropology 21:479–517.*

One of the most spectacular advances in the last 10 years in our knowledge of human genetic diversity has been the discovery of the abnormal hemoglobin genes. In this short space of time the distributions of these genes in the world's populations have become one of the best known genetic systems for any animal species. In fact, the great mass of data makes it difficult to summarize our knowledge of these genes in a single paper, and the heterogeneity of these data emphasizes once again the great genetic variability which exists among the populations of the human species. Although we know more about the hemoglobins, this is but one of the many genetic systems which the increasing precison of biochemical techniques has brought to our attention. The haptoglobins, transferrins, and others yet to be discovered will increase our knowledge of human genetic diversity still further.

Another significant advance in recent years, which preceded the discovery of the hemoglobins, was the development of the modern genetic theory of evolution. This synthesis was a theoretical advance as much as a factual one and was developed primarily from data on animals other than man. It has been applied to some extent to the blood group genes, but because we know so much more about the factors of evolution as regards the abnormal hemoglobin genes, this system is the first one for the human species for which we can discuss the factors of evolution and their interrelationships. Since, in addition, we also know the environmental circumstances which determine the direction of natural selection, the principal

Reprinted from *Evolution* 18:685–699, 1964. Reprinted with the permission of the author and publisher.

factor of evolution, we can effectively evaluate the role of culture as one of the environmental determinants of human evolution at the hemoglobin locus.

While the populational aspects of the abnormal hemoglobin genes have been of great interest to anthropologists and geneticists, biochemists have also made significant advances in the chemical structure of hemoglobin so that hemoglobin is one of the best known complex proteins. The chemical structure of this molecule has been directly related to gene action as no other has. We now know that genes are composed of DNA, which, through RNA, directs the manufacture of proteins or polypeptide chains, but for the hemoglobin molecule we know the exact changes in the molecule which are associated with the gene differences. (The biochemical advances are discussed by Ingram, 1963).

As the specific changes which genes produce have been discovered, it has been realized that similar phenotypic characteristics, whether based on observation with the naked eye or biochemical tests, can result from very different genetic structures. For example, one can talk about the gene for albinism and even calculate the mutation rate to this gene, but we now realize that literally dozens of different genetic changes may result in phenotypically similar albinism. This specificity of genes also has implications for measuring gene flow between populations. Many of the characteristics which have been used to claim genetic relationships between populations may well be due to very different genes. The abnormal hemoglobins, as the first system where we know the specific chemical changes involved, have made it possible to discuss the basic concepts of mutation, gene flow, and natural selction in a much more realistic way.

In 1953 after the development of paper electrophoresis made mass surveys for the abnormal hemoglobins quite easy, an international committee was convened to establish some orderly process for the naming of the new hemoglobins which were rapidly being discovered. This committee established the letters A, F, M, and S, for normal, fetal, met-, and sickle cell hemoglobins which had been known for some time and decided that further hemoglobins would be assigned letters in order of discovery, beginning with the letter C, and working up the alphabet. At present we are up to the letter R, but further developments have rendered this system rather unworkable as originally set up. These developments were the perfection of techniques to determine the complete chemical structure of hemoglobin. They have resulted in the discovery that hemoglobins which were being called by the same letter since they had the same electrophoretic properties were actually quite different in structure. Hence, another conference has resulted in the use of subscripts to the letters to distinguish these similar hemoglobins. These subscripts designate the place of discovery so that we now have, for example, hemoglobin G San Jose, hemoglobin G Bristol, and hemoglobin G Philadelphia.

With a few exceptions which are more complicated genetically, all of these newly discovered abnormal hemoglobins are due to the presence of a single gene, or in other words differ from normal hemoglobin in one part of their structure. When heterozygous, these genes are for the most part benign, while homozygosity or simultaneous heterozygosity for two of them result in conditions of variable severity ranging from lethality for the sickle cell homozygote in the absence of modern medicine to a slight anemia as in homozygosity for hemoglobin C. For many of the rare hemoglobins no homozygotes have been detected, but it would appear that these conditions may well be more like hemoglobin C in severity than the sickle cell gene.

Although the hemoglobin genes may still hold some surprises for us, the world distribution of these genes can be mapped in considerable detail. For purposes of further discussion the hemoglobin genes will be divided into three groups: (1) those which attain appreciable frequencies or more than 15% heterozygotes in some populations, (2) those found in intermediate frequencies or more than 1% but less than 15% heterozygotes, and (3) those found only occasionally or in less than 1% of the population. The letter designations of the hemoglobins will be used although it should be remembered that any one of these letters may indicate more than one specific gene. With this classification hemoglobins S, C, E, and thalassemia would fall into group 1; hemoglobins D, K, N, and O in group 2; and the rest in group 3. Thalassemia is a potpourri and undoubtedly contains many different "genes." This is because thalassemia is still primarily diagnosed on clinical and morphological features, and many cases which appear similar in these characteristics have been shown to have different chemical and genetic bases. Some thalassemias are chromosomal duplications due to unequal crossing over, some are probably specific structural changes in the hemoglobin molecule as are the other abnormal hemoglobins, and others may result from operator or regulator genes, whatever that means. Nevertheless, some populations have high fequencies of all thalassemias combined so that this system will be considered in the same category as hemoglobins S, C, and E, which are more specific entities.

Some 25 different rare hemoglobins have been discovered so far, although in order to discover these, extremely large samples must be collected. Many of these rare hemoglobins have been discovered in populations in the tropical and subtropical regions of the Old World which have high frequencies of abnormal hemoglobin genes, but the rare hemoglobins have also been discovered in populations outside this area. Studies from Japan indicated that these random mutants occur in about one of every 2,000 individuals examined (Shibata, 1961). We have talked about mutation as a random, recurrent process and we now have this excellent example. Furthermore, most mutations were thought to be deleterious and this appears to be true of the hemoglobins. Thus, the low frequency of abnormal hemoglobins in the Japanese, English, or Swedish populations results from a balance between mutation to these genes and selection against them. This type of selection which keeps the gene frequencies where they are has been called stabilizing selection, and the hemoglobin loci in these populations are examples of the classical theory of genetic diversity which views this diversity as a balance between mutation away from the normal genotype and natural selection weeding out these deleterious mutants. Evolution or gene frequency change has not occurred here.

The classical view of evolutionary change is usually stated as "every once in awhile a favorable mutation occurs which then replaces the older norm." For the abnormal hemoglobins this statement is wrong or at least it seems to me to be the wrong way to characterize their evolution. It is rather backward and another example of genetic determinsim which is endemic in Western thought. It is important to remember that mutation is a recurrent, continuous process, and our hominid and pongid ancestors were continually mutating and producing abnormal hemoglobins. But little evolution occurred; so little, in fact, that based on peptide fingerprinting, the hemoglobin of most of mankind is more similar to that of the chimpanzee and gorilla than it is to their fellow-man, including in some cases immediate family. The cause of evolutionary change in the human hemoglobin genes is not the occurrence of favorable mutants, but changes in the amount and direction of natural selection operating on these genes, and these changes in natural selection were the result of the development of environmental circumstances in which heterozygotes for some of these abnormal hemoglobin genes possessed a selective advantage. It was only then that these genes became an important part of some human gene pools.

While all populations which have been intensively investigated have low frequencies of some abnormal hemoglobin genes, it is only populations which have been resident for a considerable length of time in the tropical and sub-tropical regions of the Old World which have intermediate or appreciable frequencies of abnormal hemoglobins. However, there are populations in this area, such as the Australian aborigines, some Papuans, Polynesians, and Micronesians in the Asian tropics and the Bushmen, Ethiopians, and some Nilotic peoples in the African tropics, that do not have high frequencies of any abnormal hemoglobin. With the exception of thalassemia, the hemoglobins which attain high frequencies in the tropics, hemoglobins S, C, and E, are rarely found outside their areas of high frequencies except in migrant populations. Thus, they do not seem to be frequent mutants of the hemoglobin loci, but relatively rare ones.

Although thalassemia is a genetically heterogeneous entity, hemoglobins S, C, and E are quite specific, and all differ from normal hemoglobin by only a single amino acid out of the string of about 300 amino acids which comprise the identical halves of a hemoglobin molecule. Since an abnormal hemoglobin mutation presumably could occur on most of these 300 amino acids, it is obvious that the mutation rates to the hemoglobin S, C, or E gene are much less than the mutation rate to thalassemia which includes many different changes.

Since hemoglobins S, C, and E appear to be relatively rare mutants and their distributions are contiguous and somewhat restricted, gene flow appears to have been a more important factor in determining their distributions than in the case of thalassemia which is a common mutant. Of course, to explain similar frequencies of abnormal hemoglobins in any two populations, one has to wiegh the possibility of gene flow with the possibility of a separate mutation becoming established. But this is possible in the case of these three hemoglobins since all frequencies seem to be of the same specific gene mutation in each case, while for thalassemia the recognition of gene flow is difficult. It should be noted that all that sickles is not hemoglobin S; there are other hemoglobins which also produce the sickling phenomenon, but the distributions which will be discussed are based for the most part on electrophoresis tests and not on sickle cell tests with sodium metabisulfite.

All four of the abnormal hemoglobins which are found in high frequencies have some deleterious effects associated with homozygosity. In fact, it is rather surprising that thalassemia and hemoglobin S, the most widespread and most frequent of the four, have the most serious effects. Although some individuals who appear to be homozygous for either hemoglobin S or thalassemia have survived and reproduced, population studies indicate that in the relatively primitive medical conditions of the areas of Africa and Europe where high frequencies of these genes are found, the survival and reproduction of homozygotes for these genes is practically nil. Such selection against the sickle cell and thalassemia genes thus raises the question as to why there are high frequencies of these genes in some populations.

Neel (1951) first suggested the two possible answers, mutation or heterozygote superiority, and there were suggestions that malaria may be the factor which confers an increased fitness on the heterozygote. But Allison (1954a, 1954b, 1954c) first grasped the problem and attempted to answer it. His investigations, although providing strong evidence of an association between the sickle cell gene and malaria, were not conclusive; but since then investigations by Raper (1956), the Lambotte-Legrands (1957), Delbrouck (1958), and Firschein (1961) have demonstrated conclusively that sickle cell trait carriers have a selective advantage in an area with holoendemic malaria which is due primarily to *Plasmodium falciparum*. Although disbelief in the malaria hypothesis is still occasionally expressed, I think this work is an excellent example of progress in science. The question, why high frequencies of the sickle cell gene, is a legitimate one and must have an answer. In terms of the modern theory of population genetics there may be several answers, but I have never seen an alternative to the malaria hypothesis seriously advanced. And in terms of the total array of data we now possess on this gene, there is no other answer. Assuming that this is a balanced polymorphism, the factor which is balancing the polymorphism in many populations of Africa, Greece, and India would have to eliminate about 15% of the normal homozygotes each generation or about 11% of the total population. Malaria is the only cause of death which comes anywhere near eliminating this many zygotes. Thus, in terms of our theories, this question must have an answer and this is the only possible one.

Although the relationship between sickling and malaria has much evidence in its favor, practically no work has been done on the selective factors of the other abnormal hemoglobin genes. In Greece (Choremis,

Fessas, Kattamis, Stamatoyannopoulos, Zannos-Mariolea, Karaklis, and Belios, 1963), Sardinia (Ceppellini, 1957), and New Guinea (Curtain, Kidson, Gajdusek, and Gorman, 1962) the frequency of thalassemia has been shown to be correlated with the amount of malaria, and there is some evidence from Ghana (Thompson, 1962) that hemoglobin C carriers may have some resistance to malaria infections. By analogy with hemoglobin S, it has been generally assumed that malaria is the major factor involved in the other abnormal hemoglobins, but since the differences in fitness which we are attempting to detect are so much smaller for the abnormal hemoglobins, C, E, and, in most areas, thalassemia, the task is much more difficult than for the sickle cell gene. Furthermore, malaria is rapidly being controlled as a lethal disease and even being eradicated, so that there are few places left where such a relationship could be tested. Since there are also moral problems involved, I suspect that direct proof of the factors which are balancing the hemoglobin polymorphisms will never be forthcoming, except perhaps by means of some laboratory experiments which are technically not feasible at present. But making the assumption that malaria is the selective factor balancing these polymorphisms renders the entire distributions of these genes so intelligible that I think circumstantial evidence will prevail.

In the remainder of this paper malaria will be assumed to be the major factor which is balancing these polymorphisms. However, hemoglobin S seems to be balanced by falciparum malaria while this does not seem to be the case for the other abnormal hemoglobins (Livingstone, 1961). Thalassemia, for example, seems to convey some resistance to the other widespread species of malaria, quartan and benign tertian, which are due respectively to *Plasmodium malariae* and *P. vivax*. The fourth species of malaria parasite, *P. ovale*, is so rare that it need not be considered further.

Figure 1 shows the distribution of thalassemia in the Old World. It only shows the presence of thalassemia and not frequencies since these data are quite incomplete. Thalassemia is the most widespread of the abnormal hemoglobins and its distribution in the Old World is almost as extensive as the distribution of endemic malaria, with the

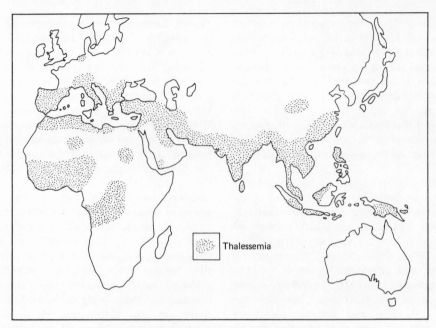

Figure 1. The distribution of thalassemia in the Old World.

very striking exception of East Africa. A very few individuals who appear to be simultaneously heterozygous for hemoglobin *S* and a thalassemia gene have been discovered in East Africa. Strangely enough, on the edge of East Africa among the Arab and Greek communities of Khartoum, thalassemia apparently attains its highest frequencies in the world (Vella and Hassan, 1961; Vella and Ibrahim, 1961).

Occasionally, a thalassemia gene is encountered outside this area in Swiss, German, Japanese, English, and some others. On the map I have tried to indicate the areas where there apppear to be a significant number of cases or percentages of thalassemia. This association with few exceptions between endemic malaria and thalassemia, in addition to confirming the malaria hypothesis, indicates other factors in the population dynamics of the abnormal hemoglobins. Thalassemia, as a number of specific genes, has a higher mutation rate than the more specific abnormal hemoglobins; so that when malaria moves into an area, the first genes with an increased fitness which it is likely to encounter are thalassemia genes. Thus, as malaria has spread, it has brought thalassemia right behind it. For example, malaria appears to have spread rather recently through the islands of the southwest

Pacific and is still spreading today through the Solomons. The Solomons and the New Hebrides are one of the few places in the tropics where there are anopheline mosquitoes and no malaria. Although malaria seems to have spread there from Southeast Asia, there has been little gene flow from the Indonesian populations to New Guinea. Hence in the New Guinea populations there are appreciable frequencies of thalassemia and another red cell gene, glucose-6-phosphate dehydrogenase deficiency, whose population genetics appears to be determined by approximately the same factors as thalassemia. In addition, there is a correlation between the amount of malaria and thalassemia in New Guinea (Curtain, Kidson, Gajdusek, and Gorman, 1962). Both are found in the lowlands but not in the highlands.

Turning now to the distribution of hemoglobin *E*, which is shown on Fig. 2, it can be seen to have a rather restricted distribution on the mainland of Southeast Asia and in the Indonesian archipelago. This gene appears to have spread by gene flow out through Indonesia as far as Celebes and Timor. Since the mutation rate to this very specific chemical change would be much less than that to thalassemia, gene flow seems to be a reasonable assumption for this contiguous distribution. Among the Bugis of southern

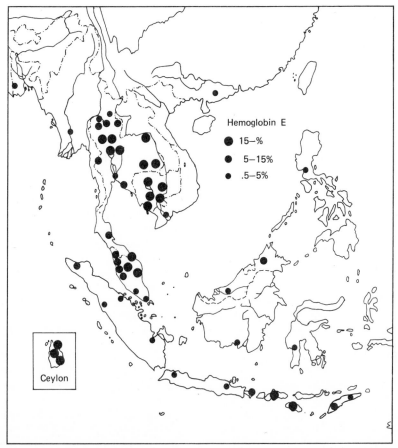

Figure 2. Percentage incidence of individuals with hemoglobin *E* in the populations of Southeast Asia. The percentages computed for each population in Figures 2, 3, 4, and 5 include both heterozygotes and homozygotes for the respective abnormal hemoglobin. Because of the problem of differentiating homozygotes from individuals simultaneously heterozygous for an abnormal hemoglobin and a thalassemia gene, estimation of the gene frequencies was not attempted. The variability in the percentages used, however, is an approximate measure of the variability in the frequency of the abnormal hemoglobin gene.

Celebes and some of the other peoples in this area hemoglobin *O* attains frequencies of about 2% and is almost unique to these populations (Lie-Injo and Sadono, 1958). As is the case with other hemoglobins, with intermediate frequencies, hemoglobin *O* is found at the forefront of the wave of advance of one of the more widespread hemoglobins which are found in high frequencies, in this case hemoglobin *E*. Hemoglobin *O*, like other intermediate hemoglobins, appears to be a random mutant that in the absence of one of the hemoglobins with greater selective advantage such as hemoglobin *E*, has been selected for and increased in these peripheral populations.

In contrast to Africa and hemoglobin *S*, the distribution of hemoglobin *E* in Southeast Asia is more spotty and erratic. This is related to the fact that all species of human malaria are not as solidly endemic on every village and farm in Southeast Asia. This in turn is due primarily to the vectors of malaria there. On the mainland of Southeast Asia, *Anopheles minimus* is the major vector of malaria but in Malasia it is a similar species, *A. maculatus*. These vectors breed principally in small, cool, fast-flowing, sunlit streams and hence are found in great numbers only in the hilly regions of Southeast Asia, where the forest has been cut down. In contrast to Europe where malaria and marshes were intimately associated because of the nature of the anopheline vectors, in Southeast Asia the deltas and great river valleys are not particularly malarious. Thus, around Bangkok and in the delta of the Mekong River in South Vietnam there is little malaria and low frequencies of hemoglobin E. On the other hand, the foothills are intensely malarious and the more primitive slash-and-burn agriculturalists of these areas have high frequencies of hemoglobin E. No data on the frequency of hemoglobin E in the hunters of this area such as the Semang are available, but due to the ecology of the vectors, there is practically no malaria in the unbroken tropical forest. It is only when the forest has been cut down that A. maculatus becomes very frequent in Malasia and A. minimus elsewhere. A. maculatus, however, does not particularly prefer human blood and can be diverted to biting cattle if these are available. Hence, in primitive slash-and-burn agriculturalists with few cattle such as the Senoi there are high frequencies of hemoglobin E. But as more livestock are present and more human manipulation of the landscape occurs, malaria and A. maculatus tend to decrease.

In mainland Southeast Asia it has been recently demonstrated that A. balabacensis is an important vector in addition to A. minimus (Eyles, Wharton, Cheong, and Warren, 1964). Since this mosquito is associated with forests and appears most numerous in villages surrounded by forest, it is perhaps responsible for much of the malaria in the sparsely populated areas. In the region of Cambodia where Eyles et al. (1964) worked, the parasite rates were very high and these populations also have very high frequencies of hemoglobin E.

In the swamps of parts of Malasia and into Indonesia, there are two other vectors of malaria, Anopheles sundaicus and A. umbrosus. A. umbrosus breeds in fresh-water, shaded mangrove swamps and when the trees are cut down becomes scarce, while A. sundaicus is found only along the coast in brackish water. Thus, malaria is rather spottily distributed in Indonesia, but can become a very severe disease in places. On Borneo the efficient vectors of malaria are relatively absent and most of the malaria is due to A. leucosphyrus which breeds in shaded water and is associated with tropical forest. The Dyaks have less malaria and low frequencies of hemoglobin E, while the Muruts of North Borneo have more malaria and a higher frequency of hemoglobin E.

To the west hemoglobin E is occasionally encountered in Nepal and in Bengal there is a frequency of about 4%, but the greater part of India is characterized by high frequencies of hemoglobin S. Some hemoglobin E has been reported in Eti-Turks and Greeks, but it may be derived from other mutations and does not represent gene flow from the east, although that possibility exists. With these exceptions there appears to be a strong border in the neighborhood of Calcutta with hemoglobin E predominating to the east and hemoglobin S to the west. This line coincides with the two general avenues of the penetration of agriculture into the South Asian tropical forest. Most of peninsular India and the Ganges River valley were populated by peoples from the west, while the Nagas and other tribes of the North East Frontier are linguistically and culturally related to peoples of Burma and southern China. However, it should be noted that few studies have been done on the Nagas or the other tribes of this area, but an assorted sample of Burmese did have a high frequency of hemoglobin E.

The only groups to the west which have high frequencies of hemoglobin E are some Vedda villages on Ceylon. An earlier report (Aksoy, Bird, Lehmann, Mourant, Thein, and Wickremaisinghe, 1955) showed a very low frequency, but recently some villages are reported to have 30% hemoglobin E carriers (Wickremaisinghe, Ikin, Mourant, and Lehmann, 1963). The investigators imply that this indicates a genetic relationship to the Senoi but there is little evidence for it. Assuming that the genes are the same, it seems to indicate gene flow from Southeast Asia. Hemoglobin E is also found occasionally in the other inhabitants of Ceylon so this seems to be quite likely. It should be noted that the Veddas are now living in settled villages, have mixed considerably with the Tamils and Sinhalese, and the villages with the high frequencies of hemoglobin E are located in the north part of Ceylon which has hyperendemic malaria. Other studies of similar villages of Tamils and Sinhalese are needed, but since they are not considered to have "ethnological" significance they have not been investigated. To postulate that the presence of this gene in the Veddas and Senoi is the result of their common ancestry which goes back to a time when hunters and gatherers were sparsely distributed throughout Southeast Asia does not accord at all with our knowledge of the operation of natural selection on this gene.

Hemoglobin *E* then seems to have followed the spread of malaria through Southeast Asia. On the other hand, the spread of the conditions which gave rise to holoendemic malaria in India to the west of Calcutta appear to have come from Asia Minor. This part of India has hemoglobin *D* and thalassemia in the north, while hemoglobin *S* is found over most of the Indian peninsula, as is shown on Fig. 3. Many gaps on the map are not necessarily areas where hemoglobin *S* is absent but just where no studies have been carried out. However, populations of the plains of Madras and Kerala have been examined and no sickling is found. And strange as it may seem, these areas also have little malaria. The populations which have very high frequencies of hemoglobin *S* are found in the Western and Eastern Ghats and the Bastar Hills. Here in these areas the vector of malaria, *A. fluviatilis*, is like those of Southeast Asia in that it breeds in the little streams in the hills. These areas are characterized by holoendemic malaria while the coastal plains have little. On the Deccan Plateau of Mysore and Hyderabad malaria tends to occur in epidemics which are dependent on the breeding of the malaria vector, *A. culicifacies*, which in turn is dependent on the monsoon. Although not many studies of abnormal hemoglobin have been done on the plateau, there seem to be lower frequencies.

The high frequencies of hemoglobin *S* in South India also are found in tribal peoples, most of whom are slash-and-burn agriculturalists but some, like the Paniyans, verge on hunting and gathering. On the other hand, the castes, with the exception of the Mahars, seem to have much lower frequencies even in the same general areas, than the tribal peoples. This seems reasonable since malaria is not endemic in the cities of southern India because there is no "rainbarrel" vector there.

The question as to whether the hemoglobin *S* genes in India are derived from the same source as those in Africa is a real problem. Assuming that these are examples of the same mutation chemically speaking, then the restricted distribution of hemoglobin *S* in Africa, the Middle East, and India seems to indicate that this gene is a rather

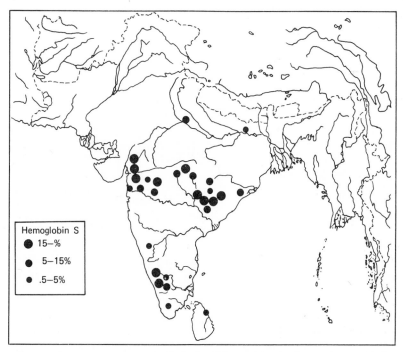

Figure 3. Percentage incidence of individuals with hemoglobin *S* in the populations of India.

rare mutant. None of the populations with high frequency are very distant from others and hence gene flow has presumably occurred.

Turning to Africa and the Middle East, Fig. 4 shows the distribution of hemoglobin C. This gene is restricted to West and North Africa and the high frequencies in West Africa are found in the more primitive tribes that speak Gur languages. The one exception is the Wakura who inhabit the northernmost mountains in the Cameroons. They appear to be long resident in the area and are surrounded by the Kanuri and Shuwa Arabs among whom there are extremely high frequencies of hemoglobin S and no hemoglobin C. One of the problems associated with hemoglobin C is whether it is replacing hemoglobin S or vice versa, or perhaps there is an equilibrium frequency with both present. The fitness values of the genotypes involved in this triallelic system undoubtedly vary throughout this area, but I think a good case can be made for the hemoglobin S gene replacing hemoglobin C. I think it can be shown that hemoglobin S will replace almost any other abnormal hemoglobin gene or thalassemia.

From the fact that the frequency of hemoglobin S carriers is 30 to 40% in many

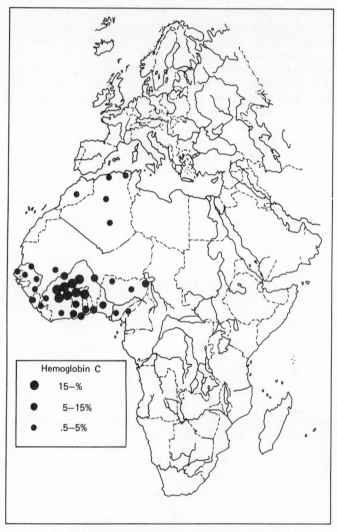

Figure 4. Percentage incidence of individuals with hemoglobin C in the populations of North and West Africa.

populations in this part of the world, one can estimate that the fitness of the *AS* heterozygote must be 1.2 to 1.3 times the fitness of the normal homozygote, assuming that the sickle cell homozygote has a fitness of zero. On the other hand, since thalassemia only occurs up to 25% of some populations, the fitness of the thalassemia heterozygote must be about 1.1 times that of normals. Homozygotes for hemoglobin *C* do not have the very serious anemia of either sickle cell or thalassemia homozygotes. If we estimate the fitness of the homozygous *C* genotype at from 0.6 to 0.8 that of the normal genotype, then, since a *C* gene frequency of 0.15 is as high as the equilibrium *C* gene frequency could possibly be with only *C* present, the maximum fitness value of the hemoglobin *C* heterozygote would be about 1.08 times the normal fitness, which we arbitrarily set as 1.00. Given these fitness values, we can attempt to determine which of these genes, hemoglobin *C, S,* or thalassemia, will replace the others or whether instead there is an equilibrium point with more than one of them present. The general conditions for the existence of an equilibrium with three genes present have been solved by Li (1955), Kimura (1956), Penrose, Smith, and Sprott (1956), and Mandel (1959), and Bodmer and Parsons (1961) have solved the conditions as to whether any one of a series of alleles will increase when introduced into a population at a low frequency. However, the differential equations involving gene frequency change at a multi-allelic locus are nonlinear and nonhomogeneous and hence a general solution is not possible by the methods of classical mathematical analysis; but one can use a computer to obtain specific solutions to these equations. I was rather amazed to find that the sickle cell gene will increase under a great variety of conditions. It will completely replace the hemoglobin *C* gene and will take over from the thalassemia gene although there is a stable equilibrium with about 15% sickle cell genes and 2% thalassemia. In both cases it takes about 50 generations or about 1,000 years for the sickle cell gene to replace the *C* or thalassemia gene. In evolutionary perspective this is a very short time span; in fact, it is about the most rapid rate at which one gene can replace another. Thus, what seem to be the most plausible estimates of the

fitness values of the abnormal hemoglobin genotypes imply that the sickle cell gene is extremely predatory and will eliminate other such genes.

This analysis has many implications for the distributions of the *S* and *C* genes. In West Africa their distributions have raised the problem as to whether there is an equilibrium with both genes present as Allison (1956) has maintained, or whether one gene is replacing the other. According to this analysis the *S* gene should be replacing the *C* gene, and this seems reasonable. Since there are populations in the western part of West Africa with low frequencies of both genes, it appears that the *S* gene was introduced into this area from the east and north, and historically it is known that a great deal of gene flow did occur in this direction. Since the highest frequencies of the *C* gene are found in the rather primitive Gur-speaking peoples who have received less such gene flow, it appears that the *C* gene was present here before the *S* gene and is now being replaced.

Figure 5 shows how the hemoglobin *S* gene has spread throughout the Old World. In East Africa the *S* gene has replaced all the other abnormal hemoglobins, while to the north in the Mediterranean area, *S* is only found in high frequencies in North Africa and parts of Greece and Turkey. However, Barnicot, Allsion, Blumberg, Deliyannis, Krimbas, and Ballas (1963) have shown that there is an inverse correlation between the *S* and thalassemia gene frequencies in the malarious areas of Greece, which indicates that they are in competition and that one is replacing the other. The *S* gene does not seem to have reached Sardinia which seems expectable since it is one of the more isolated areas of Italy with less contact with and presumable gene flow from the outside.

The fact that the *S* gene will increase rapidly in a malarious environment no matter what other genes are present implies that any mutant *S* gene would most likely increase. Thus, the fact that there are many malarious areas without high frequencies of the *S* gene and that the high frequencies of this gene are in rather contiguous populations indicates that the *S* gene is a rare mutant and that the distribution of this gene is due primarily to gene flow among the populations within which it occurs.

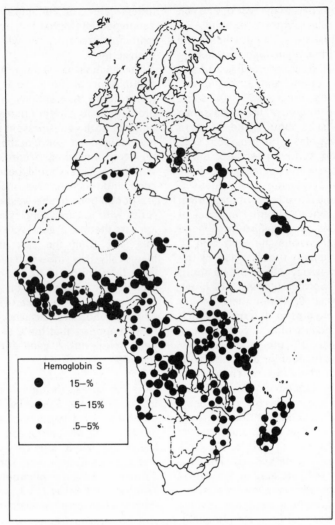

Figure 5. Percentage incidence of individuals with hemoglobin *S* in the populations of Africa, Europe, and Southwest Asia.

CONCLUSIONS AND SUMMARY

The preceding interpretation of the distributions of the abnormal hemoglobins in terms of the factors which we know control gene frequency change has several general implications. First, natural selection is the major factor determining differences in gene frequency, and for the abnormal hemoglobins this natural selection is determined by the presence of holoendemic malaria and its high cost of life. The evolution of this type of malaria is in turn dependent upon a sedentary way of life for which agriculture seems to be a necessary prerequisite in most environments. Agriculture and hence high frequen-

cies of abnormal hemoglobins are relatively recent events in human evolution. The penetration of agriculture into the tropical regions of Asia came from two centers, China and the Middle East. The penetration from China through Southeast Asia to Indonesia is associated with the spread of hemoglobin *E*, while the spread of agriculture from the Middle East through peninsular India and Africa is associated with the spread of the hemoglobin *S* gene. Where these two movements met in the vicinity of Calcutta is also the border between the high frequencies of these genes, with *S* to the west and *E* to the east.

We have learned a great deal about the

evolutionary process from the abnormal hemoglobins since they are the first genetic system in man to which we can apply genetic theory in any detailed way. They also emphasize the important relationship between man's cultural and biological evolution. The evolution of gene frequency differences has often been called "race formation." With reference to abnormal hemoglobin, such a label seems not only grossly inappropriate but false when the implications of the concept of race are taken into consideration. In addition, the distributions of the abnormal hemoglobin genes are not at all related to the traditional races of man, although one can still read that the sickle cell gene is a Negroid character. With reference to the hemoglobins, Coon (1962: 663) has recently stated, "To me, at least, it is encouraging to know that biochemistry divides us into the same subspecies that we have long recognized on the basis of other criteria," a statement which I think the detailed arguments of this paper have shown to be false with respect to the hemoglobins. If natural selection is considered to be one of the major factors contributing to the gene frequency differences which exist among the hundreds of thousands of human breeding isolates, then the gene frequencies will vary with the intensity of selection as do the abnormal hemoglobins and not with "race." If, as Mayr (1963) has recently emphasized, subspecies are artificial units of the classifier and not major units of evolution, it is time anthropologists stopped considering them as such. Between the "natural" units of species and breeding population, there is no natural unit according to the genetic theory, and to attempt to reconcile race with the genetic theory of evolution is to use old concepts to express new ideas which leads to nothing but confusion since we all learn what race basically is in childhood. In this paper I have attempted to describe and explain the distribution of one particular genetic system in man. This has been done without using the concept of race; I think the same can be done for any genetic system.

LITERATURE CITED

Aksoy, M., G. W. G. Bird, H. Lehmann, A. E. Mourant, H. Thein, and R. L. Wickremaisinghe. 1955. Hemoglobin E in Asia. J. Physiol., 130: 56P–57P.

Allison, A. C. 1954a. Protection afforded by sickle-cell trait against subtertian malarial infection. British Med. J., 1: 290–294.

———. 1954b. The distribution of the sickle-cell trait in East Africa and elsewhere, and its apparent relationship to the incidence of subtertian malaria. Trans. Roy. Soc. Trop. Med. and Hygiene, 48: 312–318.

———. 1954c. Notes on sickle-cell polymorphism. Ann. Human Gen., 19: 39–57.

———. 1956. Population genetics of abnormal human hemoglobins. Acta Gen. et Statistica Med., 6: 430–434.

Barnicot, N. A., A. C. Allison, B. S. Blumberg, G. Deliyannis, C. Krimbas, and A. Ballas. 1963. Hemoglobin types in Greek populations. Ann. Human Gen., 26: 229–236.

Bodmer, W. F., and P. A. Parsons. 1961. The initial progress of new genes with various genetic systems. Heredity, 15: 283–299.

Ceppellini, R. 1957. I meccanismi evolutivi nelle popolazioni umane. Suppl. a La Ricerca Scientifica, 27: 3–23.

Choremis, C., P. Fessas, C. Kattamis, Stamatoyannopoulos, L. Zannos-Mariolea, A. Karaklis, and G. Belios. 1963. Three inherited red-cell abnormalities in a district of Greece, thalassemia, sickling, and glucose-6-phosphate-dehydrogenase deficiency. Lancet, 1: 907–909.

Coon, C. S. 1962. The origin of races. Knopf, New York.

Curtain, C. C., C. Kidson, D. C. Gajdusek, J. G. Gorman. 1962. Distribution pattern, population genetics and anthropological significance of thalassemia and abnormal hemoglobins in Melanesia. Amer. J. Phys. Anthrop., 20: 475–483.

Delbrouck, J. 1958. Contribution a la genetique de la sicklemie. Ann. Soc. Belge de Med. Trop., 38: 103–133.

Eyles, D. E., R. H. Wharton, W. H. Cheong, and McW. Warren. 1964. Studies on malaria and Anopheles balabacensis in Cambodia. Bull. World Health Org., 30: 7–21.

Firschein, L. 1961. Population dynamics of the sickle-cell trait in the black Caribs of British Honduras, Central America. Amer. J. Human Gen., 13: 233–254.

Ingram, V. M. 1963. The hemoglobins in genetics and evolution. Columbia University Press, New York.

Kimura, M. 1956. Rules for testing stability of a selective polymorphism. Proc. Nat. Acad. Sci., 42: 336–340.

Li, C. C. 1955. The stability of an equilibrium and the average fitness of a population. Amer. Nat., 89: 281-296.

Lambotte-Legrand, J., and C. Lambotte-Legrand. 1958. Notes complementaire sur la drepanocytose. Ann. Soc. Belge de Med. Trop., 38: 45–54. I. Sicklemie et malaria.

Lie-Injo, L. E., and M. D. Sadono. 1958. Haemoglobin O (Buginese X) in Sulawesi. Brit. Med. J., 1: 1461–1463.

Livingstone, F. B. 1961. Balancing the human hemoglobin polymorphisms. Human Biol., 33: 205–219.

Mandel, S. P. H. 1959. The stability of a multiple allelic system. Heredity, 13: 289–302.

Mayr, E. 1963. Animal species and evolution. Harvard Univ. Press, Cambridge.

Neel, J. V. 1951. The population genetics of two inherited blood dyscrasias in man. Cold Spring Harbor Symp. Quant. Biol., 15: 141–158.

Penrose, L. S., S. M. Smith, and D. A. Sprott. 1956. On the stability of allelic systems, with special reference in haemoglobins A, S, and C. Ann. Human Gen. 21: 90–93.

Raper, A. B. 1956. Sickling in relation to morbidity from malaria and other diseases. Brit. Med. J., 1: 965–966.

Shibata, S. 1961. Hemoglobinopathy, with special reference to the abnormal hemoglobins found in Japan. Bull. Yamaguchi Med. School, 8: 197–207.

Thompson, G. R. 1962. Significance of haemoglobins S and C in Ghana. British Med. Jour., 1: 682–685.

Vella, V., and M. M. Hassan. 1961. Thalassemia major in a Sudanese Arab family. J. Trop. Med. and Hygiene, 64: 199–201.

———., and S. A. Ibrahim. 1961. The frequency of thalassemia minor in a Greek community. J. Trop. Med. and Hygiene, 64: 202–206.

Wickremaisinghe, R. L., E. W. Ikin, A. E. Mourant, and H. Lehmann. 1963. Blood groups and haemoglobins of the Veddas. J. Roy. Anthrop. Inst., 93: 117–125.

29

POPULATION DIFFERENCES IN RED AND GREEN COLOR VISION DEFICIENCY: A REVIEW, AND A QUERY ON SELECTION RELAXATION[1]
Richard H. Post

Students of human evolution have long been aware that many of the recent changes in human form have been reductions in various features that clearly were of survival value in earlier times. Evidence showing the reduction in jaws and teeth is presented in selections 24 and 25 and the evolutionary mechanism involved (the PME) is discussed in selections 2 and 3. Our presentation so far, however, has been chiefly from the perspective of features visible in the human skeleton—the only perspective available to the student of the fossil record.

Variation in the strength of development of traits discernible only in living populations can also be assessed from the same point of view, and the person who has made the most concerted attempt to do so is Dr. Richard H. Post. Post's article was published just before the PME was proposed. While Post makes a clear case for the reduction of a structure following the relaxation of selective pressure, the PME provides the mechanism for this occurrence.

Although the area in which Post has pioneered is rich and fascinating, it has attracted little attention, and almost all the attempts to extend the model to deal with traits other than color vision have been pursued by Dr. Post himself.

Post, Richard H. 1962. Population differences in vision acuity: a review, with speculative notes on selection relaxation. *Eugenics Quarterly* 9:189–212.

———. 1963. "Colorblindness" distribution in Britain, France, and Japan: a review with notes on selection relaxation. *Eugenics Quarterly* 10:110–118.

———. 1964. Hearing acuity variation among negroes and whites. *Eugenics Quarterly* 11:65–81.

———. 1965. Notes on relaxed selection. *Anthropologischer Anzeiger* 29:186–195.

———. 1966a. Breast cancer, lactation, and genetics. *Eugenics Quarterly* 13:1–9.

———. 1966b. Pilot study: population differences in the frequency of spina bifida occulta. *Eugenics Quarterly* 13:341–352.

———. 1966c. Deformed nasal septa and relaxed selection, I. *Eugenics Quarterly* 13:101–112.

———. 1969a. Deformed nasal septa and relaxed selection, II. *Social Biology* 16:179–196.

———. 1969b. Tear duct size differences of age, sex and race. *American Journal of Physical Anthropology* 30:85–88.

———. 1969c. Population differences of tear duct size: implications of relaxed selection. *Social Biology* 16:257–269.

Sex-linked color vision deficiency merits more consideration as a genetic trait for the study of population and race differences than has been given it, to judge from the relatively small number of reports in the literature of physical anthropology and human genetics. Certain details of the genetic basis may be unclear and a certain proportion of phenotypic classifications doubtful because of imperfect testing techniques, but the fact of relatively simple genetic control is

[1]This paper is dedicated to Professor L.C. Dunn in recognition of his long and distinguished career.

The review was written while the author was supported in part by USPHS Grant A–4108.

certain. In almost all cases it is fully penetrant by early childhood and does not vary in manifestation. Furthermore, in certain situations the comparison in frequency estimates between two samples in the same city or region, or among several samples in the same region, show considerable resemblance or homogeneity.

The present review aims to assemble frequency estimates from as many population samples as possible and to discuss them briefly with regard to race, geographical propinquity, and the long term effects of selection. The estimates are presented in two tables. Red and green deficiencies are pooled together in the first table (as they are in most reports) and separated in the second. Such separation permits making rough estimates of mutation rates. In both tables the populations are divided into three habitat groups: A) hunters and food gatherers; B) populations somewhat removed from hunting in time or in habitat, but less removed than those in C—also, populations descended from mixtures between A and C; C) populations farthest removed from hunting in time, or habitat, or both. The marked clustering of low frequencies in A and of high frequencies in C is considered as evidence of the relaxation of the intensity of natural selection against "colorblindness" in habitat C as compared with A. The hypothesis of relaxation is discussed.

UNCERTAIN POINTS IN GENETICS

The principal genetic question is whether the alleles for the two red deficiencies protanopia (P) and protanomaly (P_2)—to use the most current terminology—share the same locus with those for the two green deficiencies deuteranopia (D) and deuteranomaly (D_2), or whether they occupy two separate loci on the X-chromosome. The former hypothesis is implicit in the procedure followed in most population studies of summing all male protans and deuterans regardless of the type or degree of deficiency in order to make an estimate of the frequency of over-all "red-green colorblindness." Females are reported separately, if at all. It is often assumed that there are two degrees of each type of deficiency, hence perhaps four distinct X-linked alleles. But this is not certain: there may be three alleles of each

type, perhaps more (Jaeger, 1950, 1951; Pickford, 1950). The hypothesis of two loci is favored by most geneticists and, while evidence for it has been accumulating for some time (Franceschetti, 1928; Sorsby, 1951; Adam, 1961), it cannot yet be said to be proven. The question is well reviewed by Stern (1959), who comments: "At present, the differences between the two hypotheses is of little practical importance."

Some indication of the degree of this practical importance can be shown by a simple illustration based upon the rounded mean prevalence rates reported among males in samples of European populations. These are close to .01 for each of the first three phenotypes, P, P_2, and D, and .05 for the fourth, D_2 (Stern, 1959). Taking these as rough estimates of the corresponding gene frequencies, under the single locus hypothesis the total frequency of sex-linked color-deficient phenotypes would be estimated at 0.08 (the sum), and the frequency of normals as $1 - 0.08 = 0.92$. Under the hypothesis of two loci, however, the total frequency of deficient males would be slightly less than this, since some X-chromosomes would bear both a P and a D allele. Thus the frequency of males with normal color vision would be $(1.00 - 0.02 = 0.98)$ times $(1.00 - 0.06 = 0.94)$, or 0.9212. The frequency of those with color deficiencies would be 0.0788, consisting of protanopes $(0.02 \times 0.94 = 0.0188)$; of deuteranopes $(0.06 \times 0.98 = 0.0588)$; and of males with both deficiencies $(0.02 \times 0.06 = 0.0012)$. The discrepancy in phenotype frequency estimates between the two hypotheses for European populations is thus seen to be negligible, and it would be still lower for non-European populations, all of which have lower prevalence rates.

The unsatisfactory "fit" between the combined rate of both types of deficiency in females and the square of the combined rate in males in most population studies is at first glance disturbing (Danforth, 1924; Majima, 1961). However, in the two largest of the European studies in Table 1, the red and green deficiencies are reported separately. This permits Chi-square tests to be made (Table 3) of the fit between the "colorblind" females observed and the number expected from squaring the frequency estimates of males, after separating the red and green data in each study. A satisfactorily close fit is

Table 1

PREVALENCE RATES OF RED-GREEN COLOR VISION DEFICIENCY (WITH SQUARE ROOT OF FEMALE RATES)

Population	Males No.	Rate	Females No.	Rate	(s.r.)	Author
A. Hunters and Food Gatherers						
Eskimo fullbloods	297	.025	273	.004	(.063)	Skeller, 1954
Australian aborigines, fullbloods	4455	.019	3201	.0003	(.018)	Mann, 1956
Fiji Islanders	200	0				Mann, 1956
" "	608	.008	99	0		Geddes, 1946
Navajo Indians	535	.011	456	.007	(.084)	Garth, 1933
Ramah Navajo	163	.025	197	.010	(.100)	Spuhler, 1951
Several other groups pooled, North American Indian fullbloods	392	.020				Clements, 1930
" , plus Sioux	562	.025	337	0		Garth, 1933
Brazilian Indians	230	0	129	0		Mattos, 1958
Brazilian Caingangs (Parana)	164	.043	135	0		Salzano, 1961
Brazilian Caingangs (Parana)	43	.070				Fernandes, 1957
Brazilian Carajas (Goyaz)	35	.057				Junqueira, 1957
Kotas (India)	28	.610	11	.550	(.742)	Sarkar, 1958
Total	7,712	.020				
B. Populations Somewhat Removed from Hunters in Time or in Habitat, but Less Removed than C; also, Populations Descended from Mixtures between A and C.						
Eskimo "halfbloods"	132	.066	123	.008	(.089)	Skeller, 1954
Australian aborigines of mixed descent ("half-castes")	181	.032	173	0		Mann, 1956
Several groups of American Indians of mixed descent, pooled:						
Southwest, U.S.A.	232	.012	202	0		Clements, 1930
" , plus Sioux	480	.052	523	.008	(.089)	Garth, 1933
Mexicans, Mexico City	571	.023	494	.006	(.077)	"
Mexicans in Colorado	523	.025	469	.009	(.095)	"
Brazilians: Negroes and mulattoes, mixed	250	.088				Kalmus, 1957
African Negroes in Uganda, Ruanda-Urundi, and the Congo:						
Bechuanas	407	.030	574	.004	(.063)	Squires, 1942
Bugandas	537	.019				Simon, 1951
Batutsis	1000	.025				Hiernaux, 1953
Bahutus	1000	.027				"
Belgian Congo	929	.017				Appelmans, 1953
American Negroes in the United States:						
Virginia	2019	.039	722	.001	(.032)	Crooks, 1936
N.C. and Tennessee	538	.039	496	.008	(.089)	Garth, 1933
Connecticut (fullblood)	205	.034				Clements, 1939
" (mixedblood)	118	.042				"
Colorado	254	.028	165	0		Garth, 1933
Polynesians (Tonga)	67	.075	68	0		Beaglehole, 1939
Total	9,443	.033				

thus obtained, whereas pooling of the red and green data gives a worse fit, as anticipated. These results add to the evidence for the two-loci hypothesis, and therefore indicate that estimates of the total frequencies of sex-linked "red-green colorblindness" alleles in populations based upon overall prevalence rates of males are slightly too high.

Other genetic doubts arise over such

Table 1
PREVALENCE RATES OF RED-GREEN COLOR VISION DEFICIENCY (WITH SQUARE ROOT OF FEMALE RATES)

Population	Males No.	Rate	Females No.	Rate	(s.r.)	Author
C. Populations Farthest Removed from Hunters, in Time or in Habitat						
Arabs (Druses)	337	.100				Kalmus, 1961
Belgians, students	9540	.074				De Lact, 1935
" army recruits	760	.090				De Waale, 1946
" " "	1243	.086				François, 1957
British, students	1338	.088				Nelson, 1938
" Air Force cand.	16180	.066				Grieve, 1946
" Royal Navy enlisted men, from nine regions of the U.K.:						
London	6000	.068				Vernon, 1943
East Coast England	6000	.070				"
No. Central England	6000	.074				"
Northwest England	6000	.077				"
South Wales	6000	.078				"
So. Central England	6000	.089				"
Southwest England	6000	.095				"
Northeast Scotland	6000	.054				"
West of Scotland	6000	.077				"
Scotch, Glasgow	989	.078	676	.006	(.077)	Pickford, 1951
" students	138	.072				Gray, 1944
" "	360	.075				Collins, 1937
Chinese, Peiping	1164	.069	1132	.017	(.130)	Chang, 1932
Chengtu	1115	.063				Kilborn, 1934
Chengtu, students	7542	.050	3519	.007	(.084)	Chan, 1950
mixed	7333	.056	3001	.015	(.122)	Fang, 1942
mixed	36301	.050	19672	.008	(.089)	Chun, 1958
Czechoslovakians	656	.105				Janouskova, 1951
French	914	.086				Chabau, 1955
Germans, Berlin	6863	.077	5604	.004	(.063)	Schmidt, 1936
Indians:						
Six endogamous groups in Bombay (the first four are Brahmins).						
VNB	100	.100				Sanghvi, 1949
DRB	100	.030				"
DYB	100	.030				"
KB	100	.050				"
CKP	100	.010				"
M	200	.020				"
Brahmins, Madras	153	0				Sirsat, 1956
" , Benares	86	.012				Sirsat, 1956
Six Gujarati groups in western India:						
Brahmins, ABS	100	.090				Vyas, 1958
Tribesmen, TD	106	.028				"
Other castes: KV	100	.050				"
BHS	100	.010				"
CL	100	.060				"
LPC	100	.030				"
Samples from 6 tribes of Gujarat:						
Koli	67	.090	63	0		Vyas, unpub. MS
Naika	36	.028	46	0		" " "
Dhodia	45	0	40	0		" " "
Gamit	147	.027	51	0		" ;; "
Bhil	142	.007	27	0		" " "
Dhanka	11	.018	102	0		" " "
Andhra Pradesh	292	.075	272	.004	(.063)	Dronamraju, 1961

Table 1
PREVALENCE RATES OF RED-GREEN COLOR VISION DEFICIENCY (WITH SQUARE ROOT OF FEMALE RATES)

Population	Males		Females			Author
	No.	Rate	No.	Rate	(s.r.)	
Eight endogamous groups:						
Brahmins, GSB	100	.050	100	0		Varde, 1962
Other castes: SKP	100	.030	100	0		"
AG	100	.010	89	0		"
CH	111	.036	96	0		"
DK	83	.012	51	0		"
MH	93	.022	99	0		"
LP	100	.020	100	0		"
LG	155	.026	48	0		"
Japanese:						
24 Prefectures (11 districts), arranged from north to south:						
Karafuto (Karafuto)	2180	.036	1139	.007	(.084)	Sato, 1935
Hokkaido (Hokkaido)	9689	.039	5980	.003	(.055)	"
Aomori (Tohoku)	1205	.036	690	.004	(.063)	"
Yamagata "	11420	.042	10165	.008	(.089)	"
Fukushima "	4151	.040	3960	.005	(.071)	"
Tochigi (Kanto)	6641	.040	3945	.006	(.077)	"
Gunma "	5977	.039	4835	.006	(.077)	"
Saitama "	7960	.040	2161	.008	(.089)	"
Chiba "	11125	.039	8041	.009	(.095)	"
Tokyo "	23845	.040	10119	.008	(.089)	"
Kanagawa "	1135	.039	489	.008	(.089)	"
Ishikawa (Chubu)	12115	.043	11018	.006	(.077)	"
Yamanashi (Kanto)	10115	.040	9810	.009	(.095)	Sato, 1935
Gifu (Chubu)	15844	.040	9807	.007	(.084)	"
Shizuoka "	8705	.038	5560	.006	(.077)	"
Aichi "	19435	.040	11265	.008	(.089)	"
Nara (kinki)	14398	.040	10341	.006	(.077)	"
Shimane (Chugoku)	10365	.038	7345	.006	(.077)	"
Hiroshima "	8672	.040	5681	.006	(.077)	"
Okayama "	9435	.039	4913	.007	(.084)	"
Ehime (Shikoku)	13566	.036	8699	.006	(.077)	"
Kochi "	13985	.036	10633	.006	(.077)	"
Kumamoto (Kyushu)	18385	.040	12344	.006	(.077)	"
Kagoshima "	8366	.040	7982	.007	(.084)	"
Hiroshima	809	.049				Schull, 1962
Nagasaki	1157	.048				"
Tokyo	1524	.051				Nakajima, 1960
Sado, north	1338	.031	1314	.002	(.045)	Nagasima, 1949
" , central	3547	.035	3235	.002	(.045)	"
" , south	1671	.074	1582	.010	(.100)	"
Shizuoka	1524	.050	1509	.003		Majima, 1960
Jewish students at N.Y.U.; all four grandparents Jews:						
	529	.076				Shuey, 1936
(Russian descent)	260	.081	("about half" of same group)			
Jews, Denver, Colo.	200	.040	175	0		Garth, 1933
Jews (immigrants in Israel but for last sample):						
Ashkenazim (from north-east & central Europe)	568	.095				Kalmus, 1961
Sephardim (from south-east Europe)	140	.064				"
North Africa	318	.066				"
Kurdistan & Turkey	495	.065				"
Iraq and Iran	742	.044				"
Yemen and Aden	404	.052				"

Table 1
PREVALENCE RATES OF RED-GREEN COLOR VISION DEFICIENCY (WITH SQUARE ROOT OF FEMALE RATES)

Population	Males No.	Rate	Females No.	Rate	(s.r.)	Author
Palestine-born	143	.063				"
mixed, Middle East	191	.059				"
Norwegians, Oslo	2005	.101	2200	.009	(.095)	Schiotz, 1922
Norwegians, Oslo	9047	.080	9072	.004	(.063)	Waaler, 1927
Persians, Tabriz	949	.045				Plattner, 1959
Philippinos	959	.042	977	.002	(.045)	Nolasco, 1949
Russians (urban)	1343	.093				Flekkel, 1955
White Russia	312	.087	387	.010	(.100)	Kuzovleva, 1937
Komi S.S.R. (South)	366	.071				Cheboksarov, 1936
" (East)	426	.044				"
" (West)	227	.013				"
In Brazil (immigrants)	25	.016	38	0		Freire-Maia, 1960
Swiss, Basel	2000	.080	3000	.004	(.063)	von Planta, 1928
" "	1036	.082				Wieland, 1933
" "	1000	.090				Bally, 1954
Turks, Istanbul	473	.053	217	0		Garth, 1936
"White" groups, immigrants overseas:						
Australia	558	.073	327	.006	(.077)	Mann, 1956
New Mexico	346	.038	390	.008	(.089)	Garth, 1933
Stanford University	1286	.082	436	.009	(.095)	Miles, 1929
Denver, Colorado	795	.084	232	.013	(.114)	Garth, 1933
Baltimore, Maryland	448	.078	487	.016	(.126)	Haupt, 1922
Brazil, rural	247	.060				Kalmus, 1957
" , Rio de Jan.	147	.075				"
Total	436,853	.0507				

questions as penetrance (Knox, 1958) in hemizygous males and in each of the several genotypes of females other than the homozygous normal (Schmidt, 1934; Pickford, 1948, 1953; Jablonski, 1957), and whether still other color deficiencies than those involving red and green may be sex-linked. Clarification of these questions may be expected to lead to methods of refining gene frequency estimates in populations based on phenotype counts. However, it is believed that some value may accrue in the meantime to the examination of overall prevalence rates made from field reports on samples of males, at least in outlining some of the characteristics of certain populations.

THE DATA

While the present tabulation has been aimed to include all the published population data on sex-linked color vision deficiency which are based on testing with the Ishihara plates, the compiler is well aware that there must be many omissions and would appreciate readers notifying him of them. Red and green deficiencies are pooled in Table 1 in the interest of directing attention to major differences between populations. Prevalence rates among females are cited from the relatively few studies supplying them. The square root of each female rate is given, despite the several errors which this figure entails. The two deficiencies are separated in Table 2 for those studies which report them separately.

It is probable that the tabulation includes about all the errors to which any set of data could be subject. The imperfections in testing techniques are too well-known to be discussed here (Dunlap, 1942; Hamilton, 1944; Hardy, 1946). The studies are dated from 1922 through 1962. Description of sampling procedure is often unsatisfactory. Despite its inherent weaknesses, justification for the tabulation will be found, it is hoped, in demonstrating the resemblances between certain pairs of populations and the homogeneties among certain groups of populations, and also in suggesting an explanation for some of these differences.

DISCUSSION OF TABLE I

Perhaps the most striking observation is the high degree of consistency of the rates among the 33 samples from Europe, Great Britain and the United States, most of which lie fairly close to 0.08 (excluding the Russians of western Komi S. S. R. who, incidentally, are rather different from other Russians in their blood group frequencies). Only four samples fall below .07 and only six exceed .089. The English samples are remarkably uniform, particularly the three rates .070, .068, and .066 from, respectively, the East Coast of England, Greater London, and the area thereabouts whence the plurality of the Air Force candidates hail. Four of the five Scottish rates are certainly close together—.072, .075, .077, and .078. The fifth, from the Northeast of Scotland, is a wide deviant (.054) which will be discussed later. (Each of the nine British Navy series is said to contain at least 6,000 observations.) Other close matches are seen in the two samples of school boys in Basel, Switzerland, with rates of .080 and .082; two from Oslo, Norway, with .101 and .080; three from Belgium with .074, .086, and .090.

Samples from more widely separated populations of the same race are also notable for their consistencies. Thus, five samples of Chinese—all of good size and one enormous—have rates of .050, .050, .056, .063, and .069. Twenty-four of the Prefectures of Japan sampled by the Ministry of Education and reported by Sato (1935) have an impressively narrow range of rates—.036 to .042, with an overall mean of .0395, based on 259,060 school boys. Turks in Istanbul and Persians in Tabriz are not far apart with .053 and .045, respectively. Samples from five populations of African Negroes are more scattered, with .017, .019, .025, .027, and .030; in contrast, five samples of American Negroes have rates of .028, .034, .039, .039, and .042. Samples of Mexicans in Mexico City and in Colorado are as close as .023 and .025, respectively.

The samples were divided into the three habitat groups A, B, and C defined above as a step in the search for evidence of the hypothesis of selection relaxation. In the case of color vision deficiencies, this evidence would have to depend upon assumptions which have never been demonstrated but which do not seem to be unreasonable. First, it is assumed that color vision deficiency has been a handicap of some moment among the hunting and food-gathering populations. of group A, with an approximate equilibrium between the elimination by natural selection of genes which produce deficient color vision and their origin through mutation. Since all members of a hunting society must constantly find their way through unmarked wildlands under all conditions of color and light in their unending quest for food and for all the raw materials required by domestic industries, considering particularly the frequency in primitive societies of stresses when the penalties for deficient color vision are most dire, the assumption that color vision deficiency is a definite handicap may be entertained seriously. Furthermore, it must be assumed that in settled habitats such as those of populations in group C the handicap imposed by deficient color vision has been *completely* removed, and thus that the rate of selective elimination of genes producing color vision deficiency is no greater than that of the genes producing normal color vision. (This discussion raises many points which cannot be answered yet, among them the marked superiority of some "colorblind" persons in recognizing camouflage.)

Acting on these assumptions, the difference between the overall prevalence rates of samples of populations of group A contrasted with those of C may be taken as evidence of the result of diminished selection pressure against the deficiency-producing alleles in the second habitat group as compared with that in the first. The overall rates for groups A, B and C in Table 1 are respectively .020, .032, and .051 based on pooled sample sizes of 7,712, 9,443, and 436,853 males. While the diversity of the composition of the samples in each group is too great to justify refined estimates of statistical significance of the difference between A and C, its magnitude (.051 − .020 = .031) is impressive and merits serious consideration as evidence in support of the relaxation hypothesis.

Further examination of Table 1 fails to suggest any basis for grouping the various samples other than on the basis of habitat. The lowest rates are of samples from aborigines of Australia, Fiji, America, and India, most of the last being "tribes" still living in a quasi-hunting habitat. The highest rates are of Caucasian samples, but not far below them are the five samples of Chinese and eight of Indian Brahmins. With such great diversity of races and geographical locations among the samples within either a high or a low range of rate, it seems impossible to use either race or propinquity as a major basis for classification. Indeed, the only basis which can be found is habitat as here defined.

The only flagrant exceptions to the association between rate and habitat are the three small samples of Brazilian Indian fullbloods and the Kotas of India, the rates of which are too high for A. While all four samples may be suspected of coming from small gene pools and therefore of being subject to the eccentricities of genetic drift, the possibilities of a prevailingly higher rate among Brazilian aborigines (at least in the two tribes sampled) than among those of North America is seriously entertained by Salzano (1961), and a similar explanation might apply to the Kotas. Their high rate reminds one of the Todas, another Indian tribal group, whose rate (0.128) is the highest on record. It was reported by Rivers (1905) among 320 males and is considered reliable even though the measurements were made before the development of the Ishihara test.

Race is further discounted because the low rates among all North American Indians in contrast with the high rates of the Chinese. Further illustrations of negative associations between race and rate may be found in the studies based on color vision deficiency tests developed earlier than that of the Ishihara plates, which are tabulated by Clements (1930) and others.

Further evidence of relaxation may be seen in the low rate of .054 for the 6,000-odd British Navy recruits from the Northeast of Scotland which was noted above. This is the lowest rate of all the samples of Caucasians in the present tabulation, the closest to it being .066 for the 16,180 candidates for the Air Force—and it seems reasonable to suspect that this last may be as low as it is because the sample may not have been drawn at random, insofar as men conscious of having any color vision deficiency might

reasonably spare themselves the trouble of being rejected by an organization so well-known for its high standards of testing. The Northeast of Scotland is one of the least industrialized and urbanized areas in the United Kingdom. Further, it was the last of the major areas to emerge from the habitat which might be called paleolithic, in which one might speculate that the survival value of abnormal color vision would have been lower than under the habitats which followed it, which might be called neolithic. In contrast, the longest history of neolithic habitat in the United Kingdom in undoubtedly to be found in the South of England, and it is here that the highest rates of color vision deficiency are found—.095 in Southwestern England and .089 in South Central England—in areas where the first sedentary cultures developed and flourished and where the longest history is found of the civilization of Rome.

Relaxation is also suggested by the higher rates of several samples of Indian Brahmins in contrast with those of other castes and of the tribes still in a quasi-hunting habitat.

DISCUSSION OF TABLE 2; MUTATION RATE ESTIMATES

Under the two-loci hypothesis the prevalence rate among males of the red or the green deficiencies may be used as estimates of the frequency of each corresponding set of mutant alleles, assuming complete penetrance at the youngest ages tested. Since the degree of deficiency cannot be really well defined by even the most careful testing, and since the number of alleles is in doubt, pooling of the various degrees of deficiency of each type is desirable. It entails no loss in accuracy. Following Fernandez (1957) and Junqueira (1957), the mutants producing the red deficiencies (protans) may be designated as cv^P1, and those producing the green deficiencies (deuterans), cv^d2. Their prevalence rates are shown in Table 2-A, B, and C for all 31 of the population samples in which the prevalence of red and green deficiencies are reported separately (4 in Table 2-A, 6 in B and 21 in C).

By scanning the columns of Table 2 it is noted that the prevalence rates of cv^P1 and cv^d2 support the relaxation hypothesis as well when considered separately as do the

Table 2
PREVALENCE RATES OF PROTANS AND DEUTERANS IN THE 31 SAMPLES OF MALES FROM TABLE 1 FOR WHICH RED AND GREEN DEFICIENCY RATES AR REPORTED SEPARATELY.

Population (cvp)	Sample size (cvd2)	Protans	Deuterans	Doubtful	Total	Author
A. Hunters and Gatherers						
Brazilian Indians	230	0	0		0	Mattos
Carajas, Goyaz	35	0	.057		.057	Junqueira
Caingangs, Parana	43	.023	.047		.070	Fernandes
N.A. Indians, mixed	392	.005	.015		.020	Clements
B. As Described in Table 1						
African Negroes	407	.010	.020		.030	Squires
American Negroes, Va.	2019	.010	.029		.039	Crooks
" " , Conn.	205	.010	.025		.035	Clements
" " , ob-viously with admixture	118	.008	.034		.042	"
N.A. Indians, several groups mixed, partly of white descent	232	.004	.008		.012	Clements
Brazilian Negroes and mulattoes	250	.020	.068		.088	Kalmus
C. As Described in Table 1						
Arabs (Druses)	337	.021	.077	.002	.100	Kalmus
Belgians	1243	.024	.062	.001	.087	Francois
British: English	1338	.025	.063		.088	Nelson
British: S.W. Scotland	989	.028	.050		.078	Pickford
Germans, Berlin	6863	.025	.052		.077	Schmidt
Indians, Andhra Pradesh	292	.033	.043		.076	Dronamraju
Japanese in Brazil	62	.032	.097		.129	Kalmus
Jews in Israel (all immigrants but last sample):						
Ashkenazim	568	.030	.062	.003	.095	Kalmus
Sephardim	140	.029	.021	.014	.064	"
Kurdistan & Turkey	495	.018	.044	.003	.065	"
Iraq and Iran	742	.010	.032	.002	.044	"
Yemen and Aden	404	.022	.025	.005	.052	"
Middle East, mixed	191	.022	.032	.005	.059	"
North Africa	318	.019	.044	.003	.066	"
Palestine	143	.014	.049		.063	"
Norwegians, Oslo	9047	.019	.061		.080	Waaler
Persians, Tabriz	949	.006	.039		.045	Plattner
Swiss, Basel	2000	.022	.058		.080	von Planta
" "	1036	.021	.061		.082	Wieland
Whites in Brazil:						
Rio de Janeiro	147	.020	.054	.001	.075	Kalmus
Rural	247	.016	.053		.069	"

joint rates in Table 1. Hunters have the lowest rates, populations farthest removed from hunting have the highest rates, while populations moderately removed from the hunting habitat have intermediary rates. (This conclusion is based in part on the

Table 3

CHI-SQUARE TESTS OF FIT BETWEEN THE NUMBERS OF "COLORBLIND" FEMALES OBSERVED AND THE NUMBERS EXPECTED FROM SQUARING THE FREQUENCIES AMONG MALES.a

	Numbers of Females			
	Observed	Expected	Difference	(1 d.f.)
(A) Separately for Red and Green Deficiencies				
von Plant, 1928				
Number green deficient	10	9.9188	0.0812	
Number not green deficient	2990	2990.0812	0.0812	
Total	3000	3000.		0
Number red deficient	3	1.4520	1.5480	
Number not red deficient	2997	2998.5480	1.5480	
Total	3000	3000.		1.65
				P about 0.20
Waaler, 1927				
Number green deficient	37	33.6509	3.3491	
Number not green deficient	9035	9038.3491	3.3491	
Total	9072	9072.		0.33
Number red deficient	4	3.3558	0.6442	
Number not red deficient	9068	9068.6442	0.6442	
Total	9072	9072.		0.12
(B) Red and Green Deficiencies Pooled				
Number "colorblind"	57	67.2329b	10.2329	
Number not "colorblind"	9805	9794.7671	10.2329	
Total	9862	9862.		1.57
				P about 0.21

a(A) Separately for the red and the green deficiencies in the two largest samples in Table I which report the two sexes and the two deficiencies separately; (B) Pooled red and green deficiencies, in 7 other samples of European descent in Table I which report the sexes separately, but in which the two color deficiencies are pooled, viz. Garth, 1933; Mann, 1956; Miles, 1929; Kuzovleva, 1937; Pickford, 1951; Schiotz, 1922; Schmidt, 1955.

bOf 12,838 males tested, 1,060 were "colorblind," i.e., 0.08256737. The square of this rate, 0.00681737 multiplied by 9862 females, gives the expected number of females "colorblind," or 67.2329.

Table 4

MEANS AND VARIANCES OF RATES OF $cv^{P}1$ AND $cv^{d}2$ AMONG THE FOUR SAMPLES OF NEGROES, SEVEN SAMPLES OF EUROPEANS, AND EIGHT SAMPLES OF JEWS TESTED IN ISRAEL, IN TABLE 2. WEIGHTED MEANS OF THE POOLINGS OF EACH SET OF SAMPLES ARE GIVEN IN PARENTHESES, ALSO THE RATIO OF THE WEIGHTED MEANS.

Samples	Number (pooled)	Protans $cv^{P}1$ Mean	Variance	Deuterans $cv^{d}2$ Mean	Variance	Ratio $\dfrac{cv^{P}1}{cv^{d}2}$
A. Four samples of Negroes	2,749	.0096 (.0102)	.000001	.0267 (.0273)	.000037	(.37)
B. Seven samples of Europeans	22,518	.0229 (.0222)	.000011	.0581 (.0577)	.000027	(.38)
C. Eight samples of Jews in Israel	3,001	.0204 (.0193)	.002995	.0388 (.0403)	.000178	(.48)

sample of 230 Brazilian Indians reported by Mattos (1958) in which there is not one case of color vision deficiency, but it is not supported by the two samples of 35 and 43 Brazilian Indians, which have high rates, as noted above.)

Certain details are brought out more clearly by rearrangements for three subgroups as in Table 4, these subgroups being Negroes, continental Europeans, and Jews tested in Israel. Pooled rates show Europeans and Jews to be indistinguishable in the frequency of protans (.0222 and .0193, respectively), but the former have higher rates of deuterans than the latter (.0577 and .0403). Thus the ratio of the pooled rates of cv^P1 and cv^d2 is .38 for Europeans and .48 for Jews. The Negro rates are less than one-half those of the Europeans in both deficiencies, and the Negro ratio is .37. The variances of the rates are considerably higher for both types of deficiency among the eight Jewish samples than among the seven samples of Europeans or the four of Negroes. The latter are particularly homogeneous in cv^P1. Many interesting details of differences in the rates of the two types of color vision deficiency among populations are brought out in Table 2, and are too numerous for comment here.

The relatively high homogeneity of the prevalence rates of the seven European samples for both types of deficiency tempts one to hazard making an estimate of the mutation rates at the two loci. Assuming that selection against both sets of alleles which produce color vision deficiency became negligible following the introduction of domestic animals and agriculture with the Neolithic era, it would follow that cv^P1 has increased from approximately .005 to .02 during the ensuing interval, a change of .015; similarly, that cv^d2 increased from .015 to .06, a change of .045 (viz. Tables 2-A and 4-B). Acting on these assumptions, both increases must be attributed solely to mutation, or to net mutation after subtracting any possible reverse mutation. Estimating the elapsed time as 3,000 years or 120 generations, the mutation rate per generation would be .015 ÷ 120 = 0.000125 for the aggregate of alleles which produce protans and .045 ÷ 120 = 0.000375 for those producing deuterans. If 4,000 years are allowed instead of 3,000, as might be more reasonable for some of the populations, the mutation rates become 0.00009375 and 0.00028125; if 5,000 years are allowed, they would be 0.000075 and 0.000225, respectively. Whatever date is assigned to the earliest neolithic culture in Europe, it would seem reasonable to suppose that the hunting habitat was displaced during many generations fairly gradually and slowly and perhaps centuries thereafter, and that complete relaxation may not have been achieved until perhaps about Iron Age times.

To speculate briefly in another direction, we might consider the selection force necessary to maintain protanopia and deuteranopia among hunting populations when selection and mutation are in equilibrium at the gene frequencies estimated above, i.e., .005 and .015, respectively. Since selection is theoretically the quotient of the mutation rate divided by the gene frequency (when the loss in the frequency of a mutant allele per generation is balanced by replacements of this allele by mutation) or $s = \frac{3u}{q}$ (Li, 1961), we may make estimates of "s" by substituting the above values for q and use maximum and minimum mutation rates arbitrarily chosen as 10^{-4} and 10^{-5} for "u." The resulting selection forces seem intuitively rather low, namely, from 7 to 200 "genetic deaths" per 10,000 colorblind persons per generation:

estimates of mutation rate	$u = 10^{-4}$	$u = 10^{-5}$
protanopia, with q = .oo5	s = .02	s = .002
deuteranopia, with q = .015	s = .007	s = .0007

NOTE ON RELAXATION

The concept of relaxed selection, with consequent reduction of fitness in plants and animals under domestication and in man under the gradual changes in habitat resulting from the growth of culture, has been widely discussed since the earliest days of Darwinism. Examples are readily cited in the failure of one or another variety of domestic plant to survive without cultivation in competition with wild plants; the failure of dogs' ears, among most breeds, to stand erect and turn towards a particular sound; the small size of the human fifth toe. Perhaps most of the speculation in man has concerned traits or conditions or functions under genetic control which have benefitted the most from advances in modern medical therapy (such as diabetes), or in public health (such as the hereditary form of endemic goiter), or in living standards (such as pulmonary tuberculosis), rather than those which are believed to have been under relaxed selection for several millenia (such as acuity of vision and hearing). The advances in medicine, public health, and living standards have been so marked that it is not difficult to imagine the survival of many persons today who might not have been able to live long enough to reproduce had they been born several thousand years ago when selection was, in certain respects, more rigorous.

The confusion resulting from this speculation has been great, and particularly damaging to eugenics. Some clarification may come from considering the following suggestions. (1) The concept of relaxed selection should not be applied to an entire species, including the human species, but rather to specific hereditary traits to be considered one at a time. (2) Two distinct habitats are implied, each with its own rate of selection pressure—a higher rate in an aboriginal or "wild" or "natural" habitat, usually of the past, and a lower rate in a "protected" habitat, usually of the present. The selection pressure of the second habitat is called "relaxed" only when compared with that of the first. (3) A mutant allele which is suspected of having increased in frequency in the second habitat as a result of such relaxation in selection pressure must be considered to have no adaptive advantage in this habitat over the "wild type" gene. If it is supposed to have an adaptive advantage in the new habitat, the resulting evolutionary change would properly be attributed to progressive adaptation, not to relaxation. (4) A relaxed selection rate might be further qualified as one which is lower than the rate of mutation with respect to a specific mutant allele in the second of two specific habitats, disregarding the possibility of reverse mutation. If the selection is completely relaxed, i.e., zero, it follows that the population frequency of the mutant allele being considered in the second habitat is approximately the product of its net mutation rate times the number of generations under such relaxation, plus its frequency in the first habitat. (Since the frequency of a mutant allele would increase progressively with each generation under such circumstances, the frequency of the "wild type" gene remaining at risk of

mutation would correspondingly decrease, but at a continuously diminishing rate. Therefore the previous statement is an approximation.)

The best traits for studying relaxation are those under simple genetic control (as contrasted with control by multiple genes) having congenital manifestation or full penetrance at a fairly early age, relative stability in all habitats, susceptibility to rather precise measurement, and significant variation in frequency among different populations in a variety of habitats. At least two of these habitats should be under contrasted selective pressures as far as these can be estimated by the necessarily subjective methods at hand.

Perhaps the red and green color vision deficiencies are among the best traits for the study of selection relaxation. They fulfill the above requirements and offer a certain literature of population studies. Whether or not they demonstrate the phenomenon of relaxation, however, is a question which each student of evolution must answer independently.

SUMMARY

1. Some of the genetic hypotheses and uncertainties in sex-linked color vision deficiency are noted.
2. Prevalence rates of red and green color deficiencies are tabulated for all the population samples found in the literature so far, as estimated by testing males with the Ishihara color cards.
3. Among the lowest rates are those of the aborigines in Australia, Brazil, Fiji, and North America. The highest rates are of samples in Europe and the Far East, including Brahmins of India. Intermediary rates are of Negroes in Africa and the Americas, other groups in India, and various hybrid groups.
4. All of the lower rates are of populations with simple or primitive cultures until recently, for which it might be assumed that color vision deficiency would be a handicap in life in the unmarked wildlands. Under stress this handicap would frequently be fatal. There is no concrete evidence for this assumption, but it seems reasonable.
5. All of the higher prevalence rates except

for three based on very small samples are of populations which have had pastoral-agricultural economies and settled habitats for at least three millenia. It is assumed that in these habitats a "colorblind" person of either sex could be as successful in living and procreating as a person of normal color vision; again, no concrete evidence for this assumption is known.

6. From the above considerations the total frequency of alleles producing the red color vision deficiencies are roughly estimated to have increased from .005 to .02 in European populations during about 120 generations; the green, from .015 to .06. Assuming that selection at both loci has been completely relaxed during this time, the net mutation rates (discounting reverse mutation) for all deficiency-producing mutant alleles at each locus are then $.015 \div 120 = .000125$ or 1.25×10^{-4} for protans, and $.045 \div 120 = .000375$ or 3.75×10^{-4} for deuterans, per generation. If 160 generations are allowed, the rates become 9.375×10^{-5} and 2.8125×10^{-4}, respectively.

7. Under the above assumptions, which are purely speculative and not discussed in this paper, the frequencies of protans and deuterans have increased in recent millenia in Europe and may be expected to continue to increase in the future (unless their reproductive rate should change in relation to that of persons with normal color vision).

ACKNOWLEDGMENTS

Grateful appreciation is expressed to Professors L.R. Dice, J.V. Neel, J.N. Spuhler, and W.J. Schull for their helpful comments, and to Assistant Professor Frank B. Livingstone and L.D. Sanghvi, Visiting Lecturer, for unpublished data from Japan and India, respectively.

BIBLIOGRAPHY

Adam, A., 1961. Linkage between deficiency of G-6-Ph dehydrogenase deficiency and colour-blindness. Nature, 189:686.

Appelmans, M., J. Weyts and J. Vankam. 1953. Bull. Soc. Belge. Ophthalmol., 103:226. (Quoted by François, 1957.)

Bally, C., 1954. Unfallmed Beruf., 47:100. (Quoted by François, 1957.)

Beaglehole, Ernest, 1939. Tongan colour-vision. Man, 39:170–172.

Chabau, A., 1955. (Quoted by François, 1957.)

Chan, E., and W.S. Mao, 1950. Colour-blindness among the Chinese. Brit. J. Ophthalmol., 34:744–745.

Chang, S.P., 1932. Statistics on color-blindness among students in Peiping (in Chinese). Nat. Med. J. China, 18:806. (Quoted by Chan, 1950, and by Kilborn and Beh, 1934.)

Cheboksarov, N., 1936. Blood groups and color-blindness in Comi. J. Anthropol. (Moscow), 1936:396–413.

Chun, Y., C. Jun-Chin, F. Pao-Hua and Y. Nai-Hua., 1958. Color-blindness among the Chinese. Chinese Med. J., 76: 283–284.

Clements, F., 1930. Racial differences in color-blindness. Am. J. Phys. Anthropol., 14: 417–432.

Collins, M., 1937. Brit. Assoc. Ann. Rept. (Quoted by François, 1957.)

Crooks, K.B.M., 1936. Further observations on color blindness among Negroes. Human Biol., 8: 451–458.

Danforth, C.H., 1924. The problem of incidence in color blindness. Am. Naturalist, 58: 447–456.

De Laet, M., and P. Van DeCalseyde, 1935. Bull. Roy. Acad. Med. Belge., 1:46; 5:15. (Quoted by François, 1957.)

De Waele, G., 1946. Vlaamsche Opvoedk. Tydsch,. 26:240, 305. (Quoted by François, 1957.)

Dronamraju, K.R., and P. Meerakhan, 1961. Frequency of colour blindness in Andhra Pradesh school children. Ann. Human Genet., 25:107–110.

Dunlap, K., and R.D. Loken, 1942. Anomalies of color vision. Science, 96:251–252.

Fang, A., and A. Liu, 1942. Nat. Med. J. China, 28:170. (in Chinese) (Quoted by Chan, 1950.)

Fernandes, J.L., P.C. Junqueira, H. Kalmus, F. Ottensooser, R. Pasqualin and P. Wishart, 1957. P.T.C. thresholds, colour vision and blood factors of Brazilian Indians. Ann. Human Genet., 22:16–21.

Flekkel, A.B., 1955. Concerning the problem of differential diagnosis of colorblindness. Dokl. Akad. Nauk. SSSR, N.S. 100:57–60 (in Russian).

Franceschetti, A., 1928. Die bedeutung der einstellungsbreite am anomalskop fur die diagnose der einzelnen typen der farbensinnstörunger, usw. Schweiz. Med. Wochschr., 52:1273–1279.

François, J., G. Verriest, V. Mortier, and R. Vanderdonck, 1957. De la fréquence des dyschromatopsies congenitales chez l'homme. Annales d'Oculistique, 190:5–16.

Freire-Maia, A., N. Freire-Maia and A. Quelce-Salgado, 1960. Genetic analysis in Russian emigrants. Am. J. Phys. Anthropol., 18:235–240.

Garth, T.R., 1933. The incidence of colorblindness among races. Science, 77:333–334.

Garth, T.H., 1936. Color blindness in Turkey. Science, 84:85.

Geddes, W.R., 1946. The colour sense of Fijian natives. *Brit. J. Psychol.*, 37:30.

Gray, R.C., 1944. Incidence of colour vision weakness. *Nature*, 153:657.

Grieve, J., 1946. Incidence of defective colour vision. *Nature*, 157:376.

Hamilton, W.F., A.P. Briggs and R.E. Butler, 1944. The testing of color vision in relation to vitamin-A administration. *Am. J. Physiol.*, CXL:578–579.

Hardy, L.H., G. Rand and M.C. Rittler, 1946. The H-R-R polychromatic plates. *A.M.A. Arch. Ophthalmol.*, 51 (2):216–218.

Haupt, I., 1922. The Nela test for color blindness applied to schoolchildren. *J. Comp. Psych.*, 6:291–302.

Hiernaux, J. and H. Van Der Borght, 1953. La fréquence du Daltonisme chez les Batutsi et Bahutu du Ruanda-Urundi. *Ann. Soc. Belge. Med. Trop.*, 33:43–46.

Jablonski, W.M., 1957. Heredity of green-blindness. *Brit. J. Ophthalmol.*, 41:86–87.

Janouskova, K., 1951. *Csl. Oftal.*, 7:182. (Quoted by François, 1957.)

Jaeger, W., 1950. Systematic investigation of "incomplete" congenital total colorblindness. *Arch. Ophthalmol.*, 150:509–528.

Jaeger, W., 1951. Giebt es kombinationsformen der verschiedenen typen angeborener farbensinnstörung? *Arch. Opthalmol.*, 151:229–248.

Junqueira, P.C., H. Kalmus and P. Wishart, 1927. P.T.C. thresholds, color vision and blood factors of Brazilian Indians. *Ann. Human Genet.*, 22.22–25.

Kalmus, H., 1957. Defective colour vision, P.T.C. and drepanocytosis in samples from 15 Brazilian populations. *Ann. Human Genet.*, 21:313–317.

Kalmus, H., A. Amir, O. Levine, E. Barak and E. Goldschmidt, 1961. The frequency of inherited defects of color vision in some Israeli populations. *Ann. Human Genet.*, 25:51–55.

Kherumian, R. and R.W. Pickford, 1959. *Hérédité et Fréquence des Anomalies Congénitales du Sens Cromatique.* Vigot Frères, Paris.

Kilborn, L.G., and Y.T. Beh, 1934. The incidence of colorblindness among the Chinese. *Science*, 79:34.

Knox, George, 1958. An estimation from pedigree data of gene frequency of color blindness. *Brit. J. Prevent. Social Med.*, 12:193–196.

Kuzovleva, V.A., 1937. Genetics of Daltonism. *J. Anthropol.* (Moscow), 1937 (3):70–71 (in Russian).

Majima, A., et al, 1961. Studies on the genetic carrier of color deficiency. *J. Clin. Ophthalmol.* (Tokyo), 15:161–168. (in Japanese).

Mann, I. and C. Turner, 1956. Color vision in native races in Australasia. *Am. J. Opthalmol.*, 41:797–800.

Mattos, R.B., 1958. Acuité visuelle et fréquence des dyschromatopsies chez les indiens bresiliens. *Arquiv. Brasil de Oft.* 21 (2):105–253. (Reviewed in *Annales d'Oculist*, 192:157–158, 1959.)

Miles, W., 1929. One hundred cases of colorblindness detected with the Ishihara Test. *J. Gen Psych.*, 2:535–543. (Quoted by Clements, 1930.)

Nagasima, T., 1949. On the distribution of colorblindness in the Island of Sado. *Minzoku Eisei*, 16:76–78 (in Japanese).

Nakajima, A., M. Yoshimoto, N. Ito, K. Kimura, A. Majima and S. Awaya, 1960. Distribution of eye diseases among school children. *Rinsho Ganka 14 (11) Supplement*, Nov. 15, 1960. (in Japanese).

Nelson, J.H., 1938. Anomalous trichromatism and its relation to normal trichromatism. *Proc. Phys. Soc.*, 50:661–702.

Nolasco, J.B., and D. Rodil, 1949. Students seeking admission to the University of the Philippines in Manila. *Arch. Ophthalmol.*, N.S. 41:20–23.

Pickford, R., 1947. Colour vision deficiencies in the West of Scotland. *Nature*, 160: (4062):335.

Pickford, R.W., 1948. Color vision of heterozygotes for sex-linked red-green defects. *Nature*, 163 (4151):804.

Pickford, R.W., 1950. Three pedigrees for colour blindness. *Nature*, 165:82.

Pickford, R.W., 1951. *Individual differences in colour vision.* The Macmillan Co., New York.

Pickford, R.W., 1953. Inheritance of minor color vision variations. *Nature*, 171:1167.

Pickford, R.W., 1959. Some heterozygous manifestations in colour blindness. *Brit. J. Physiol. Optics*, 16:83–95.

von Planta, P., 1928. Die Häufigkeit der angeborenen Farbensinnstörungen bei Knaben und Mädchen und ihre Festellung durch die üblichen klinischen Proben. *von Graefe's Arch. Ophthalmol.*, 120:253–281.

Plattner, F., 1959. Häufigheit angeborener Störungen des Rot-grün-sinnes in Perisch-Aserbeidschan. *von Graefe's Arch. Ophthalmol.*, 161:237–238.

Rivers, W.H.R., 1905. Observations on the senses of the Todas. *Brit. J. Psych.*, 1:334.

Salzano, F.M., 1961. Rare genetic conditions among the Caingang Indians. *Ann. Human Genet.*, 25:123–130.

Sanghvi, L.D., and V.R. Khanolkar, 1949. Data relating to seven genetical characters in six endogamous groups in Bombay. *Ann. Eugen.*, 15:52–64.

Sanghvi, L.D., 1953. Comparison of genetical and morphological methods for a study of biological differences. *Am. J. Phys. Anthropol.*, 11:384–404.

Sanghvi, L.D., 1962. Unpublished data.

Sarkar, S.S., 1958. Blood groups and colour blindness among the Kotas of the Nilgiris. *Sci. Cult.* (Calcutta), 25:379–380.

Sato, S., 1935. Statistical observations on congenital abnormalities in color vision in Japan. *Acta Soc. Ophthalmol. Jap.*, 38:2227–2230. (in Japanese).

Schiotz, I., 1922. Rotgrünblindheit als Erbeigenschaft. *Klin. Mbl. Augenheilk.* 68:498–526.

Schmidt, Ingeborg, 1934. Ueber manifeste Heterozygotie bei Konduktorinnen für Farbensinstörungen. *Klin. Monatsbl. für Augenheilkunde*, 92:456–465.

Schmidt, I., 1936. *Z. Bahnartz*, 2: (Quoted by François, 1957).

Schmidt, I., 1955. A sign of manifest heterozgygosity in carriers of color deficiency. *Am. J. Optometry and Arch. Am. Acad. Opt.*, 32:404–408.

Schuey, A., 1936. The incidence of color-blindness among Jewish males. *Science*, 84:228.

Schull, W.J., 1962. Unpublished data.

Simon, K., 1951. Colour vision of Buganda Africans. *E. African Med. J.*, 28 (2):75–80.

Sirsat, S.M., 1956. Effect of migration on some genetical characters in six endogamous groups in India. *Ann. Human Genet.*, 21:145–154.

Skeller, E., 1954. Anthropological and ophthalmological studies on the Angmagssalik Eskimos. Reitzels, Copenhagen. Republished from *Meddelelser om Grønlande*, 107 (4):1–231.

Sorsby, Arnold, 1951. *Genetics in ophthalmology.* Mosby, St. Louis, Mo.

Spuhler, J.N., 1951. Some genetic variations in American Indians. In: *Physical anthropology of the American Indian.* (W.S. Laughlin, ed). New York: Viking Fund, Inc. 177–202.

Squires, B.T., 1942. Colour vision and colour discrimination amongst the Bechuana. *Trans. Roy. Soc. S. Africa*, 29:29–34.

Stern, Curt, 1960. *Principles of human genetics.* W.H. Freeman, San Francisco, Calif. (Second edition.)

Varde, D.S., and L.D. Sanghvi, 1961. Unpublished data.

Vernon, P.E., and A. Straker, 1943. Distribution of colour-blind men in Great Britain. *Nature*, 152:690.

Vyas, G.N., H.M. Bhatia, D.D. Banker and N.M. Purandare, 1958. Study of blood groups and other genetical characters in six Gujarati endogamous groups in western India. *Ann. Human Genet.*, 22:185–199.

Vyas, G.N., H.M. Bhatia, P.K. Sukumaran, V. Balkrishnan and L.D. Sanghvi, 1961. *Study of blood groups, abnormal haemoglobins and other genetical characters in some tribes of Gujarat.* (in press).

Waaler, G.H.M., 1927. Über die Erblichkeitsverhältnisse der verschiedenen Arten von angeborener Rotgrünblindheit. *Acta Ophthalmol.*, 5:309–345.

Wieland, M., 1933. Untersuchungen über Farbenschwäche bei Konduktorinnen. *von Graefe's Arch. Ophthalmol.*, 130:441–462.

Wright, W.D., 1946. *Research on normal and abnormal colour vision.* Kimpton, London.

30

SUNBURN
Farrington Daniels, Jr., Jan C. van der Leun, and Brian E. Johnson

Variation in skin color was the basis for the old concept of race, valued in folklore and politics, even though, as we have tried to show, the concept itself is a hindrance to our understanding of human biological variation. The fact of skin color variation remains one of the best-known aspects of human difference, and, if only to satisfy the curiosity of the average reader, this alone would warrant our treatment of the subject.

What, then, is the biological significance of variation in skin color? As it happens, the answers to that question have generated as much controversy among biologists as the use of skin color to establish racial categories. Long ago there was the ethnocentric assumption that "white" was the original color of mankind, with the darker colors representing lapses toward depravity, and the equally ethnocentric view that "black" was the original color of mankind, with the lighter shades representing varying degrees of progress toward perfection—perfection of course being white. A version of this still lingers on in recent attempts to defend the view that skin pigment is really a nonadaptive trait and just represents the innate difference in old established racial stocks (Blum 1961). This argument, however, is no better than saying "in the beginning, God created black and white," and really is not an explanation at all.

Most of the discussion now is between the group that claims that the principal role of skin pigment is to prevent the overproduction of calciferol (the calcifying hormone often called vitamin D2) (Loomis 1970), and the group that claims that pigment protects against the cancer-producing effects of the ultraviolet component of sunlight (Daniels, van der Leun, and Johnson, 1968, reprinted here). The problem with Loomis' view is that it cannot account for the existence of greater amounts of skin pigment in the tropics since hypervitaminosis or overproduction of calciferol (vitamin D2) does not occur in lightly pigmented people exposed to tropical sunlight. Ultimately Loomis' view cannot account for the existence of pigment at all. Daniels' view, on the other hand, nicely accounts for the presence of pigment in the tropics where ultraviolet induced skin cancer is absent in people with dark skin and common in those with light skin, but by itself, this view cannot explain what advantage is gained by the reduction in the amount of pigment visible in the inhabitants of more northern latitudes.

Since we are reprinting Daniels' article, it is obvious that we favor his position in the controversy. Further, we think we can account for the decrease in pigment in populations that have been long-term residents in areas remote from the tropics by suggesting that selection in these areas has been relaxed, giving the PME a chance to operate. Depigmentation, then, is not so much a positive advantage as it is the consequence of relaxed selection.

Blum, Harold F. 1961. Does the melanin pigment of human skin have adaptive value? *The Quarterly Review of Biology* 36:50–63.

Loomis, W. Farnsworth. 1970. Rickets. *Scientific American* 223(6):76–91.

Urbach, Frederick (ed.). 1969. *The Biologic Effects of Ultraviolet Radiation (With Emphasis on the Skin).* Pergamon, Oxford. 704 pp.

Sunburn is notoriously the unpleasant consequence of pleasant expectations. Typi-

From *Scientific American* 219:1:38–46. Copyright 1968 by Scientific American, Inc. All rights reserved. Reprinted with the permission of the author and publisher.

cally the victim lies down for a happy time under a warm sun with a cool breeze playing over his exposed skin. His nose clears, his muscles relax, his tension is eased, and he may doze off. He (or, to be sure, she) comes to feel refreshed, reposed—and then uncomfortable. The skin may already be tender and feel slightly burned. During the next few hours it becomes redder and more painful and may swell or blister. In severe cases more deep-seated consequences may follow within 12 hours: fever, chills, nausea and perhaps prostration. The sufferer receives from his fellows the same kind of sympathy that is accorded to the victim of a hangover. As the burned layers of the epidermis peel off in the ensuing days and the skin becomes pale again, the victim may be left without even the satisfaction of a socially admired tan.

We live in an environment of solar radiation that is essential for the existence of life on our planet and at the same time is potentially lethal to living matter. The dangerous portion of the sun's radiation is at the short-wavelength end of the spectrum: from the X rays through the ultraviolet rays [see Figure 1]. Life on the earth is made possible by the attenuation of these rays in their journey through the earth's atmosphere, which filters out the shorter wavelengths. Oxygen in the outer part of the atmosphere absorbs these rays and forms ozone (O_3), which in turn acts as an effective filter blocking almost all the ultraviolet radiation at wavelengths up to 2,900 angstrom units. (The visible spectrum lies between 3,8000 and 7,6000 angstroms.) Hence the ultraviolet rays of shortest wavelength do not reach the earth's surface. A substantial amount of ultraviolet radiation between the wavelengths of 2,900 and 3,200 angstroms does penetrate to the surface. This minute portion of the solar spectrum is what produces sunburn.

Obviously the sunburn hazard is greater at high altitudes (for example on mountain ski slopes), where the ultraviolet rays have traversed less of the atmosphere. On such

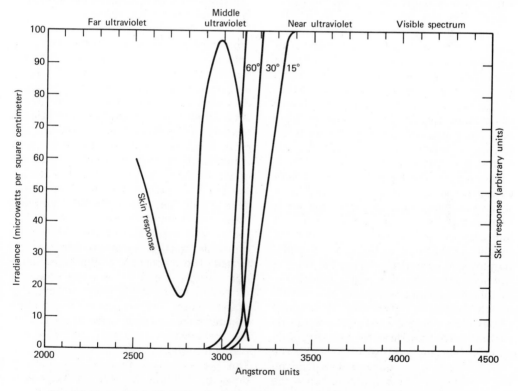

Figure 1. Human skin is affected by ultraviolet radiation at wavelengths from 2,500 to 3,150 angstrom units in length. One curve on the graph shows that the effect varies with the wavelength. Almost all solar ultraviolet radiation below 2,900 angstrom and above 3,200 angstroms is filtered out by the atmosphere. The wavelengths that affect the skin most intensely lie in a narrow band on each side of 3,000 angstroms. Atmospheric scattering also weakens solar ultraviolet radiation: the black curves show the amount of energy at various wavelengths reaching the ground when the sun is respectively 60, 30 and 15 degrees above the horizon.

slopes the radiation is also intensified by reflection from the snow. The amount of ultraviolet radiation reflected, like the amount of light, is high from snow and sand, low from vegetation and water. Sunburn is particularly common at the beach because of reflection from the sand and one's exposure to scattered ultraviolet rays from the entire hemisphere of the sky. Under these conditions untanned skin may be affected in as little as 10 to 20 minutes. Contrary to a common notion, two or three hours on the beach is by no means a short exposure. People are misled at the beach by the cooling effect of the breeze and the water. Not feeling an intense heating effect from the sun, they do not realize that they are nonetheless being burned by the invisible ultraviolet rays.

Why is it that basking in the early-morning or late-afternoon sun almost never produces sunburn, even on the brightest summer day? The answer is simply that, when the sun is low in the sky, its radiation must pass through a greater thickness of the atmosphere, and the atmosphere selectively scatters the shorter wavelengths. The longer wavelengths of light get through, which accounts for the yellow, orange and red tints of the sunrise and the sunset. The shorter waves at the blue end of the visible spectrum are largely blocked out, and of course the still shorter waves of ultraviolet radiation are scattered and attenuated even more.

This suggests that sun-worshipers, particularly those with a sensitive skin, would be wise to do their sunbathing when the sun is not too high. A simple "sunburn dial" can indicate the safe times of day and the duration of exposure needed to avoid painful burning and to start producing the tan that our society equates with health and leisure. In this instrument the shadow of a vertical needle shows the elevation of the sun, and circles drawn on the horizontal dial can be calibrated to prescribe the safe length of exposure for any given solar elevation. The "safe" exposure of course will depend on the individual's skin sensitivity; hence the dial should be calibrated to specify different exposures for skins of high, medium and low sensitivity.

The skin's main defense against ultraviolet radiation lies in the brown-to-black pigment known as melanin. The melanin polymer is synthesized by special cells called melanocytes; these cells are descended from nerve cells that migrate out of the central nervous system during embryonic development. (Their kinship to nerve cells is indicated by the fact that they have many dendrites, or threadlike extensions [see Figure 2].) In the melanocytes melanin is produced by a series of oxidations of the amino acid tyrosine with the aid of the enzyme tyrosinase. In its final polymerized form the pigment, bound to protein molecules, is aggregated in granules that typically are between a tenth of a micron and two microns in diameter. The melanocytes inject these granules through their dendrites into the cells of the epidermis that manufacture the tough protein keratin. A considerable amount of the melanin moves into the horny outer layer of the skin as the keratin-producing cells move to the surface and flatten out to form this layer. The amount and dispersion of melanin in the epidermis determines the color of a person's skin.

Even in an untanned skin melanin serves to protect the genetic material of the cells in the epidermis by concentrating in a cap that screens the nucleus of each cell against ultraviolet radiation. In tanned or naturally dark skin the supply of melanin is greatly augmented. The tanning of the skin in response to ultraviolet irradiation involves more than one mechanism. First there is an immediate darkening of the skin as the result of the oxidation of pigment that is already present in a bleached form. (The degree and duration of this tanning without sunburn varies greatly among individuals.) Meanwhile the enzyme tyrosinase, which in fair skin is ordinarily inactive, somehow becomes activated. The mechanism of this activation is not entirely clear; it may be that the ultraviolet radiation inactivates an inhibitor of tyrosinase. The activation of tyrosinase initiates increased production of melanin by the melanocytes and the injection of this pigment into the keratin-producing cells. The process takes four or five days to develop, and the tan reaches its peak in about a week and a half, after which, without further exposure, it gradually fades over a period of months.

The melanin in a well-tanned or naturally dark skin is so effective a shield that it reduces the amount of ultraviolet radiation

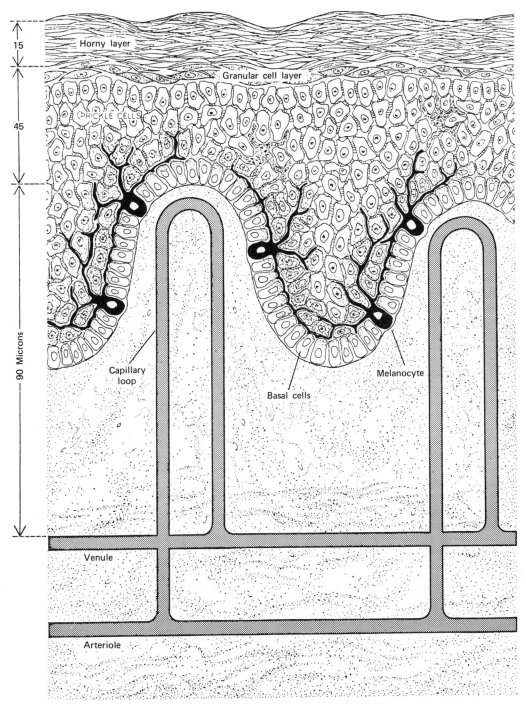

Figure 2. Zones of skin affected by the ultraviolet light wavelengths that produce sunburn are shown in a schematic cross section. The hill-and-dale boundary between the epidermis *(top)* and the dermis below allows capillary vessels to come to within 65 microns of the skin surface. Ultraviolet radiation causes enlargement of the vessels and produces the characteristic redness of sunburned skin.

penetrating to the underlying dermis by 90 percent or more. Melanin is not, however, the only defense against sunburn. A tanned skin can suffer sunburn from intense exposure to ultraviolet radiation before the tan has faded, and it is well established that even dark-skinned Negroes can become sunburned on an initial visit to the beach. Conversely, an albino skin can develop some tolerance to ultraviolet radiation although it has no pigment. Clearly the human skin must contain other protections against this radiation. One of these is the horny layer at the skin surface. This layer scatters and absorbs radiation, and it becomes thicker after sunburn. Another possible protective agent is urocanic acid, a substance in the epidermis that is an effective absorber of ultraviolet rays. On exposure to the radiation the "trans" molecular form of this substance is changed to the alternate "cis" form, and the change is reversible. Thus urocanic acid may absorb the ultraviolet energy in a chemical reaction and then dissipate the energy harmlessly in a reversal of the reaction.

The large industry devoted to protection of the human epidermis against the sun attests to the human propensity for trusting to artificial rather than natural defenses. The antisunburn ointments and lotions fall into three general categories (see Figure 3): (1) substances such as p-aminobenzoic acid, which absorb the wavelengths between 2,900 and 3,150 angstroms; (2) substances such as the benzophenones, which absorb all the ultraviolet wavelengths, and (3) opaque preparations containing zinc oxide or titanium oxide, which provide a total shield for very sensitive skins. Unfortunately most preparations do not adhere well or are uncomfortably greasy. It is difficult to find one that will serve for all purposes; a preparation that is satisfactory for a fishing trip may cause discomfort by interfering with sweating in a hot location such as a tropical beach. The best protection for anyone who must expose himself to the noonday sun is to build up the skin's tolerance by starting with small doses of sun and gradually increasing the exposure over a period of weeks. Most skins cannot

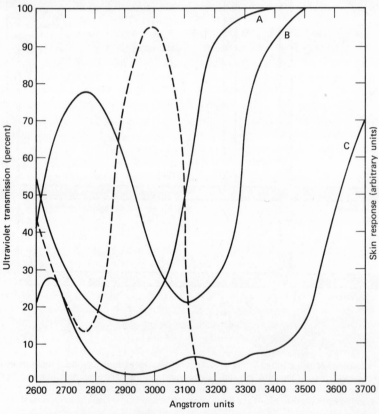

Figure 3. Screening compounds that absorb some or all ultraviolet wavelengths are the key ingredients in antisunburn lotions. Of the three compounds illustrated, two (a, b) selectively absorb part of the radiation that most intensely affects the skin. The third (c) almost completely absorbs the entire ultraviolet spectrum. For total protection opaque ointments such as zinc oxide can be applied.

take hours of sunshine at a first sitting, any more than a man can run two miles without training for it.

Let us now look in detail at the physiological and chemical effects of ultraviolet radiation on the skin. More than a century ago the English physician John Davy (brother of Sir Humphry Davy) investigated this subject with experiments conducted under the Mediterranean sun at noon in midsummer. The reddening of the skin giving the first sign of sunburn is caused by a dilatation of the venules that bring more blood near the skin surface. After a longer exposure to the sun the arterioles also become dilated, with a consequent increase in blood flow, a rise in the skin temperature and of course intensified erythema (redness).

Nowadays most studies of the effects are carried out not with natural sunlight but with ultraviolet lamps of one kind or another that make it possible to measure the doses precisely and to examine the skin's reactions to particular wavelengths. The lamps used for these experiments may be of the carbon-arc, the mercury-arc or the xenon type. In one notable respect the skin's response to exposure under these lamps is strikingly different from the response to natural sunlight. At low or moderate doses from a lamp the erythema that signals sunburn may be greatly delayed, sometimes as much as eight hours after the exposure. (A user of a sun lamp should therefore limit himself to a brief exposure. If he waits until he sees signs of redness, he may already have suffered a severe burn.) The emission spectra of artificial sources differ considerably from the spectrum of sunlight, both in wavelengths and in energy distribution. Since the skin's response to ultraviolet radiation varies with wavelength, the difference between a "natural" sunburn and one from an artificial source is not surprising. It is possible that the longer erythema-producing wavelengths in sunlight, together with a heating effect, are responsible for the early appearance of erythema on exposure to the sun.

Where does ultraviolet radiation produce the primary injury—in the epidermis or in the dermis? This question has been debated for nearly a century and is still undecided. The Danish physician Niels Finsen, who received a Nobel prize in 1903 for his discovery that skin tuberculosis could be treated with ultraviolet radiation, suggested that the radiation acts on the dermis, because the erythema originates there. A generation later other investigators, principally Sir Thomas Lewis of Britain, swung opinion to the view that the primary target is the epidermis and that injury to this layer releases a substance that causes the dilation of the blood vessels in the dermis. One argument in favor of the epidermal theory is that the delay in the onset of erythema can be explained on the basis that time is needed for a substance to diffuse out of the epidermis and affect the blood vessels in the dermis. About 1960 the dermal theory began to swing back into favor. The observational evidence is so complicated, however, that some current hypotheses propose that both the epidermis and the dermis are attacked by ultraviolet radiation, some wavelengths of the radiation doing injury to the epidermis and others to the dermis.

The detailed evidence on ultraviolet effects is mainly biochemical. Intensive studies have been made of the effects of ultraviolet irradiation on tissues, cells and specific substances. The picture presented by the findings is ambiguous, to say the least. The complexity of the situation is suggested by the experimental information on enzymes and other proteins. It is well known that very high doses of ultraviolet radiation can break down protein molecules, and specifically that such dosage can inactivate enzymes by breaking their disulfide bonds. Studies of sunburned skin tissue, however, show no loss of enzymes.

The significance of ultraviolet effects on other proteins in the skin tissues is likewise unclear. Certain changes have been found to take place in the proteins of the skin's horny layer, but no connection has been established between these changes and damage to the deeper tissues. Ultraviolet radiation also alters proteins, notably collagen, in the dermis.

Does a sunburn dose of ultraviolet damage the genetic material—deoxyribonucleic acid—of the skin cells? On the basis of studies of the effects of ultraviolet radiation on the cells of microorganisms there is reason to believe this radiation may produce certain chemical changes in DNA, but no such change has yet been detected in the

DNA of irradiated skin cells. As a general rule the sensitivity of cells to radiation damage is associated with cell division. In skin cells there is little evidence of such damage. The cells in the basal layer of the epidermis, the only ones capable of dividing, do appear to be affected by moderate doses of ultraviolet radiation. The radiation briefly inhibits the synthesis of DNA, but the cells quickly recover that ability.

It has long been assumed that DNA and proteins were the primary targets of ultraviolet damage, because the relationship between wavelength and the production of erythema was similar to the absorption spectra of these substances. In our work at the Cornell University Medical College we have asked: What other specific structures in the skin cells may be particularly vulnerable to ultraviolet damage? The radiation has been found to reduce the phospholipid content of skin and to alter its cholesterol. Since these substances are important contributors to the stability of cell membranes, research attention has been drawn to testing the effects of ultraviolet radiation on membranes, including the envelopes around subcellular particles. Our studies have focused particularly on the cell organelles known as lysosomes.

The lysosomes are tiny intracellular bodies that act as the cell's digestive system and apparently are involved in the aging of the cell [see "The Lysosome," by Christian de Duve; *Scientific American*, May, 1963]. They are packed with hydrolytic enzymes. Many investigators believe lysosomes play an important role in converting the living cells of the epidermis into the horny material that is continuously being formed as the protective outer surface of the skin. Examination of the epidermal cells with the electron microscope has not yielded absolutely clear evidence of the presence of lysosomes in these cells, but biochemical analysis shows that lysosomes are indeed present: the epidermal cells contain the enzyme acid phosphatase, known to be an identifying component of lysosomes.

Now, a number of cell investigations have disclosed that the thin, single-layer membrane of the lysosome is particularly susceptible to damage by ultraviolet radiation —more susceptible, for example, than the membrane of the mitochondrion (another intracellular body) or the complex membrane of the cell as a whole. We have shown that a moderately high dose of ultraviolet rays of the sunburn wavelengths reduces the amount of acid phosphatase in the skin of mice, and similar exposure of human skin also yields evidence of the rupture of lysosomes by this radiation. Moreover, in skin that has been sunburned the epidermis has a scattering of cells that are shrunken and appear to be prematurely keratinized (hornified), which suggests that the sunburn dose may have released hydrolytic enzymes by rupturing lysosomes. It is possible that substances discharged from the lysosomes may also be responsible for characteristic symptoms of severe sunburn such as dilatation of the blood vessels and fever.

The sunburn reaction can be minimized by administering drugs, such as aspirin or hydrocortisone, that stabilize lysosomes against breakdown. Experiments with rat skin in vitro, however, have shown that even though cell breakdown may be prevented by hydrocortisone, after irradiation the basal skin cells lose their normal capacity for division. It may well be that in these experiments the radiation alters the DNA.

The skin is a site of continuous cell birth and death, controlled by a feedback regulatory system that normally matches the birth rate to the death rate. The cells of the epidermis differentiate into the dead material of the horny layer, which is continuously shed from the skin surface in the form of minute flakes. As the old cells die, cell division in the basal layer of the epidermis produces new cells, so that the epidermis's cell population, and apparently its thickness, is maintained at a constant level. The control system involves certain metabolites supplied to the living cells and the feedback of a specific inhibitor of cell mitosis (called the chalone-epinephrine complex of Bullough) from the upper levels of the epidermis.

Sunburn produces a form of damage to the epidermis that impairs these control mechanisms, with the result that cell division goes on unchecked for a time. In moderately sunburned skin this increase in mitosis reaches its peak at 72 hours, whereas if horny material is simply stripped from the surface (say with Scotch tape), the step-up of cell division for replacement reaches its peak at about 48 hours. Consequently in sunburned skin the entire epidermis becomes thickened; indeed, the thickness of the epidermis more than doubles within 48 hours after a mild sunburn. The abnormal thickness may last for six weeks.

The transient uncontrolled multiplication of cells that follows a single exposure of the skin to ultraviolet radiation is similar in many respects to that produced by exposure to a single dose of a chemical carcinogen. The mechanisms involved are perhaps the same in both cases. It is now well established that ultraviolet radiation can produce skin cancer. This has been shown experimentally in mice, and there is much clinical evidence of the same effect in man. Fair-skinned people are particularly prone to develop skin cancers; the cancers occur mainly in exposed areas of the head and the back of the hands, and the affected skin shows other evidence of radiation damage. These signs of damage—commonly found in ranchers, sailors and others who spend a great deal of time outdoors—include thinning of the skin, dark blotches of melanin, chronic redness of the skin and sometimes yellowing from an increase of elastic fibers in the dermis. When the cancers arise in the epidermal layers, they can usually be treated successfully if caught before they have become invasive. Ultraviolet exposure can also, however, generate the highly dangerous malignant melanomas; which arise from the pigment cells.

Skin cancer is a particularly important problem for persons of northern European descent (particularly Irish or Scottish) who work outdoors in the perpetual sunshine of the U.S. Southwest, South Africa or Australia. This is not to say that dark-skinned peoples are immune. In dark skin, however, epidermal tumors usually stem not from ultraviolet radiation but from chronic lesions such as burns or unhealed ulcers.

To round out the story of the hazards from sunlight we must note that under certain conditions the skin can suffer injury from wavelengths other than ultraviolet, including radiation in the visible region of the spectrum. In one way or another the skin may become photosensitized, so that substances in the epidermis absorb radiation that normally would be harmless, with a consequent formation of free radicals and peroxides that

produce cell damage. The photosensitization can be produced by certain chemicals that come into contact with the skin and even by some taken orally, and this hazard is increasingly a matter of concern in this chemical age. Many chemicals commonly used in industry, in drugs and in cosmetics, perfumes and antibacterial soaps are capable of photosensitizing human skin. A classic example of compounds with this property is the group of plant substances known as furocoumarins, which sensitize the skin to wavelengths in the range from 3,200 to 3,800 angstroms. Herbs (such as *Ammi najus*) that contain these substances have been used in Egypt and India for thousands of years to treat vitiligo ("white spot" disease), and the substances had a flurry of popularity as suntan pills a few years ago.

Exposure to sunlight can precipitate or exacerbate several well-known skin diseases, among them lupus erythematosus, a grave condition marked by patches of discoloration and scars. Some of the sunshine hazards are curiously complex. For example, the skin can be sensitized to light (specifically at the wavelength of 4,000 angstroms) by an abnormality in the metabolism of porphyrins, precursors of hemoglobin, that results in the concentration of porphyrins in the skin. A person with this condition may develop urticarial skin eruptions (like those characteristic of hives) shortly after exposure to the sun. For many such people the only remedy is to stay out of the sun, at least between 9:30 A.M. and 3:30 P.M., or clothe the skin completely with opaque covering.

We have deliberately left a discussion of the beneficial effects of sunshine for the conclusion of our article, because the constructive aspects of this radiation surely outweigh the destructive ones for both animal and plant life.

The best-known specific benefit of exposure of the skin to the sun is the production of vitamin D. This vitamin is essential for the absorption and metabolism of calcium, and a deficiency of the vitamin in growing children results in the bone disease called rickets. Ultraviolet radiation brings about the synthesis of a form of the vitamin (D-3) in the human epidermis through the conversion of 7-dehydrocholesterol. A certain daily dose of radiation at the wavelength of 2,970 angstroms, applied to 200 square centimeters (about 30 square inches) of skin, has been found to be sufficient to cure rickets, and this dose is only about 5 percent of the amount that would be required to produce a perceptible sunburn. Sunlight is not effective in supplying this dose when the sun is lower than 35 degrees above the horizon. Since in many parts of the world the sun remains below that height for several winter months, inhabitants of those regions need vitamin D in their food, and this of course is also true for children elsewhere who avoid the sun. The rickets problem was essentially eliminated in the U.S., for all but undernourished children, after the late Harry Steenbock of the University of Wisconsin discovered in the 1920's that vitamin D could be produced by irradiating milk and other foods with ultraviolet rays; within a few years poisoning by an excess of vitamin D became more of a medical problem than rickets. Some evolutionists have speculated that overproduction of vitamin D in the skin by sunshine may have been a factor in preventing the development of white races in the Tropics, but we have found no reports indicating that fair-skinned dwellers in the Tropics are particularly prone to form the calcium deposits that are characteristic of vitamin-D poisoning. Apparently the formation of vitamin D by the epidermis under ultraviolet exposure is self-limiting: as the exposure continues beyond a certain point the vitamin begins to break down, presumably because it is converted to other substances.

Basking in the sun confers many benefits besides the synthesis of vitamin D, some that are known and undoubtedly many others that have not yet been explored. The practice is common to many species of animals. In cold-blooded animals the sun's warmth can determine the body temperature; in warm-blooded animals it can supplement the heat of metabolism when that is necessary in a cold climate. In hairless man the sun's drying effect on the skin surface prevents bacterial and fungus infections. Unquestionably there are also health-giving systemic effects. Studies in northern Europe and the U.S.S.R. have shown that indoor workers and those in lands of weak sunshine improve in physical fitness when they are given moderate supplementary doses of ultraviolet radiation. Engineers in the U.S. are investigating this means of enhancing the healthfulness of working environments.

31
HUMAN ADAPTATION TO HIGH ALTITUDE
Paul T. Baker

The species Homo sapiens lives in the greatest diversity of environmental circumstances of any vertebrate. We think of the stresses encountered by arctic and tropical populations and of populations in areas ranging from extremely wet to extremely dry. There have been studies exploring the cultural and biological adaptations made to all of these conditions, and most of these studies are well known. In most extreme situations, however, the numbers of people encountered are so small as to be insignificant when balanced against the bulk of mankind living under conditions that we consider more usual. The exception to this is the high altitude situation. Baker's estimate of ten million people for the Andean altiplano represents a population of substantial size in any context, and certainly the cultural contributions of the Incas in the Andes and the Tibetans in the Himalayas were at least in proportion.

The two selective forces encountered at high altitudes are cold and reduced oxygen pressure. The matter of adaptation to cold is relatively well known (Edholm and Lewis 1964; Irving 1966; Laughlin 1966; Scholander et al. 1958), and includes maintenance of body heat by raising the metabolism and prevention of excess heat loss by selection for shortened extremities. We have less knowledge about altitude adaptations. It is not known how much is just acclimatization and how much is hereditary; and much of the basic research is quite recent and still incomplete. Increased chest and lung capacity associated with hyperventilation ability is the most obvious adaptation, but this coincides with a decrease in the oxygen gradient between the alveoli of the lungs and the blood in the pulmonary arteries. Other known adaptations are an increase in the number of red cells (polycythemia) and a shift in the affinity of hemoglobin for oxygen mediated by 2,3 diphosphoglycerate (DPG), one of the phosphorylated intermediaries in the glycolytic pathway of red cell metabolism (Brewer and Eaton 1971; Harrison et al. 1969; Hegnauer 1969; Hock 1970; Hurtado 1964; Monge and Monge 1966; and Weihe 1964). Research on demography (De Jong 1970) and growth (Frisancho and Baker 1970) in high altitude populations also is proceeding, and our knowledge is increasing so rapidly that any attempt at a survey will be out of date by the time it reaches print and still further out of date by the time it is republished. So be it.

Brewer, George J., and John W. Eaton. 1971. Erythrocyte metabolism: interaction with oxygen transport. *Science* 171:1205–1211.

De Jong, Gordon F. 1970. Demography and research with high altitude populations. *Social Biology* 17:114–119.

Edholm, O.G., and H.E. Lewis. 1964. Terrestrial animals in cold: man in polar regions. In D.B. Dill (ed.) *Handbook of Physiology, Section 4, Adaptation to Environment.* American Physiological Society, Washington, D.C. pp. 435–446.

Frisancho, A.R., and P.T. Baker. 1970. Altitude and growth: a study of the patterns of physical growth of a high altitude Peruvian Quechua population. *American Journal of Physical Anthropology* 32:279–292.

Harrison, G.A., C.F. Küchemann, M.A.S. Moore, A.J. Boyce, T. Baju, A.E. Mourant, M.J. Godber, B.G. Glasgow, A.C. Kopeć, D. Tills, and E.J. Clegg. 1969. The effects of altitudinal variation in Ethiopian populations. *Physiological Transactions of the Royal Society of London, Series B, Biological Sciences* 256:147–182.

Hegnauer, A.H. (ed.). 1969. *Biomedicine of High Terrestrial Elevations.* U.S. Army Medical Research and Development Command, Washington, D.C. 323 pp.

Hock, Raymond J. 1970. The physiology of high altitude. *Scientific American* 222(2):52–62.

Hurtado, Alberto. 1964. Acclimatization to high altitudes. *In* W.H. Weihe (ed.) *The Physiological Effects of High Altitude.* Macmillan, New York. pp. 1–17.

Irving, Laurence. 1966. Adaptations to cold. *Scientific American* 214:94–101.

Laughlin, W.S. 1966. Genetical and anthropological characteristics of arctic populations. *In* P.T. Baker and J.S. Weiner (eds.) *The Biology of Human Adaptability.* Oxford University Press, London. pp. 469–495.

Monge, Carlos M., and Carlos C. Monge. 1966. *High Altitude Diseases: Mechanism and Management.* C.C. Thomas, Springfield, Ill. 97 pp.

Scholander, P.F., H.T. Hammel, J.S. Hart, D.H. LeMessurier and J. Steen. 1958. Cold adaptation in Australian aborigines. *Journal of Applied Physiology* 13:211–218.

Weihe, Wolf H. (ed.). 1964. *The Physiological Effects of High Altitude.* Pergamon (distributed by Macmillan, New York). 351 pp.

Stretching along western South America from Colombia to Chile lies a large section of the Andean plateau, or *Altiplano,* which rises above 2500 meters (about 8250 feet) (Fig. 1).

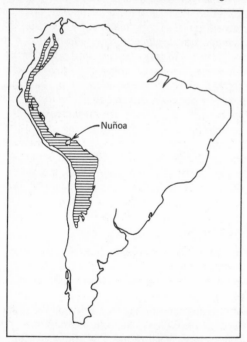

Figure 1. The high-altitude areas of South America and the location of Nuñoa. Shading indicates altitude of 2500 meters (8200 feet) or more.

This area is suitable for human habitation up to the permanent snow line, which is generally above 5300 meters (17,590 feet). There are now more than 10 million people

living in this zone, and the historical and archeological records indicate that it has been densely populated for a long time. Indeed, before Europeans arrived, the Inca empire, which had its center in this zone, formed one of the two major civilizations of the Western Hemisphere and, in A.D. 1500, probably contained about 40 percent of the total population of the hemisphere.

With such a history, one would assume this to be an ideal environment for man and the development of his culture. Yet, in point of fact, modern man from a sea-level environment ("sea-level man") finds this one of the world's more uncomfortable and difficult environments. The historical records show that such was the case even in the 1500's, when the Spanish complained of the "thinness of the air," moved their capital from the highlands to the coast, and reported that, in the high mining areas, the production of a live child by Spanish parents was a rare, almost unique, phenomenon (1). Today this environmental zone remains the last major cultural and biological center for the American Indian. The population has an extremely low admixture of genes from European peoples and virtually none from African peoples. The few cities are Hispanicized, but the rural areas retain a culture which, in most aspects, antedates the arrival of the Spaniards.

It would be far too simplistic to suggest that this unique history is explicable entirely on the basis of the effects of altitude on sea-level man. Yet, there is sound scientific evidence that all sea-level men suffer characteristic discomfort at high altitudes, the degree of discomfort depending upon the altitude. There is evidence, also, of long-term or permanent reduction in their maximum work capacity if they remain at these altitudes, and evidence that they undergo a number of physiological changes, such as rises in hemoglobin concentrations and in pulmonary arterial pressure. In a few individuals the initial symptoms develop into acute pulmonary edema, which may be fatal if untreated. On the basis of less complete scientific evidence, other apparent changes are found for sea-level man at high altitudes: temporary reduction in fertility, reduction in the ability of the female to carry a fetus to term, and a high mortality of newborn infants (2, 3).

With these problems in mind, a group of scientists from Pennsylvania State University, in collaboration with members of the Instituto de Biología Andina of Peru, decided to investigate the biological and cultural characteristics of an ecologically stable Peruvian Quechua population living in traditional fashion at a high altitude. We chose for study the most stable population known to us at the highest location reasonably accessible. It was hoped that some insight could be gained into the nature of this quite obviously successful and unusual example of human adaptation. In this article I review some of the results available from this continuing study.

The general problem may be defined by three questions: (i) What are the unique environmental stresses to which the population has adapted? (ii) How has the population adapted culturally and biologically to these stresses? (iii) How did the adaptive structures become established in the population?

Our basic method of study, in attempting to answer these questions, was a combination of ecological comparisons and experimental analysis.

THE STUDY POPULATION

The population chosen for study lives in the political district of Nuñoa, in the department of Puno in southern Peru. In 1961 the district had a population of 7750 and an area of about 1600 square kilometers. Geographically, the district is formed of two major diverging river valleys, flat and several kilometers broad in the lower parts but branching and narrow

above. These valleys are surrounded by steep-sided mountains. In the lower reaches of the valley the minimum altitude is 4000 meters; the higher parts of some valleys reach above 4800 meters. The intervening mountains rise, in some parts, to slightly above 5500 meters.

The climatic conditions of the district are being studied from weather stations on the valley floors and on the mountain sides at different altitudes. From present records, the pattern seems fairly clear. The lower valley floor appears to have an average annual temperature of about $8°C$ with a variation of only about $2°C$ from January, the warmest month, to June, the coldest. This is much less than the diurnal variation, which averages about $17°C$. The seasonal variation in temperature is due almost entirely to cloud cover associated with the wet season. Some snow and rain fall in all 12 months, but significant precipitation begins around October, reaches its peak in January, and ends in April. Since the diurnal variation is high, some frost occurs even in the wet months. Mean temperatures fall in proportion to increases in altitude (by about $1°C$ per 100 meters), but, because of the sink effect in the valleys, minimum temperatures on the valley floors are usually somewhat lower than those on the lower mountain sides.

Except for two small areas of slow-growing conifers, almost all of the district is grassland. Because of the existing climatic and floral conditions, herding has become the dominant economic activity. Alpaca, llama, sheep, and cattle, in that order, are the major domestic animals. Agriculture is limited to the cultivation of frost-resistant subsistence crops, such as "bitter" potatoes, quinoa, and cañihua (species of genus Chenopodium). Even these crops can be grown only on the lower mountain sides and in limited areas on the lower valley floors. In recent years, crop yields have been very low because of drought, but they are low even in good years.

A single town, also called Nuñoa, lies within the district and contains about one-fourth of the district's population; the other three-fourths live in a few native-owned settlements called allyus, or on large ranches or haciendas, which are frequently owned by absentee landlords. The social structure may be loosely described as being made up of three social classes: a small (less that 1 percent) upper class, whose members are called *mestizos;* a larger intermediate class of individuals called *cholos;* and the Indians, or *indígenas,* who constitute over 95 percent of the population. Membership in a given social class is, of course, based on a number of factors, but the primary ones are degree of westernization and wealth. Race appears to be a rather secondary factor, despite the racial connotations of the class designations: *mestizos,* of mixed race; *cholos,* transitional; *indígenas,* indigenous inhabitants. Biologically the population is almost entirely of Indian derivation.

By Western economic and medical-service standards, this district would be considered very poor. If we exclude the *mestizo,* we find per capita income to be probably below $200 per year. The only medical treatment available in the district is that provided by a first-aid post. The upper class has access to a hospital in a neighboring district. Yet repeated surveys suggest that the diet is adequate, and that death rates are normal, or below normal, for peasant communities lacking modern medicine. Indeed, this population must be viewed as being one nearly in ecological balance with its technology and its physical environment.

Superficial archeological surveys reveal that the central town predated the Spanish conquest, and suggest that the district population has been fairly stable for at least 800 or 900 years.

From this general survey of the Nuñoa population and its environs we have concluded that the unusual environmental stresses experienced by this population are hypoxia and cold; other stresses, more common to peasant groups in general, which the Nuñoa population experiences are specific infectious diseases, the problems of living in an acculturating society, and, possibly, nutritional deficiencies.

HYPOXIA

At elevations such as those of the district of Nuñoa, the partial pressure of atmospheric oxygen is 40 percent or more below the values at sea level. As noted above, such a deficiency of oxygen produces a multitude of physiological changes in sea-level man, at all ages. We therefore attempted to evaluate the native Indian's responses to altitude at all stages of the life cycle.

Demography

A survey of more than 10 percent of the population revealed an average completed fertility of about 6.7 children for each female. This is quite a high fertility by modern standards, but there was no evidence of voluntary birth control, and cultural practices appeared in many ways designed to provide maximum fertility; under these conditions, 6.7 children is no more than average. This same survey, partially summarized in Table 1, did not show an unusually high rate of miscarriage but did reveal two unusual features. (i) The earliest age at which any woman gave girth to a child was 18 in the low valleys and something over 18 at higher elevations. The average age of first pregnancy was also higher for women at the higher altitudes. (ii) The sex ratio was highly unusual in that there was a large number of excess males. Furthermore, there was a higher mortality of females than of males throughout the period of growth. In an associated study of newborns it was found that, for Quechua mothers in Cuzco (altitude, 3300 meters), placenta weights at childbirth were higher and infant birth weights were lower than corresponding weights for comparable mothers near sea level (4). Finally, an analysis of the Peruvian census showed that, as in the United States, the mortality of newborn infants is higher at higher elevations; this does not appear to be primarily a socioeconomic correlation. From the results so far obtained, we conclude that fecundity and survival through the neonatal period is probably adversely affected by high altitude, even in the native populations of high-altitude regions. However, it is clear that the Nuñoans can still maintain a continuing population increase. Our data do not provide a basis for deciding whether, at high altitudes, fecundity and survival of offspring through the neonatal period are greater for natives than they are for immigrant lowlanders (5).

Growth

Intensive studies on growth were carried out on over 25 percent of the Nuñoa-district children, from newborn infants to young

Table 1

STATISTICS ON REPRODUCTION AND VIABILITY OF OFFSPRING FOR THE DISTRICT OF NUÑOA, BASED ON A SAMPLE OF APPROXIMATELY 14 PERCENT OF THE POPULATION OF THE DISTRICT.

Sample	Married women						Sex ratio (males to females) of offspring		Mortality of offspring (%)[b]	
	Number in sample	Mean age (yr)	Mean age at first pregnancy (yr)	Off-spring (No.)	Mean number of offspring per woman	Mean number of surviving offspring per woman	At birth	Surviving[a]	Male	Female
Total sample	136	36.2	19.5	608	4.5	3.2	124	129	30	33
Sample of postmeno-pausal individuals	31	45	20.1	207	6.7	4.4	113	146	27	44

"Surviving" refers to time of the census.
During the period of growth.

415

Table 2
STATURE AND WEIGHTS OF NUÑOA INFANTS AND OF INFANTS IN THE UNITED STATES.

Age (months)	Stature, males (cm)		Stature, females (cm)		Weight, males (kg)		Weight, females (kg)	
	Nuñoa	U.S.	Nuñoa	U.S.	Niñoa	U.S.	Nuñoa	U.S.
6	62	66	61	65	6.9	7.6	6.6	7.3
12	71	75	69	74	7.9	10.1	7.3	9.7
24	76	87	75	87	9.9	12.6	9.0	12.3

people up to the age of 21. A number of unusual growth features were apparent shortly after birth. Thus, as shown in Table 2, a slower rate of general body growth than is standard in the United States is apparent from a very early age. In addition, developmental events such as the eruption of deciduous teeth and the occurrence of motor behavior sequences occur late relative to U.S. standards. For example, the mean number of teeth erupted at 18 months was 11.5 for Nuñoa infants as compared with 13 for U.S. infants. The median age at which Nuñoa children briefly sat alone was 7 months, and the median age at which they walked alone was 16.2 months. These data were collected by means of the technique developed by Bayley, who reported that the median ages at which U.S. children sat and walked alone were 5.7 months and 13.2 months, respectively (see 6).

Some of the growth characteristics in later development are shown in Figs. 2 and 3. In these growth studies it was possible to compare our results with cross-sectional data for groups from lower elevations (Huánuco and Cajamarca, 2500 meters; Lima and Ica, 300 meters). We have also collected some semi-longitudinal data in order to evaluate growth rates. These combined data (7) showed, for Nuñoa children, (i) lack of a well-defined adolescent growth spurt for males, and a late and poorly defined spurt for females; (ii) a very long period of general

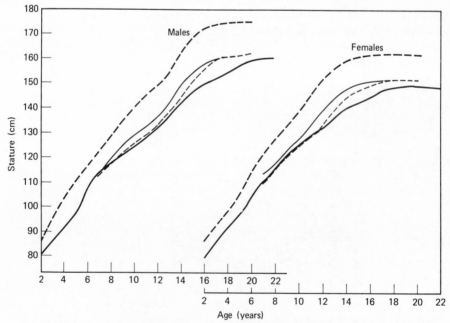

Figure 2. The growth of Nuñoa children as compared to that of other Peruvian populations and of the U.S. population. (Heavy dashed lines) U.S. population; (light solid lines) Peruvian sea-level population; (light dashed lines) Peruvian moderate-altitude (1990 to 2656 meters) population; (heavy solid lines) Nuñoa population (altitude, 4268 meters).

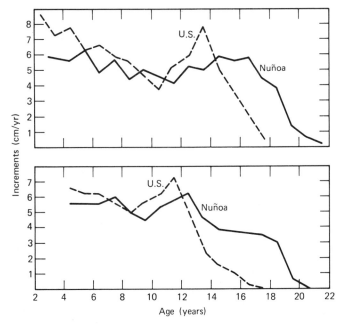

Figure 3. Rates of general body growth for children in Nuñoa as compared with that for children in the United States. (Top) Males; (bottom) females.

body growth; and (iii) larger chest sizes, in all dimensions and at all ages, than those of children from lower elevations.

In explanation of the unusual growth aspects of the Nuñoa population, at least three hypotheses may be suggested: (i) all Quechua have an unusual growth pattern, genetically determined; (ii) malnutrition and disease are the prime causes; (iii) hypoxia is the major factor. Our present data are not adequate for testing these hypotheses. However, a number of observations suggest that hypoxia is a major factor. As discussed below, we have been unable to find any evidence of widespread malnutrition or of unusual disease patterns. What data are available on the growth of other Quechua show growth patterns different from those found for the Nuñoans (8). Finally, hypoxia has been shown to affect growth in a number of animals other than man (3).

Work physiology

The most striking effect of high altitude (4000 meters) on newcomers, apparent after the first few days of their stay, is a reduced capacity for sustained work. This reduction is best measured through measurement of the individual's maximum oxygen consumption. For young men from a sea-level habitat, the reduction is in the range of 20 to 29 percent;

the men who had received physical training generally showed a greater reduction than the untrained (9). Some rise in maximum oxygen consumption occurs during a long stay at high altitudes, but studies extending over periods of as much as a year have failed to show a recovery to even near low-altitude values for adult men (10).

Maximum oxygen consumption for any individual or group is controlled by a large number of factors, among which the level of continuing exercise is of major importance. Among young men of European descent, mean values for maximum oxygen consumption range from below 40 milliliters of oxygen per kilogram of body weight for sedentary groups, through 45 milliliters per kilogram for laborers, up to more than 55 milliliters per kilogram for highly trained runners (11). The high degree of variability in this parameter makes it difficult to determine whether the native of a high-altitude region has a work capacity different from that of an individual from a low-altitude habitat, and makes it even more difficult to determine whether the complex physiological differences between groups from high and low altitudes have resulted in a better adaptation, with respect to work capacity, for the high-altitude Quechua.

In order to help clarify these questions, we determined maximum oxygen consumption

Table 3

SOME DATA FROM TESTS OF MAXIMUM OXYGEN CONSUMPTION (MAX V_{O_2}) AT HIGH AND LOW ALTITUDES FOR CONTRASTING POPULATIONS.

| | Subject | | | | | | | Response[a] | | | | |
Group of subjects	Altitude at which tested (m)	Duration of exposure to high altitude	Number	Mean age (yr)	Mean height (cm)	Mean weight (kg)	Max V_{O_2} (liter/min)	Aerobic capacity[b] (ml/kg/min)	Maximum ventilation (liter/min)	Ventilation equivalent[c] (V/V_{O_2} min)	Maximum heart rate (beat/min)	Oxygen pulse (ml/beat)
Nuñoa Quechua	4000	Life	25	25	160	57	2.77	49.1	75	27.3	171	16.0
U.S. white researchers	300		6	30	183	79	3.92	50.4	131	33.7	185	21.2
U.S. white researchers	4000	4 weeks	12	27	181	75	2.78	38.1	91	32.9	173	16.6
U.S. white athletes	300		6	20	179	71	4.58	64.2	131	28.8	175	26.5
U.S. white athletes	4000	4 weeks	6	20	179	71	3.14	46.6	105	33.7	172	19.4
Quechua from sea level	100		10	22	160	62	3.01	49.3	108	36.2	187	16.7
Quechua from sea level	4000	4 weeks	10	22	160	62	2.67	44.5	87	33.4	190	14.5
Peruvian students												
Quechua	3830	Life	10	23.8	162	60	2.79	46.8	72	25.8	188	15.1
White	3830	Life	13	23.5	169	61	2.62	42.8	74	28.2	186	14.2

[a]The measurements were made by means of a bicycle ergometer in 10-minute progressive exhaustion tests.

[b]Aerobic capacity is the maximum oxygen consumption per kilogram of body weight and, as such, is the most significant measure available of the success of the individual's (and, by inference, the group's) biological oxygen transport system. It is also assumed to be one of the best measures available for judging an individual's work capacity relative to his body size.

[c]Ventilation equivalent is the ventilation volume per unit oxygen uptake per unit time. The lower the value, the greater the relative efficiency in supplying oxygen.

for a number of carefully selected samples of contrasting populations; in all cases the method of determination was the same. Some of the results of these studies are presented in Table 3. It should be noted that the individuals referred to as White Peruvian students are so classified on the basis of morphology, and it is quite possible that they contain some admixture of native Quechua genes.

On the basis of results obtained for students alone, one investigator surmised that the differences in maximum oxygen consumption for high-altitude and low-altitude groups might be only a matter of life-long exposure, plus a high state of physical fitness in the highland Quechua (12). In an article based on partial results (13), some of the investigators, including myself, pointed out that trained athletes from lower altitudes could, at high altitudes, achieve the same oxygen consumption per unit of body weight as the Nuñoa native. While the data now available support the idea that physical training and life-long exposure to hypoxia act to increase maximum oxygen consumption, these two factors appear insufficient to explain the total results. The data, instead, suggest that a fairly random sample of Nuñoa males between the ages of 18 and 40 have a vastly greater maximum oxygen consumption than a group of reasonably physically fit researchers from the United States. The oxygen consumption of the Nuñoans also significantly exceeded that of young native students from lower altitudes, and equaled that of a group of highly trained U.S. athletes who had spent a month at high altitude. Furthermore, the heart rate and ventilation rate for the Nuñoans remained low. The Nuñoans do walk more than people from the United States, but nothing in the personal history of the Nuñoa subjects suggested that they had experienced physical training or selection comparable to that involved in becoming a college track athlete. To me, the data suggest that a high-altitude Quechua heritage confers a special capacity for oxygen consumption at 4000 meters. In the absence of more precise data, such a conclusion remains tentative. However, the data can certainly be interpreted as showing that the Nuñoa native in his high-altitude habitat has a maximum oxygen consumption equal to, or above, that of sea-level dwellers in their oxygen-rich environments. This conclusion is in agreement with the results obtained by Peruvian researchers (2).

COLD

The microenvironment

By the standards of fuel-using societies, the temperatures in the Nuñoa district are not very low, and we would consider the typical daily weather equivalent to that of a pleasant fall day in the northern United States. However, the lack of any significant source of fuel made us suspect that at least some segments of the population might suffer from significant cold stress. As mentioned above, few trees grow in the district, and those that do are slow-growing. At present, these trees are used primarily as rafters for houses; only an occasional member of the upper class uses wood for cooking. The fuel used almost universally for cooking is dried llama dung or alpaca dung. This dung provides a hot but rapid fire, and is burned in a clay stove, which provides little external heat. Since cooking is done in a building separate from the other living quarters, only the women and children benefit from the fire. Bonfires are lit only on ceremonial occasions; the winter solstice is celebrated by a pre-Hispanic ceremony in which many bonfires are lit all over the district. The use of fires during solstice ceremonies throughout the world is often considered an act of sympathetic magic to recall the sun. For Nuñoans it may also recall the warmth.

The houses of the native pastoralists, with walls of stacked, dry stone and roofs of grass, provide no significant insulation. Measurements made within the dwelling units generally showed the temperature to be within 2° or 3° C of the outdoor temperature. This is in sharp contrast to the situation in the adobe houses used by the upper classes, by some agriculturalists in the Nuñoa district, and by all classes in slightly lower areas of the Altiplano. Adobe houses provide good insulation, and indoor temperatures are frequently 10°C above outdoor temperatures during the cold nights of the dry season.

From this analysis and other observations we concluded that the Nuñoa native depends upon his own calories for heat, and relies, for heat conservation, primarily upon his clothing and upon certain customs, such as spending the early evening in bed and having as many as four or five individuals sleep in the same bed. His clothing is layered and bulky, with windproof materials on the outside. Thus, it provides good insulation for his body. However, the Nuñoa native's wardrobe does not include gloves, and the only foot coverings are sandals occasionally worn by men. The insulating effect of native clothing was tested under laboratory-controlled cold conditions. It was found that at 10°C the clothing increased mean body temperature of hands and feet despite the lack of gloves and shoes.

From the total assessment we concluded that the Nuñoa native probably experiences two types of exposure to cold: (i) total-body cooling during the hours from sunset to dawn and (ii) severe cooling of the extremities, particularly in the daytime during periods of snow and rain. To assess the degree of stress due to cold we took measurements of rectal and skin temperatures of individuals in samples selected by sex, age, and altitude of habitat. These studies indicated that at night the adult women experience very little stress from cold, whereas adult men showed some evidence of such stress. During the day, women, because they are less active than men, may experience slight stress from cold, whereas men do not, except for their extremities. Active children show no evidence of such stress; however, during periods of inactivity, as at night, their skin temperature and rectal temperature are low.

Indeed, at these times, all indices show an inverse relationship between age, size, and body temperatures (14).

Physiological responses

In order to characterize the Nuñoa native's responses to cold, we used three types of laboratory exposures: (i) total-body cooling at 10°C with nude subjects, for 2 hours; (ii) cooling of the subject's hands and feet at 0°C, for 1 hour; (iii) cooling of the feet with cold water. The subjects were Nuñoa males and females, North American white males, and Quechua males from low-altitude habitats.

Some results of the studies of total-body cooling are summarized in Table 4. Since the Nuñoa Indians are smaller than either the coastal Indians or U.S. whites, the data are presented in terms of surface area (15). Viewed in this way, the data show that the native Quechua from a high-altitude habitat produced more body heat during the first hour than individuals from low-altitude habitats, but produced amounts similar to those for such individuals during the second hour. By contrast, heat loss was much greater for the Nuñoans than for members of the other groups during the first hour and similar during the second hour. The findings on heat loss are perhaps the more interesting, since they conform with results of two other studies of cooling responses in native Quechua from high-altitude habitats (16).

When the source of the greater heat loss was closely examined, it proved to be almost

Table 4

EXCHANGE OF BODY HEAT AS EXEMPLIFIED IN HEAT PRODUCTION AND HEAT LOSS. THE VALUES ARE AVERAGES FOR TWO EXPOSURES AT 10°C, EXPRESSED ON THE BASIS OF BODY-SURFACE AREA.

Subjects	Heat loss[a] (kcal/m²)				Heat production (kcal/m²) Number		
	in sample	1st 60 minutes	2nd 60 minutes	Total time	1st 56 minutes[b]	2nd 60 minutes	Total time
Whites	19	51.5	62.2	113.7	29.6	11.8	41.4
Nunoans	26	58.1	65.5	123.6	51.0	12.9	63.9
Lowland Indians	10	54.7	65.5	120.2	30.1	14.7	44.8

[a]Heat not replaced by metabolic activity.

[b]Because perfect equivalence in body temperature prior to exposure to cold was not achieved, heat loss in the first 4 minutes of exposure has been excluded from this calculation.

entirely the product of high temperatures of the extremities, and these temperatures, in turn, seem to be produced by a high flow of blood to the extremities during exposure to cold. When a comparison was made, as between Nuñoa males and females, of the temperatures of the extremities, the women were found to have warmer hands and somewhat colder feet. In both sexes the temperatures for hands and feet were significantly above corresponding values for white male subjects. The specific studies of hand and foot cooling made with exposures of types ii and iii shed further light on the subject, showing that the maximum differences between populations occurred with moderate cold exposure: that the high average temperatures of hands and feet were the result of a slow decline in temperature with less temperature cycling than is found in whites; and that the population differences were established by at least the age of 10 (the youngest group we could test) (17).

Since the oxygen exchange between hemoglobin and tissue bears a close positive relationship to temperature (18), it is clear that, when the temperature of the peripheral tissues remains high, more oxygen is available to these tissues. Therefore, the high temperatures of the extremities of the Nuñoans at low atmospheric temperatures may be considered not only an adaptation to cold but also a possible adaptation to hypoxia.

NUTRITION AND DISEASE

In the complex web of adaptations that are necessary if a peasant society is to survive, adequate responses to nutritional needs and prevalent diseases are always critical. For a people living at high altitude, these responses are important to an interpretation of the population's response to altitude and cold.

Nutrition

The analysis of nutritional problems in the Nuñoa district has proceeded through a number of discrete studies, including a study of dietary balance in individuals, a similar study for households, an analysis of food intake by individuals, and a study of the metabolic cost, to the community, of food production. Of these studies, the first two have been completed, the third is in the

analysis stage, and the fourth is in the data-collection stage. The results to date suggest that the Nuñoa population has a very delicate, but adequate, balance between nutritional resources and needs.

The dietary-balance study was carried out with six native adult males, chosen at random. Food requirements were predicted from U.N. Food and Agriculture Organization standards, on the basis of weight and temperature. The food used in the study consisted wholly of native foodstuffs and was prepared by a native cook. The results showed that, for these individuals, protein, caloric, and fluid balance remained good, and indicated that caloric and protein balance was good prior to the time of the study (19). The household survey suggested that nutrition for the population as a whole was generally adequate, although the method did not permit conclusions on the adequacy of nutrition for special subgroups, such as children and pregnant women (20).

The household survey also suggested that the diet might be somewhat deficient in vitamin A and ascorbic acid. Subsequent, more detailed surveys of individuals now cast doubt on the validity of this conclusion and suggest that, if malnutrition exists, it is probably no more common than in U.S. society. Indeed, in the light of the modern concept of "overnutrition," we might even say that the Nuñoans have a better dietary balance than the U.S. population. As noted above, the balance is delicate, and there must be years and times of the year when certain dietary deficiencies exist. Furthermore, the balance is subtle. To cite an example, the basic foods available are very low in calcium, yet adequate calcium is obtained, primarily by use of burned limestone as a spice in one type of porridge (21).

Disease

Our data on infectious disease are particularly inadequate. Health questionnaires are almost useless, since native concepts of health are only partially related to modern medicine. The indígenas attribute over 50 percent of all illness and death to susto, a word best translated as "fright." As noted above, no regular medical treatment is available, so records are lacking, even for a subsample. In our general survey we encountered the usual variety of infectious diseases and had the impression that respiratory ailments, such as tuberculosis and pneumonia, were common. On the other hand, we did not find evidence of deficiency diseases—not even goiters.

Perhaps the most striking results of the survey were those relating to cardio-vascular disease. In the survey, heart murmers were common among children, but no evidence of myocardial infarction or stroke was seen. Casual blood pressures of individuals from age 10 to 70 + were taken. They revealed a complete absence of hypertension; the highest pressure encountered was 150/90 mm-Hg. Other researchers have reported similar results for high-altitude populations, and it has been suggested that hypoxia may directly reduce the incidence of hypertension (22). In an attempt to trace the etiology of the low blood pressures, we subdivided our sample into a series of paired groups, first into lower- and higher-altitude groups, next into urban and rural groups, finally into more acculturated and less acculturated groups.

Significant differences in the effect of age on blood pressure appear when the sample is divided on the basis of any of these three criteria. However, it is not possible to assess the extent to which the environmental factors are independently related to blood pressure, since the total sample is too small to provide six independent subsamples large enough to give meaningful analytical results. It is our present belief that acculturation is the most significant of the factors, since altitude, urban residence, and acculturation are interrelated within the Nuñoa district population and the group differences are most striking when acculturation is taken as the criterion of subdivision. Children aged 10 to 20 years were classified as "acculturated" if they were in school, whereas children in the same age bracket who were not in school were classified as "unacculturated." Among adults, evidence of schooling, knowledge of

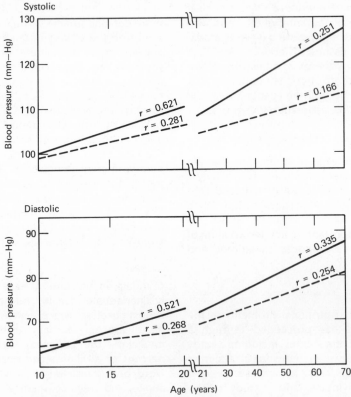

Figure 4. Changes with age in the blood pressure of male Nuñoa natives, according to level of acculturation. (Solid lines) More acculturated; (dashed lines) less acculturated; r, Pearson correlation coefficient.

Spanish, and use of modern clothing and specific material items, such as radios, were taken as signs of acculturation.

The results of these comparisons are shown in Figs. 4 and 5. Certainly the regressions cannot be taken as evidence that altitude does not affect blood pressure, since none of the Nuñoa males, even those in the acculturated group, have high blood pressures in old age. However, the analysis does show that, within a native population living at high altitude, something associated with the process of acculturation into general Peruvian society leads to significant increases in systemic blood pressure with age. Similar results have been reported for peasant and "primitive" populations at low altitudes, and some researchers have attributed the increase to psychological stress associated with modern culture (23). Such an explanation might apply to the results of our study, but it does not appear safe to conclude that this is the case before carefully examining nutritional and disease correlates. The available nutritional data are being examined for evidence of possible nutritional differences between the groups.

DISCUSSION AND CONCLUSIONS

From earliest recorded history it has been recognized that men from different populations vary in physical (that is, anatomical) characteristics and in cultures, but it is only recently that the variety of *physiological* differences has been revealed. The physiological differences so far shown are of the same general magnitude as the anatomical variations. That is, the available information suggests a basic commonality with respect to functions such as temperature regulation, energy exchange, and response to disease, but comparison of different populations has revealed a number of specific variations in response to environmental stress.

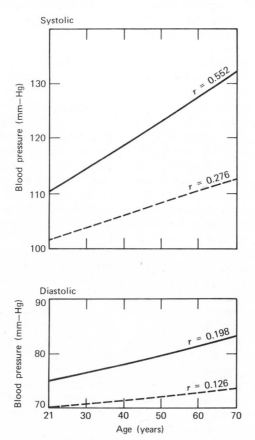

Figure 5. Changes with age in the blood pressure of female Nuñoa natives, according to level of acculturation. (Solid lines) More acculturated; (dashed lines) less acculturated; r, Pearson correlation coefficient.

Probably the most controversial aspect of these new findings concerns the mechanisms underlying the physiological differences. Because of the time and expense involved in studying the problem, population samples have often been small. Thus, with respect to specific findings, such as the high oxygen-consumption capacity reported by some workers for natives living at high altitudes, it has been suggested that biased sampling explains the difference. Other differences have been explained in terms of short-term acclimatization or of variations in diet or in body composition. Of course, genetic differences and long-term or developmental acclimatization have also been suggested, but the short-term processes have been more commonly accepted as explanations because they are based on known mechanisms.

We believe that a more general application of the extensive and intensive methods used in studying the Nuñoa population is a necessary next step in the search for the sources of differences in functional parameters in different populations. Thus, with respect to the Nuñoa population, a study of growth alone would probably have led to the conclusion that the observed differences in growth were the result of malnutrition.

On the other hand, the results of the growth study considered together with results of detailed studies of nutritional and other responses suggest hypoxia as a better explanation. Similar examples could be cited, from other aspects of the program, to show that a set of integrated studies of a single population can provide insights not obtainable with data pertaining to a single aspect of population biology.

In general, the data are still not adequate to treat the third question originally posed, on the sources of adaptation. Indeed we cannot even clearly differentiate genetic factors from long-term and developmental acclimatization. For this purpose one would require comparable data on several populatins that vary in genetic structure, in altitude of habitat, and in other aspects of environmental background. Fortunately, collection of such data is contemplated as part of the Human Adaptability Project of the International Biological Programme. The importance of understanding the sources of population differences seems obvious in a world where the geographical and cultural mobility of peoples is greater than it has ever been throughout history.

It seems clear that the native of the high Andes is biologically different from the lowlander, and that some of the differences are the result of adaptation to the environment. How well and by what mechanisms a lowland population could adapt to this high-altitude environment has not yet been adequately explored. Moreover, almost nothing is known about the biological problems faced by the highlander who migrates to the lowlands.

SUMMARY

The high-altitude areas of South America are in many ways favorable for human habitation, and they have supported a large native population for millennia. Despite these facts, immigrant lowland populations have not become predominant in these areas as in other parts of the New World, and lowlanders experience a number of biological difficulties on going to this region.

In order to learn more about the adaptations which enable the native to survive at high altitudes, an intensive study of a native population is being carried out in the district of Nuñoa in the Peruvian Altiplano. In this area hypoxia and cold appear to be the most unusual environmental stresses. Results to date show a high birth rate and a high death rate, the death rate for females, both postnatal and prenatal (as inferred from the sex ratio at birth), being unusually high. Birth weights are low, while placenta weights are high. Postnatal growth is quite slow relative to the rate for other populations throughout the world, and the adolescent growth spurt is less than that for other groups. The maximum oxygen consumption (and thus the capacity for sustained work) of adult males is high despite the reduced atmospheric pressure at high altitude. All lowland groups brought to this altitude showed significant reductions in maximum oxygen consumption. The Nuñoa native's responses to cold exposure also differ from those of the lowlander, apparently because blood flow to his extremities is high during exposure to cold. The disease patterns are not well known; respiratory diseases appear common, whereas there seems to be almost no cardiovascular disease among adults. Systemic blood pressures are very low, particularly those of individuals living in traditional native fashion. Nutrition appears to be good, but analysis of the nutrition studies is continuing.

The results of these studies are interpreted as showing that some aspects of the natives' adaptation to high altitudes require lifelong exposure to the environmental conditions and may be based on a genetic structure different from that of lowlanders.

REFERENCES AND NOTES

[1] C. Monge, *Acclimatization in the Andes* (Johns Hopkins Press, Baltimore, 1948).

[2] *Life at High Altitudes: Proceedings of the Special Session held during the Fifth Meeting of the PAHO Advisory Committee* (Pan American Health Organization, Washington, D.C., 1966); *Arch. Inst. Biol. Andina* (this is a new journal devoted entirely to the subject of acclimatization at high altitude; address, Apartado 5073, Lima, Peru).

[3] E.J. Van Liere and J.C. Stickney, *Hypoxia* (Univ. of Chicago Press, Chicago, 1963).

[4] J.P. McClung, *Amer. J. Phys. Anthropol.* 27, 248 (1967).

C. Hoff, thesis, Pennsylvania State University (1968).

[6] T.S. Baker, A.V. Little, P.T. Baker, "Infant Development at High Altitude," in preparation.

[7] P.T. Baker, R. Frisancho, R.B. Thomas, in *Human Adaptability to Environments and Physical Fitness*, M.S. Malhotra, Ed. (Defense Institute of Physiology and Allied Sciences, Madras, India, 1966).

[8] R. Frisancho, thesis, Pennsylvania State University (1966).

[9] E.R. Buskirk, J. Kollias, R.F. Akers, E.K. Prokop, E. Picon-Reategui, *J. Appl. Physiol.* 23, 259 (1967).

[10] From results of a study of adult men over a 1-year period and inferences from cardiovascular changes found only in the high-altitude newborn, Velasquez concludes that adults from lowland regions can never adapt to high altitudes as well as natives do [T. Velasquez, in *The Physiological Effects of High Altitude*, W.H. Weihe, Ed. (Macmillan, New York, 1964)].

[11] K.L. Andersen, in *The Biology of Human Adaptability*, P.T. Baker and J.S. Weiner, Eds. (Clarendon, Oxford, 1966).

[12] R.B. Mazess, thesis, University of Wisconsin (1967).

[13] J. Kollias, E.R. Buskirk, R.F. Akers, E.K. Prokop, P.T. Baker, E. Picon-Reategui, *J. Appl. Physiol.* 24, 792 (1968).

[14] J.M. Hanna, thesis, University of Arizona (1968); P.T. Baker, in *Human Adaptability and Its Methodology*, H. Yoshimura and J. S. Weiner, Eds. (Japan Society for the Promotion of Sciences, Tokyo, 1966).

[15] P.T. Baker, E.R. Buskirk, J. Kollias, R.B. Mazess, *Human Biol.* 39, 155 (1967).

[16] P.T. Baker, in *The Biology of Human Adaptability*, P.T. Baker and J.S. Weiner, Eds. (Clarendon, Oxford, 1966); R.W. Eisner and A. Bolstad, "Thermal and Metabolic Responses to Cold Exposure of Andean Indians at High Altitude," *Ladd Air Force Base Tech. Rep. AALTOR 62–64* (1963).

[17] M.A. Little, thesis, Pennsylvania State University (1968).

[18] This conclusion is based on the shift in the oxygen disassociation curve produced by lowering blood temperature. A standard graph, such as that presented by Consolazio and his associates [C.F. Consolazio, R.E. Johnson, L.J. Pecora, *Physiological Measurements of Metabolic Functions in Man* (McGraw-Hill, New York, 1963), p. 112] illustrates this effect.

[19] E. Picon-Reategui, "Food Requirements of High Altitude Peruvian Natives," unpublished.

[20] R.B. Mazess and P.T. Baker, *Amer. J. Clin. Nutr.* 15, 341 (1964).

[21] P.T. Baker and R.B. Mazess, *Science* 142, 1466 (1963).

[22] M.J. Fregly and A.B. Otis, in *The Physiological Effects of High Altitude*, W.H. Weihe, Ed. (Macmillan, New York, 1964).

[23] N.A. Scotch, *Amer. J. Public Health* 53, 1205 (1963).

[24] The data presented in this article represent the work of many scientists on the project. I particularly want to cite the contributions of Drs. E.R. Buskirk, J. Kollias, G. DeJong, and G. Escobar (all affiliated with the Pennsylvania State University) and of E. Picon-Reateguie (Universidad de San Marcos), M. Little (Ohio State University), R. Frisancho (University of Michigan), R. Mazess (University of Wisconsin), and J. Hanna (University of Hawaii). I also want to note the invaluable assistance of Mr. Victor Barreda and the officials of the Nuñoa district. The research is continuing as a U.S. project under the International Biological Programme. The primary financial support for the project was provided by the U.S. Army Medical Research and Development Command under contract DA–49–193–MD–2260. Additional support was provided by that Command (contract DA–49–193–MD–2709), by the Public Health Service (grant IROI HD–01756–01), by the National Institutes of Health (grant GM–07325–03), and by the Pennsylvania State University and the Instituto de Biología Andina.

32

ON CREEPING JENSENISM
C. Loring Brace and Frank B. Livingstone

The last few selections have dealt with traits that can be measured readily and in which individuals and populations can easily be compared. Now we turn to a trait that defies simple definition; that can be measured indirectly at best; and in which it may be difficult to compare individuals and meaningless to compare populations. We refer to what is called intelligence. Culturally defined categories such as originality, sensuality, lovableness, and willpower are no less real, but for a variety of historical reasons, intelligence has been invested with a great deal of importance, particularly in America.

In the absence of a controlling hereditary aristocracy, entrance to positions of wealth and power are based on achievement, and the fiction is maintained that achievement is solely the result of applied ability. But one needs a degree in law or business to start on the trail of legislative or corporate achievement, and that degree requires a college education. This, however, is hardly within the realm of expectation for the offspring of a family that has no tradition of literacy and exists below the federally established poverty level.

Enter the question of race. Well over half of the black people in America subsist below the poverty level. Their legacy is one of educational deprivation and blocked opportunity with no hope for breaking out of the trap that was legislated by white hostility. The language spoken differs in grammar and vocabulary from standard American English. Yet black children are given IQ tests based on familiarity with white middle class values and linguistic behavior. When they do not measure up to white norms, the difference is regarded as innate and their ultimate failure is considered foreordained. In effect they are blamed for the poverty that produced them. This is a classic example of the unwarranted use of an unjustified concept for the purpose of maintaining social inequality.

Within the last few years, the doctrine of white supremacy has been resurrected, clothed in modest if piously hypocritical language, and given forceful advocacy by the Berkeley, California, educational psychologist Arthur R. Jensen. No effort was made to set linguistic and experiential factors equal before testing; the nature of the concept of heritability was misrepresented; and opposing evidence was simply ignored. The results were received with immediate enthusiasm in the South (see the dismay expressed by Brazziel 1969), and Jensen's testimony was used by Congressman John R. Rarick of Louisiana in an effort to stop desegregation (see the Congressional Record of July 1, 1970. pp. H 6319–H 6326.)

Other social scientists were quick to respond (Brace, Gamble, and Bond 1971, Klineberg 1971). Because of its anthropological flavor, we reprint one of the responses here.

> Brace, C.L., G.R. Gamble, and J.T. Bond (eds.). 1971. *Race and Intelligence.* Anthropological Studies No. 8. The American Anthropological Association, Washington, D.C. 75 pp.
>
> Brazziel, William F. 1969. A letter from the South. *Harvard Educational Review 39* (2):348–356.
>
> Klineberg, Otto. 1971. Black and White in international perspective. *American Psychologist 26:*119–128.

Concern about the meaning of the physical differences between human populations dates back to before the dawn of written history, but it did not really become a major issue until the Renaissance, when the revolution in ocean-going transportation brought large numbers of diverse people physically face to face. The superior technology of the Europeans enabled them to coerce and exploit the peoples encountered, many of whom were forcibly uprooted and relocated as slaves. While one could argue that this was one of the most extraordinary examples of barbarism in the annals of "civilization," it was justified at the time, not so much on the basis of race, but because the people being enslaved were "heathens." Actually the "Christianity" of the unprincipled and largely illiterate slaving crews was often a convenient fiction, and the real reasons why the slave trade continued were greed and the force of firearms.

The phenomenon of the Christianized (and even literate) slave removed the initial rationale, but, needless to say, the institution persisted. Economics and the established social order in the American South assured its perpetuation while the Calvinistic fatalism of the North tended to maintain the status quo with little question. For example, in 1706 that godly Puritan, Cotton Mather, heartily supported the Christianization of "the Negro" on the one hand, while arguing on the other that baptism does not entitle a slave to liberty (Osofsky 1967:389). Although Quakers publicly and repeatedly extended Christian principles to the extreme of condemning slavery from the latter third of the seventeenth century on, this did not become a matter of general concern until the winds of "enlightenment" ushered in the Age of Reason, complete with elegant statements on the nature of man and human rights, and culminating in the American Revolution. Backlash followed the excesses of the revolutions in Santo Domingo and France, and it was more than half a century before the momentum of the Enlightenment was regained and slavery was finally abolished—in name, at least. (For excellent and detailed historical treatment, see Jordan 1968 and Stanton 1960.)

The intellectual legacy from late eighteenth century idealism, however, is apparent in the continuing debate concerning the meaning of human physical differences.

Clouding this debate has been another legacy of considerably less exalted origins. This legacy survives in the wretched social and environmental surroundings that continue to characterize the living conditions of Negroes in the United States. Quite recently there has been an explicit recognition of this situation—witness the belated extension (in 1954 and 1969) of eighteenth century Constitutional guarantees to Americans of African ancestry—but, at the same time, there has also been a continuation of the attempts to justify bloc differences in human treatment that began when slavery was already an accomplished fact.

Enforced inferior status—slavery—was initially justified by the heathen state of African peoples. All the other attributes of Negroes were automatically stigmatized and, although the justification changed through time, their association with inferiority has remained a continuing item of faith. Black skin color was regarded as the result of the curse placed on Ham and all his descendants. Negroes then were identified with the Biblical Canaanites, their servitude was considered justified by Noah's curse, and their attributes were regarded as visible evidence of the Lord's displeasure. With the rise of a rational world view in the latter part of the eighteenth century, this became an increasingly unsatisfactory explanation to thoughtful men. Separate creations—separate and unequal—were suggested, although this was offensive to the faithful who preferred something which remained compatible with the Biblical original pair. The result was a pre-Darwinian development of a form of evolution by means of a crudely conceived kind of natural selection (Smith 1965). Inevitably, however, vested interests of a social and political nature clouded all efforts at objectivity, as they continue to do. The record of published attempts to justify existing social inequalities on the basis of innate or biological differences extends unbroken from the Renaissance era of exploration and subsequent colonization (Jordon 1968) through the nineteenth century (Barzun 1965, Stocking 1968) to the present day. The association with events that maximize human misery (epitomized in the American Civil War and World War II for instance) is so clear that each new attempt to justify differential treatment of large numbers of human beings, often prejudged en masse, should be examined with the greatest of care.

We offer this cautionary preamble because yet another such attempt has been made, this time couched in the language of modern science, published in circumstances which tend to enhance its prestige, and given widespread if uncritical publicity. The presentation we refer to is Jensen's (1969a) monograph-length article in the *Harvard Educational Review*. Pointing up the obvious seriousness of its implications is the fact that the very next issue of the *Review* (Vol. 39, Spring 1969) contained responses from more than a half-dozen scholars. Many of the points raised are well-taken, but, in the haste of immediate reaction, documentation was incomplete, important aspects were missed entirely, and organization suffered.[1] Adding further to this unfortunate confusion is the treatment it has been given in the popular press. The discussion in the prestigious *New York Times Magazine* (Edson 1969), attempting journalistic impartiality, presents the various arguments and rebuttals as though they were all of equal probability. The result has been the widespread circulation of conclusions which are possibly pernicious, and certainly premature, to a readership which, though highly literate, is largely unable to make a reliable independent evaluation.

Seen in perspective, "jensenism, n. the theory that IQ is largely determined by the genes" (Edson 1969), is the extreme if logical outcome of the preoccupation which the field of behavior genetics has had with the "defeat" of the environmentalist heritage of Watsonian behaviorism (Hirsch 1967b: 118–119). The extreme of the environmentalist position is best expressed in Watson's (1924:82) famous dictum:

Give me a dozen healthy infants . . . and I'll guarantee to take any one at random and train him to become any type of specialist I might select—doctor, lawyer, artist, merchant-chief and, yes, even beggar-man and thief, regardless of his . . . abilities . . . and race of his ancestors.

Fulminations against this position by committed racists, who anathemize it as "equalitarian doctrine," are well known (Putnam 1961). Objections to extreme environmental-

ism have also been repeatedly offered by students of behavior genetics, one of whom, Hirsch, has variously characterized it as a "counterfactual assumption" (1961:480), a "counterfactual dogma" (1963), and a "counterfactual . . . postulate" (1967a), based on "fallacious reasoning" and "excessively anti-intellectual" (1967b). Both these positions, the racist and the behavior geneticist, represent reactions to the emotionally based humanitarianism in much of recent social science.

Leaving the racists out of it for the moment, it is evident that the advances in behavior genetics and ethology must be considered of prime importance among the recent major developments in biological, psychological, and anthropological science. This has led to the organization of many symposia and fostered the production of a series of popular books such as those by Lorenz (1966), Ardrey (1966), Morris (1968, 1969), and Tiger (1969). Questions being asked include "Why are men aggressive?" "Does man have a pair bond?" and "Is there such a thing as male bonding?" The interest in basic human biology is apparent, and much of this new questioning is concerned with supposed "species-specific" characteristics of man, although there is a tendency to postulate a genetic cause for human behavioral differences—Lorenz's (1966:236) discussion of Ute aggression, for example. Given these recent trends, it seems inevitable that attention would be focused on intelligence differences and that genetic causation should be stressed.

In the general picture, caution should be urged on two accounts, and Jensen's work illustrates what can happen when neither problem is adequately considered. First, the distinction between individual and population performance should be clearly perceived; and, second, if genetic differences are to be the object of concern, thorough control of the environmental component of observed variation should be achieved.

Considering the first issue, one of the roots of the problem is the inability of Western science—and biological science in particular—to recognize and differentiate between individual and populational phenomena. Certainly birth rates, death rates, or intelligence levels are the result of individual performances, but their variability among human populations is not primarily due to individual genetic differences, however much these may be involved. Many of the recent discussions of incest, inbreeding, and sexual behavior demonstrate the same inability to differentiate populational and individual phenomena (Roberts 1967; Livingstone 1969). Ironically, Hirsch, one of the people most responsible for the trend of research which Jensen has carried to something of an extreme, has apparently sensed the fact that the approach he has promoted is being carried too far and has recently articulated a brief critique which could be applied to Jensen's work (Hirsch 1968:42):

What is the relative importance of genetic endowment and of environmental milieu in the development of the intelligence of an individual? The answers given to that question . . . have nothing to do with an individual, nor are they based on the study of development. The answers have been based on the test performance of a cross-section of a population of individuals at a single time in their lives.

In his critical comment, Kagan (1969) in fact notes that Jensen makes no effort to resolve this issue.

Turning to the environmental component in observed behavior, we see that again Jensen has made little effort to grapple with the problem. Admittedly, the thrust of recent work in behavior genetics has been to discount the environmental contribution, but, again, Hirsch, who has been a major part of this thrust, has recently provided a warning against excesses in this direction. While he refers to the heredity-environment question as "a pseudo-question to which there is no answer" (1968:42), he goes on to warn that

it should also be noted that one cannot infer from a high heritability value that the influence of environment is small or unimportant, as so many people try to do [1968:43, emphasis Hirsch's].

To illustrate the unwarranted extreme of what Medawar (1961:60) has called "geneticism," Hirsch refers to the controversial pronouncements of William B. Shockley, Nobel laureate in physics. (For excerpts of Shockley's speech, see Birch 1968:49, and for a responsible rebuttal, see Crow, Neel, and Stern 1967). Mention of Shockley in this regard is particularly important since Jensen was apparently much impressed by Shockley when he was visiting Stanford in 1966–67. The result was what has been called his "most unfortunate speech" illustrating "the dangers of inappropriate use of both the concept of heritability and that of race by the biometrically unsophisticated" (Hirsch 1967a: 434). Jensen's speech, in turn, provided the background for the article which is the focus of our concern here.

The first half of Jensen's article is a comprehensive review of quantitative genetics. He concludes this review with the statement (1969a:65) that

the question of whether heritability estimates can contribute anything to our understanding of the relative importance of genetic and environmental factors in accounting for average phenotypic differences between racial groups (or any other socially defined group) is too complex to be considered here.

Since heritability estimates are specific to the populations studied—at the time studied—and since they vary considerably with environmental circumstances, Jensen, as quoted, correctly expresses the problem and should have stopped there. He does not stop, however, and proceeds under the assumption that there is a definite intelligence heritability of .8. Not only is this the highest found, but it is based on twin data, which are most unlikely to differentiate the environmental component.[2] This estimate he then generalizes to all humanity.

Despite his statement that the matter is "too complex," his further discussion of racial differences apparently implies that the preceding review of quantitative genetics supports his view. It does not. Furthermore we fail to see how, after pointing out that environment can change IQ by as much as 70 points, he can make the statement that "in short it is doubtful that there is any significant environmental effect on IQ."

For purposes of comparison, let us take the case of stature. As a "trait," it is sufficiently complex to warrant the expression of doubts concerning simplistic treatment, although it is somewhat less of a "typological reification" (Hirsch 1968:44) than intelligence. Treating them for the moment as though they were comparable traits, it is evident that both are under polygenic control. Proceeding with this in mind, Kagan (1969), in his initial reaction to Jensen's article, cites the difference in stature between rural and urban populations in Latin America to show the effect of environment on an inherited trait. Hunt (1969), on his part, makes casual mention of stature in colonial Jamestown, Plymouth, and during the American Revolution, noting the radical changes that have taken place since that time.[3]

Other examples are well known and documented, but perhaps the changes in Sweden and the Low Countries in the past 100 years constitute a better example (Chamla 1964). Stature certainly has a major genetic component. Estimates concerning its heritability vary widely, although they average about .5, comparable to the average for IQ despite what Jensen claims. For example, Kagan and Moss (1959) have found an average correlation of .43 between parents and offspring for IQ, and an average correlation of .36 for stature. In the past 100 years, or about four generations, very little genetic change could have occurred, particularly when one considers the lack of evidence for strong selection. However, in that time, the stature of the average adult male in many European countries has changed 4–5 in., or almost two standard deviations. Since populational differences in IQ are at most about one standard deviation, we do not see why anyone would maintain that the same amount of nongenetic change could not occur where IQ is concerned—particularly when the trend of IQ increase is not only known but, in some cases, even greater than the trend for increase in stature.

The principal reason for the observed increase in stature appears to be a change in nutrition, particularly an increase in the amount of protein in the diet. A similar increase in stature is occurring in Japan (Kimura 1967), and there is a strong correlation between stature and protein intake (Takahashi 1966). Recently evidence has been accumulating to suggest that mental development can be markedly influenced by nutritional inadequacy—particularly where protein-calorie malnutrition occurs during the period in development when the brain is growing most rapidly (Cravioto, DeLicardie, and Birch 1966; Davison and Dobbing 1966; Eichenwald and Fry 1969).

Brain weight, amount of brain protein, and RNA increase linearly during the first year of human life—all being directly proportional to the increase in head circumference. The amount of brain DNA is regarded as a good indication of cell number and, although it largely ceases to increase at six months, it too maintains a direct relation to head circumference during the first year of life (Winick and Rosso 1969). With this in mind, it is of grim interest to note that in cases of severe malnutrition, head circumferences have been recorded that were two standard deviations below the mean for normal children of the same age. Brain weight and protein were reduced proportionately, while DNA content was reduced at least as much and in some cases more (Winick and Rosso 1969:776). In one instance, rehabilitation was tried on malnourished children and behavioral recovery was measured by the Gesell method. Children who were under six months of age on admission retained their deficit, leading to the conclusion (Cravioto and Robles 1965:463) that "there is a high possibility that at least the children severely malnourished during the first six months of their lives might retain a permanent mental deficit." In another instance, recovery of head circumference following early malnutrition lagged way behind other aspects of growth recovery (Graham 1968, esp. Fig. 3).

The studies cited above deal principally with the consequences of malnutrition in Latin America, but the record from Africa is equally clear: small fetal and neonatal brain sizes among the starving people of Biafra (Gans 1969), decreased cranial circumference and reduced brain weight among the malnourished of Uganda (Brown 1965, 1966), reduced cranial circumference and lower intelligence test scores in the Cape Coloured of South Africa. In the latter case, the reduction in circumference and test score was in comparison with a control population, also of Cape Coloured, but one which was not suffering from severe malnutrition. The differences were statistically significant ($P = < .01$) but, interestingly enough, there was no significant difference between the parents of the two groups (Stoch and Smythe 1963, 1968).

One could argue that the works we have mentioned deal principally with extremes of malnutrition, and, in fact, Jensen does so, claiming that there is little extreme malnutrition in the United States. Yet with substantially more than half of the American black population living at or below the poverty level as defined by the US Department of Health, Education, and Welfare, with the shocking deprivation recently and belatedly brought to the attention of the US Congress (Javits 1969; Hollings and Jablow 1970), and with the obstacles to survival facing the American poor so graphically depicted by Coles (1969), it would be most surprising if malnutrition did *not* contribute something to the lowering of intelligence test scores in American Negroes—all other things being equal, which, of course, is not the case.

Before leaving strictly biological matters, we should note that deprivation need not be extreme for its consequences to show. Admittedly, these data are derived from studies on experimental animals rather than on human beings, but this can hardly justify ignoring their implications. Inadequate nutrition delays development of the myelin nerve sheaths in rats, and the deficit is not completely made up. The importance of this particular study is to be seen in the fact that the deprivation was that of the lower end of the "normal" range and did *not* constitute "starvation" (Dobbing 1964:508). Demonstration of the reduction in cell number of other brain tissues following early deprivation is equally clear (Dickerson 1968:335; Dobbing 1968:195). Not surprisingly, the behavioral consequences are also apparent (Eichenwald and Fry 1969:646):

Protein deprivation in early life not only causes . . . behavioral changes but also reduces the capacity of the experimental animal to learn at a later age. Furthermore, rats born of and suckled by malnourished mothers are similarly deficient in their learning capacity.

So far we have stressed the role of nutrition—particularly protein calorie malnutrition—in the stunting of mental development. Vitamin deficiency, illness susceptibility, and chronic ill-health all contribute to a malnutrition-disease syndrome (see Scrimshaw and Gordon 1968) which, given nothing else, whould certainly lower performance levels on intelligence tests. These factors alone can go a long way towards accounting for the differences in the tested intelligence of the world's populations, but they constitute only a part of the nongenetic background of testable mental performance. However, strictly experiential factors can have an even more pronounced effect on intelligence test performance and may completely mask the nutritional and genetic factors.

Obviously there are many problems associated with estimating the heritability of behavioral traits. Data on IQ tests derived from family studies do indicate a genetic component, although this may in fact be somewhat less than the heritability for physical traits. The heritable component is extremely difficult to separate from the nonheritable component in assessing the results of most tests of complex behavior, and it is apparent that Jensen really does not make the effort to do so. The cumulative interaction of particular types of experience with facets of biological maturation produces an elaboration that is extremely difficult to assess in terms of what percentage of which part is represented in the end-product. This is what Hirsch meant when he referred to the nature-nuture problem as a "pseudo-question to which there is no answer," but if Jensen expects to demonstrate the credibility of his conclusions, it is a question to the solution of which he must direct research efforts more carefully planned and better controlled than any that have yet been undertaken or even proposed.[4]

Studies on the heritability of behavioral traits in *Drosophila* are frequently cited to bolster estimates on behavioral heritability in man, but, even ignoring the enormous phylogenetic gap, recent research has shown the heritability of the oft-mentioned geotactic and phototactic responses to be quite low. Richmond (1969), for example, found the heritability of both to be less than .2 in all cases and not significantly different from .0 in one instance. Dobzhansky and Spassky (1969) found realized heritabilities for these traits to be below .1.

We should like to make it quite clear that we do not deny the existence of a genetic component that contributes to differences in performance on IQ tests—*within* a single population, where conditions of early experience and education are relatively similar. The differences, however, are less important than implied by Jensen.[5] For example, he has noted that there are significant correlations between the IQ scores of adopted children and their real parents, while correlations with their foster parents tend to be nonsignificant. However, he does not mention the fact that adopted children consistently display a substantially higher IQ than their biological parents. Skodak and Skeels (1949) found that the average IQ of the real mothers was 86 while that of their children adopted into other families was 106—well over a whole standard deviation higher. Surely this indicates that, with an improved socioeconomic background, one can accomplish in one generation a change that is greater than any difference between racial or religious groups in the United States. The overwhelming component of this difference is certainly environmental.

In their review of behavior genetics, Spuhler and Lindzey (1967) come to much the same conclusion with regard to racial differences in IQ. While citing many cases of behavioral differences among humans which have a known genetic basis, they show that there is a very significant relationship between IQ and educational expenditure. They conclude (1967:405): that "we do not *know* whether there are significant differences between races in the kinds and frequencies of polygenes controlling general intellectual ability." In our turn, we do not see how anyone would disagree with this statement, but would go further. We suggest that it is possible to explain all the measured differences among major groups of men primarily by environmental factors, while noting, on the other hand, that it is not possible to provide genetic explanations which are evolutionarily plausible for most of these differences.

Within a given population there certainly is a spectrum of the inherited component of "intelligence," and there may be some association between this and certain demanding occupations, but from the perspective of biological evolution, the time depth of the professions in question is so shallow that little change in the genetic structure of the population can have occurred. Furthermore, Jensen's reaffirmation of the time-honored

assumption that there are average differences in innate intelligence between social classes is also without demonstrable foundation and is very probably incorrect. At the top end of the social scale in America, the initial establishment of position may have had some relationship to ability, although demonstrable unprincipled ruthlessness was at least as important (Lundberg 1968). Once established, position is retained with little relation to the continuing presence of ability in the families in question, and reproductive behavior is notoriously unrelated to the *intellectual* attributes of the partners chosen.

At the bottom of the social hierarchy there is one outstanding factor that makes suspect any claims concerning inherited ability. This factor is poverty. It is not unexpected that "in most settings there is a positive association between poor nutrition and poor social conditions" (Richardson 1968:355). And if this itself does not assure retardation in the development of mental ability, an atmosphere of social impoverishment certainly does. Inculcation into the ways of "the culture of poverty" (Lewis 1966) does not train people to perform well on IQ tests. Nor has ability or its lack had much to do with recruitment into the ranks of the extremely poor. Mere possession of a black skin was sufficient until quite recently and, with the addition of certain geographic provisos, still is.

One of Jensen's basic assumptions is made explicit in the comment printed with his approval in *The New York Times Magazine* (Sept. 21, 1969, p. 14). In this he clearly regards "intelligence as the ability to adapt to civilization," adding that "races differ in this ability according to the civilizations in which they live." Building on this, he further assumes that "the Stanford-Binet IQ test measures the ability to adapt to Western civilization," an ability in which he claims American Negroes to be inferior to "Orientals," with the clear implication that, as a blanket category, they are far less well-endowed than American whites. For an educated man to hold such beliefs is regrettable, but for a presumed "scientist" to be allowed to publish them in a popular journal without informed editorial supervision is an example of the unfortunate failure of intellectual responsibility.

First of all, "Western civilization," if this is

indeed a valid category in this context, is largely a product of the Industrial Revolution and has a maximum time depth of little more than two centuries. Even if natural selection had been operating at maximum efficiency during this time, it would have been hard put to change a polygenic trait as much as a full standard deviation for an entire population. In terms of actual reproductive performance, there is little reason to believe that the intellectually highly endowed were in fact favored to such an extent. If it is fair to make such sweeping judgments, we can make a case for the fact that most of the labor roles which were created by and ensured the success of the Industrial Revolution—and, hence, Western civilization—required relatively little learning and no creative decision-making on the part of their occupants. This, of course, is why child labor was practical until it was outlawed. In terms of the kind of folk knowledge and unwritten tradition necessary for survival, it is perhaps fair to claim that the average European (i.e., peasant) of the sixteenth century lived a life that had more elements of similarity with that of the average West African than it did with that of the descendents of either one in the Europe or America of the twentieth century.

Obviously in saying this we are making a value judgment that cannot be proven one way or the other, but, nevertheless, it would appear to square with the data of both anthropology and history rather better than Jensen's suggestion that races differ in intelligence "according to the civilizations in which they live." Considering the fact that, with a few numerically unimportant exceptions, all human populations now live under conditions characterized by cultural adaptations—"civilizations" in Jensen's terms—that are radically different from those of their lineal predecessors only a few thousand years ago (and often much less), it is reasonable to conclude that no races are really adapted to the "civilizations in which they live."

The time is not so long past when instructing Negroes in the mechanics of reading and writing was contrary to law in parts of the American South. Educational opportunities remain drastically substandard, and there is scarcely a rudimentary form of the tradition in child-rearing, so characteristic of the middle and upper-middle classes,

which promotes literacy as the key to wordly success. When used to compare groups with different cultural backgrounds, the Stanford-Binet IQ test is less a comparative measure of ability than an index of enculturation into the ways of the American middle class. Since Negroes have been systematically (see the account in Woodward 1966) denied entrance to the middle-class world, it is not surprising that their learned behavior is measurably different from that on which the IQ test is based. Certainly before the results of IQ tests can be taken as indicating inherited differences in ability, some cognizance should be taken of the effect of tester expectation on performance (Rosenthal 1966), or motivation in its various aspects (Katz 1967), and of the results of nonverbal tests where conceptual styles of the groups being studied are markedly different (Cohen 1969).

Finally, Jensen's assertion that intelligence or brain differences must exist among the "races" of man is an argument by analogy which ends up assuming what he presumably was trying to demonstrate. As he notes, separate breeding isolates will very likely show differences on some genetic characteristics which will be due to the various evolutionary forces. In most cases, these differences, if at all considerable, will coincide with differences in selective forces to which the populations are subject. To conclude from this perfectly reasonable genetic statement, as Jensen does, that it is "practically axiomatic" that two populations will be different in any characteristic having high heritability (1969a:80) and, ergo, that the races of man differ in their genetic capacities for intelligence or in the genetic properties of their brains is simply a non sequitur. Certainly it is contrary to all we have learned from evolutionary biology. All human populations have 10 fingers, 10 toes, 2 eyes, and 32 teeth per individual. These all have high heritability and some variability within human isolates, but are constant between isolates. This is primarily due to the operation of natural selection, a factor which Jensen deemphasizes.

Behavior or brain function is obviously under the control of many loci, and, equally obviously, it is subject to the influence of natural selection. If differences exist at these loci among human populations, these differences would be correlated with differences in the forces of selection. These in turn would be reflected in the cultural and behavioral attributes designed to counteract them. Within any continent there are as many differences in cultural and behavioral adaptation as there are between continents.

However, implicit and even explicit in much of behavior genetics is the assumption that cultural differences are caused by genetic differences. The anthropological findings that cultural differences represent responses to varying environmentally imposed selective forces are simply ignored. Selective force distributions do not neatly coincide as a rule. Some may covary in some areas, some may show crosscutting distributions, and others may vary completely at random with respect to each other. Given this situation, we have elsewhere suggested that, in order to make sense out of human biological variation, the typological gestalt of the race concept be abandoned and human adaptation be studied trait by trait in the contexts where the relevant selective forces have been at work (Livingstone 1962, 1964; Brace 1964a, b). We cannot resist adding the comment that this approach, if taken seriously, can completely defuse the potentially explosive situation which Jensen has created.

Jensen (1969a:89) cites the Harlows (Harlow and Harlow 1962) to the effect that if the average IQ were lower and thus fewer geniuses were produced, then there would be fewer people to make inventions and discoveries and thus cultural evolution would have been slower. We suggest that, just as mutation rate does not control the speed of biological evolutionary change, neither does the frequency of the occurrence of genius have anything to do with the rate of cultural evolution. We can even offer a converse suggestion and raise the suspicion that levels of cultural complexity are inversely related to IQ. Survival takes less innate wit for the socially and economically privileged than it does for those to whom culture does not offer ready-made solutions for most of life's problems. It is possible that the average level of intelligence is highest among populations where culture is least complex. Post-Pleistocene food preparation techniques, including, especially, pots in which boiling was easy and common, have rendered the human dentition of far less importance to survival than before. The

sharp reductions in the Post-Pleistocene human face are concentrated in the dentition and have proceeded farthest in just those people whose forebears have been longest associated with "high civilization" (Brabant and Twiesselmann 1964:55). Is it not possible that supraregional political and economic organization increased the survival chances of any given individual without regard for his inherited ability? Why then should we not expect an average lowering of basic intelligence to accumulate under such circumstances? We offer this solely as an hypothesis for possible testing. Jensen, on the other hand, feels that failure to test the hypothesis that Negroes are intellectually inferior for genetic reasons may constitute "our society's greatest injustice to Negro Americans" (1969c:6). Unless there is a latent racist bias to the kind of research Jensen feels is urgent,[6] it is difficult to see why the testing of the hypothesis we have outlined above is not considered at least of equal importance with the testing of its converse, and yet the possibility is not even mentioned, let alone seriously entertained. Ironically, the possible consequences of our failure to take this issue seriously will be enormous for all Americans, but particularly for non-Negro Americans, i.e., "whites."

Knowledge of both cultural and biological dimensions is required for a full understanding of the human condition. The stress on "geneticism" (to use Medawar's word again) should be tempered by an insistence that the environmental component be thoroughly controlled. Certainly as much effort and sophistication should be devoted to this task as to comparative performance assessments. Jensen's work is conspicuously lacking in this regard. As such, it is the logical antithesis to the old environmentalist thesis. Perhaps the synthesis will contain the reasonable parts of each.

Finally, in the words of Jensen (1969:78), "If a society completely believed and practiced the ideal of treating every person as an individual, it would be hard to see why there should be any problems about "race" per se." Unfortunately Jensen ignores this ideal in practice and, in the absence of adequate control, insists on treating a substantial portion of the American population as though a stereotype were sufficient and as though the individual could be ignored. In effect this guarantees that there *will* continue to be problems about race per se and that Jensen and his like will only intensify them.

NOTES

[1]Since the preparation of this manuscript (for the November 1969 Annual Meeting of the American Anthropological Association), another paper by Jensen has appeared (1969b) in conjunction with more thoroughly documented critiques in the summer issue of the *Harvard Educational Review*. Some of the points we raise are discussed in greater detail than in our presentation, but since other important ones are not even mentioned we have decided to let our paper stand substantially as originally written.

[2]For an elegant demonstration of the inappropriateness of Jensen's use of twin data, see the critique by Light and Smith (1969). Fehr (1969) also shows the inaccuracy of Jensen's use of twin data to arrive at his assumed heritability level.

[3]Jensen (1969b) offers a rebuttal to the somewhat anecdotal accounts of Kagan and Hunt but, again, uses a single debatable account to generalize for all mankind.

[4]This criticism of Jensen's approach has been eloquently and forcefully made by Stinchcombe (1969) and Deutsch (1969).

[5]The interaction of heredity and environment in the development of a trait has been brought into focus by Stinchcombe (1969), but an even more important point is made by Gregg and Sanday in their contribution to this present volume. They note that heritability figures for given traits will vary in inverse proportion to the similarity of the environments of the populations being considered. This illustrates the generalization offered some time ago by Lerner (1958:63, italics his): "The heritability of a given trait may differ from one population to another, or vary in the same population at different times . . . *strictly speaking, any intra-generation estimate of heritability is valid only for the particular generation of the specific population from which the data used in arriving at it derive.*" As Hirsch (1969:138) has phrased it, "Heritability is a property of populations and not of traits."

[6]The regretful comment made by a collaborator and admirer of Jensen's experimental research is worth quoting here: "I believe the impact of Jensen's article was destructive; that it has had negative implications for the struggle against racism and for the improvement of the educational system. The conclusions he draws are, I believe, unwarranted by the existing data and reflect a consistent bias towards a racist hypothesis" (Deutsch 1969:525).

REFERENCES CITED

Ardrey, R. 1966 The Territorial Imperative. New York: Delta.

Bajema, C.J. 1963 Estimation of the Direction and Intensity of Natural Selection in Relation to Human Intelligence by Means of the Intrinsic Rate of Natural Increase. Eugenics Quarterly 10:175–187.

Barzun, Jacques 1965 Race: A Study in Superstition. New York: Harper Torchbooks.

Birch, Herbert G. 1968 Boldness and Judgment in Behavior Genetics. *In* Science and the Concept of Race. M. Mead, T. Dobzhansky, E. Tobach, and R. Light, eds. New York: Columbia University Press.

Brabant, H., and F. Twiesselmann 1964 Observations sur l'Évolution de la Denture permanente humain en Europe Occidentale. Bulletin du Groupement International pour la Recherche scientifique en Stomatologie 7:11–84.

Brace, C.L. 1964a The Concept of Race. Current Anthropology 5:313–320.

——— 1964b A Non-Racial Approach Toward the Understanding of Human Diversity. *In* The Concept of Race. M.F.A. Montagu, ed. New York: Free Press.

Brown, Roy E. 1965 Decreased Brain Weight in Malnutrition and Its Implications. East Africa Medical Journal 42:584–595.

——— 1966 Organ Weight in Malnutrition with Special Reference to Brain Weight, Developmental Medicine and Child Neurology 8:512–522.

Chamla, M-C. 1964 L'accroisement de la Stature en France de 1800 à 1960; Comparison avec les pays d'Europe occidentale. Bulletins et Mémoires de la Société d'Anthropologie de Paris, Série 11, 6:201–278.

Cohen, Rosalie A. 1969 Conceptual Styles, Culture Conflict, and Nonverbal Tests of Intelligence. American Anthropologist 71:828–856.

Coles, Robert 1969 Still Hungry in America. Cleveland: New American Library.

Cravioto, J., E.R. DeLicardie, and H.G. Birch 1966 Nutrition, Growth and Neuro-Integrative Development: An Experimental and Ecologic Study. Pediatrics 38:319–372.

Cravioto, J., and B. Robles 1965 Evolution of Adaptive and Motor Behavior During Rehabilitation from Kwashiorkor. American Journal of Orthopsychiatry 35:449–464.

Crow, James F., James V. Neel, and Curt Stern 1967 Racial Studies: Academy States Position on Call for New Research. Science 158:892–893.

Davison, A.N., and J. Dobbing 1968 Myelination as a Vulnerable Period in Brain Development. British Medical Bulletin 22:40–44.

Dickerson, J.W.T. 1968 The Relation of the Timing and Severity of Undernutrition to Its Effect on the Chemical Structure of the Central Nervous System. *In* Calorie Deficiencies and Protein

Deficiencies. R.A. McCance and E.M. Widdowson, eds. London: J.A. Churchill.

Dobbing, J. 1964 The Influence of Nutrition on the Development and Myelination of the Brain. Proceedings of the Royal Society of London, Series B, Biological Sciences 159:503–509.

——— 1968 Effects of Experimental Undernutrition on Development of the Nervous system. In Malnutrition, Learning and Behavior. N.S. Scrimshaw and J.E. Gordon, eds. Cambridge: MIT Press.

Dobzhansky, T., and B. Spassky 1969 Artificial and Natural Selection for Two Behavioral Traits in Drosophila pseudoobscura. Proceedings of the National Academy of Sciences 62:75–80.

Edson, Lee 1969 jensenism, n. the theory that IQ is largely determined by the genes. The New York Times Magazine, August 31, pp. 10–11, 40–41, 43–47.

Eichenwald, Heinz F., and Peggy Crooke Fry 1969 Nutrition and Learning. Science 163:644–648.

Gans, Bruno 1969 A Biafran Relief Mission. The Lancet 1969–I:660–665.

Graham, G.G. 1968 The Later Growth of Malnourished Infants: Effects of Age, Severity and Subsequent Diet. In Calorie Deficiencies and Protein Deficiencies. R.A. McCance and E.M. Widdowson, eds. London: J.A. Churchill.

Hirsch, Jerry 1961 Genetics of Mental Disease Symposium, 1960: Discussion: The Role of Assumptions in the Analysis and Interpretation of Data. American Journal of Orthopsychiatry 31:474–480.

——— 1963 Behavior Genetics and Individuality Understood: Behaviorism's Counterfactual Dogma Blinded the Behavioral Sciences to the Significance of Meiosis. Science 142:1436–1442.

——— 1967a ed. Behavior Genetic Analysis. New York: McGraw-Hill.

——— 1967b Behavior-Genetic, or "Experimental," Analysis: The Challenge of Science Versus the Lure of Technology. American Psychologist 22:118–130.

——— 1968 Behavior-Genetic Analysis and the Study of Man. In Science and the Concept of Race. M. Mead, T. Dobzhansky, E. Tobach, and R. Light, eds. New York: Columbia University Press.

Hollings, Ernest F., as told by Paul Jablow 1970 We Must Wipe out Hunger in America. Good Housekeeping, January, pp. 68–69, 144–146.

Hunt, J.McV. 1969 Has Compensatory Education Failed? Has It Been Attempted? Harvard Educational Review 39:278–300.

Javits, Jacob 1969 Hunger in America. Playboy, December, p. 147.

Jensen, Arthur R. 1969a How Much Can We Boost IQ and Scholastic Achievement? Harvard Educational Review 39:1–123.

——— 1969c Arthur Jensen Replies. Psychology Today 3:4, 6.

Jordan, Winthrop D. 1968 White over Black: American Attitudes Toward the Negro, 1550–1812. Chapel Hill: University of North Carolina Press.

Kagan, Jerome S. 1969 Inadequate Evidence and Illogical Conclusions. Harvard Educational Review 39:274–277.

Kagan, J.S., and H.A. Moss 1959 Parental Correlates of Child's IQ and Height: A Cross-Validation of the Berkeley Growth Study Results. Child Development 30:325–332.

Katz, Irwin 1967 Some Motivational Determinants of Racial Differences in Intellectual Achievement. International Journal of Psychology 2:1–12.

Kimura, K. 1967 A Consideration of the Secular Trend in Japanese for Height and Weight by a Graphic Method. American Journal of Physical Anthropology 27:89–94.

Lewis, Oscar 1966 The Culture of Poverty. Scientific American 215:19–25.

Livingstone, Frank B. 1962 On the Nonexistence of Human Races. Current Anthropology 3:279–281.

——— 1964 On the Nonexistence of Human Races. In The Concept of Race. Ashley Montagu, ed. New York: Free Press of Glencoe.

——— 1969 Genetics, Ecology and the Origins of Incest and Exogamy. Current Anthropology 10:45–61.

Lorenz, Konrad 1966 On Aggression. New York: Bantam.

Lundberg, Ferdinand 1968 The Rich and the Super-Rich: A Study in the Power of Money Today. New York: Lyle Stuart.

Medawar, P.B. 1961 The Future of Man. New York: Mentor.

Morris, Desmond 1968 The Naked Ape. New York: McGraw-Hill.

——— 1969 The Human Zoo. New York: McGraw-Hill.

Osofsky, Gilbert 1967 The Burden of Race: A Documentary History of Negro-White Relations in America. New York: Harper and Row.

Putnam, Carleton 1961 Race and Reason: A Yankee View. Washington: Public Affairs Press.

Richardson, Stephen A. 1968 The Influence of Social-Environmental and Nutritional Factors on Mental Ability. In Malnutrition, Learning and Behavior. N.S. Scrimshaw and J.E. Gordon, eds. Cambridge: MIT Press.

Richmond, R.C. 1969 Heritability of Phototactic and Geotactic Responses in Drosophila pseudoobscura. American Naturalist 103:315–316.

Roberts, D.F. 1967 Incest, Inbreeding and Mental Abilities. British Medical Journal 4:336–337.

Rosenthal, Robert 1966 Experimenter Effects in Behavioral Research. New York: Appleton-Century-Crofts.

Scrimshaw, Nevin S., and John E. Gordon (eds.) 1968 Malnutrition, Learning and Behavior, Cambridge: MIT Press.

Skodak, M., and H.M. Skeels 1949 A Final

Follow-up Study of One Hundred Adopted Children. Journal of Genetic Psychology 75:85–125.

Smith, Samuel Stanhope 1965 An Essay on the Causes of Variety of Complexion and Figure in the Human Species (reprint of the 1810 version). Winthrop D. Jordan, ed. Cambridge: The Belknap Press.

Spuhler, J.N., and G. Lindzey 1967 Racial Differences in Behavior. *In* Behavior-Genetic Analysis. Jerry Hirsch, ed. New York: McGraw-Hill.

Stanton, William 1960 The Leopard's Spots: Scientific Attitudes Toward Race in America, 1815–59. Chicago: University of Chicago Press.

Stoch, Mavis B., and P.M. Smythe 1963 Does Undernutrition During Infancy Inhibit Brain Growth and Subsequent Intellectual Development? Archives of Diseases of Childhood 38:546–552.

1968 Undernutrition During Infancy, and Subsequent Brain Growth and Intellectual Development. *In* Malnutrition, Learning and Behavior. N.S. Scrimshaw and J.E. Gordon, eds. Cambridge: MIT Press.

Stocking, George W., Jr. 1968 Race, Culture and Evolution: Essays in the History of Anthropology. New York: Free Press.

Takahashi, E. 1966 Growth and Environmental Factors in Japan. Human Biology 38:112–130.

Tiger, Lionel 1969 Men in Groups. New York: Random House.

Watson, J.B. 1924 Behaviorism. New York: W.W. Norton.

Winick, Myron, and Pedro Rosso 1969 Head Circumference and Cellular Growth of the Brain in Normal and Marasmic Children. The Journal of Pediatrics 74:774–778.

Woodward, C. Vann 1966 The Strange Career of Jim Crow. New York: Galaxy Book.

SUPPLEMENTARY REFERENCES

Deutsch, Martin 1969 Happenings on the Way Back to the Forum: Social Science, IQ, and Race Differences Revisited. Harvard Educational Review 39:523–557.

Fehr, F.S. 1969 Critique of Hereditarian Accounts of "Intelligence" and Contrary Findings: A Reply to Jensen. Harvard Educational Review 39:571–580.

Harlow, H.F., and M.K. Harlow. 1962 The Mind of Man. *In* Yearbook of Science and Technology, pp. 31–39.

Hirsch, Jerry 1969 Biosocial Hybrid Vigor Sought, Babel Discovered. *Review of* Genetics: Second of a Series on Biology and Behavior, edited by David C. Glass. Contemporary Psychology 14:138–139.

Jensen, Arthur R. 1969b Reducing the Heredity-Environment Uncertainty: A Reply. Harvard Educational Review 39:449–483.

Lerner, I. Michael 1958 The Genetic Basis of Selection. New York: John Wiley.

Light, Richard J., and Paul V. Smith 1969 Social Allocation Models of Intelligence: A Methodological Inquiry. Harvard Educational Review 39:484–510.

Stinchcombe, Arthur L. 1969 Environment: The Cumulation of Effects Is Yet to be Understood. Harvard Educational Review 39:511–522.

33

INTELLECTUAL DEVELOPMENT OF CHILDREN FROM INTERRACIAL MATINGS
Lee Willerman, Alfred F. Naylor, and Ntinos C. Myrianthopoulos

"If A can prove, however conclusively, that he may, of right, enslave B, why may not B snatch the same argument and prove equally that he may enslave A. You say A is white, and B is black. It is color, then; the lighter having the right to enslave the darker? Take care. By this rule, you are slave to the first man you meet with fairer skin than your own. You do not mean color exactly? You mean the whites are intellectually the superiors of the blacks and, therefore, have the right to enslave them: Take care again. By this rule, you are to be slave to the first man you meet with an intellect superior to your own."

Abraham Lincoln

In his discussion of race and intelligence, A.R. Jensen produces figures showing a fifteen point (one standard deviation) difference in the average IQ scores of blacks and whites in America. Ignoring the genesis of IQ in the individual and the difference between the white and the black experience in America, he claims that 80 percent of IQ is controlled by heredity alone and that the black-white difference is too large to be accounted for by environment.

We reprint the following research report because, in spite of the technical complexity of the statistical and analytical procedure, the experimental design is quite clear. The evidence reported is simply incompatible with Jensen's claims.

Both sexes contribute about equally to the inherited component of their children's intellectual capacities, so, in assessing the children of a mating where the parents were of different races, it should make no difference whether the mother is white or black so long as the father is not the same color as the mother. But, as Willerman and his associates show, there is a difference. When the mother is black, the IQ scores of the male children are one standard deviation below those of the female children—the same difference shown in the scores of the black and white populations in the work reported by Jensen, yet no such male-female difference shows up in either the black or the white populations at large. But if the mother is white and the father black, there is no significant difference between the male and female children. In addition, there is a fifteen point IQ gap between male and female children when the mother is unmarried—but only if she is black. No such gap appears when children of unmarried white mothers and black fathers are measured.

These differences are fully as dramatic as the population differences that Jensen attributes to heredity alone. Yet because of the way Willerman's study was controlled, it is apparent that heredity cannot be the cause. Some kind of environmental shaping effect must be involved. The effect that different environmental conditions can have on the development of the brain (Rosenzweig et al. 1972) and the pitfalls of the incautious use of the concept of heritability have recently been shown (Bodmer and Cavalli-Sforza 1970; Hirsch 1970; McCall 1970). In view of the focus of Jensen and his supporters, we are greatly in need of more information on the nature and mode of operation of the environmental influences that Willerman and others have proven to exist.

Bodmer, Walter F., and L.L. Cavalli-Sforza. 1970. Intelligence and race. *Scientific American* 223(4):19–29.

Hirsch, Jerry. 1970. Behavior-genetic analysis and its biosocial consequences. *Seminars in Psychiatry* 2(1):89–105. Invited address presented to the XIXth

International Congress of Psychology, London, England, July 30, 1969, and
dedicated to T. Dobzhansky on his seventieth birthday.

McCall, Robert B. 1970. Intelligence quotient pattern over age: comparisons
among siblings and parent-child pairs. *Science* 170:644–648.

Rosenzweig, Mark R., E.L. Bennett, and M.C. Diamond. 1972. Brain changes in
response to experience. *Scientific American* 226(2):22–29.

Abstract. *Interracial offspring of white mothers obtained significantly higher IQ scores at 4 years of age than interracial offspring of Negro mothers, suggesting that environmental factors play an important role in the lower intellectual performance of Negro children.*

If racial differences in intelligence test performance are determined by additive genetic factors which are not sex-linked, then test scores for children of interracial crosses might be independent of maternal race. But if test differences between races are largely environmental in origin, the mothers' race should have an effect on children's performance since she is the primary socializing agent during the preschool years (1). In our analysis we assume (in the absence of data) that the mean intelligence of the parents does not differ with either maternal or paternal race combination.

Dichotomous assignment of individuals to either the Negro or white group is inaccurate and suspect on both genetic and social grounds because American Negroes share approximately 21 percent of their genes with non-Negroes (2) and because 70 percent of a sample of American Negroes has reported a white ancestor (3). Nevertheless, such designations have proven useful in providing insights concerning the occurrence of many biological and social phenomena (4).

The Collaborative Study of Cerebral Palsy, Mental Retardation, and other Neurological and Sensory Disorders of Infancy and Childhood provides data which may be useful in disentangling some of the genetic and environmental interactions. This study is currently following the children born to approximately 42,000 women who registered during pregnancy in 12 institutions throughout the United States (5). These children are routinely given standardized neurological and psychological examinations at various intervals during the first 8 years of life.

Among the information collected before birth of a child is the race and schooling of

the father and the race, schooling, and marital status of the mother. The degree of underreporting of fathers of a different race probably depends on the mother's race; white women would tend to report that the father was Negro because it would become obvious at birth; Negro mothers might not report a white mate because light skin is common in Negro infants.

The frequency of interracial mating (disregarding marital status) in the Collaborative Study is approximately 0.38 percent. This should not be taken to be indicative of the rate for the United States since the current sample is approximately 50 percent Negro and is drawn from urban hospital registrants rather than from less-biased census data.

Of the 186 liveborn offspring of interracial matings identified in the Collaborative Study only 88 had reached the age of 4 years and were tested with the Stanford-Binet, abbreviated Form L-M (6), at the time this study was undertaken. The IQ's come from only 10 of the 12 collaborating institutions since the two southernmost ones (Charity Hospital, New Orleans, and University of Tennessee) provided no cases. The IQ's were obtained routinely during the course of regularly scheduled testing for all children in the Collaborative Study.

In another study (7) the mean IQ for control children from uniracial matings matched for hospital of birth and socioeconomic and marital status to the present sample was 104.3 for the children of white matings and 97.4 for the children of Negro matings. The mean IQ for the present sample is 98.7.

The children were also measured and weighed at birth, and their gestational ages were calculated from the mothers' report of her last menstrual period. Interracial matings involved 61 white and 27 Negro mothers; 38 of the children were male and 50 female.

Table 1
Characteristics of samples of interracial matings by race of mother. Results are mean ± standard deviation. Numbers in parentheses are the number of subjects.

Maternal education (years)	Paternal education (years)	Weight of child at birth (g)	Length of child at birth (cm)	Gestation (weeks)
		White mother		
10.9 ±2.2 (61)	11.5 ± 2.3 (46)	3207 ±573 (60)	49.8 ±2.6 (59)	40.1 ±2.5 (61)
		Negro mother		
11.0 ±2.5 (27)	11.0 ± 2.5 (21)	3228 ±567 (27)	50.1 ±2.5 (27)	40.2 ±2.6 (26)

Table 1 shows comparative statistics of available data on maternal education, paternal education, birth weight, birth length, and duration of gestation by race of the mother of the interracial child. As judged by t-tests, none of the differences approach statistical significance, and there is, in particular, no suggestion that intrauterine experience or parental education favors the child of a white mother. However, it would be premature to exclude from further consideration differential infection rates or nutritional differences. Because of these close similarities, adjustment for the above variables in the statistical analysis of IQ differences is unnecessary.

Mean education of all white mothers in the Collaborative Study whose 4-year-old children were given the IQ test is 11.1 years, as compared to 10.9 years for the white mothers in Table 1. The 10.4 years for all Negroes in the Collaborative Study whose children were tested at 4 years of age is somewhat lower

than the 11.0 years in Table 1 for Negro mothers (8). Comparative figures are not available for paternal education.

In the interracial sample 36 percent of the white mothers and 26 percent of the Negro mothers were unmarried at the time of registration. Comparative figures for the entire Collaborative Study are 12 and 23, respectively. Thus, in the present sample, interracial whites have a lower frequency of marriage and Negroes have a higher frequency.

In assessing the postnatal effect of the race of the mother on the IQ of the 4-year-old child it seemed desirable to take into account the marital status of the mother and the sex of the baby since both these factors have been reported as being of importance (9, 10). The data showing the three-way combinations of maternal race, sex, and marital status in Table 2 were analyzed from two approaches. The first involved entering the data

Table 2
The IQ scores of 4-year-old children categorized by race of mother, sex of child, and marital status. Married implies either legal or common law; unmarried implies single, divorced, separated, or widowed. Results are the mean ± standard deviation. The numbers in parentheses are the numbers for each sample.

Race of mother	Sex of child	Marital status	IQ scores
White	Male	Unmarried	94.7 ± 12.1 (7)
White	Male	Married	100.8 ± 18.3 (20)
White	Female	Unmarried	100.3 ± 15.7 (15)
White	Female	Married	103.8 ± 18.0 (19)
Mean			100.9 ± 16.8 (61)
Negro	Male	Unmarried	67.5 ± 23.2 (2)
Negro	Male	Married	88.4 ± 11.0 (9)
Negro	Female	Unmarried	88.6 ± 13.7 (5)
Negro	Female	Married	105.1 ± 14.1 (11)
Mean			93.7 ± 16.9 (27)
Mean of all			98.7 ± 16.8 (88)

into a computer program that performed a three-way analysis of variance with least squares adjustments for disproportionality in sample sizes. Statistical interactions were not significant in this analysis and the significant main effects (F = 4.2 for 3 and 80 d.f.; P = .008) have additive interpretations.

The first member of each dichotomy, Negro or white mother, male or female child, and married or unmarried marital status, was assigned a score of zero and the second member a score of one. Application of regression procedures yielded the following slopes and standard errors for the main effects: 8.36 ± 3.75 IQ points for race, 8.14 ± 3.52 for sex, and 8.30 ± 3.73 for marital status. If the ratio of each coefficient to its standard error is treated as having a t distribution, all are significant in the 5 to 1 percent range.

However, the interaction between marital status and the mothers' race may be considerable, with marital status resulting in bigger differences among the children of Negro mothers. The maternal race-marital status effect is 13.6 ± 8.4 and, though not statistically significant, is so sizable that it merits further analysis. Similarly, the sex effect seems larger among the children of Negro mothers. In this case the slope is 14.1 ± 7.7, again not statistically significant, but sufficiently large to deserve continued study, especially since the failure to observe statisti-

cally significant interactions on these variables is very likely due to small cell sizes.

The data were therefore partitioned in a manner which focused on the two-way interactions, first ignoring sex (Table 3), then ignoring marital status (Table 4). The results indicate that if sex is ignored, maternal race is significant only among the children of unmarried mothers (P < .05), and that among Negro mothers it is the children of the unmarried with the low IQ's (P < .05). Alternatively, if marital status is ignored, maternal race is significant only among males (P < .05), and among Negro mothers, it is the male children who have the low IQ's (P < .05). Therefore, the male children of unmarried Negro mothers have the lowest IQ's. Among white mothers, the effects of marital status and sex are less, though always consistent with the findings for the children of Negro mothers.

Interpretation of the race effect should be tentative since the number of interracial subjects is small. The evidence presented here suggests that environmental factors may play an important role in the lower intellectual performance of Negro preschool children.

Despite no observed differences in mean educational attainment by race of mother, it is possible that child-rearing practices vary between the two groups. Racial differences in dialect usage would tend to militate against the children of Negro mothers on IQ

Table 3
The IQ scores of 4-year-old children categorized by race and marital status of mother (see Table 2).

Race of mother	Marital status	IQ scores
White	Unmarried	98.5 ± 14.7 (22)
White	Married	102.3 ± 18.2 (39)
Negro	Unmarried	82.6 ± 16.1 (7)
Negro	Married	97.6 ± 12.8 (20)

Table 4
The IQ scores of 4-year-old children categorized by race of mother and sex of child (see Table 2).

Race of mother	Sex of child	IQ scores
White	Male	99.2 ± 17.0 (27)
White	Female	102.3 ± 17.0 (34)
Negro	Male	84.6 ± 12.9 (11)
Negro	Female	99.9 ± 14.0 (16)

tests, for example. Performance on intelligence and achievement tests might also reveal differences in favor of the white mothers.

The significant sex effect on IQ in favor of females has been reported before the Collaborative Study data (10) and is only one of many cognitive tasks which show females superior to males. Tasks involving relatively simple perceptual motor skills, such as speed of naming colors, reading, typing, and coding speed, all show female superiority (11). However, tasks requiring restructuring of the stimulus field, such as finding a simple pattern embedded in a more complex one, have shown consistent sex differences in favor of males (11). It was suggested that sex differences on cognitive tasks may be more adequately explained by physiological differences rather than by child-rearing differences between the sexes. Recent research suggesting a specific perceptual deficit associated with the absence or abnormality of one X chromosome in patients with Turner's syndrome is consistent with that hypothesis (12).

The association of single marital status with lower IQ performance has been documented before with interpretation based on increased disorganization in one-parent families (9). Since females tend to do most of the child-rearing during the early years even in two-parent families, the relationship remains to be clarified. Lewis (13) pointed out that negative effects on children associated with one-parent families tend to diminish when socioeconomic status is controlled. If maternal education can be taken as an index of socioeconomic status, the unmarried group differs only slightly from the mean for the entire sample given in Table 1 [white mothers, 10.5 years (n = 22); Negro mothers, 11.3 years (n = 7)]. Since the designation of marital status is assigned during pregnancy and there is no information available on whether the postnatal years of the child did in fact agree with this original designation, no firm conclusions can be drawn.

REFERENCES AND NOTES

[1] H. Simmons and P. Schoggen, in The Stream of Behavior, R.G. Barker, Ed. (Appleton-Century-Crofts, New York, 1963), p. 70.

[2] T.E. Reed, Science 165, 762 (1969).

[3] M.J. Herskovits, Pediat. Semin. 33, 30 (1926).

[4] A. Damon, Soc. Biol. 16, 69 (1969).

[5] H.W. Berendes, in Research Methodology and Needs in Perinatal Studies, S.S. Chipman, A.M. Lilienfeld, B.G. Greenberg, J. F. Donnelly, Eds. (Thomas, Springfield, Ill., 1966), p. 118. The Collaborative Study, supported by the National Institute of Neurological Diseases and Stroke, has the following participants: Boston Lying-in Hospital; Brown University; Charity Hospital, New Orleans; Children's Hospital of Buffalo; Children's Hospital of Philadelphia; Children's Medical Center, Boston; Columbia University; Johns Hopkins University; Medical College of Virginia; New York Medical College; Pennsylvania Hospital; University of Minnesota; University of Oregon; University of Tennessee; Yale University; and the Perinatal Research Branch, NINDS.

[6] L.M. Terman and M.A. Merrill, Stanford-Binet Intelligence Scale (Houghton Mifflin, Boston, 1960).

[7] L. Willerman, A.F. Naylor, N.C. Myrianthopoulos, J.A. Churchill, unpublished data.

[8] S.H. Broman, J. Khanna, J. Weber, in preparation.

[9] M. Deutsch and B. Brown, J. Soc. Issues XX, 24 (1964).

[10] J.E. Singer, M. Westphal, K.R. Niswander, Child Devel. 39, 103 (1968); L. Willerman, S.H. Broman, M. Fiedler, ibid. 41, 69 (1970).

[11] B.M. Broverman, E.L. Klaiber, Y. Kabayashi, W. Vogel, Psychol. Rev. 75, 23 (1968).

[12] J. Money, J. Psychiat. Res. 2, 223 (1964).

[13] H. Lewis, in The Moynihan Report and the Politics of Controversy, L.E. Rainwater and W.L. Yancey, Eds. (M.I.T. Press, Cambridge, Mass., 1967), p. 314.

34

A COMMENTARY ON THE BEHAVIOR GENETICS OF RACE, SOCIAL CLASS, AND IQ
Sandra Scarr-Salapatek

Much of the confusion surrounding the current discussion of intelligence, race, and social class stems from assumptions and misconceptions concerning heritability. The coefficient of heritability—h^2—is the relation between the total observed variance of the trait under observation and the proportion of the trait that is under genetic control. Total, or phenotypic, variance is represented by $\sigma^2{}_P$ and is composed of genetic variance, $\sigma^2{}_G$, plus environmental variance, $\sigma^2{}_E$. Hence $\sigma^2{}_P = \sigma^2{}_G + \sigma^2{}_E$. Since the coefficient of heritability is the proportion of genetic variance to total variance for a trait,

$$h^2 = \frac{\sigma^2{}_G}{\sigma^2{}_G + \sigma^2{}_E}$$

But there are problems with this concept. The environmental contribution to total variance is not a fixed amount. It can vary through time for a given population; it is almost certainly different from one population to another; and it varies between sections and individuals of a single population. Not only that, the interaction between the genetic and environmental contributions to total phenotypic variance is not simple or additive as the formula suggests.

Heritability for a given trait, then, is not a fixed figure. It can vary from 0 to 1.0 without indicating which factor is contributing how much to total variance (Lewontin 1970a, 1970b). Over twenty years ago the late British geneticist R. A. Fisher remarked that the coefficient of heritability is "one of those unfortunate short-cuts which have emerged in biometry for lack of a more thorough analysis of the data" (Fisher 1951:217). The behavior-geneticist Jerry Hirsch concludes that "the plain facts are that in the study of man a heritability estimate turns out to be a piece of 'knowledge' that is both deceptive and trivial" (1970:98).

This may be true when it has been used to claim that the tested IQ of black and white Americans is different because blacks are genetically inferior (see the balanced critique by Gage 1972), but as Scarr-Salapatek has shown, there is a somewhat inverse utility in the measure. She has shown that there is a substantial difference in the coefficient of heritability for IQ between black and white schoolchildren, and also between the upper and lower socioeconomic levels of the white sample. This finding alone casts grave doubts on the attempts to suggest that racial differences are basically of genetic origin. But she goes still further and shows how the coefficient can be used as an indicator of environmental conditions. When the circumstances for the development of intelligence are optimal, as in the socially advantaged part of the white population, then the variation that does show up will be due more to genetic factors than to environment. Where conditions do not favor the development of the IQ, the variance will reflect a greater degree of the influence of these unfavorable conditions. A high heritability coefficient, as in the privileged white sample, should be an index that conditions are favorable. A low coefficient indicates environmental deprivation. Dr. Scarr-Salapatek's original and ingenious use of her data from a study of twins in Philadelphia shows how heritability estimates can be calculated for a relatively large sample and how they indicate the favorable or unfavorable conditions for intellectual development. Blacks and low-status whites how low coefficients while high-status whites have high ones. In this case, then, the coefficient of heritability is a measure of environmental privilege.

Fisher, R. A., 1951. Limits to intensive production in animals. *British Agricultural Bulletin* 4:217–218.

Gage, N. L., 1972. Replies to Shockley, Page and Jensen. *Phi Delta Kappan* 53:422–427.

Hirsch, Jerry. 1970. Behavior-genetic analysis and its biosocial consequences. *Seminars in Psychiatry* 2:89–105.

Lewontin, Richard C. 1970a. Race and intelligence. *Bulletin of the Atomic Scientists* 26:2–8.

———. 1970b. Further remarks on race and the genetics of intelligence. *Bulletin of the Atomic Scientists* 26:23–25.

Who among us can deny that both genes and environments are required for the development of human traits? Yet, it seems that voices from the left and right shout about environmental and genetic determinants of IQ as though there were mutually exclusive explanations for the development of intelligent human behavior.

Here I will try to clarify "Three D's" of genetics and to relate these to studies on race, social class and IQ. The first D is *determination,* the second is *difference,* and the third is *development.* A clear distinction of the genetic meanings of determination, difference, and development is critical to understanding the current acrimony over individual and group differences in IQ, since a large part of the confusion rests on the misuse of these terms. When someone speaks of the genetics of intelligence, he may be referring to any of these three terms, and herein lies the mischief.

It is obvious that genes play a crucial part in the *determination* of intelligence through their pathways to brain anatomy and physiology. Without a brain, intelligent behavior would not exist. Let me quickly add that environmental determination has the same claim: without oxygen, nutrients, and stimulation, the brain would not survive to be intelligent. The absolute necessity of both genes and environments for intelligence is so obvious that the point need not be labored.

The idea of genetic determination is seen as a threat to environmentalism only because it is misunderstood. The inheritors of Mendel's ideas have not yet penetrated the inner reaches of the behavioral sciences to root out pre-evolutionary thought. Mendel knew full well that his pea plants had to have soil,

From a paper delivered at the New York Academy of Sciences, April 11, 1972, which was based on another article that appeared in *Science, 174* (December 24, 1971). pp. 1285–1295.

and that the composition of the soil affected the final phenotypes. No soil yields no plants; poor soil yields weak plants. Mendel happened upon some single gene characteristics that had full penetrance or full correspondence between genotype and phenotype—a lucky break for him. Now we know that for many complex human behaviors there is no simple correspondence between single genes and behaviors like intellectual abilities and mental illnesses. The genetic determination depends on many genes and many mechanisms which produce the person's responsiveness to environmental conditons. The genetic expression of complex behavioral traits may be modified to a considerable extent by environmental characteristics, but they are nonetheless as genetically determined as single-gene traits. Only the gene action-behavior pathways differ. It is in this area that cell geneticists and biochemists investigate the physiological links between genes and phenotypes.

If every human behavior is, in this trival sense, genetically determined, what is all the furor about? The question currently at issue pertains to *genetic differences* among us. This is the question of "how much of the phenotypic variance among people(s) is contributed by genetic variance and how much by environmental variance." The intellectual history of genetic differences descends from Darwin through Galton to the present-day population geneticists. Darwin, of course, focused on phenotypic variation as adaptation to varying environments, and on the non-random selection of reproducing individuals, again in response to environmental conditions. His theory of evolution was designed to account for the observed diversity of life forms and their changes over time. Darwin knew nothing of Mendel. The integration of Mendelian ideas of gene segregation and recombination and Darwinian ideas of variation and change is still not complete in genetics, so that we behavioral scientists need not be embarrassed by our confusion.

In the Darwinian tradition, population geneticists ask questions about the origin of differences among us without respect to known gene loci or to specific gene-action pathways. Rather, the methods of population genetics require only phenotypes that vary among people of different genetic and environmental relatedness. Phenotypic diversity is analyzed as a function of these two parameters.

Also in the Darwinian tradition animal breeders have explored the heritability of various characteristics with an eye to improving phenotypes through selective breeding. The higher the proportion of additive genetic variance in a trait (narrow heritability), the faster changes can be brought about by breeding only desirable phenotypes. The method worked for many years before genes were known to exist. Even in 1971, Jerry Hirsch was moved to say that "a gene is an inference from a breeding experiment"![1] Surely someone with an electron microscope could be goaded into disagreement, but the point remains that Darwinian and Mendelian traditions have led to quite different contemporary thought, and confusion for nongeneticists.

The field of behavior genetics includes investigators of both Mendelian and Darwinian ancestry, and occasional hybrids who may benefit from some heterosis (hybrid vigor). The work reported here grew out of the Darwinian tradition of investigating the origins of *differences* among people. But I am also a hybrid—a peculiar sport, perhaps —because my primary interest in behavior genetics is psychological development. Development is the third D of genetics.

Developmental psychology has a long history of ambivalence about biological theories and a recent history of biology-rejection. At the present time, Darwinism is creeping into the literature through ethology with its concern for species variation and through behavior genetics with its concern for individual differences. I hope that some synthesis of social and biological thought will result in new developmental theories, lest we be swept back into another era of naive environmentalisms or naive instinct theory.

Genetic theory is by nature developmental theory. As I see it, development is the common concern of Mendelian, Darwinian and environmental theories, a perfect ground for integration. In a few cases of abnormal development, we can trace an integration of the results from genetic and environmental investigations, as in phenylketonuria, PKU. PKU was first detected in two severely retarded siblings who had a peculiar smell and pigmentation that was lighter than expected. Fölling, in the Mendelian tradition, laboriously traced the metabolic pathways between a single gene and its expression in retarded intellectual development. The history of environmental treatment for PKU with low phenylalanine diets is now a familiar story. I need add only that pedigree and population studies have shown the distribution of the guilty gene to be about 1 in 75 people in white populations and to have different frequencies in other populations.

PKU is a prize example of genetic-environmental research on human behavior. While there are more examples of the single-gene sort, we cannot be certain how long it will take for normal human development to become amendable to elegant, integrated research. Problems abound; for example, for most of the behaviors that interest us, many genes and many environmental events contribute to normal development. When a gross aberration occurs in the developmental process or in the final phenotype, we can often detect the problem. But what variations in normal genotypes and normal environments contribute how much, at what time, to the developing phenotype? Some would claim that a dialectical interaction between organism and environment make analysis of the components senseless.[2] I would propose that we can disentangle individual genotypes, gene pathways and environmental factors from the synthetic process, even if I do not know exactly how. At least we must try if we are ever to understand (and perhaps control) developmental processes.

Let me give just one example of this kind of integrated developmental study. Language acquisition is a fascinating behavioral development with *species-specific* qualities (all normal children in all populations learn a symbolic language but other species ordinarily do not), *individual differences* (some children in all populations speak earlier and more fluently than others), a *regular developmental sequence* (all normal children acquire speech between 18 and 48 months of age), and *environmental variation*. These four characteristics of speech make it a good candidate for behavior-genetic analysis. In addition, language abilities have been subject to selection for many thousands of years, yet are not critical to reproduction, which, if true, would eliminate most genetic variation.

While ethologists like Peter Marler are investigating the species qualities of speech, call, and song, several students of developmental behavior genetics are looking at individual variation in language development. Mittler in England, and Karen Fischer and Lynn Waterhouse at the University of Pennsylvania, have all shown important genetic sources of variation in the acquisition of vocabulary and certain syntactic features of language and important environmental variation in other features of speech. The essential aspect of the Fischer-Waterhouse study is its investigation of both genetic and environmental hypotheses to account for language development over time. In developmental studies we must ultimately be concerned with the mechanisms of genetic and environmental determination and the sources of individual variation, a combination of both Mendelian and Darwinian methods.

This long excursion into genetic terminology and its consequences has been a preamble to the following report on my own as yet incomplete work on the nature of intellectual development. This study arose out of my curiosity in 1967 about the heritability of IQ differences in various populations which had not been studied, particularly the black group and the socially disadvantaged portions of both black and white populations.*

The heritability of intelligence in white, middle-class populations of school-aged children and adults has been repeatedly estimated to account for 60 to 80 percent of the total variance in general intelligence scores, however measured.[3] Yet Jensen (3, pp. 64–65) has noted many limitations to the available data on heritability.

*The following portions of this paper are edited from the report that appeared in *Science*, 1971, 174, 1285–1295.

It is sometimes forgotten that such (heritability) estimates actually represent average values in a population that has been sampled and that they do not necessarily apply either to differences within the various subpopulations or to differences between subpopulations . . . All the major heritability studies have been based on samples of white European and North American populations, and our knowledge of intelligence in different racial and cultural groups within these populations is nil. For example, no adequate heritability studies have been based on samples of the Negro population of the United States.

After carefully examining the intelligence data on the black and white populations, Jensen hypothesized that the average genetic potential of the black population may not be equal to that of the white population. Others[4] have interpreted the same racial differences in mean IQ (intelligence quotient) within an environmental framework, often naively and without good evidence for their competing hypotheses. Dislike of a genetic hypothesis to account for racial differences in mean IQ scores does not equal disproof of that hypothesis. Evidence for genetic or environmental hypotheses must come from a critical examination of both explanations, with data that support one.

As every behavioral geneticist knows, the heritability of a behavioral characteristic is a function of the population in which it is measured.[5] There is no reason to assume that behaviors measured in one population will show the same proportion of genetic and environmental variances when measured in a second population whose distributions of genetic or environmental characteristics, or both, differ in any way from those of the first population. Racial and social class groups are, for many purposes, sufficiently different populations so that generalization from one to another is highly questionable.[6]

The sociological literature on social class and racial differences in style of life, nutrition, child-rearing practices, and the like describes population differences in distributions of environments. These population differences must affect the development of phenotypic (observed) IQ[7] and the relative proportions of genetic and environmental variances in IQ scores.

Distributions of genotypes for the development of behavioral characteristics may also vary from one population to another. Except for single-gene characteristics such as Huntington's chorea, microcephaly, and the like, we know very little about genotypic variability among populations for behavioral development. Because identified single-gene characteristics are known to occur with varying frequencies among populations, it is assumed that genes for polygenic characteristics may also be distributed somewhat differently among groups.

TWO MODELS OF IQ, SOCIAL CLASS, AND RACE

There are two major, competing hypotheses for predicting the relation among social class, race, and IQ—the environmental disadvantage hypothesis and the genotype distribution hypothesis. Both hypotheses make differential predictions about the proportions of genetic and environmental variance in IQ within lower and higher social class groups.

The term "environmental disadvantage" refers to the largely unspecified complex of environmental factors associated with poverty that prevents an organism from achieving its optimum development. The biological environmental disadvantages have been reviewed by Birch and Gussow,[8] and studies on social environmental disadvantages have been reviewed by Deutsch, Katz, and Jensen.[9]

Race and social class are terms that refer to socially defined subgroups of the human population. Reproduction is more likely to occur between people in the same subgroup than between people in different subgroups. There is no question that races are partially-closed breeding groups with a great deal more endogamy than exogamy. It is also true that social class groups (groups whose members have attained a certain educational and occupational status) within races practice more endogamy than exogamy.[6] Social mobility from generation to generation does not upset the notion of social classes as somewhat different breeding groups, in terms of IQ levels, because the distribution of IQ's within each occupational level is reestablished in each generation of adults.[10] Brighter children in families at all but the top

social levels tend to be upwardly mobile, whereas duller siblings at all but the bottom class level tend to be downwardly mobile.[11] Social class groups may be thought of as endogamous primarily for IQ (as expressed in occupational and educational acheivements).

Social class groups may represent both different distributions of parental genotypes for IQ and different rearing environments for children. Although fathers' average IQ scores may vary by 50 points or more from top professional groups to unskilled laborers, their children's average IQ's differ by 25 points or less.[10][11]

The mean differences in children's IQ's by social class reflect differences in both parental genotypes and rearing environments, which covary to a large extent in the development of IQ. Crucial evidence on the genetic and environmental components from adopted children is very limited, but Skodak and Skeels[12] revealed a 20 point rise in the IQ of adopted children over that of their biological mothers. The distribution of adopted children's IQ's was also shifted beyond the values expected by regression to a mean above average of the population, presumably by their better social environments.

Social class groups, then, are subdivisions of races and represent different distributions of parental genotypes, as well as different rearing environments. There is no comparable statement that can be made about racial groups: whereas races represent different rearing environments, no statements can be made concerning different distributions of parental genotypes for IQ. Since there is no direct test possible for distributions of genotypic IQ, it is impossible to assert that such distributions for the two races are "equal" or "different". Races do constitute different rearing environments in two respects. First proportionately more blacks than whites are socially disadvantaged, thus more black children are reared under lower-class conditions; second, being black in the United States may carry with it a social burden not inflicted on any white.

The environmental disadvantage hypothesis assumes that lower-class whites and most blacks live under suppressive[13] conditions for the development of IQ. In brief, the disadvantage hypothesis states: (i) unspecified environmental factors affect the development of IQ, thereby causing the observed differences in mean IQ levels among children of different social classes and races; (ii) blacks are more often biologically and socially disadvantaged than whites; and (iii) if disadvantage were equally distributed across social class and racial groups, the social class and racial correlations with IQ would disappear. The envoromental disadvantage hypothesis predicts that IQ scores within advantaged groups will show larger proportions of genetic variance and smaller proportions of environmental variance than IQ scores for disadvantaged groups. Environmental disadvantage is predicted to reduce the genotype-phenotype correlation[14] in lower-class groups and in the black group as a whole.

The genetic differences hypothesis, as it

Model 1: Environmental advantage as the determinant of group differences in IQ.

Assumptions:
1. Genotypic distribution by social class for phenotypic IQ of children (no differences).

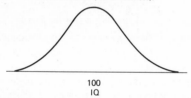

100
IQ

2. Environmental effects on the development of IQ by SES (large effect).

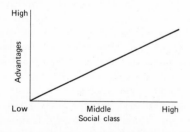

Prediction: Lower h^2 in disadvantaged groups.

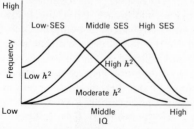

Figure 1. Environmental disadvantage, model 1 (h^2 is heritability for twins; SES is socioeconomic status).

Model 2: Genetic differences as the primary determinant of group differences in IQ.

Assumptions:
1. Genotypic distribution by social class for phenotypic IQ of children (differences).

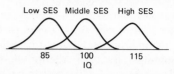

2. Environmental effects on the development of IQ by SES (small effect).

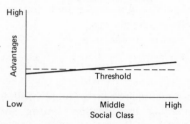

Prediction: Equal h^2 in all groups.

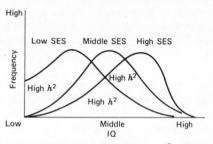

Figure 2. Genetic differences, model 2 (h^2 is heritability for twins; SES is socioeconomic status).

applies to social class groups within races, centers on the issues of assortative mating by IQ and selective migration, based on intelligence, within the social structure. Social class differences in mean IQ are assumed to be principally genetic in origin and to result from the high heritability of IQ throughout the population, assortative mating for IQ, and a small covariance term that includes those education advantages that brighter parents may provide for their brighter children.[3,6] Social class differences in phenotypic IQ are assumed to reflect primarily the mean differences in genotype distribution by social class; environmental differences between social class groups (and races) are seen as insignificant in determining total phenotypic variance in IQ. Therefore, the proportion of genetic variance in IQ scores is predicted to be equally high for all social class groups (and for both races). Figures 1 and 2 present models 1 and 2, respectively, as they apply to social class.

In model 1, there are assumed to be equal distributions of genotypes across social classes. In model 2, there are assumed to be unequal distributions of genotypes for IQ, the lower class having proportionally more genotypes for low IQ and the upper social groups having proportionally more genotypes for high IQ. Environmental effects of social class are posited to be strong in model 1 and very weak in model 2.

COMPETING PREDICTIONS

Both models account for the observed social class data on IQ, but they make competing predictions about the proportion of genetic variance. In model 1, environmental factors are predicted to reduce the mean and the heritability of IQ in the lower social class groups and raise both in the higher social groups. Model 2 predicts equally high heritabilities for all groups, regardless of rearing environments and regardless of mean scores. Estimated heritabilities by social class and race provide a new way of evaluating the adequacy with which the two hypotheses account for observed differences in mean IQ by social class. Racial differences may also be examined if the following rationale is always considered.

To the extent that the same environmental factors are assumed to affect the development of IQ in the same way in both black and white populations, predictions can be made about the sources of racial differences in mean IQ scores. If certain biological deprivations (such as low weight at birth, poor nutrition) are known to be more prevalent in lower class groups of both populations and more prevalent among blacks than whites, then the two models can make differential predictions about the effects of these sources of environmental variance on the proportion of genetic variance in each population. Given a larger proportion of disadvantaged children within the black group, the environmental disadvantage hypothesis must predict smaller proportions of genetic variance to account for differences in phenotypic IQ among blacks than among whites, as whole populations. Since the genotype distribution hypothesis predicts no differences in the proportion of genetic variance for social class groups within the races, it should predict the same proportions of genetic variance in the two races.

To the extent that different environmental factors are assumed to affect the development of IQ in black and white populations, or the same environmental factors are assumed not to affect the development of IQ in the same way, or both, no differential predictions about the origin of racial differences can be made by the two models. If all black children are disadvantaged to an unknown degree by being reared as blacks in a white-dominated society, and no white children are so disadvantaged, it is impossible to estimate genetic and environmental variances between the races. Only if black children could be reared as though they were white, and vice versa, could the effects of different rearing environments on the genotype distribution of the two races be estimated.

Some combinations of models 1 and 2 may be found to account best for phenotypic variability within and between groups. The clear opposition of models 1 and 2 as explanations for the same IQ, racial, and social class data was presented to demonstrate the differential predictions that can be generated about proportions of genetic variance in different populations.

TWIN SAMPLE

An alphabetic roster of all students enrolled in the Philadelphia public schools in April 1968 was examined for children with the same last name, the same birth dates, and the same home address. Children who met the three criteria were identified as twins.

Of the 250,258 children in kindergarten through grade 12, 2042 were identified as twins, including 492 opposite-sex pairs and 1028 same-sex pairs.

The racial distribution of these twins was 26 percent white and 64 percent black. The corresponding figures for the entire public school population were 41 percent white and 59 percent black. The twins' racial distribution was discrepant from the total population by 5 percent, which can be accounted for by the substantially higher rate of fraternal twinning among blacks.[15]

In a large sample of twins it is tactically difficult to differentiate the monozygotic (identical) and dizygotic (fraternal) groups directly. Direct approaches to zygoity could be discarded in favor of the indirect, statistical approach, which is advocated by Burt,[3]

Vandenberg, Sandon, and Husen.[16] The reasoning is as follows: the percentage of opposite-sex pairs is known in any complete population survey, and, obviously, all identical twins are same-sex pairs. By applying the Weinberg formula, the proportion of monozygotic twins can be easily obtained. There will always be approximately the same proportion of same-sex pairs as opposite-sex pairs because of the distribution of sexes. It is then a simple matter to estimate the percentage of monozygotic pairs as follows: 100 − 2 (percent of opposite-sex pairs) = percent of monozygotic pairs. Percentage estimates for monozygotic and dizygotic groups were done separately for each racial group.

Once the proportion of monozygotic and dizygotic twins is known, the correlations for same-sex and opposite-sex groups can be used to estimate the correlation coefficients for monozygotic and dizygotic twins within the same-sex sample. By converting correlation coefficients to z scores, the same-sex intraclass coefficient can be apportioned according to the percentages of monozygotic pairs in the same-sex group, so that:

$$r_{iss} = \frac{\% \ SS_{dz} (r_{ios}) + \% \ SS_{mz} (X)}{\% \ SS_{mz + dz}}$$

where r_{iss} = the coefficient of correlation between intelligence scores of same-sex twins within a social class;

$\% \ SS_{dz}$ = the percent of same-sex twins in the intraclass twin population that are dizygotic;

r_{ios} = the coefficient of correlation between intelligence scores of opposite-sex twins within a social class;

$\% \ SS_{mz}$ = the percent of same-sex twins in the intraclass twin population that are monozygotic;

$\% \ SS_{mz + dz}$ = the total percent of twins in the intraclass twin population that are same-sex pairs—both monozygotic and dizygotic;

and X = the coefficient of correlation between intelligence scores of the monozygotic twins in the intraclass twin population —this is the unknown to be solved for.

On the basis of seven independent studies including more than 1000 pairs of same-sex and 100 pairs of opposite-sex twins, Burt[3] found the average correlations for intelligence to be .76 and .57, respectively. From these coefficients, he was able to estimate the correlation for monozygotic and dizygotic groups at .89 and .56, respectively. These estimates match very closely the correlations found for intelligence in samples of monozygotic and dizygotic twins whose zygosity had been determined by blood-grouping procedures.

In the Philadelphia sample, 30 percent of the white pairs and 34 percent of the black pairs were found to be of opposite sexes. Therefore, by the Weinberg formula, 40 percent of the whites and 32 percent of the blacks were estimated to by monozygotic pairs. The higher proportion of monozygotic twins in the white population matched the figures reported[16] for a complete age-group of British children taking the 11 + examinations.

The final samples were considerably smaller than the original 1521 pairs found, for several reasons. First, since standardized tests were not administered to the kindergarten or first-grade groups, 282 pairs were lost. Second, one or both members of 124 pairs were found to be enrolled in special classes, to whom the test used in this study were not given. Third, the absence of one or

Table 1
FINAL SAMPLE PAIRS BY RACE AND TEST SCORES

Test scores	Black	White
Aptitude only	315	194
Achievement only	129	75
Aptitude and achievement	191	88
Total pairs	635	357

both twins on the days that tests were administered eliminated an additional 123 pairs. Combined losses of 529 pairs with aptitude or acheivement scores, or both, for each twin, as shown in Table 1.

SOCIAL CLASS MEASURES

Within both the black and white groups, social class variables were used to assign pairs to relatively advantaged and disadvantaged groups. The public school data on parental occupation, income, and education were incomplete and too unreliable for these purposes. Instead, census tract information from the 1960 U.S. Census was used.

Every pair had a census tract designation for which median income and educational data were available. Although census tracts in an urban area are designed to provide maximum homogeneity within tracts, they are still imperfect measures of individual SES (socioeconomic status) characteristics. Relatively advantaged and disadvantaged groups could be designated by neighborhood SES, however, since peer associations and school characteristics would be reflected in the census tract data. To the extent that the social disadvantage hypothesis pertains to the life-style, in addition to within-family environment, the census tract data were appropriate.

Social-class assignment was made by establishing a median level of income and educational characteristics for the total number of census tracts from which the twin sample was drawn, regardless of race. Cross-tabulations of above- and below-median levels of income and education provided three groups: one below the census tract medians for both income and education; one above the median of both; and a third above in one and below in the other. On this basis, the three groups were designated as below median, above median, and middle status.

APTITUDE AND ACHIEVEMENT TESTS

Results from several tests were available in the 1968–69 school year for children in the Philadelphia school district from second through twelfth grade.[17] All children in grades three through eight who were in regular academic classrooms were given the Iowa Tests of Basic Skills, which test long-term development of intellectual skills.[18] These are highly reliable group tests[19] that are used to measure scholastic achievement in many school districts across the nation.

Since a different aptitude test was given in every second school grade, it was impossible to obtain a sufficiently large number of pairs for reliable test-by-test results. It was decided, therefore, to combine aptitude test results across tests and age ranges, and to treat them as age-appropriate, equivalent forms of the same test. This radical decision was based primarily on the roughly equivalent structure of the aptitude tests. All have at least two principal subtests, a verbal and a nonverbal (or numerical), as well as a total score. Some tests, such as the Differential Abilities Test, have additional subtests to measure spatial, mechanical, and other abilities not included in more scholastically-oriented tests, such as the School and College Ability Tests. Thus, the total scores based on all subtests are not strictly equivalent; nor are the nonverbal tests, which may be based primarily on arithmetic reasoning or may include abstract reasoning as well. The verbal scores are the most nearly equivalent from test to test, and thus are the most reliable for comparisons across grades.

No a priori assumptions were made about the appropriateness of standardized aptitude tests for different social-class and racial groups. Although there exists a popular notion that standardized tests are less predictive of scholastic achievement in disadvantaged groups, this has generally been unsupported by research.[20] This hypothesis was tested, however, by examining the correlations between aptitude and achievement scores for each racial and social-class group.

Since the generalizations were never intended to exceed the limits of aptitude test and IQ scores, no extensive discussion of the epistemological issue, "What do IQ tests measure?" will be attempted here. Suffice it to say that variance in IQ and aptitude test scores have been shown to have strong genetic components in other studies of white populations, and that the appropriateness of these measures for other racial and social-class samples will be considered later in this report.

DISTRIBUTION OF SCORES

An initial look at the distribution of scores within the samples of twins from Philadelphia indicated that the scores were far from normal. The low mean value, especially in the black population, and the skew of the distributions required careful normalization of the scores before any heritability analyses could be attempted. Thus, the results are reported in three sections: first, the distributions of scores and their transformations; second, the analyses of data on twins; and third, the heritability and estimated proportions of variance in the scores by race and social class.

The distributions of aptitude scores, based on national norms were divided first by race and then by race and social class. The means and standard deviations of the scores were markedly different by race; the mean aptitude scores of whites were slightly below the national mean of 50, while the mean aptitude scores of blacks were one standard deviation below the national mean. There was almost one standard deviation between the means of the two races (Table 2).

On measures of aptitude, the racial groups had surprisingly large differences, once social class was considered (Table 3). The mean of the below-median white group equalled or surpassed the mean of the above-median black children on verbal, nonverbal, and total aptitude scores. The social-class divisions among whites separated the aptitude means of the subpopulations by approximately four-fifths of a standard deviation. The comparable divisions among blacks produced a difference on one-quarter of a standard deviation between children below and above the medians for the 280 census tracts in which the twins lived.

Table 2

MEANS AND STANDARD DEVIATIONS (σ) OF NATIONAL SCORES FOR INDIVIDUALS BY RACE.

Aptitude test	Black (N = 1006)		White (N = 560)	
	Mean	σ	Mean	σ
Verbal	30.3	18.2	45.9	21.2
Nonverbal	32.7	19.1	47.9	21.8
Total	28.9	18.5	46.1	20.8

Table 3

MEAN AND STANDARD DEVIATIONS (σ) OF NATIONAL SCORES ON COMBINED APTITUDE TESTS FOR INDIVIDUALS BY RACE AND SOCIAL CLASS (Q INDICATES QUARTILE).

Statistics	Black			White		
	Below (N = 634)	Middle (N = 236)	Above (N = 134)	Below (N = 114)	Middle (N = 106)	Above (N = 340)
			Verbal			
Mean	29.0	30.9	35.3	36.4	43.9	49.8
σ	(17.7)	(17.2)	(20.8)	(18.6)	(22.6)	(20.4)
Q	15-28-39	19-31-43	23-32-46	22-38-50	28-42-56	38-41-63
			Nonverbal			
Mean	32.0	32.7	35.9	38.3	44.5	52.2
σ	(19.2)	(18.7)	(19.3)	(18.0)	(22.5)	(21.5)
Q	17-32-44	20-32-46	20-34-50	25-39-50	29-43-59	36-51-68
			Total			
Mean	27.7	29.7	33.0	34.8	43.4	50.9
σ	(18.1)	(18.1)	(20.3)	(16.9)	(21.4)	(20.2)
Q	15-26-39	15-30-41	19-29-47	23-37-47	29-42-56	38-52-65

Table 4

Intercorrelations of test scores by race and social class [nonverbal (NV), total (T), vocabulary (Vo), reading (R), language (L), arithmetic (A), composite (C)]

Black

Test	Aptitude		Total	Achievement			
	Verbal	Non-verbal		Vocabulary	Reading	Language	Arithmetic
Below-median group (N=351)							
NV	.57						
T	.84	.87					
Vo	.56	.44	.54				
R	.56	.47	.59	.64			
L	.59	.54	.64	.67	.67		
A	.53	.58	.62	.57	.66	.67	
C	.64	.57	.67	.82	.84	.86	.83
Middle Group (N=125)							
NV	.71						
T	.90	.89					
Vo	.54	.47	.56				
R	.64	.56	.66	.66			
L	.67	.54	.65	.66	.75		
A	.60	.53	.60	.64	.72	.73	
C	.70	.59	.70	.83	.89	.90	.85
Above-median group (N=51)							
NV	.53						
T	.82	.86					
Vo	.60	.35	.53				
R	.62	.56	.68	.71			
L	.68	.55	.71	.74	.87		
A	.55	.65	.68	.61	.81	.77	
C	.67	.57	.71	.83	.94	.93	.87

White

Test	Aptitude		Total	Achievement			
	Verbal	Non-verbal		Vocabulary	Reading	Language	Arithmetic
Below-median group (N=60)							
NV	.44						
T	.81	.83					
Vo	.53	-.04	.31				
R	.62	.30	.51	.61			
L	.76	.28	.61	.69	.79		
A	.67	.37	.59	.58	.77	.79	
C	.75	.26	.58	.81	.87	.92	.89
Middle group (N=43)							
NV	.57						
T	.88	.85					
Vo	.81	.49	.71				
R	.84	.59	.79	.88			
L	.71	.51	.69	.75	.85		
A	.60	.52	.63	.64	.71	.77	
C	.78	.61	.77	.86	.93	.94	.85
Above-median group (N=147)							
NV	.66						
T	.81	.88					
Vo	.71	.49	.59				
R	.68	.53	.60	.78			
L	.69	.61	.66	.73	.74		
A	.70	.70	.74	.66	.71	.78	
C	.77	.64	.72	.87	.90	.88	.87

Social-class groups of children were far more differentiated among whites than among blacks, despite the same criteria for assignment.

Comparisons across racial groups showed that disadvantaged white children scored in a pattern similar to that of black children, while the middle and above-median white groups had much higher means. Variances were not reliably different across races.

Compared to the national distribution, the twins in Philadelphia scored poorly. Instead of mean scores of 50, all black groups and white groups of below-median and middle status had mean performance scores in the 20 to 40 range. Only the above-median whites had mean scores close to the national average. A comparison of the means and variances of the twins' scores with those of all Philadelphia children showed that the twins were indeed representative of their respective racial and social-class groups, and were only slightly handicapped by their twinship.

Since the scores based on national norms were skewed with the Philadelphia samples, the scores for each test were normalized, separately by racial groups, to a mean of 50 and a standard deviation of 10, in order to develop comparable data for blacks and whites. Since the means and variances of the two racial groups were arbitarily set as equal, there were no longer any differences based on race in the distributions of scores. In every test, there were significant social-class differences and significant class-by-race interaction terms, which reflected the fact that social-class differences in mean scores were much greater among whites than blacks.

Correlational analyses of all test scores by race and social class were done to examine the equivalence of measurement among groups. Correlations among aptitude and achievement scores were substantial and quite similar in all groups, regardless of race or social class (Table 4). It is difficult to argue that the dimensions of performance measured in the different racial and social-class groups were not comparable. The most parsimonious explanation of similar patterns of correlations is that there are similar underlying dimensions. It is impossible to argue that "nothing" is being measured by these tests in disadvantaged groups, because the prediction from aptitude to achievement

scores is approximately as good in the below-median as in the middle black groups, and is certainly as good in the black groups as it is in the white groups.

ANALYSES OF TWINS BY RACE AND SOCIAL CLASS

It was hypothesized in model 1 that social-class conditions of life would affect twin similarities and resulting estimates of genetic variances. The potentially restricting effects of lower-class life on the development of genetically-based individual differences could tend to reduce within-pair correlation coefficients in the lower-class groups, whereas better environmental opportunities could allow a greater range of phenotypic individual differences in the middle-class groups. Model 2 predicted that similar proportions of genetic variance would be found across social-class groups because mean differences in scores were assumed to arise from differences in genotype distributions.

In the below-median SES groups of both races, the same-sex correlation exceeded the opposite-sex coefficient only once (black verbal aptitude). The failure of same-sex correlations to exceed opposite-sex coefficients left the estimated monozygotic correlations and heritability statistics indeterminant. It is unlikely that the correlations for monozygotic twins were lower than those for the same-sex dizygotic twins, but it is senseless to assign a value when r_{ios} is greater than r_{iss}. The most likely interpretation of this result is that the greater genetic correlation between monozygotic twins was not sufficient to increase the same-sex correlations above the values obtained for opposite-sex twins. Thus, genetic factors cannot be seen as strong determinants of aptitude scores in the disadvantaged groups of either race.

In the middle- to above-median SES groups, the same-sex correlations exceeded the opposite-sex correlations for all three aptitude scores in both races. The most likely inference from these data is that both genetic and environmental components of variance contributed to the similarity of within-pair scores in the advantaged group. For the disadvantaged group, the failure of same-sex correlations to exceed opposite-sex coefficients makes it doubtful that the proportion of genetic variance in the lower-class group equals that of the advantaged group.

Total variance was generally larger in the advantaged than in the disadvantaged groups of both races. This finding reflects the great phenotypic variability of advantaged children, as predicted in model 1. The intraclass correlations were found to be comparable for blacks and whites within social classes.

As noted earlier, the proportion of genetic variance in disadvantaged groups was low but indeterminant, except for verbal aptitude among blacks. Aptitude scores in advantaged groups all showed heritability estimates of greater than zero, except in the nonverbal scores of whites. Verbal aptitude scores which were most comparable from test to test had the highest heritability for both blacks and whites.

The aptitude tests sampled in Philadelphia showed moderate heritabilities of 27 to 72 percent of the total variance in advantaged populations and practically no heritable variance in the disadvantaged populations. The heritabilities of aptitude scores reported in this study apply only to the tests used and to these populations, not to other tests administered to other groups in other ways.

MEAN SCORES AND GENETIC VARIANCE

The lower mean scores of disadvantaged children of both races can be explained in large part by the lower genetic variance in these scores. A "deprived" or unfavorable environment for the development of phenotypic IQ unfavorably affects mean scores, phenotypic variability, genetic variance in phenotypes, and the expression of individual differences.[14] No study of human family correlations to date has looked at all of these effects of suppressive environments. In a landmark study of mice, however, Henderson[5] has demonstrated that suppressive environments reduce the amount of genetic variance in performance, reduce phenotypic variability, and reduce mean performance scores. The percentage of genetic variance in the scores of standard-cage-reared animals was one-fourth that of animals with enriched environments (10 percent versus 40 percent). Not only did genetic variance account for a larger portion of the variance among animals with enriched environments, but their performance on the learning task was vastly superior to that of their relatively deprived littermates.

Although generalizations from genetic studies of the behavior of mice to genetic studies of the behavior of human beings are generally unwarranted (because mechanisms of development vary greatly among species), the role that a better rearing environment played in the development of genetic individual differences among Henderson's mice finds an obvious parallel with the effects of advantaged SES homes in this study.

From studies of middle-class white populations, investigators have reached the conclusion that genetic variability accounts for about 75 percent of the total variance in IQ scores of whites. A closer look at children reared under different conditions shows that the percentage of genetic variance and the mean scores are very much a function of the rearing conditions of the population. A first look at the black population suggests that genetic variability is important in advantaged groups, but much less important in the disadvantaged. Since most blacks are socially disadvantaged, the proportion of genetic variance in the aptitude scores of black children is considerably less than that of the white children, as predicted by model 1.

"Disadvantage" has been used as a term throughout this paper to connote all of the biological and social deficits associated with poverty, regardless of race. As long as these environmental factors were considered to be the same, and to act in the same way on children of both races, then racial differences in scores could be discussed. Unquantified environmental differences between the races—either different factors or the same factors acting in different ways—preclude cross-racial comparisons. Informed speculation is not out of order at this point, however.

Those cultural differences between races that affect the relevance of home experience to scholastic aptitudes and achievement may be of primary importance in understanding the remaining racial differences in scores, once environmental deficits have been accounted for. In a series of studies of African children's scholastic performance, Irvine found that many sources of variation that are important for European and American scores are irrelevant for African children (21, p. 93).

Of environmental variables studied in population samples, including socio-economic status, family size, family position, and school quality, only school quality showed significant and consistent relation to ability and attainment tests. Other sources of variation were irrelevant to the skills being learned.

For the black child in Philadelphia, the relevance of extrascholastic experience is surely greater than it is for the tribal African. But one may question the equivalence of black and white cultural environments in their support for the development of scholastic aptitudes. As many authors of an environmental persuasion have indicated,[4,22] the black child learns a different, not a deficient, set of language rules, and he may learn a different style of thought. The transfer of training from home to school performance is probably less direct for black children than for white children.

The hypothesis of cultural differences in no way detracts from the predictive validity of aptitude tests for the scholastic achievement of black children. The correlations between aptitude and achievement are equally good in both racial groups. But the cultural differences hypothesis does speak to the issue of genetic and environmental components of variance. If most black children have limited experience with environmental features that contribute to the development of scholastic skills, then genetic variation will not be as prominent a source of individual phenotypic variation; nor will other between-family differences, such as SES level, be as important as they are in a white population. School-related experiences will be proportionately more important for black children than for white children in the development of scholastic aptitudes. The Coleman report[23] suggested that scholastic environment does have more influence on the performance of black children than it does on the performance of white children. The generally lower scores of black children can be fit adequately to the model 1 hypothesis, with the additional interpretation of cultural differences to account for the lower scores of black children at each social-class level.

The differences in mean IQ between the races can be affected by giving young black children rearing environments that are more conducive to the development of scholastic aptitudes. Or the differences in performance can simply be accepted as differences, and not as deficits. If there are alternate ways of being successful within the society, then differences can be valued variations on the human theme,[24] regardless of their environmental or genetic origins. Haldane[25] has suggested that, ideally, different human genotypes would be found to respond most favorably to different environmental conditions—that genotype-environment interactions would exist for many human characteristics. From a genetic point of view, varied adaptations are useful to the species and permit the greatest flowering of individual differences. Socially invidious comparisons, however, can destroy the usefulness of such differences.

It remains for us to discover the genetic mechanisms and pathways that determine individual patterns of development, and to combine that knowledge with varied environmental strategies to enhance the development of all children. In education and in psychology we give lipservice to individual differences. Yet, our research techniques and statistics highlight central tendencies. Since we know that genotypic and experiential factors combine to produce individual differences in development, we must adopt research strategies that explore the origins of those differences.

It is critical to remember that individual children are the reality to be explained, not the error term in an experimental analysis of average scores.

REFERENCES

[1] J. Hirsch in *Intelligence*, R. Cancro, Ed. (Grune & Stratton, New York), p. 95.

[2] K. Riegel, *Psychological Bulletin*, in press.

[3] L. Erlenmeyer-Kimling and L.F. Jarvik, *Science*, 142, 1477 (1963); S.G. Vandenberg, in *Genetics*, D. Glass, Ed. (Rockefeller Univ. Press, New York, 1968), pp. 3–58; *Acta Genet. Med. Gemellol.* 19, 280 (1970). C. Burt, *Brit. J. Psychol.* 57, 137 (1966). A.R. Jensen, *Harv. Educ. Rev.* 39, 1 (1969a). ———. in *Disadvantaged Child*, J. Hellmuth, Ed. (Brunner-Mazel, New York, 1970), vol. 3, pp. 124–257.

[4] T.F. Pettigrew, *A Profile of the Negro American* (van Nostrand, Princeton, N.J., 1964). S. Baratz and J. Baratz, *Harv. Educ. Rev.* 40, 29 (1970).

[5] M. Manosevitz, G. Lindzey, D. Thiessen, *Behavioral Genetics: Methods and Research* (Ap-

pleton-Century-Crofts, New York, 1969). N. Henderson, *J. Comp. Physiol. Psychol.* 3, 505 (1970).

[6]I. Gottesman in *Handbook of Mental Deficiency: Psychological Theory and Research*, N. Ellis, Ed. (McGraw-Hill, New York, 1963), pp. 253-295; F. Weizmann, *Science* 171, 589 (1971). I. Gottesman, in *Social Class, Race, and Psychological Development*, M. Deutsch, I. Katz, A. Jensen, Eds. (Holt, Rinehart & Winston, New York, 1968), pp. 11-51. C.V. Kiser, *Eugen. Quart.* 15, 98 (1968).

[7]A genotype is the genetic makeup of an individual. The term may refer to one, several, or all loci. Genetic variance refers to the differences among individuals that arise from differences in genotypes. A phenotype is the sum total of all observable characteristics of an individual. Phenotypic variance refers to the observable differences among individuals.

[8]H. Birch and J. Gussow, Disadvantaged Children: *Health, Nutrition and School Failure* (Harcourt, Brace & World, New York, 1970).

[9]M. Deutsch, I. Katz, A. Jensen, Eds., *Social Class, Race and Psychological Development* (Holt, Rinehart & Winston, New York, 1968).

[10]C. Burt, *Brit. J. Statist. Psychol.* 14, 3 (1961). R. Herrnstein *Atl. Mon.* 228, 43 (September 1971).

[11]J. Waller, thesis, University of Minnesota (1970).

[12]M. Skodak and H. Skeels, *J. Genet. Psychol.* 75, 85 (1949).

[13]Suppressive environments are those which do not permit or evoke the development of genetic characteristics. "Suppose, for example, that early experience in the manipulation of objects is essential for inducing hoarding behavior. Genetic differences in this form of behavior will not be detected in animals reared without such experience". J.L. Fuller and W.R. Thompson, *Behavior Genetics* (Wiley, New York, 1960), p. 65.

[14]The genotype-phenotype correlation is generally expressed as the square root of the heritability of a characteristic in a given population

$$(r_{pg} = \sqrt{h^2}).$$

[15]H. Strandskov and E. Edelen, *Genetics*, 31, 438 (1946).

[16]S.G. Vandenberg, quoted in C. Burt (3). F. Sandon, *Brit. J. Statist. Psychol.* 12, 133 (1959). T. Husen, *Psychological Twin Research* (Almquist and Wiksele, Stockholm, 1959).

[17]Aptitude tests used in this study are Primary Mental Abilities (2nd grade): *verbal meaning, perceptual speech, *number facility, spatial relations, and *total; Lorge-Thorndike Intelligence Tests (4th grade): *verbal, *non-verbal, and *total; Academic Promise Tests (6th grade): abstract reasoning, numerical, *nonverbal total, language usage, verbal, *verbal total, and *total; Differential Abilities Tests (8th grade): *verbal reasonings, *numerical ability, abstract reasoning, space relations, mechanical reasoning, clerical speed and accuracy, language usage, and *total (scholastic aptitude); School and College Ability Tests (10th grade): *verbal, *quantitative, and *total; Test of Academic Progress (12th grade): *verbal, *numerical, and *total. Achievement tests used are Iowa Tests of Basic Skills (3rd through 8th grades): *vocabulary, *reading comprehension, *language total, work-study skills, *arithmetic total, and *composite (average of five scores). Asterisks indicate scores reported.

[18]H. Stevenson, A. Friedrichs, W. Simpson, *Child Develop.* 41, 625 (1970).

[19]O. Buros, Ed. *The Sixth Mental Measurements Yearbook* (Gryphon Press Highland Park, N.J., 1965).

[20]J. Stanley, *Science* 171, 640 (1971).

[21]S. Irvine, *J. Biosoc. Sci.* 1 (Suppl.), 91 (1969).

[22]S. Houston, *Child Develop.* 41, 947 (1970); F. Williams, in *Language and Poverty*, F. Williams, Ed. (Markham, Chicago, 1970), pp. 1–10; C. Cazden, ibid., pp. 81–101.

[23]U.S. Commission on Civil Rights, *Racial Isolation in the Public Schools* (Government Printing Office, Washington, D.C., 1967).

[24]D. Freedman, in *Progress in Human Behavior Genetics*, S.G. Vandenburg, ed. (Johns Hopkins Press, Baltimore, 1968), pp. 1–5.

[25]J.B.S. Haldane *Ann. Eugen.* 13, 197 (1946).

35

BOOK REVIEWS: UNKNOWNS IN THE IQ EQUATION
Sandra Scarr-Salapatek

One might have expected that the professional scholars would have risen in unanimous opposition to the gambit promoted by Jensen. While the majority has indeed done so, there has been a surprising amount of support for him from various quarters. The legacy of typological racism in the intelligence testing movement remains strong and represents the continuation of the idea, promoted by Sir Francis Galton a century ago and his followers Karl Pearson in England and G. Stanley Hall in America, that intelligence is a fixed entity determined by heredity (see the excellent critique of this idée fixe by Hunt 1972). Prominent among the current supporters of Jensen's approach are Stanford engineer, William Shockley (noted for his role in the invention of the transistor), and psychologists H. J. Eysenck and Richard Herrnstein. No one is better qualified to comment on the recently published major claims than Dr. Scarr-Salapatek whose review is reprinted here.

The controversy continues and the flood of books and articles is clearly just getting under way (Brace, Gamble, and Bond 1971; Cunningham 1972; Hunt 1972; Richardson, Spears, and Richards 1972).

Brace, C. L., G. R. Gamble, and J. T. Bond (eds.). 1971. *Race and Intelligence.* Anthropological Studies No. 8. American Anthropological Association, Washington, D.C. 75 pp.

Cunningham, Michael. 1972. *Intelligence: Its Organization and Development.* Academic Press, N.Y. 174 pp.

Hunt, J. McVicker (ed.). 1972. *Human Intelligence.* transaction books. New Brunswick, N.J. 283 pp.

―――. 1972. The role of experience in the development of competence. *In* J. McVicker Hunt (ed.) *Human Intelligence.* transaction books. New Brunswick, N.J. pp. 30–52.

Richardson, K., D. Spears, and M. Richards (eds.). 1972. *Race and Intelligence: The Fallacies Behind the Race-IQ Controversy.* Penguin, Baltimore. 206 pp.

Environment, Heredity, and Intelligence. Compiled from the *Harvard Educational Review.* Reprint Series No. 2. Harvard Educational Review, Cambridge, Mass., 1969. iv, 248 pp., illus. Paper, $4.95.

The IQ Argument. Race, Intelligence and Education. H. J. Eysenck. Library Press, New York, 1971. iv, 156 pp., illus. $5.95.

IQ. Richard Herrnstein, in the *Atlantic,* Vol. 228, No. 3, Sept. 1971, pp. 44–64.

IQ scores have been repeatedly estimated to have a large heritable component in United States and Northern European white populations (1). Individual differences in IQ,

From *Science 174* (17 December 1971): 1223–1228. Copyright 1971 by the American Association for the Advancement of Science. Reprinted by permission of the author and publisher.

many authors have concluded, arise far more from genetic than from environmental differences among people in these populations, at the present time, and under present environmental conditions. It has also been known for many years that white lower-class and black groups have lower IQ's, on the average, than white middle-class groups. Most behavioral scientists comfortably "explained" these group differences by appealing to obvious environmental differences between the groups in standards of living, educational opportunities, and the like. But recently an explosive controversy has developed over the heritability of between-group differences in IQ, the question at issue being: If individual differences within the white population as a whole can be attributed largely to heredity, is it not plausible that the average differences between social-class groups and between racial groups also reflect significant genetic differences? Can the former data be used to explain the latter?

To propose genetically based racial and social-class differences is anathema to most behavioral scientists, who fear any scientific confirmation of the pernicious racial and ethnic prejudices that abound in our society. But now that the issue has been openly raised, and has been projected into the public context of social and educational policies, a hard scientific look must be taken at what is known and at what inferences can be drawn from that knowledge.

The public controversy began when A. R. Jensen, in a long paper in the *Harvard Educational Review*, persuasively juxtaposed data on the heritability of IQ and the observed differences between groups. Jensen suggested that current large-scale educational attempts to raise the IQ's of lower-class children, white and black, were failing because of the high heritability of IQ. In a series of papers and rebuttals to criticism, in the same journal and elsewhere (2), Jensen put forth the hypothesis that social-class and racial differences in mean IQ were due largely to differences in the distributions of these populations. At least, he said, the genetic-differences hypothesis was no less likely, and probably more likely, than a simple environmental hypothesis to explain the mean difference of 15 IQ points between blacks and whites (3) and the even larger average IQ differences between professionals and manual laborers within the white population.

Jensen's articles have been directed primarily at an academic audience. Herrnstein's article in the *Atlantic* and Eysenck's book (first published in England) have brought the argument to the attention of the wider lay audience. Both Herrnstein and Eysenck agree with Jensen's genetic-differences hypothesis as it pertains to individual differences and to social-class groups, but Eysenck centers his attention on the genetic explanation of racial-group differences, which Herrnstein only touches on. Needless to say, many other scientists will take issue with them.

EYSENCK'S RACIAL THESIS

Eysenck has written a popular account of the race, social-class, and IQ controversy in a generally inflammatory book. The provocative title and the disturbing cover picture of a forlorn black boy are clearly designed to tempt the lay reader into a pseudo-battle between Truth and Ignorance. In this case Truth is genetic-environmental interactionism (4) and Ignorance is naive environmentalism. For the careful reader, the battle fades out inconclusively as Eysenck admits that scientific evidence to date does not permit a clear choice of the genetic-differences interpretation of black inferiority on intelligence tests. A quick reading of the book, however, is sure to leave the reader believing that scientific evidence today strongly supports the conclusion that U.S. blacks are genetically inferior to whites in IQ.

The basic theses of the book are as follows:

1. IQ is a highly heritable characteristic in the U.S. white population and probably equally heritable in the U.S. black population.
2. On the average, blacks score considerably lower than whites on IQ tests.
3. U.S. blacks are probably a non-random, lower-IQ, sample of native African populations.
4. The average IQ difference between blacks and whites probably represents important genetic differences between the races.
5. Drastic environmental changes will have to be made to improve the poor phenotypes that U.S. blacks now achieve.

The evidence and nonevidence that Eysenck cites to support his genetic hypothesis of racial differences make a curious assortment. Audrey Shuey's review (5) of hundreds of studies showing mean phenotypic differences between black and white IQ's leads Eysenck to conclude:

All the evidence to date suggests the strong and indeed overwhelming importance of genetic factors in producing the great variety of intellectual differences which we observe in our culture, and much of the difference observed between certain racial groups. This evidence cannot be argued away by niggling and very minor criticisms of details which do not really throw doubts on the major points made in this book [p. 126].

To "explain" the genetic origins of these mean IQ differences he offers these suppositions:

White slavers wanted dull beasts of burden, ready to work themselves to death in the plantations, and under those conditions intelligence would have been counterselective. Thus there is every reason to expect that the particular sub-sample of the Negro race which is constituted of American Negroes is not an unselected sample of Negroes, but has been selected throughout history according to criteria which would put the highly intelligent at a disadvantage. The inevitable outcome of such selection would of course be a gene pool lacking some of the genes making for higher intelligence [p. 42].

Other ethnic minorities in the U.S. are also, in his view, genetically inferior, again because of the selective migration of lower IQ genotypes:

It is known [sic] that many other groups came to the U.S.A. due to pressures which made them very poor samples of the original populations. Italians, Spaniards, and Portuguese, as well as Greeks, are examples where the less able, less intelligent were forced through circumstances to emigrate, and where their American progeny showed significantly lower IQ's than would have been shown by a random sample of the original population [p. 43].

Although Eysenck is careful to say that these are not established facts (because no IQ tests were given to the immigrants or nonimmigrants in question?), the tone of his writing leaves no doubt about his judgment. There is something in this book to insult almost everyone except WASP's and Jews.

Despite his conviction that U.S. blacks are genetically inferior in IQ to whites, Eysenck is optimistic about the potential effects of radical environmental changes on the present array of Negro IQ phenotypes. He points to the very large IQ gains produced by intensive one-to-one tutoring of black urban children with low-IQ mothers, contrasting large environmental changes and large IQ gains in intensive programs of this sort with insignificant environmental improvements and small IQ changes obtained by Headstart and related programs. He correctly observes

that, whatever the heritability of IQ (or, it should be added, of any characteristic), large phenotypic changes may be produced by creating appropriate, radically different environments never before encountered by those genotypes. On this basis, Eysenck calls for further research to determine the requisites of such environments.

Since Eysenck comes to this relatively benign position regarding potential improvement in IQ's, why, one may ask, is he at such pains to "prove" the genetic inferiority of blacks? Surprisingly, he expects that new environments, such as that provided by intensive educational tutoring, will not affect the black-white IQ differential, because black children and white will probably profit equally from such treatment. Since many middle-class white children already have learning environments similar to that provided by tutors for the urban black children, we must suppose that Eysenck expects great IQ gains from relatively small changes in white, middle-class environments.

This book is an uncritical popularization of Jensen's ideas without the nuances and qualifiers that make much of Jensen's writing credible or at least responsible. Both authors rely on Shuey's review (5), but Eysenck's way of doing it is to devote some 25 pages to quotes and paraphrases of her chapter summaries. For readers to whom the original Jensen article is accessible, Eysenck's book is a poor substitute; although he defends Jensen and Shuey, he does neither a service.

It is a maddeningly inconsistent book filled with contradictory caution and incaution; with hypotheses stated both as hypotheses and as conclusions; with both accurate and inaccurate statements on matters of fact. For example, Eysenck thinks evoked potentials offer a better measure of "innate" intelligence than IQ tests. But on what basis? Recently F. B. Davis (6) has failed to find any relationship whatsoever between evoked potentials and either IQ scores or scholastic achievement, to which intelligence is supposed to be related. Another example is Eysenck's curious use of data to support a peculiar line of reasoning about the evolutionary inferiority of blacks: First, he reports that African and U.S. Negro babies have been shown to have precocious sensorimotor development by white norms (the difference, by several accounts, appears only in gross motor skills and even there is slight). Second, he notes that by three years of age U.S. white exceed U.S. black children in mean IQ scores. Finally he cites a (very slight) negative correlation, found in an early study, between sensorimotor intelligence in the first year of life and later IQ. From exaggerated statements of these various data, he concludes:

These findings are important because of a very general view in biology according to which the more prolonged the infancy the greater in general are the cognitive or intellectual abilities of the species. This law appears to work even within a given species [p. 79].

Eysenck would apparently have us believe that Africans and their relatives in the U.S. are less highly evolved than Caucasians, whose longer infancy is related to later higher intelligence. I am aware of no evidence whatsoever to support a within-species relationship between longer infancy and higher adult capacities.

The book is carelessly put together, with no index; few references, and those not keyed to the text; and long, inadequately cited quotes that carry over several pages without clear beginnings and ends. Furthermore, considering the gravity of Eysenck's theses, the book has an occasional jocularity of tone that is offensive. A careful book on the genetic hypothesis, written for a lay audience, would have merited publication. This one, however, has been publicly disowned as irresponsible by the entire editorial staff of its London publisher, New Society. But never mind, the American publisher has used that and other condemnations to balance the accolades and make its advertisement (7) of the book more titillating.

HERRNSTEIN'S SOCIAL THESIS

Thanks to Jensen's provocative article, many academic psychologists who thought IQ tests belonged in the closet with the Rorschach inkblots have now explored the psychometric literature and found it to be a trove of scientific treasure. One of these is Richard Herrnstein, who from a Skinnerian background has become an admirer of intelligence tests—a considerable leap from shaping the behavior of pigeons and rats. In contrast to Eysenck's book Herrnstein's popular account in the *Atlantic* of IQ testing and its values is generally responsible, if overly enthusiastic in parts.

Herrnstein unabashedly espouses IQ testing as "psychology's most telling accomplishment to date," despite the current controversy over the fairness of testing poor and minority-group children with IQ items devised by middle-class whites. His historical review of IQ test development, including tests of general intelligence and multiple abilities, is interesting and accurate. His account of the validity and usefulness of the tests centers on the fairly accurate prediction that can be made from IQ scores to academic and occupational acheivement and income level. He clarifies the pattern of relationship between IQ and these criterion variables: High IQ is a necessary but not sufficient condition for high achievement, while low IQ virtually assures failure at high academic and occupational levels. About the usefulness of the test, he concludes:

An IQ test can be given in an hour or two to a child, and from this infinitesimally small sample of his output, deeply important predictions follow—about schoolwork, occupation, income, satisfaction with life, and even life expectancy. The predictions are not perfect, for other factors always enter in, but no other single factor matters as much in as many spheres of life [p. 53].

One must assume that Herrnstein's enthusiasm for intelligence tests rests on population statistics, not on predictions for a particular child, because many children studied longitudinally have been shown to change IQ scores by 20 points or more from childhood to adulthood. It is likely that extremes of giftedness and retardation can be sorted out relatively early by IQ tests, but what about the 95 percent of the population in between? Their IQ scores may vary from dull to bright normal for many years. Important variations in IQ can occur up to late adolescence (8). On a population basis Herrnstein is correct; the best early predictors of later achievement are ability measures taken from age five on. Predictions are based on correlations, however, which are not sensitive to absolute changes in value, only to rank orders. This is an important point to be discussed later.

After reviewing the evidence for average IQ differences by social class and race, Herrnstein poses the nature-nurture problem of "which is primary" in determining phenotypic differences in IQ. For racial groups, he explains, the origins of mean IQ differences are indeterminate at the present time because we have no information from heritability studies in the black population or from other, unspecified, lines of research which could favor primarily genetic or primarily environmental hypotheses. He is thoroughly convinced, however, that individual differences and social-class differences in IQ are highly heritable at the present time, and are destined, by environmental improvements, to become even more so:

If we make the relevant environment much more uniform (by making it as good as we can for everyone), then an even larger proportion of the variation in IQ will be attributable to the genes. The average person would be smarter, but intelligence would run in families even more obviously and with less regression toward the mean than we see today [p. 58].

For Herrnstein, society is, and will be even more strongly, a meritocracy based largely on inherited differences in IQ. He presents a "syllogism" (p. 58) to make his message clear:

1. If differences in mental abilities are inherited, and
2. If success requires those abilities, and
3. If earnings and prestige depend on success,
4. Then social standing (which reflects earnings and prestige) will be based to some extent on inherited differences among people.

Five "corollaries" for the future predict that the heritability of IQ will rise; that social mobility will become more strongly related to inherited IQ differences; that most bright people will be gathered in the top of the social structure, with the IQ dregs at the bottom; that many at the bottom will not have the intelligence needed for new jobs; and that the meritocracy will be built not just on inherited intelligence but on all inherited traits affecting success, which will presumably become correlated characters. Thus from

the successful realization of our most precious, egalitarian, political and social goals there will arise a much more rigidly stratified society, a "virtual caste system" based on inborn ability.

To ameliorate this effect, society may have to move toward the socialist dictum, "From each according to his abilities, to each according to his needs," but Herrnstein sees complete equality of earnings and prestige as impossible because high-grade intelligence is scarce and must be recruited into those critical jobs that require it, by the promise of high earnings and high prestige. Although garbage collecting is critical to the health of the society, almost anyone can do it; to waste high-IQ persons on such jobs is to misallocate scarce resources at society's peril.

Herrnstein points to an ironic contrast between the effects of caste and class systems. Castes, which established artifical hereditary limits on social mobility, guarantee the inequality of opportunity that preserves IQ heterogeneity at all levels of the system. Many bright people are arbitrarily kept down and many unintelligent people are artificially maintained at the top. When arbitrary bounds on mobility are removed, as in our class system, most of the bright rise to the top and most of the dull fall to the bottom of the social system, and IQ differences between top and bottom become increasingly hereditary. The greater the environmental equality, the greater the hereditary differences between levels in the social structure. The thesis of egalitarianism surely leads to its antithesis in a way that Karl Marx never anticipated.

Herrnstein proposes that our best strategy, in the face of increasing biological stratification, is publicly to recognize genetic human differences but to reallocate wealth to a considerable extent. The IQ have-nots need not be poor. Herrnstein does not delve into the pyschological consequences of being publicly marked as genetically inferior.

Does the evidence support Herrnstein's view of hereditary social classes, now or in some future Utopia? Given his assumptions about the high heritability of IQ, the importance of IQ to social mobility, and the increasing environmental equality of rearing and opportunity, hereditary social classes are to some extent inevitable. But one can question the limits of genetic homogeneity in social-class groups and the evidence for his syllogism at present.

Is IQ as highly heritable throughout the social structure as Herrnstein assumes? Probably not. In a recent study of IQ heritability in various racial and social-class groups (9), I found much lower proportions of genetic variance that would account for aptitude differences among lower-class than among middle-class children, in both black and white groups. Social disadvantage in prenatal and postnatal development can substantially lower phenotypic IQ and reduce the genotype-phenotype correlation. Thus, average phenotypic IQ differences between the social classes may be considerably larger than the genotypic differences.

Are social classes largely based on hereditary IQ differences now? Probably not as much as Herrnstein believes. Since opportunities for social mobility act at the phenotypic level, there still may be considerable genetic diversity for IQ at the bottom of the social structure. In earlier days arbitrary social barriers maintained genetic variability throughout the social structure. At present, individuals with high phenotypic IQ's are often upwardly mobile; but inherited wealth acts to maintain genetic diversity at the top, and nongenetic biological and social barriers to phenotypic development act to maintain a considerable genetic diversity of intelligence in the lower classes.

As P. E. Vernon has pointed out (10), we are inclined to forget that the majority of gifted children in recent generations have come from working-class, not middle-class, families. A larger percentage of middle-class children are gifted, but the working and lower classes produce gifted children in larger numbers. How many more disadvantaged children would have been bright if they had had middle-class gestation and rearing conditions?

I am inclined to think that intergenerational class mobility will always be with us, for three reasons. First, since normal IQ is a polygenic characteristic, various recombinations of parental genotypes will always produce more variable genotypes in the offspring than in the parents of all social-class groups, especially the extremes. Even if both parents, instead of primarily the male, achieved social-class status based on their IQ's, recombinations of their genes would always produce a range of offspring, who would be upwardly or downwardly mobile relative to their families of origin.

Second, since, as Herrnstein acknowledges, factors other than IQ—motivational, personality, and undetermined—also contribute to success or the lack of it, high IQ's will always be found among lower-class adults, in combination with schizophrenia, alcoholism, drug addiction, psychopathy, and other limiting factors. When recombined in offspring, high IQ can readily segregate with facilitating motivational and personality characteristics, thereby leading to upward mobility for many offspring. Similarly, middle-class parents will always produce some offspring with debilitating personal characteristics which lead to downward mobility.

Third, for all children to develop phenotypes that represent their best genotypic outcome (in current environments) would require enormous changes in the present social system. To improve and equalize all rearing environments would involve such massive intervention as to make Herrnstein's view of the future more problematic than he seems to believe.

RACE AS CASTE

Races are castes between which there is very little mobility. Unlike the social-class system, where mobility based on IQ is sanctioned, the racial caste system, like the hereditary aristocracy of medieval Europe and the caste system of India, preserves within each group its full range of genetic diversity of intelligence. The Indian caste system was, according to Dobzhansky (11), a colossal genetic failure—or success, according to egalitarian values. After the abolition of castes at independence, Brahmins and untouchables were found to be equally educable despite—or because of—their many generations of segregated reproduction.

While we may tentatively conclude that there are some genetic IQ differences between social-class groups, we can make only wild speculations about racial groups. Average phenotypic IQ differences between races are not evidence for genetic differences (any more than they are evidence for environmental differences). Even if the heritabilities of IQ are extremely high in all races, there is still no warrant for equating within-group and between-group heritabilities (12). There are examples in agricultural experiments of within-group differences that are highly heritable but between-group differences that are entirely environmental. Draw two random samples of seeds from the same genetically heterogeneous population. Plant one sample in uniformly good conditions, the other in uniformly poor conditions. The average height difference between the populations of plants will be entirely environmental, although the individual differences in height within each sample will be entirely genetic. With known genotypes for seeds and known environments, genetic and environmental variances between groups can be studied. But racial groups are not random samples from the same population, nor are members reared in uniform conditions within each race. Racial groups are of unknown genetic equivalence for polygenic characteristics like IQ, and the differences in environments within and between the races may have as yet unquantified effects.

There is little to be gained from approaching the nature-nurture problem of race differences in IQ directly (13). Direct comparisons of estimated within-group heritabilities and the calculation of between-group heritabilities require assumptions that few investigators are willing to make, such as that all environmental differences are quantifiable, that differences in the environments of blacks and whites can be assumed to affect IQ in the same way in the two groups, and that differences in environments between groups can be "statistically controlled." A direct assault on race differences in IQ is vulnerable to many criticisms.

Indirect approaches may be less vulnerable. These include predictions of parent-child regression effects and admixture studies. Regression effects can be predicted to differ for blacks and whites if the two races indeed have genetically different population means. If the population mean for blacks is 15 IQ points lower than that of whites, then the offspring of high-IQ black parents should show greater regression (toward a lower population mean) than the offspring of whites of equally high IQ. Similarly, the offspring of low-IQ black parents should show less regression than those of white parents of equally low IQ. This hypothesis assumes that assortative mating for IQ is

equal in the two races, which could be empirically determined but has not been studied as yet. Interpretable results from a parent-child regression study would also depend upon careful attention to intergenerational environmental changes, which could be greater in one race than the other.

Studies based on correlations between degree of white admixture and IQ scores *within* the black group would avoid many of the pitfalls of between-group comparisons. If serological genotypes can be used to identify persons with more and less white admixture, and if estimates of admixture based on blood groups are relatively independent of visible characteristics like skin color, then any positive correlation between degree of admixture and IQ would suggest genetic racial differences in IQ. Since blood groups have not been used directly as the basis of racial discrimination, positive findings would be relatively immune from environmentalist criticisms. The trick is to estimate individual admixture reliably. Several loci which have fairly different distributions of alleles in contemporary African and white populations have been proposed (14). No one has yet attempted a study of this sort.

h² AND PHENOTYPE

Suppose that the heritabilities of IQ differences within all racial and social-class groups were .80, as Jensen estimates, and suppose that the children in all groups were reared under an equal range of conditions. Now, suppose that racial and social-class differences in mean IQ still remained. We would probably infer some degree of genetic difference between the groups. So what? The question now turns from a strictly scientific one to one of science and social policy.

As Eysenck, Jensen, and others (15) have noted, eugenic and euthenic strategies are both possible interventions to reduce the number of low-IQ individuals in all populations. Eugenic policies could be advanced to encourage or require reproductive abstinence by people who fall below a certain level of intelligence. The Reeds (15) have determined that one-fifth of the mental retardation among whites of the next generation could be prevented if no mentally retarded persons of this generation reproduced. There is no question that a eugenic program applied at the phenotypic level of parents' IQ would substantially reduce the number of low-IQ children in the future white population. I am aware of no studies in the black population to support a similar program, but some proportion of future retardation could surely be eliminated. It would be extremely important, however, to sort out genetic and environmental sources of low IQ both in racial and in social-class groups before advancing a eugenic program. The request or demand that some persons refrain from any reproduction should be a last resort, based on sure knowledge that their retardation is caused primarily by genetic factors and is not easily remedied by environmental intervention. Studies of the IQ levels of adopted children with mentally retarded natural parents would be most instructive, since some of the retardation observed among children of retarded parents may stem from the rearing environments provided by the parents.

In a pioneering study of adopted children and their adoptive and natural parents, Skodak (16) reported greater *correlations* of children's IQ's with their natural than with their adoptive parents' IQ's. This statement has been often misunderstood to mean that the children's *levels* of intelligence more closely resembled their natural parents' which is completely false. Although the rank order of the children's IQ's resembled that of their mothers' IQ's, the children's IQ's were higher, being distributed, like those of the adoptive parents, around a mean above 100, whereas their natural mothers' IQ's averaged only 85. The children, in fact, averaged 21 IQ points higher than their natural mothers. If the (unstudied) natural fathers' IQ's averaged around the population mean of 100, the mean of the children's would be expected to be 94, or 12 points lower than the mean obtained. The unexpected boost in IQ was presumably due to the better social environments provided by the adoptive families. Does this mean that phenotypic IQ can be substantially changed?

Even under existing conditions of child rearing, phenotypes of children reared by low-IQ parents could be markedly changed by giving them the same rearing environment as the top IQ group provide for their children. According to DeFries (17), if children whose parents average 20 IQ points below the population mean were reared in

environments such as usually are provided only by parents in the top .01 percent of the population, these same children would average 5 points *above* the population mean instead of 15 points below, as they do when reared by their own families.

Euthenic policies depend upon the demonstration that different rearing conditions can change phenotypic IQ sufficiently to enable most people in a social class or racial group to function in future society. I think there is great promise in this line of research and practice, although its efficacy will depend ultimately on the cost and feasibility of implementing radical intervention programs. Regardless of the present heritability of IQ in any population, phenotypes can be changed by the introduction of new and different environments. (One merit of Eysenck's book is the attention he gives to this point.) Furthermore, it is impossible to predict phenotypic outcomes under very different conditions. For example, in the Milwaukee Project (18), in which the subjects are ghetto children whose mothers' IQ's are less than 70, intervention began soon after the children were born. Over a four-year period Heber has intensively tutored the children for several hours every day and has produced an enormous IQ difference between the experimental group (mean IQ 127) and a control group (mean IQ 90). If the tutored children continue to advance in environments which are radically different from their homes with retarded mothers, we shall have some measure of the present phenotypic range of reaction (19) of children whose average IQ's might have been in the 80 to 90 range. These data support Crow's comment on h^2 in his contribution to the *Harvard Educational Review* discussion (p. 158):

It does not directly tell us how much improvement in IQ to expect from a given change in the environment. In particular, it offers no guidance as to the consequences of a new kind of environmental influence. For example, conventional heritability measures for height show a value of nearly 1. Yet, because of unidentified environmental influences, the mean height in the United States and in Japan has risen by a spectacular amount. Another kind of illustration is provided by the discovery of a cure for a hereditary disease. In such cases, any infor-

mation on prior heritability may become irrelevant. Furthermore, heritability predictions are less dependable at the tails of the distribution.

To illustrate the phenotypic changes that can be produced by radically different environments for children with clear genetic anomalies, Rynders (20) has provided daily intensive tutoring for Down's syndrome infants. At the age of two, these children have average IQ's of 85 while control-group children, who are enrolled in a variety of other programs, average 68. Untreated children have even lower average IQ scores.

The efficacy of intervention programs for children whose expected IQ's are too low to permit full participation in society depends on their long-term effects on intelligence. Early childhood programs may be necessary but insufficient to produce functioning adults. There are critical research questions yet to be answered about euthenic programs, including what kinds, how much, how long, how soon, and toward what goals?

DOES h² MATTER?

There is growing disillusionment with the concept of heritability, as it is understood and misunderstood. Some who understand it very well would like to eliminate h^2 from human studies for at least two reasons. First, the usefulness of h^2 estimates in animal and plant genetics pertains to decisions about the efficacy of selective breeding to produce more desirable phenotypes. Selective breeding does not apply to the human case, at least so far. Second, if important phenotypic changes can be produced by radically different environments, then, it is asked, who cares about the heritability of IQ? Morton (21) has expressed these sentiments well:

Considerable popular interest attaches to such questions as "is one class or ethnic group innately superior to another on a particular test?" The reasons are entirely emotional, since such a difference, if established, would serve as no better guide to provision of educational or other facilities than an unpretentious assessment of phenotypic differences.

I disagree. The simple assessment of phenotypic performance does not suggest any particular intervention strategy. Heritability estimates can have merit as indicators of the effects to be expected from various types of intervention programs. If, for example, IQ tests, which predict well to acheivements in the larger society, show low heritabilities in a population, then it is probable that simply providing better environments which now exist will improve above average performance in that population. If h^2 is high but environments sampled in that population are largely unfavorable, then (again) simple environmental improvement will probably change the mean phenotypic level. If h^2 is high and the environments sampled are largely favorable, then novel environmental manipulations are probably required to change phenotypes, and eugenic programs may be advocated.

The most common misunderstanding of the concept "heritability" relates to the myth of fixed intelligence: if h^2 is high, this reasoning goes, then intelligence is genetically fixed and unchangeable at the phenotypic level. This misconception ignores the fact that h^2 is a population statistic, bound to a given set of environmental conditions at a given point in time. Neither intelligence nor h^2 estimates are fixed.

It is absurd to deny that the frequencies of genes for behavior may vary between populations. For individual differences within populations, and for social-class differences, a genetic hypothesis is almost a necessity to explain some of the variance in IQ, especially among adults in contemporary white populations living in average or better environments. But what Jensen, Shuey, and Eysenck (and others) propose is that genetic racial differences are necessary to account for the current phenotypic differences in mean IQ between populations. That may be so, but it would be extremely difficult, given current methodological limitations, to gather evidence that would dislodge an environmental hypothesis to account for the same data. And to assert, despite the absence of evidence, and in the present social climate, that a particular race is genetically disfavored in intelligence is to scream "FIRE! . . . I think" in a crowded theater. Given that so little is known, further scientific study seems far more justifiable than public speculations.

REFERENCES AND NOTES

[1]For a review of studies, see L. Erlenmeyer-Kimling and L. F. Jarvik, *Science* 142, 1477 (1963). Heritability is the ratio of genetic variance to total phenotypic variance. For human studies, heritability is used in its broad sense of total genetic variance/total phenotypic variance.

[2]The *Harvard Educational Review* compilation includes Jensen's paper, "How much can we boost IQ and scholastic achievement?," comments on it by J. S. Kagan, J. McV. Hunt, J. F. Crow, C. Bereiter, D. Elkind, L. J. Cronbach, and W. F. Brazziel, and a rejoinder by Jensen. See also A. R. Jensen, in J. Hellmuth, *Disadvantaged Child*, vol. 3 (Special child Publ., Seattle, Wash., 1970).

[3]P. L. Nichols, thesis, University of Minnesota (1970). Nichols reports that in two large samples of black and white children, seven-year WISC IQ scores showed the same means and distributions for the two racial groups, once social-class variables were equated. These results are unlike those of several other studies, which found that matching socio-economic status did not create equal means in the two racial groups [A. Shuey (5); A. B. Wilson, *Racial Isolation in the Public Schools*, vol. 2 (Government Printing Office, Washington, D.D., 1967)]. In Nichols's samples, prenatal and postnatal medical care was equally available to blacks and whites, which may have contributed to the relatively high IQ scores of the blacks in these samples.

[4]By interaction, Eysenck means simply $P = G + E$, or "heredity and environment acting together to produce the observed phenotype" (p. 111). He does not mean what most geneticists and behavior geneticists mean by interaction; that is, the *differential* phenotypic effects produced by various combinations of genotypes and environments, as in the interaction term of analysis-of-variance statistics. Few thinking people are not interactionists in Eysenck's sense of the term, because that's the only way to get the organism and the environment into the same equation to account for variance in any phenotypic trait. How much of the phenotypic variance is accounted for by each of the terms in the equation is the real issue.

[5]A. Shuey, *The Testing of Negro Intelligence* (Social Science Press, New York, 1966), pp. 499–519.

[6]F. B. Davis, *The Measurement of Mental Capacity through Evoked-Potential Recordings* (Educational Records Bureau, Greenwich, Conn., 1971). "As it turned out, no evidence was found that the latency periods obtained . . . displayed serviceable utility for predicting school performance or level of mental ability among pupils in preschool through grade 8" (p. v).

[7]*New York Times*, 8 Oct. 1971, p. 41.

[8]J. Kagan and H. A. Moss, *Birth to Maturity* (Wiley, New York, 1962).

[9]S. Scarr-Salapatek, *Science*, in press.

[10]P. E. Vernon, *Intelligence and Cultural Environment* (Methuen, London, 1969).

[11]T. Dobzhansky, *Mankind Evolving* (Yale Univ. Press, New Haven, 1962), pp. 234–238.

[12]J. Thoday, *J. Biosocial Science* 1, suppl. 3, 4 (1969).

[13]L. L. Cavalli-Sforza and W. F. Bodmer, *The Genetics of Human Populations* (Freeman, San Francisco, 1971), pp. 753–804. They propose that the study of racial differences is useless and not scientifically supportable at the present time.

[14]T. E. Reed, *Science* 165, 762 (1969); *Am. J. Hum. Genet.* 21, 1 (1969); C. MacLean and P. L. Workman, paper at a meeting of the American Society of Human Genetics (1970), Indianapolis).

[15]E. W. Reed and S. C. Reed, *Mental Retardation: A Family Study* (Saunders, Philadelphia, 1965); *Social Biol.* 18, suppl., 42 (1971).

[16]M. Skodak and H. M. Skeels, *J. Genet. Psychol.* 75, 85 (1949).

[17]J. C. DeFries, paper for the C.O.B.R.E. Research Workshop on Genetic Endowment and Environment in the Determination of Behavior (3–8 Oct. 1971, Rye, N.Y.).

[18]R. Heber, *Rehabilitation of Families at Risk for Mental Retardation* (Regional Rehabilitation Center, Univ. of Wisconsin, 1969). S. P. Strickland, *Am. Ed.* 7, 3 (1971).

[19]I. I. Gottesman, in *Social Class, Race, and Psychological Development*, M. Deutsch, I. Katz, and A. R. Jensen, Eds. (Holt, Rinehart, and Winston, New York, 1968), pp. 11–51.

[20]J. Rynders, personal communication, November 1971.

[21]N. E. Morton, paper for the C.O.B.R.E. Research Workshop on Genetic Endowment and Environment in the Determination of Behavior (3–8 Oct. 1971, Rye, N.Y.).

[22]I thank Philip Salapatek, Richard Weinberg, I. I. Gottesman, and Leonard I. Heston for their critical reading of this paper. They are not in any way responsible for its content, however.

AUTHOR INDEX

Estes, R. D., 105
Etkin, W., 53
Everden, J. F., 80, 281
Eyles, D. E., 380
Eysenck, H. J., 458–461, 464–466

Fawcett, C. D., 275
Fernandes, J. L., 394
Fessas, P., 377
Fiedler, W., 116
Finsen, N., 407
Fischer, K., 446
Fisher, J., 369
Fisher, R. A., 11–13, 19, 30, 443, 444
Firschein, L., 377
Fitzpatrick, T. B., 14
Fitzsimmons, F. W., 122
Flannery, K. V., 349
Fleischer, R. L., 80
Ford, C. S., 43
Ford, E. B., 11, 12, 30
Fraenkel-Conrat, H., 22
Fraipont, J., 282
Franceschetti, A., 388
Franks, D., 86
Freeman, D., 64
Freeman, E. A., 369
Friedlaender, J. S., 18, 20, 27
Fries, J. C. de, 465
Frisanche, A. R., 411
Frische, J. E., 263
Fry, P. C., 431
Fuhlrott, J. C., 282

Gage, N. L., 443, 444
Gajdusek, D. C., 378
Galileo, 371
Galton, F., 444, 458
Gamble, G. R., 426, 458
Gans, B., 430
Gardner, B. T., 73
Gardner, R. A., 73
Garn, S. M., 13–15, 25, 26, 47, 50–52, 54, 269, 330, 353, 358
Garner, R. L., 138
Garrod, D., 27
Garth, T. R., 394
Gartlan, J. S., 97, 108, 109, 189
Gentner, W., 281
Gerard, R. W., 44
Gieseler, W., 284, 299
Gilbert, C., 120
Giles, E., 31, 242, 263
Gillette, J. M., 292
Gillham, N. W., 341, 365
Gillin, F. J., 7
Gillman, J., 120
Glass, B., 11–12, 31
Glickman, S. E., 82

Goffman, E., 112
Goldschmidt, W., 59, 60, 65
Goodall, J. (also van Lawick-Goodall), 47, 58, 74, 81–83, 131, 132, 139, 140, 145, 146, 181, 182, 186, 214, 257, 258
Goodman, M., 86
Goose, D., 327
Gordon, J. E., 431
Gorman, J. G., 378
Gossett, T. F., 370
Goustard, M., 74
Graebner, C., 6
Graham, G. G., 430
Grand, T. I., 86
Greene, D. C., 326, 332
Gregg, T. E., 341
Gregory, W. K., 12, 14, 25, 262, 286
Gross, H., 15
Groves, C., 138
Guenther, E. W., 287
Gussow, J., 447
Gutgesell, V. J., 255

Haag, W. G., 348
Haddon, A. C., 343
Haddow, A. J., 214
Haeckel, E., 281, 282
Hafleigh, A. S., 86
Hagmeier, E. M., 341
Haldane, J. B. S., 11, 456
Hall, G. S., 458
Hall, K. R. L., 61, 74, 75, 81, 83–85, 92, 97, 109, 116, 117, 122, 125, 129, 132, 182, 188, 239
Haller, J. S., 364
Hamburg, D., 64, 85, 131
Hamburg, E., 131
Hamilton, W. F., 392
Hammel, H. T., 412
Hardin, G., 10, 12, 282, 296
Hardy, L. H., 392
Harlow, H. F., 434
Harlow, M. K., 434
Harris, H., 13, 361
Harris, M., 366, 367
Harrison, G. A., 411
Harrison, B. J., 24
Harrisson, T., 214
Hart, J. S., 412
Hassan, M. M., 378
Hauser, O., 282
Hay, R., 222
Hayes, C., 85, 138
Hayes, K. I., 85
Heber, R., 465
Heberer, G., 40, 281, 284, 286, 299, 300
Hegnauer, A. H., 411
Heinz, H. J., 54
Heiple, H. G., 198, 247
Henderson, J. R., 86, 336